MATADOR BOOKS

Safety Fables for Today

Born in England in the mid 1970s, Laura J Cahill is a health and safety manager with over twenty years' experience spanning the utilities, oil & gas, and rail sectors. She also has extensive knowledge of fairy tales and fables, primarily picked up during her formative years. Laura's understanding of the challenges faced by real-world workers, together with her belief that fictional characters might be deployed to deliver important safety messages, provided the inspiration for this book.

Whilst her day job involves the crafting of procedures, newsletters and handbooks for organisations, this book sees Laura taking a slightly different tack from these more mainstream communication channels, as she seeks to shine a light on some key health and safety topics through a blend of storytelling and poetry. The seeds of this approach were possibly sown in the late 1980s when, aged 12, Laura scooped first prize in a local authority poster competition promoting awareness of headlice prevention, with the caption *'Don't let the louse make your head his house!'*

'Safety Fables for Today' is Laura's first book.

LAURA J CAHILL

Safety Fables for Today

Traditional Tales
with Modern Meaning

Matador
Unit E2 Airfield Business Park,
Harrison Road, Market Harborough,
Leicestershire. LE16 7UL
Tel: 0116 2792299
Email: books@troubador.co.uk
Web: www.troubador.co.uk/matador
Twitter: @matadorbooks

ISBN 978 1800465 510

British Library Cataloguing in Publication Data.
A catalogue record for this book is available from the British Library.

Printed and bound by CPI Group (UK) Ltd, Croydon, CR0 4YY
Typeset in 10pt Minion Pro by Troubador Publishing Ltd, Leicester, UK

Matador is an imprint of Troubador Publishing Ltd

This book is dedicated to those who make things work.

It's dedicated to those who work on overhead lines, keeping our lights on. It's also dedicated to those who bend, stoop and crouch down in excavations, looking after the pipework which delivers essential utilities, as well as to those who drive, dispatch and maintain trains, who get us to the places we need to be, and help to join us up as a society too.

And to anyone else who works to make life better for us all.

CONTENTS

PART TWO

THE *HOW TO...* GUIDES

APPENDICES

ACKNOWLEDGEMENTS

MARK LEWIS

The author acknowledges with grateful thanks the contribution of Mark Lewis, in providing the cover and all other illustrations for this book, which have captured perfectly the essence of these fables.

HEALTH AND SAFETY EXECUTIVE

This book contains public sector information published by the Health and Safety Executive and licensed under the Open Government Licence, version 3.0. Where used, the Health and Safety Executive has been acknowledged as the source of the information.

INTRODUCTION

I'd like to start off by saying 'thank you'. You have my sincere appreciation for buying this book. If you were lucky, you might have managed to locate a hard copy of it before you committed to parting with your money. Thanks also if you made the purchase by putting it into your 'basket' at an on-line marketplace. If this was the buying channel you pursued, it's likely you were offered a number of alternatives before you reached your final decision and clicked 'buy now'. In the course of the process, you might have been asked the question *'Have you considered 101 Dalmations?'* or been steered in the direction of other equally worthy products, with the website helpfully suggesting *'Others who purchased this book also bought Cinderella'*. But however it happened, I imagine there were a number of factors which moved you away from the 'thinking of buying' group, and towards the 'actually buying' one. And if you are yet to be persuaded to join the actually buying group, *go on...*

You didn't have to buy it. Perhaps you didn't even mean or intend to part with your hard-earned money. An *accidental* purchase of a safety book seems wrong on a lot of levels, doesn't it? Oxymoronic, even. But I suppose I can see how it might have happened. *Were you taken in by the giant/beanstalk cover illustration? Did you think it would be an easy-reader? Have you inadvertently bought it for your curious five year old?* Or, *Did you have a momentary lapse in the course of your on-line transaction, selecting 'buy now' in a split-second decision, rather than 'save for later' or even – dare I say it – 'remove from basket'?* If any of these scenarios ring true, I'm sorry. Perhaps you have no interest in safety whatsoever and are more fascinated by the pantomime or fairy tale genres. But however it happened, all I ask is that you bear with me, because my hope is that time and a reading of the first few pages of this book will serve to validate your decision as having been the right one. And let me be candid with you, things could have been far worse – you might have frittered the same amount of money away on drink, drugs or a losing lottery ticket. So before you resolve to return it, shamelessly re-gift it, or level up a wonky table with it, please give me just a few more moments of your time. In all honesty, it's the appetites of the *wonky table levellers* I'm most eager to whet. *Why?* Well, if you really care about safety – as I unashamedly do – the people you should most want to win over are the ones who say they couldn't give two hoots. And whatever your viewpoint, I'd just ask that you take a few paces back, to clear a path for the approaching *safety carnival…*

Whether you dip in and out of this book or read it in its entirety, my hope is that there might just be something of interest for you here. If you like your safety with a dash of humour and don't object to an occasional splash into a world of lost containment – *of the purely metaphorical kind, of course* – this might be the book for you. And even if your overriding interest is in poetry, provided that you have no objection to giving safety a passing thought, as and when the opportunity presents itself, I believe that you too will find something on which to ponder here. It's through breaking these – sometimes complex – subjects down into a familiar tale with a modern twist, and by identifying a few key principles and posing incidental questions along the way, that I hope to offer up some fresh perspectives for those readers who already enjoy safety. But that isn't all, because I also believe it's the moral imperative of those of us working in the field to widen its appeal to those who perhaps don't feel quite as positively about it. *The cynics. The disinterested. The disenfranchised.* And to add a splash of colour to the greyness typically associated with the profession.

And why would I want to do this? It's simply because safety done well isn't about unnecessary complexity, nor should it be the preserve of an intellectual elite. It's not the place for *impenetrable jargon.* It shouldn't be about painfully awkward adjuncts to dysfunctional processes or revisions to already cumbersome procedures. Nor should it give rise to irritating time-wasting. On the contrary, it should act as the steady pulse in the background of a complex work activity, the moment of calm thought in the midst of a challenging situation, and the beating heart that feeds individual, workplace and societal wellbeing. So whether you have decades of experience and understanding of the field, or simply an idle curiosity which stirred momentarily because of a few words in the foregoing paragraphs, I hope you find something of note here. Because, as well as providing an alternative way of looking at a variety of challenges for those involved in day-to-day activities, my hope is that these little fables might just spread the interest in some key 'risk' types to a broader audience. I realise you might be one of many thus far put off by the all too often complex terminology that has a tendency to dominate this discipline, but rest assured that all are welcome here...after all, in order for this safety mission to work, it has to be our collective endeavour!

WHERE TO START
Childish Beginnings

Don't worry! I'm not about to describe how I came into being. Nor do I propose to take you on a dreary wander through the boggy quagmires of legislation. But I just expressed a desire to refine complex subjects into basic principles, and I should probably take a moment to explain why this matters and how this book came to be. The longer I've worked in safety, the more I've realised one of the biggest challenges for all involved is communication: communicating the right information to the right people at the right time – in a way that's meaningful to them, whether they are utility pipe layers, overhead line workers, or railway workers who see to it that trains arrive and depart safely. Most of my conversations with colleagues in these sharp end occupations, and others besides, have revealed that they want to know what they *need to know,* rather than being overloaded with irrelevant information which might be *nice to know,* but hampers rather than supports their daily work activities. Let's be honest, this should come as no surprise. They are absolutely entitled to have given me this feedback – and right to have done so – however blunt it may have been in some cases! *Why?* Because, it's the purpose of those of us fortunate to work in the safety field to make working lives easier, rather than simply adding layers of complexity, which are frankly unhelpful to those up to their elbows in the mud, silt and grime of operational endeavours. I say this in no way to diminish the value of legislation, codes of practice and procedures – *far from it!* I've been variously involved in the crafting of these *literary masterpieces* and their spin-offs over the past twenty years – from commenting and drafting, through to releasing handbooks and briefing out the requirements of organisational documents, including talking to those who actually need to use and understand them. The truth is that it's the job of any safety advisor (myself included) to distil from often complex legislation, codes of practice and industry guidance, the practical bits and pieces that those doing the job actually *need* to know. *And how is anyone to know whether this alchemy has worked?* It's simple really: any communication needs to reach the right people, in the right way, and at the right time – and inspire them to do the right thing, with gladness. *And if it doesn't do this?* It has utterly failed.

It was this belief in the need for straightforward messaging that got me thinking. The messages which have stayed with me to this day – or at least some of the most vivid – were to be found in the bedtime stories mixed in with my milk, that were read to me as a child, the 'ever afters' to which had the potential to land anywhere on a spectrum between Utopia and Bedlam. They were based on repetition, and the simple actions of often well-meaning characters who added to my early understanding of the world and worked their magic in effortlessly delivering important life messages, through a charming blend of naïvety, tenderness and occasional stupidity. And, in thinking about this still further, I mused that there was perhaps a hidden depth to their endeavours that had passed me by as an infant, and that maybe the little characters that crawled, toddled and tumbled their way through my child mind might walk a little more purposively and – *dare I say it* – sensibly through the designated walkways of a grown-up workplace. Let's face it, they appear to have done precious little else of value in the intervening years; I'm not aware of a large-scale chemical manufacturer laying claims to humble porridge pot beginnings in a domestic kitchen, nor of a group of pigs having made subsequent moves to dominate the construction industry, let alone of a whimsical piper having become a market leader in alternative pest control. And yet, even for those of us who climb trees (and perhaps beanstalks), there still comes a time when the landscape we need to navigate our way through with confidence is the grown-up real-world one. So, whilst recognising that most workplaces are less densely populated by pigs, goats, bears and dragons than in the contexts pondered here, I've sought to put the transferable skills of these characters to good use.

My aim is to bring the simple messaging approach effectively employed by many a childhood fable to some safety scenarios commonly encountered in the grown-up world. And whilst these tales feature things that go 'CRACKLE!', 'POP!', or 'SQUELCH!' with an amusing – sometimes pantomime-like – quality, there is, of course, much for us to be serious about when looking at equivalent real-world events, where things which catch fire, explode or leak can have far-reaching consequences for the people, plant and places involved.

A REALITY CHECK
Grown-Up Problems

It's worth mentioning that this book is mostly about safety, but not exclusively so. The viewing of safety in a vacuum is just one of the problems faced by those of us who peddle this craft. It can be seen as a budgetary burden, rather than a legitimate cause for expenditure. It can be perceived, too, as a frivolous addition to a meeting agenda, rather than being the driving force behind a business's thought processes. But just as is true for anyone serious about adjusting mindsets, it's our job as *safety advocates* to be accepting – and even welcoming – of any such challenges to our beliefs. And, where needed, we should also take the time to stray into the fields of others to see things from their perspectives, particularly if this helps to achieve our purpose of keeping people and processes safe. This means we must promote our craft and infiltrate it within the to-do lists of others, whenever and wherever the opportunity presents itself – an approach this book tries to adopt, through acknowledging the links to risk, as well as to such ergonomic, environmental and commercial concerns as might be relevant to the subject at hand. But make no mistake, there are potential pitfalls with this, and there will no doubt be some who feel this spreads the effort too thinly. I do, however, think it's important not to be too cosseted about safety, as viewing it only in isolation runs the risk of promoting the very vacuum-based thinking we need to avoid. So with all this in mind, and before getting into the detail of the fables, let's think about who this book is for, and set some basic ground rules for effective communication. As well as being invaluable real-world rules these are, coincidentally, those that the fables – and their accompanying *modern meanings* – abide by too.

WHO THIS BOOK IS FOR
Developing Relationships

The target audience for this book is a broad one, as is reflected by both the range of characters featured in these fables and the diverse meanings that flow from them. The roles of people and other creatures we'll see depicted in the fables can be divided into three groups, which broadly align to the levels within organisational structures familiar to many readers[1]. *First,* there are *the people who do stuff* – a role usually performed by the central characters in these fables – roles which, in real life, tend to be taken on by a range of people, including 'workers', 'users', 'employees', and 'operatives'. This is a diverse group, but their common purpose is – or should be – to do stuff safely. *Second,* there are *the people who look after the people and things that do stuff* – a role assumed by those charged with looking out for the central characters of these tales, through overseeing the activities undertaken by the first group, and one which, in real-world settings, tends to be carried out by a range of different 'managers'. Numbered amongst them are not only those who look after people – the 'line managers', 'team managers', 'functional managers', and 'operational managers' – but also the 'process managers', 'depot managers' and 'performance managers' too. The purpose of this group is to look, check and see that the stuff people and things are doing – including the systems used and processes operated – are safe. And *third,* there are *the people who need to know that the people who do stuff* (the first group), *and the people who look after the people and things that do stuff* (the second group) *do it brilliantly.* Fewer of the characters featured within these fables fall into this third group than into the first or second groups. But in the real world these are the crucial roles performed by 'senior leaders' – the individuals who are ultimately accountable for making sure that any organisational activities undertaken on their watch are being performed safely. Not just once, but every time they are carried out.

Having looked at who this book is for, it's a logical next step to want to understand *what* needs to be communicated to them and *how* this is to be achieved, which is where the *rules for engagement* and *consultation considerations* come into play.

---

1. Whilst the way in which responsibilities are allocated varies from organisation to organisation, it is possible to give some broad indications of the types of roles and functions assigned to individuals, the generic scope of which has been captured within defined terms in this book's *Glossary.*

THE RULES FOR ENGAGEMENT
As easy as 1-2-3

RULE #1
STOP TO LOOK AT WHAT PEOPLE ARE DOING

In the time I've been involved in safety, I've met a lot of people. I've been lucky enough to experience working life in the utilities, energy, oil & gas, and rail sectors. I've done some work, that's true. I've also watched many people doing more work at the sharp end than me and, irritating though it can be for those being observed, watching is the lot of the safety professional. I've also read a few books and visited a few places. Some of the books I've read have been written by people who've read a lot more widely, met a lot more people, and done a lot more operational stuff with steel and pipes and flanges than me. Many have travelled more extensively too. I'll admit I've travelled a bit less and met fewer people than some, and been involved in less hard graft than many others. I don't dispute that big things can teach you big things but, for me, the epiphany moments have come from small things too. They have sprung unexpectedly from the small things learnt whilst visiting excavations in Hampshire and utility pipelines in Oxfordshire, from time spent at an operational control centre in Sussex, and during the course of trips to engineering depots on the outskirts of London. They have come, too, through observing the challenges from a train driver's cab during peak commuting times, as well as by watching the goings-on at the platform edge at London Bridge station.

I consider it a privilege to have learnt from these people and experiences, and recognise that there's always more to learn. Taking the opportunity to observe what people are doing – or are trying to do – is vital, particularly for those of us who seek to advise them. It builds common understanding and helps to drive the desire from all concerned to determine what might need to be changed and, with time, fosters a collaborative culture in which everyone wants to make things work better. This matters for the systems and processes operated by people, just as it does for their 'personal safety'. It matters too for the safety of anyone or anything else that might be impacted – even indirectly – by what they are doing.

RULE #2
LISTEN TO WHAT PEOPLE SAY (OR DON'T SAY)

If you take the time and trouble to listen, people will, by and large, tell you what's wrong! And if, like me, you operate in an advisory capacity, it's essential to remember that it's the person at the sharp end who's your ultimate customer. The ethos of the retail sector is that 'the customer is always right'. It's true to say that there are some rights and wrongs in safety – some clear must and mustn't dos – which mean the *always right* retail philosophy doesn't neatly transfer to the safety arena, but if we expect people to receive our messages, we absolutely must listen to them. *Why is this?* It's simply because, for safety to work brilliantly, we need a collective vision. The audiences with whom we want to – or sometimes simply have to – connect are as diverse as the world from which they are drawn. *There are those who have 'been there, done that, bought the t-shirt' for the last 30 years. And people who dream. And people who do as they are told. And people who don't. And people who want to do stuff faster. Or feel pressurised into doing it faster, perhaps through inexperience or a simple desire to impress others. And enthusiastic 'wet behind the ears' youngsters. And people focused just as intently on monitoring the health of their pension pots, as on the vigilant checking of gauge levels.* The thing is, we can't choose *who* does safety. Nor should we wish to. We want them all to join our mission…

…and so we have to pitch our craft flexibly, creatively even. We have to speak to the dreamers and the cynics and the embittered veterans. For those who want to be told line by line in procedural form what it is they need to do, we should do that. For those who need pictures and diagrams, we should don a smock and turn up with an easel, palette and paintbrush, if necessary. And for those who require up-to-the minute information zapped across to them in some whizzy format, we must be sympathetic to these requests and use technological advancements in service of their interests, whenever it's appropriate to do so. Finally, for those who simply don't want to talk to us, or who miss out details we would want or expect to hear, we should take some time to understand their views and motives. It might be that they disagree with the messages being put out. It could be that they have yet to be convinced, or that they hold a contrary opinion to that of the majority, which they feel is being ignored. Alternatively, and most worryingly, they might be following their own, perhaps misguided, agendas. Needless to say, whatever their reasons, our audience always matters and, in listening to what people say – or omit to say – we should be forever curious.

RULE #3
THINK ABOUT WHAT PEOPLE NEED TO STAY SAFE

People need things – including information – for all manner of reasons, in the name of safety. They hail from multiple backgrounds, performing a variety of functions and work activities, and operating at different points within work processes in all sorts of workplaces. They also act in different capacities, bringing with them a broad range of personal strengths, needs, and weaknesses. Superficially, it's true that these fables are about hogs, goats, bears and dragons but, as we shall see, these creatures hide a deeper meaning. As allegorical devices, the inhabitants of these tales are arguably less ambitious than the pigs of Orwell's 'Animal Farm'[2], but their capability to be insightful should not be dismissed out of hand. There are human equivalents to these fantastical beings who operate in the real world and whose safety always matters, whether they act as workers, operatives, or users, or perform some other vital function – functions often referred to in the course of reviewing these fables. The *way* in which people operate is important, because it affects what they need – and what they need to do – to protect their own safety and wellbeing and that of others too, and safeguard the systems and processes they operate. The question about what people need is one that any safety communication effort should seek to address. In short, it should always place people at its heart, delivering to them the information they need to know. At the right time. In the right place. And at the right point in any given process. Ultimately, the delivery of any safety message should be driven by an understanding of *who* it's for, *why* they need it and *what* it is they need.

Our efforts to communicate might need to be directed towards an engineer who tightens flange bolts to achieve leak free joints within a utility network. Or to a dispatcher who sees to it that trains safely depart from a station platform. It could be for the tiny dots of folk *up in the sky*, in all weathers, fixing overhead power lines. Or for the genius who monitors levels on a control panel, with the reaction

---

2. Orwell, G., *Animal Farm*. (Harper Collins, 2021).

speed of an enthusiastic teenage gamer. But wherever these people – and all manner of others – sit within organisational hierarchies, from the newly-recruited trainee, to the most senior person in the room, if what they do has to be done in the right way, reliably, every time – it's upon these people in all their different capacities and guises that our communication efforts should be most firmly focused. And whatever people do, and however they operate, the hope is that this book makes some key concepts, tools and principles accessible and useful to many, in a format that works for a diverse audience and opens up conversations throughout organisations.

It's quite true that simply by observing these rudimentary rules for engagement – *watching what people do, listening to what they say,* and *thinking about what they need to help them stay safe* – organisations can build for themselves the foundations of an effective communication strategy. This is no great surprise and few would dispute the benefits to safety culture that can flow from successful everyday conversations and other workforce-wide communications. But on top of this, organisations need to meet the demands of the clear legal duty which requires them to engage in more formal dialogue with employees or their representatives about health and safety matters – so called 'consultation' – the key considerations of which are outlined here.

CONSULTATION CONSIDERATIONS
Learning to Talk

In considering the fundamentals of *how* to carry out consultation and *what* it should involve, organisations within Great Britain need to be well versed in the contents of two sets of regulations, which collectively cover workplaces in which 'trade unions' are recognised, and those where they are not[3]. The nature of workplace circumstances will determine whether consultation is required under one or both sets of regulations in any given situation but, whichever type applies, when used to best effect the benefits organisations stand to win by pursuing them include: better workforce motivation; efficiency and

---

3. These are *the Safety Representatives and Safety Committees Regulations 1977* (S.I. 1977/500) and *the Health and Safety (Consultation with Employees) Regulations 1996* (S.I. 1996/1513) respectively.

quality gains, and increased productivity too. Effective consultation – seen where employees are not only provided with information, but are also listened to and their views accounted for – also tends to lead to workplaces which are healthier and safer, with better health and safety decisions being made, a stronger commitment to actions being implemented, closer collaboration on problem solving in evidence, and a greater level of co-operation and mutual trust apparent between employers and their employees.

As will soon become clear, the naïve nature of the fables that follow here makes it difficult to determine what – if any – consultation arrangements might have applied to the scenarios involved. It's for this reason that this text tends towards generalisation on this point, with suggestions made that the characters should, for instance, involve workers, communicate, proactively engage or work collaboratively with others, without necessarily being prescriptive about exactly *how* this should be done. But of course, these are the kinds of details that equivalent real-world organisations can't afford to ignore, needing as they do to be ever mindful of the broad-ranging circumstances which specifically require them to consult. *They might be seeking to introduce new systems of work, including shift patterns. They could be looking to determine their arrangements for engaging 'competent persons' to help them meet legal requirements. They might be thinking about how they give out information on work-related risks and dangers, together with the methods by which they reduce or remove them, and what employees should do if they believe they have been exposed to them. They might even simply be seeking to organise and plan health and safety training. Or they could be evaluating the health and safety consequences of proposed new technology.* These are just a few examples of the many kinds of activities likely to give rise to a need for some form of consultation to take place[4].

---

4. For further information on consultation processes, see Health and Safety Executive Guidance (2013), *Consulting Employees on Health and Safety: A brief guide to the law* (INDG232, rev.2). It is felt that to provide an exhaustive list of the potential areas where consultation should have taken place, or been overseen by, the characters featured in these fictional works would be of limited value, notwithstanding the point that it would also be impracticable to do so. For these reasons the examples of opportunities to consult with workers cited at the appropriate points throughout this text are just a sample of the many possibilities, with those chosen thought to have particular resonance for the operating circumstances of equivalent real-world organisations.

It's at this point that attention turns to this book's structure, which is in part informed by the communication and consultation aspects just outlined.

THE STRUCTURE OF THIS BOOK

This book falls into two main parts.

PART ONE contains the ten fables. In each case, a *prologue* provides some real-world safety context and practical background knowledge for the tale. There then follows the fable, which is a retelling of a (hopefully familiar) classic, with a safety embellishment upon the original version and a poetic twist. As is true of the original stories, these tales generally involve a central character trying to do or achieve something. *As such, it's the fable itself that offers an opportunity to 'stop to look at what people are doing', as expected by rule one.* At the end of each tale is a *modern meaning*, which draws out some key learning points from the events it describes, linked back to the questions posed or issues covered by its *prologue*. *This underlines the importance of the 'listen to what people say (or don't say)' thrust of rule two which, in real-world circumstances, often sets the tone for any guidance and advice that might be offered to them, further down the line.*

PART TWO contains a set of ten *How to...* Guides, the contents of which are derived from the events of the ten fables and their *modern meanings* from Part One. As well as reflecting upon the fables' topics and subtopics, the guides draw out the key points raised and provide some practical hints and tips about how to address these more broadly, primarily in a work-based context. *These guides support the 'what people need to stay safe' purpose of rule three.* They should also serve an additional purpose, by offering insights or talking points for safety or operational teams who wish to take any given topic area a stage further, when developing workplace action plans, initiatives and the like. Senior leaders might also find there are other benefits to be gained by referring to these guides, whether using them as prompts to sense-check the appropriateness of their goals and targets in the areas they cover, or to help them judge the robustness of their arrangements for managing risk.

There are other sources of information within this book too, which should be of further interest. An *Epilogue* is provided at the end of Part

One, which suggests the reporting requirements that might apply if the types of events featured in the fables were to be transplanted from these fictional scenarios into real-world workplace settings. Additionally, the *Appendices* contain supporting information, including assessments and models, as referred to by the main text. Finally, where language has been adopted which is in common use in the safety arena, but is perhaps less well-known in the wider world, these terms together with their accompanying meanings are to be found within this book's *Glossary*. Inverted commas help to draw attention to key terms the first time they are used in relation to a fable – for instance 'risk assessment' points to risk assessment being a defined term.

THE LEGAL HEALTH AND SAFETY FRAMEWORK:
THE GOAL, THE CONTROL & THE GUIDANCE
Boundary Setting

The fables in this book often show a lightness of touch towards their underlying subject matter. This approach is deliberate and is in no way intended to trivialise the issues at their heart, but rather goes hand in hand with the intention for the concepts they involve to be presented in a straightforward way. Indeed, in order to get the most from reading these tales – and the important messages they seek to convey – it's also helpful to have a rudimentary understanding of the key legal principles involved, which underpin the health and safety framework operating in Great Britain. *And so, to the basics...*

First, at the heart of our legal framework for health and safety sits the *Health and Safety at Work etc. Act 1974 (HSWA 1974)*, which sets out core obligations, duties and principles, and is goal-setting. As the bedrock of our domestic health and safety law, it basically requires those that generate risks to do what's required to understand and manage them, protecting people from harm. As such, it sets out 'general duties' for organisations to ensure 'so far as is reasonably practicable (SFAIRP)' the health and safety at work of their employees (section 2) as well as that of others (section 3), making sure that they carry out their undertakings in such a way as not to expose anyone to risk. Or, to put it another way, in respect of any risk to health and safety that an organisation creates or allows to exist, it has a duty to reduce or effectively control it to a level that is 'as low as reasonably practicable

(ALARP)'. It's commonplace for the acronyms ALARP and SFAIRP to be used interchangeably in the health and safety world, but the key point to note is that whether talking about the amount by which risks must be reduced – SFAIRP, or the level to which they are expected to be controlled – ALARP, the upshot is the same: organisations must do all that is required to avoid, reduce and effectively control them. *And what if they don't?* Well, in circumstances where a prosecution is pursued, organisations have to show that they did everything that needed to be done, and it's only where it's technically impossible for them to put in place measures to control risk – or if the time, trouble or cost of so doing outweighs the improvement to risk which would be achieved by implementing them – that they will be viewed as having done enough, a requirement referred to as the 'reverse burden of proof'[5].

Second, to help organisations work out *how* they are to identify their risks and the suitable accompanying 'control measures' needed to reduce them to ALARP levels – and so meet their obligations under health and safety law – there are regulations, which cover all manner of workplaces and work types. These are important because, whilst the goal-setting intention of *HSWA 1974* is clear, it doesn't say *how* organisations are to go about achieving the effective identification and control of their risks in practical terms, a gap that's unsurprising, given that this goal-setting – or 'self-regulation' – approach is geared towards compelling organisations to identify, understand, control and manage their own risks, rather than telling them exactly what they need to do to achieve a level of risk which is ALARP. In order to guide their decisions about the steps they need to take therefore, organisations are expected to refer to regulations, which flesh out the obligations, duties, and principles applicable to particular risks and workplaces, some of which couch expectations in general terms and others that set requirements focused on specific areas or work types. By way of example, *the Management of Health and Safety at Work Regulations*

---

5. Section 40 of *HSWA 1974* refers to this as the onus of proof, and requires the accused party to prove that it was not practicable or not reasonably practicable to do more to satisfy a duty or requirement, or that there was no better practicable means than was actually used to satisfy the duty or requirement. More commonly it is referred to as the 'reverse burden of proof', so-called because it reverses the usual presumption of English Law of innocence until guilt is proven.

1999[6] ('the Management Regulations') take the goal of preventing exposure to risk from *HSWA 1974*, adding to this the expectation for a suitable and sufficient risk assessment to be carried out[7] – which shows how the risks have been identified and suitable control measures put in place (or risk mitigation measures implemented) to reduce them to acceptable levels. So, in essence, the requirement to do a risk assessment in *the Management Regulations* both adds to, and is supportive of, the *HSWA 1974* goal of not exposing people to risks.

Third, there's guidance – which comes in all shapes and sizes – and highlights how organisations can meet the expectations of a goal-setting Act and the control requirements of regulations. Having just noted that the goal of not exposing people to risk is drawn from *HSWA 1974,* and added to this the example of the requirement to perform a risk assessment and control the risks identified by it, as taken from *the Management Regulations,* this still leaves unanswered the question of exactly *how* organisations are to go about achieving a level of risk that's acceptable. In supporting organisations with their approach to identifying risks and making decisions about the actual measures they need to adopt to control them, therefore, guidance fills this gap by – in the case of risk assessment – indicating the particular types of information it should include, and helping them to work out how risks are to be reduced and controlled, in practical terms.

It's important to note that guidance can be drawn from multiple sources, any or all of which might be appropriate, depending upon the particular circumstances. There are 'Approved Codes of Practice (ACOPs)' which have a special legal status and give direction on how to comply with the law, providing advice on how to achieve good practice. To build upon the example of risk assessment just provided, ACOPs give examples of what is meant by 'reasonably practicable' and illuminate words such as 'suitable and sufficient' as appear within the regulations, by adding to these *what* is practically required, by way of risk assessment and control, for the particular circumstances. Employers don't have to follow ACOPs but, if prosecuted for a breach of health and safety law and it's shown that they didn't follow them, a court will find them to be at fault, unless they can show they complied with the law in some other – equivalent

---

6. S.I. 1999/3242.
7. Regulation 3 of *the Management Regulations* sets out this requirement.

or better – way. There is authoritative guidance too, which fleshes out the questions raised by regulations and helps organisations with the interpretation of compliance requirements, or the provision of technical advice, originating from sources including 'regulators', such as the 'Health and Safety Executive', as well as from industry bodies. Guidance can either set out a range of possible options for controlling a risk or, in some cases, dictate specific steps to be taken to control a particular risk. And there are other 'good practice' and 'best practice' documents too, which usually evolve outside these more formal types of guidance. Typically, following good practice from an authoritative source will be enough to demonstrate compliance with health and safety law, whilst adopting best practice goes beyond this, and is an approach which indicates that an organisation is exceeding the minimum expectations. It's important for organisations to keep an eye on both good practice and best practice, however, because over time, expectations for controlling risk rise. Today's best practice becomes tomorrow's good practice and organisations need to ensure that they keep pace with requirements, checking the sufficiency of their processes and practices and making sure they meet the variable and often rising demands posed by technological change, industry challenges, and emerging risk. This requires constant vigilance and regular review, in order to ensure they do everything that is expected of them to comply with health and safety obligations, including periodically revisiting the contents of management systems to verify their continued fitness for purpose, observable through their achieving compliance with such health and safety requirements as are relevant to their undertakings.

I do recognise that this legal *stuff* may not be of interest to all readers, but whenever legislation is referred to in the context of a fable this is cited in full on the occasion of its first use, accompanied by a shortened version in brackets, this being the abbreviation used subsequently. For those who hanker after a further level of detail, references have also been variously included – signposting Acts, regulations and guidance, including ACOPs at the appropriate points throughout the text – with supplementary information provided as footnotes, where this is felt to add to the meaning of the fable at hand. Where an Act (primary legislation) has been cited, the footnote includes its year, together with its chapter number (denoted by a 'c.'

reference), this being the chronological number within the year of its enactment, whilst any reference made to a regulation (secondary legislation) is accompanied by its statutory instrument number (denoted by an 'S.I.' reference). Finally, whilst case law has been added sparingly to the text, where used, this is supported by references to the law report from which it was sourced. It is hoped that this approach keeps the main text accessible and avoids unnecessary distractions from its core messages. In the real world of course, organisations must always determine the requirements of *HSWA 1974* and any regulations applicable to their operations, as well as keeping up to speed with any relevant case law, and seeking to draw upon other guidance, codes of practice and good and best practice, which fits to the risks being considered.

A NOTE ABOUT EUROPEAN UNION EXIT
Changing Relationships

Historically, regulations have either originated as requirements under European Law – whilst Great Britain was part of the European Union – or been home-grown, sitting beneath *HSWA 1974* and developed following proposals made by the Health and Safety Executive. The UK's withdrawal from the European Union which took place on 31 January 2020, around two years before this book went to press, is unlikely to see many changes to our health and safety requirements[8].

---

8. The Health and Safety Executive has made minor amendments to regulations to remove European Union references, the examples of particular relevance to this book being minor changes to *the Health and Safety (Safety Signs and Signals) Regulations 1996 ('the Safety Signs and Signals Regulations'), the Control of Substances Hazardous to Health Regulations 2002 ('the COSHH Regulations'),* and *the Control of Major Accident Hazards Regulations 2015 ('the COMAH Regulations')* – but the present position is that requirements are to continue largely unchanged and the intention is for the high health and safety standards for which Great Britain is world-renowned to be maintained. Maintenance of the requirements of *the Safety Signs and Signals Regulations, the COSHH regulations, the COMAH Regulations,* and other affected regulations has been achieved by virtue of the *EU (Withdrawal) Act 2018* c. 16, as supported by *the Health and Safety (Amendment)(EU Exit) Regulations 2018* c. 1370. These regulations ensure the continuance of EU-derived health and safety protections within domestic law, following the UK's departure from the EU, and mean that – as this book goes to press – there is unlikely to be any material alteration to the *modern meanings* given to these fables, for the foreseeable future.

HSWA 1974 was created prior to the UK's joining of the union, is a robust piece of domestic legislation that has stood the test of time and – irrespective of any political viewpoint any of us might hold – seems likely to endure. But that doesn't mean there will be no change and our relationship with the EU, as well as the linkages between the various legal requirements – safety or otherwise – will inevitably evolve over the coming months and years. Some tweaks will be required where gaps emerge, with one area of focus being the need to find domestic substitutes for those institutions listed within legacy EU documents. This is an issue upon which *Ian's fable* – fable three – touches, with the tale raising as it does some interesting questions about the checks that might be required on *magic* lamps and, more particularly, about real-world product safety and provenance matters. Sweeping changes are perhaps unlikely but, just as with any relationship, some adjustment over time is surely inevitable.

EMERGING RISKS AND HORIZON-SCANNING
Grown-Up Risks in a Grown-Up's World

Let me level with you: this book took what seemed like an age to write, for a combination of reasons – a mixture of the need to keep down a full-time job to pay bills, coupled with a ponderous streak in the author. *That doesn't make it epic.* It just means that fables which started off as seeds of ideas tended to evolve organically, rather than in a linear fashion. Taking a protracted period of time to write something of this nature creates issues of its own. Statistics date – that's always true. But as time passes, the nature of the risk geography alters too. In this book's early stages, that might have meant a subtle change to legislation, or perhaps some updated injury figures. But we shouldn't presume that the challenges we face today will remain forever unchanged. In starting to write this book, the intention was for the concepts of 'emerging risk' and 'horizon scanning' to be little more than casual asides in *the four little pigs' fable.* Move on a few months, however, and as this book goes to press, it's against the backdrop of 'Coronavirus disease (COVID-19)' – a newly emerged infectious disease which threatens the wellbeing of us as individuals and that of broader society in a way that only those who have lived through world wars have previously been forced to contemplate – with events on a scale few could have foreseen[9]. The long term consequences of this pandemic have still to be fully determined, but it seems likely that its after-effects will be felt in the adjustment of workplace dynamics and the movement of wider societal norms for many years to come, even with the vaccine-based endeavours of clever scientists thankfully bearing fruit at the time of this book going to press[10]. These kinds of events poignantly show why it's not enough for us simply to be informed about existing risks – we must always be concerned about new risks too. As time moves on, there will undoubtedly be much to learn from this viral encounter but, at a basic level, it serves as a salutary reminder that in managing any kind of risk – as in all things – alongside the day-to-day stuff, it always pays to expect the unexpected. This matters not just on a global, national and societal scale, but for us all as individuals too.

HOW MIGHT THE SUCCESS
OF THIS BOOK BE JUDGED?

The honest answer to this question is *'I'm not entirely sure'*. If, in the coming months and years, the only evidence of this book's use is a dent from where it once propped up a wonky table, I'll know I have more still to do. On a more positive note, if this book moves even one person to think about safety with new or rekindled interest, or allows another to find joy in safety, where before they found it a tiresome irritation, then perhaps it will earn its place on a bookshelf rather than under the foot of a table leg.

---

9. The statistical data used in this book is the most up-to-date available at the time of going to press. Some changes to previous trends are already becoming apparent due to the Coronavirus disease (COVID-19) outbreak of 2020, but assessment of the enduring impact of this global pandemic has yet to be fully gauged. Whether changes to workplace incidents, injury and ill health trends are temporary or longer-lasting remains to be seen. This will likely depend upon multiple factors, not least whether the adjustments seen in work patterns and practices adopted by organisations and those who work for them will be reversed, or are here to stay.

10. The characters illustrated in this book have not been required to don 'face coverings', nor been made subject to the 'social distancing' measures that COVID-19 brought upon society, the focus here being upon the control measures routinely applied to address health and safety risks within real-world settings. It does, however, appear likely that these and other important additional measures will live long within corporate memory, even when the threat posed by this global pandemic has lessened in magnitude.

I don't profess that this book holds all the answers. If you want all the answers, then you should buy a conventional text book which takes a more mainstream line. But that's a well-trodden path and, in offering up an alternative approach, I'll be satisfied if this book simply opens up discussions and prompts questions amongst a wider audience. To this end, I welcome debate about the meanings behind, or interpretations given to, any of these fables. I also take the point that dragons, bears and pigs have so far escaped the rigours of *HSWA 1974* and its supporting legislation and guidance. But setting aside the idiosyncrasies of these and other species involved here, I'd venture to suggest that there's much to be learnt from the actions they take and the decisions they make, not to mention the simple enjoyment on offer to those who accept the invitation to embark upon this *safety safari* trip!

Now, where shall we start? Make yourself comfortable, adjust your seat pan, ensure your backrest provides lumbar support, and get a footrest if you need one. This could take a little time.

Goats it is...

LJC

PART ONE

THE SAFETY FABLES

The Three Goats Tough, Lone Working,
and
Managing the Risk of Violence and Aggression

THE GOATS' FABLE

'...the three Goats Tough retraced their steps to the spot back on the other side of the bridge, from where they had each set out, and together they reflected on the troubling events that had dogged their various work activities, in a bid to try to work out where things might have started to go wrong for them all.'

PROLOGUE

In this, the first of the fables, we accompany three goats on their various work visits, each of which requires them to pass by a less than agreeable troll. At one level, it's about goat/troll tussles. At another, it's about the particular task, location and social 'risks' faced by those who work alone and what can be done to manage these, so as to prevent them from coming to harm. It's the first of four *workers' fables* in this book which share a common purpose of showing what can be done to keep 'workers' safe – whether they are 'employees' or 'contractors' – in addition to those with whom they work or otherwise have cause to interact. Together with the three fables that follow it, this tale deals with a fundamental safety basic – in this case, lone working.

WHAT IS LONE WORKING?

The term 'lone working' describes circumstances in which work activities are carried out by workers in isolation, without the close, direct or immediate support of supervisors or colleagues. Practically speaking, if they cannot be seen or heard by their fellow workers, this tends to indicate that individuals are subject to lone working arrangements, whether forming all or part of their working day. Examples of lone workers include mobile workers in service industries who work away from their fixed base – such as postal staff, social and medical workers, engineers, and estate agents. Others who typically operate in this way include sales and service representatives visiting domestic and commercial premises, in roles commonly performed across the utilities and energy sectors. Changes to ways of working, including the continued rise of the 'gig economy', are increasing the prevalence of short-term, informal working relationships, with work delivered on-demand on a task-by-task basis, in roles often taken by lone workers.

RISK FACTORS

Some job roles and work activity types carry levels of risk which are inherently higher for lone workers than for other workers. Where workers are known to handle money, where the tasks they need to carry out are more likely to evoke a difficult or confrontational reaction from those they meet, or where there is an observable pattern to the routes they take or locations they visit, this can make them vulnerable to targeted attacks. Poor weather conditions and certain times of day – such as during the hours of darkness – can also increase risk levels. Environmental factors play a part too, with the level of risk to which lone workers are potentially exposed being raised, where there are difficulties related to layout, site conditions or location. The interactions lone workers have with other individuals are particularly crucial considerations; if members of the public might get upset or feel threatened by visits made to their homes, this can introduce additional risk to what, in the majority of cases, might be regarded as routine low risk activities. Some people can pose more of a threat than others too. Where, for instance, those being visited are suffering from a physical condition, or where their state of mind is poor – even if only temporarily – this places lone workers at increased risk. Under such circumstances, workers can unwittingly find themselves on the receiving end of 'violence', aggression or upset, or more vulnerable to being taken advantage of by customers or members of the public.

Examples of occupations susceptible to these adverse situations include bailiffs and others involved in debt recovery. Also, where work activities are of a sensitive nature – for instance, in the social care sector, or where there exist significant issues linked to alcohol or social deprivation – this can create sudden mood changes in 'clients' or members of the public and consequently introduce levels of risk which would not otherwise be present. It's important for organisations to recognise and address each of these factors before allowing lone working to take place, in order to ensure that 'control measures' have been considered and adopted to protect workers, as required. But equally, it's important for lone workers to understand the part they can personally play in calming situations and controlling the risks involved.

There are several work types which are never likely to be suitable for lone workers to perform, and employers need to use 'risk assessment' to guide their decisions about appropriate supervision levels in each case. Examples of work types where lone working is likely to be ruled out altogether include: 'confined space' working, a work type which often generates the need for a supervisor to be present, together with someone assigned to the role of rescuer; working in the vicinity of exposed live electricity conductors, and performing certain roles within the health and social care sector, where unpredictable client behaviours and situations are unfortunately commonplace.

THE LEGAL CONTEXT

This fable concerns the risks associated with lone working, including the potential for lone workers to be exposed to violence and aggression. Working alone is not, of itself, against the law in Great Britain and it is often safe to do so; indeed, when well-managed, lone working can also increase productivity and flexibility and reduce organisational costs. It is, however, important for the health and safety risks associated with the practice to be identified, and for these to be addressed by appropriate arrangements being put in place, before work starts.

The risks to lone workers arise principally because there is no-one to assist them, a factor which makes more acute the need for effective risk assessment arrangements. This need for risk assessment is one that runs across all risk types and is the process by which organisations identify, analyse and evaluate their risks, in addition to instituting the accompanying control measures. The *Health and Safety at Work etc. Act 1974*[11] ('*HSWA 1974*') calls for a risk assessment to be carried out for lone workers where such working practices exist – as a vital aspect of establishing a 'safe system of work'[12]. Taken in conjunction with the supporting *Management of Health and Safety at Work Regulations 1999*[13] ('*the Management Regulations*'), this means that steps need to be taken to avoid or control risks, where identified as necessary to protect the workers involved[14]. This duty is to be fulfilled in conjunction with

---

11. 1974 c. 37.
12. Section 2(2)(a) of *HSWA 1974* sets out the requirement for employers to provide safe systems of work, alongside a range of other general duties towards their employees, to be found elsewhere within section 2.
13. S.I. 1999/3242.
14. Regulation 3 of *the Management Regulations* sets out the requirement for employers to carry out risk assessments.

the corresponding requirements placed upon all employees to take reasonable care for their own health and safety and that of others affected by their acts or omissions at work[15] and to co-operate with their employer or others in the meeting of their obligations[16]. It's worth noting that if an employer is found to be at fault and in breach of legislative requirements, due to lone workers being threatened, attacked or injured at work, they could face prosecution and, upon conviction, imprisonment, with the organisation also facing fines.

A well-known and tragic example which highlights the possible consequences which can befall lone workers, where lone working risks are ineffectively managed, is that of *Ashleigh Ewing's case*[17]. Ashleigh Ewing, a mental health charity worker, was killed when she was sent to the home of Ronald Dixon, a paranoid schizophrenic, to deliver a letter informing him that he was in debt. She had been asked to do this on the last day of her probationary period of employment. Dixon, who had a known history of mental health issues, became angry and stabbed Ewing multiple times with kitchen knives and a pair of scissors. These events took place just months after Dixon had been detained outside the gates of Buckingham Palace for threatening to kill the Queen, whom he believed to be his mother. It was found that the charity concerned had not conducted a risk assessment on Dixon for three years. Had this been effectively performed, with Dixon's mental state taken into account, Ewing would not have been sent unaccompanied to his property and her tragic killing would likely have been avoided. The carrying out of a robust risk assessment – together with a revisiting of the organisation's lone working policy – would undoubtedly have resulted in the charity abandoning its lone working practice and adopting a joint visit approach in its place.

Dixon admitted manslaughter on the grounds of diminished responsibility and was ordered to be detained indefinitely at a high security mental health facility. The charity admitted breaching section 2(1) of *HSWA 1974*, which requires employers to ensure the

---

15. Section 7(a) of *HSWA 1974* sets out the duty for employees to take reasonable care for their own health and safety at work, and that of others too.

16. Section 7(b) of *HSWA 1974* sets out the requirement for employees to co-operate with their employers as regards any measures they adopt to comply with any duties imposed upon them by legislation.

17. For further details of the Ashleigh Ewing case (*case no: 4110872*), see the Health and Safety Executive's website www.hse.gov.uk.

health, safety and welfare of their employees. The prosecutor stated that the charity had '...*failed to identify and respond to the increasing risks to which Ewing was exposed in the course of employment...*', highlighting that, whilst it had not *caused* Ewing's death, further risk assessments and training should have been carried out by the organisation in order to protect her. The charity was ordered to pay £50,000. Following the inquest, the charity stated: '*We offer our sincere sympathy to her family. We deeply regret the failings which have been identified. Our practices and controls have been completely reviewed and revised.*'

Ashleigh Ewing's tragic story shows the true impact of lone working incidents, both for the individuals involved and those employing them. The gravity of the outcome in that case – for all concerned – demonstrates the critical need to identify risks to lone workers and underlines the importance of putting in place robust control measures, so as to protect these individuals from harm and prevent organisational exposure to fines and criminal penalties.

THE VALUE OF RISK ASSESSMENT

The case of Ashleigh Ewing is one of many that highlight the crucial role played by risk assessment in securing the safety and welfare of those subject to lone working arrangements. As is true for other risk types, this is the vital first stage to managing risks effectively. Risk assessment outcomes help to shape the choices employers make about control measures. In the context of lone working, risk assessment determines the level of risk associated with the practice and, where this is deemed to be unacceptably high, informs and steers the development of processes which mitigate or otherwise restrict it. If a risk assessment concludes that it isn't possible for work to be carried out safely by a lone worker – as is the case where violence and aggression risks are highlighted – this needs to be addressed by making arrangements to provide them with help or back-up. In making decisions about whether lone working is acceptable, it's important to note that some tasks may routinely be deemed too difficult or dangerous to be carried out by unaccompanied workers. This extends to circumstances in which work is undertaken at another employer's workplace; in such cases, it's crucial for the host employer to advise of any identified risks, with the accompanying control measures for the work activity being agreed upfront, and checks also made that relevant site rules are in place and observed for the location visited.

Taking a simplistic view of the nature of risks encountered in the course of lone working shows that these can be broadly divided into three different types. Some are practical concerns, directly linked to the nature of the tasks lone workers perform. Other challenges that arise relate to the work environment. And a third category covers the social interactions between workers and the people they encounter, as they go about their work activities. In deciding whether the practice of lone working is acceptable, employers should seek to answer a few key questions, to help evaluate the robustness of their arrangements for worker safety and welfare, given the particular circumstances. These include: *'Does the work involve the lifting of objects which are too large for one person?', 'Is there a risk of violence and aggression?', 'Have there been reports of attacks at this location, or in the course of particular work types being carried out?'*, and, *'Are there any other reasons why the individual involved might be more vulnerable than others and placed at particular risk if they work alone?'* (as could be the case for those who are young, pregnant, disabled or trainees, where the employer's *'duty of care'* is higher). If the answer to any of these questions is *'yes'*, lone working is unlikely to be viewed as an appropriate option. It's only where control measures can be put in place to sufficiently mitigate the risk, that lone working is permissible.

Training is a basic requirement under general health and safety law[18], but is particularly crucial in lone working situations, where there is limited supervision available to control, guide and help workers. It can also be instrumental in enabling them to cope with unexpected circumstances and potential exposure to violence and aggression. Lone workers may also need more training than other workers, as they are less likely to be able or inclined to ask for help in difficult situations. They need to be sufficiently experienced and fully understand the risks involved and precautions required, so as to enable them to account for issues particular to their work tasks and locations, together with any relating to the people with whom they might come into contact.

---

18. Section 2(2)(c) of *HSWA 1974* requires employers to provide employees with *'...such information, instruction, training, and supervision as is necessary to ensure, so far as is reasonably practicable, the health and safety at work of...employees...'*

THE FOCUS OF THIS FABLE

This fable looks at three lone workers, who just so happen to be goats. It explores the trio's behaviours, as well as the consequences of their actions, both for their own safety and that of their co-workers. It also considers the task-based risks commonly faced by this type of worker, in addition to location and social risks, based upon the nature of the characters' interactions with their work environment and others around them. In so doing, it prompts questions relevant in a real-world context, including: *'Who is working alone?'*, *'What are they doing?'* and *'Are they okay?'* As we shall see, from an – on the face of it – simple set of circumstances, come a number of important practical measures that can be taken to keep lone workers safe, whatever the nature of their employment status might be.

So, without further ado, let's follow each of the goats in turn, as they embark upon their journeys under the bridge...

THE FABLE

Once upon a time, there lived the three Goats Tough. They represented three generations of the same family and worked for the same energy supplier, but with very different roles and responsibilities. The continued service they had shown to the same employer over the years was a source of great pride for them all, and the three Goats Tough couldn't imagine working anywhere else! They worked from any location, within reason, enabling the organisation to meet the needs of its customers, keeping their homes warm and water hot.

There was Little Goat Tough...
He liked to jump. He was also a recently qualified meter fitter. He installed meters. He was a happy young goat, without a care in the world.

There was Middle Goat Tough...
He liked to have fun. He was a meter reader. He read meters and maintained metering equipment, following the installations carried out by Little Goat Tough and others like him. In truth, he liked his work, but wasn't keen on all the information he had to put into and take from company systems about the jobs he was doing, a process which he found

to be long-winded and tiresome. He just wanted to do what he needed to do, pack up, and get home to relax at the end of a working day.

There was Big Goat Tough...

He liked to eat grass. He worked in the revenue services' team, helping to recover debt for the organisation. He visited commercial and domestic premises, investigating, detecting and remedying instances of faulty metering, potential theft of gas, and abstraction of electricity[19], which stopped additional costs being passed on to bill-paying customers. Where it was suspected that 'energy theft' might have taken place, he was responsible for the securing of evidence too, liaising with local authorities as and when needed. In the more tricky cases, this also involved obtaining and executing rights of entry warrants from the local magistrates' court and dealing with local authorities and government agencies. But perhaps the most rewarding part of his role, as Big Goat Tough saw it, was that he was helping to avert the risks to safety – including fires, explosions and electrocutions – that interference with electricity and gas meters, pipes and wires could variously cause. There was no denying that his could be a difficult job at times, but one which he found hugely rewarding too. He was very proud of all he'd accomplished with the organisation, over the years.

There was a bridge...

A big troll had a home under the bridge. The big troll had a long history of drink and drug-related issues, which made him somewhat aggressive and his behaviour unpredictable. The bridge he called home was situated in one of the less desirable parts of town and was known by locals to be a no-go area at certain times of day. One by one, on separate occasions, the three Goats Tough each had to walk under the bridge and past the big troll, to fulfil their responsibilities and carry out their various work duties. They knew of no other route by which to reach their work location.

Tippetty-tap-tippetty-tap-tippetty-tap! Little Goat Tough approached the bridge, as he wanted to go under it. He was carrying the meter he was about to install. Up jumped the troll. He said, 'I want

---

19. Abstraction of electricity is a criminal offence, under the *Theft Act 1968*, c.60, section 13. See www.stayenergysafe.co.uk for details on how to report a suspected case of energy theft. [viewed 1 May 2021].

to beat you up!' *Little Goat Tough was frightened. The troll was angry.* 'No, no!' said Little Goat Tough. 'I have to install this meter. My dad – Middle Goat Tough – will be along some time soon to read and maintain the meter. He is big and fat. You can beat *him* up!'

'Yes,' said the troll. '*Yes, I can!* I can beat Middle Goat Tough up!' he said, thinking to himself that beating up a bigger, fatter goat would be a more enjoyable challenge. 'You can go under the bridge.'

Tippetty-tap-tippetty-tap-tippetty-tap! Little Goat Tough was under the bridge. He soon emerged on the other side of the bridge and swiftly carried out his meter installation work. Once finished, he started jumping around again, because jumping was his favourite thing to do. Little Goat Tough was so happy, he decided he would stay on the other side of the bridge.

Some time later...

Tippetty-tap-tippetty-tap-tippetty-tap! Along came Middle Goat Tough, to read and maintain the meter which Little Goat Tough had installed. He knew that Little Goat Tough was beyond the bridge, happily eating grass. 'Little Goat Tough is beyond the bridge.' he said. 'He has some grass to eat. I can go under the bridge, read and maintain the meter and when I am finished, eat some grass with him.'

Tippetty-tap-tippetty-tap-tippetty-tap! Middle Goat Tough was under the bridge. Up jumped the troll. He said, 'I want to beat you up!' *Middle Goat Tough was very frightened. The troll was very angry.* 'No, no!' said Middle Goat Tough. 'I have to read and maintain a meter. My dad – Big Goat Tough – will be along some time soon. You can beat *him* up!'

Privately, Middle Goat Tough knew that Big Goat Tough would soon be visiting customers who had failed to settle their bills, that he was somewhat short-tempered and more than a match for any troll. But he did not let on about this, instead preferring to use these insights to his advantage, by simply implying that a bigger challenge lay in prospect for the troll.

'Yes,' said the troll. '*Yes I can!* I can beat Big Goat Tough up!' said the troll, thinking to himself that beating up the biggest, most experienced of the Goats Tough would be sure to win him the respect and favour of the goat-fighting troll fraternity. 'You can go under the bridge.'

Tippetty-tap-tippetty-tap-tippetty-tap! Middle Goat Tough was under the bridge. He soon emerged on the other side of the bridge and wasted no time at all in carrying out his meter reading and maintenance work. Once finished, he found there was lots of space in which he could frolic about and have fun, which was good, because frolicking was his favourite thing to do. Like Little Goat Tough who had gone before him, he was so happy, he decided he would stay on the other side of the bridge.

Some more time later...

Big Goat Tough set out on his way to pursue debts from non-paying customers who had failed to keep up with their gas and electricity payments, on the other side of the bridge. Dusk had fallen and the whole area felt a bit seedier than usual. But this did not deter Big Goat Tough. Looking into the distance, through to the other side of the bridge, he could just pick out Little Goat Tough and Middle Goat Tough eating some grass, silhouetted against the dim light beyond. Eating grass was Big Goat Tough's favourite thing to do. *Oh, how he envied them.*

'Little Goat Tough and Middle Goat Tough are over the other side of the bridge eating some grass, having finished their work for another day,' he said. 'I can go under the bridge, recover some debt from a non-paying customer and, when I am finished, eat some grass with them.'

Tippetty-tap-tippetty-tap-tippetty-tap! Big Goat Tough was under the bridge. Up jumped the troll. He said, 'I want to beat you up!' *Big Goat Tough was not frightened.* This wrong-footed the troll, as he was used to being one step ahead, when it came to matters of bridge-based politics.

'No, no!' said Big Goat Tough. 'I want to beat *YOU* up! I also want to recover debt, as I'm investigating instances of faulty metering, potential theft of gas and abstraction of electricity.' This made the troll even more angry, as some of his troll friends lived in the houses just beyond the bridge and they resented paying for gas and electricity, feeling these to be basic troll needs – just like air and occasional exposure to natural light.

Big Goat Tough had a feeling that things might be about to turn nasty...

He wasn't wrong. A few harsh words were exchanged between goat and troll, and some rather unpleasant, garbled guttural noises could be heard coming from the troll's direction. The troll became *even more than* even more angry, causing him to be unsteady on his feet. In his rage, he tripped over one of the bottles in an area beneath the bridge that was strewn with litter. It had to be said, he wasn't the tidiest or most observant of trolls. Up he went – up into the air – before landing flat on his face! Fortunately, he wasn't injured, but it was fair to say that his pride was somewhat dented by the incident.

Undeterred, Big Goat Tough continued on under the bridge. He *tippetty-tapped* over the troll. He *tippetty-tapped* his way past an old gas holder[20], due for demolition. And he continued *tippetty-tapping* onwards, to recover debt from one of the troll's friends, who lived in one of the houses just beyond it. He was met at the house that belonged to the troll's friend by a warrant officer, who helped him with the debt recovery.

Tippetty-tap-tippetty-tap-tippetty-tap! And, with the debt recovery having been accomplished, Big Goat Tough *tippetty-tapped* his way to join Little Goat Tough and Middle Goat Tough. Big Goat Tough was delighted at this outcome, having been reunited with the other Goats Tough and with there being lots of lush grass for him to happily munch his way through. The three Goats Tough had fun in the grass. They ate and ate and ate. 'We like it here...' they said, before reflecting: '...but things could have turned out *very* differently for us...'

For even though things had panned out well for the three Goats Tough on this occasion, they knew in their hearts that they had been lucky and the trio agreed there were a number of aspects of their working practice that needed looking at, as a priority. If only they had communicated with each other, things would likely have been much more straightforward for them all. Little Goat Tough and Middle Goat Tough felt particularly sheepish (which was funny, given that they were goats), thinking they could have done more, perhaps by sharing stories of the difficulties they had each faced on their journeys under the bridge to carry out their various work activities, or maybe by referring to notes held on company systems, which Middle Goat Tough was known to find tiresome. But one thing was for sure, the realisation was dawning amongst them all that had they better communicated with each other, or behaved a little differently, this might have prevented Big Goat Tough from being exposed to the troll's violence and aggression. And even Big Goat Tough had to admit that, in the face of such situations,

---

20. Gas holders are large containers in which natural gas can be stored near atmospheric pressure at ambient temperatures, acting as a buffer and thus, removing the need for continuous gas production. The capability of modern gas distribution networks to function at full capacity without needing to have recourse to storage – due to larger and upgraded underground pipe networks – means that programmes for their decommissioning, demolition and associated land remediation are now well advanced in the UK, allowing the sites on which they are situated to be brought back into beneficial use. Some examples remain, but these structures are fast becoming the archaic relics of our industrial past. Arguably the most prominent remaining example is that of gasholder no.1 in Kennington, London (*built 1877-9, grade II listed*) situated next to the Oval cricket ground.

his behaviours and responses only ever seemed to make things worse.

Some time passed...

Rumours of the recent rise in reported attacks on lone working goats were rife in the organisation where the three Goats Tough worked. The Head of Safety had been tasked to investigate this alarming trend. With this in mind, the three Goats Tough retraced their steps to the spot back on the other side of the bridge, from where they had each set out, and together they reflected on the troubling events that had dogged their various work activities, in a bid to try to work out where things might have started to go wrong for them all.

They related their experiences to the Head of Safety who, having considered these and carried out her own investigation, summarised the situation thus:

'Here's a tale of three goats, filled with hope and ambition,
Three meter workers, keen on family tradition...

Little Goat set off first – the meter work *kid*
A goat with much still to learn, but who loved what he did.
When done with his work, this goat's joy knew no bounds,
Being happy with life, he would just jump around.

Middle Goat headed out next, a technology hater,
He shunned system alerts and ignored warning data.
He could have stopped for a moment or paused, just to think,
To regain control of a risk, that sat on the brink...

But this didn't happen, so the chances were lost,
As Big Goat Tough was to find out, it could have been to his cost!
He followed on last, as head of the herd,
But the risks that he took were, frankly, absurd;
In dealing with others, he simply caused confrontation
Never seeking to calm, only adding frustration.

This goat chose the wrong *gargoyle*, a troll clearly unhappy,
Inciting his anger, which turned the troll snappy.
The goats failed to liaise with those gone before,
All these bridge-based 'near misses', they seemed to ignore.

The warnings had been there, the area of town
A high-risk location, of known ill-renown.
To people, places, or tasks they gave not a thought
So the lessons were lost, due to a lack of reports.

They were dicing with danger, these gambolling goats,
They gambled too – with the troll – who went for their throats!
They were lucky, it's true, their fun swiftly resumed,
But success in the future should not be presumed.

As for organisations, those that fail to learn
Should regard *trolls under bridges* as a constant concern…
And not just troll risks, but other risks too,
Whether far off, on the horizon, or closer in view.'

And together the three Goats Tough made a pact that they would never again allow themselves to be outwitted by a troublesome troll. The organisation carried out a fundamental review of its approach to lone working, including the associated violence and aggression risks and, along with some other colleagues, the three Goats Tough signed up for a course on managing difficult situations.

And they all lived happily (and non-confrontationally) ever after…

MODERN MEANING

From what may, on first impressions, appear to be quite a short and simple fable come a number of important lessons. The focus here is a broad one, concerning the general risks associated with lone working, rather than those particular to the activities of energy suppliers, as used in the tale's fictional example. The lone working risks reviewed here can broadly be divided into three categories: *first,* task-based risks, being risks due to working unsupervised, ineffective information flows and technology, and risk assessment failings; *second,* location risks, such as those arising from work settings, workplaces and customers' home conditions, and *third* and finally, social risks, including verbal abuse, physical aggression, or attacks of any kind, which can stem from the behaviours of, or interactions with, other individuals.

TASK-BASED RISKS

Whilst there will always be aspects of a social and environmental nature inherent to lone working, risks related to the tasks performed by their workers are areas over which organisations ordinarily have the greatest level of direct control, hence why they are considered first here.

Analysis of this fable highlights fundamental weaknesses in the goats' approach, seemingly rooted in a failure by their organisation to assess the metering activities undertaken by its lone workers. In equivalent real-world scenarios, some tasks – such as the debt recovery activity performed by Big Goat Tough – are more likely than others to provoke a difficult or confrontational reaction, which the risk assessment needs to reflect. And, as the fable notes, some times of day, such as during the hours of darkness, make risk levels higher too. Risk assessment outcomes are crucial in this context, as they help employers to decide whether they have a problem, determine what action (if any) is required of them, and ultimately, shape effective lone working policies and arrangements, which keep their workers safe.

Gaining upfront management commitment by winning leadership buy-in to protect lone workers is key, as this sets the tone for the way in which the activities they perform are controlled across an organisation. 'Senior leaders' need to adopt a zero-tolerance approach towards violence and aggression, actively demonstrating this through their deeds and actions, and making sure that violence-prevention measures and support are in place across the full range of activities undertaken by their workforces. This includes recognition of lone workers as being a high-risk group because, whilst lone working does not automatically imply a higher risk of violence, it does increase vulnerability to it and reduce their ability to prevent incidents from escalating into more serious situations, due to the absence of proximate support from colleagues. It also means ensuring that those with medical conditions, or otherwise at higher risk, be given particular consideration within risk assessment and control processes, including medical surveillance, where appropriate. There was no management commitment evident here, but the three Goats Tough should have been able to draw confidence from knowing that they had the backing of their senior leaders, without fearing the personal repercussions that might have flowed from any decisions they needed to make. And it's worth noting that the relative inexperience of Little Goat Tough should have been a consideration too, in light of his having only recently qualified as a meter fitter. In some cases, the provision of insufficient welfare or support can be symptomatic of a poor manager/employee relationship. On the other hand, where there is a supportive organisational culture in place – with the concerns of workers being recognised and their involvement in solutions sought – this invariably leads to more positive outcomes. The support felt through a proactive management commitment helps to reduce the likelihood of lone working negatively impacting upon employees' work-related 'stress' levels too, as well as having a positive influence upon their mental 'wellbeing'. It's really important for organisations to understand the serious and long-term consequences of violence and aggression incidents for workers' psychological, physical and mental health. If these are not fully understood, the impact of work-related stress upon lone workers can prove to be devastating, as well as having wider repercussions for workforce culture.

The events of the fable would tend to suggest that there was no overarching management structure in place. This was a regrettable omission, because such organisational arrangements would have been crucial to delivering against any commitment made by senior leaders to ensure the safety and welfare of the three Goats Tough. Alas, there doesn't seem to have been any understanding of the challenges particular to these lone workers, nor evidence of a willingness on the part of management to safeguard them, at least not until the incidents that resulted were of such severity, and received in such numbers, that action simply had to be taken!

An effective lone working risk assessment should be carried out as a joint exercise, in advance of any such activities and tasks being undertaken, led by the organisation, and with input from the lone workers involved. As has already been highlighted, whilst lone working brings with it potential benefits for organisations – in terms of higher productivity, increased flexibility and reduced costs – certain circumstances can provoke an aggressive or hostile response from those with whom lone workers interact, which must be addressed. In this fable, as is often the case in real-world scenarios, the suggestion is that drug and alcohol problems were a factor. The handling of money and sensitive issues like debt, as here, are also tricky aspects which increase the likelihood of a lone worker experiencing a backlash, if left to handle a violent or aggressive customer or member of the public alone. Furthermore, the time of day at which work is carried out can have a big effect on the level of risk. Here, we are told that Big Goat Tough had set out to recover debt at dusk, meaning that '...the whole area felt a bit seedier than usual', raising the question as to whether this particular activity could have been differently scheduled. As such, the information seen in a risk assessment for the kinds of activities described here would typically include: *the context* – covering the type of work undertaken; *the environment* – encompassing location, security and access, and *the individual* – including the risk history of anyone being visited and, where possible, any known specific personal issues. Taking a step-by-step approach to risk assessment, by looking at each stage of a job in turn and working out the required control measures – including what workers need to do by way of self-help – is essential to ensuring risks are well-managed.

Upon completion of a risk assessment, a further important step is the communication of the assessment outcomes. It's imperative for all those involved – in this fable, the three lone goats – to be made aware of the contents of any relevant risk assessments, together with the identified control measures in place or available to safeguard them, and for these to be applied and followed throughout the duration of the work activity. There are various ways in which the briefing out of control measures can be achieved. It might be on a group or individual basis. It could be carried out either on or off-site. And it may include reference being made to paper-based or system-generated assessments, or a mixture of the two. But however organisations choose to communicate their risk assessment outcomes, it's generally most beneficial for this to be undertaken just before work begins. Having a good understanding of the tasks, risks and relevant control measures, and giving workers the opportunity to ask questions, including addressing any concerns they may wish to raise before a job starts, paves the way for work activities to be conducted in a well-controlled and safe manner[21]. Looking even earlier on in the process here, it might have been possible to apply stricter recruitment criteria, such that only those suited to lone working were selected for the kinds

---

21. As outlined in this book's introduction, employers are required to have 'consultation' arrangements in place with those who carry out work, or their representatives. For this type of work, employers would be expected to provide employees with information on the risks and dangers associated with lone working, the measures put in place to get rid of or reduce these risks, and what they should do in the event of them being uncontrolled.

of roles described. This could have included confirmation at interview stage of candidates' aptitude for handling potentially confrontational situations – noted as having been a particular flaw to Big Goat Tough's actions and behaviours.

No mention is made here of any risk assessments having been carried out. Had these been undertaken, and supported by the briefing out of control measures, the Goats Tough could have been forewarned of the troll's presence, together with any other risks associated with the route to their work location. This prior knowledge would have armed them with an understanding of on-site risks and the accompanying control measures, before their arrival.

In addition to having 'generic risk assessments' in place for given activities (which tend to be particularly useful for jobs which are routine and repeatable in nature), where the potential exists for situations to change rapidly there's an acute need for lone workers to be trained and competent in 'dynamic risk assessment' too. Ensuring that workers are adept at making quick on-the-spot risk assessments helps them to evaluate their 'personal safety', given the context of the particular circumstances in front of them, and to take appropriate actions in order to avert potential danger, which is personally beneficial to them and to others with whom they interact. In addition to the general failing in risk assessment already explored here, this fable highlights shortfalls in dynamic risk assessment. These weaknesses are perhaps not all that surprising given that dynamic risk assessments often build upon generic risk assessment outcomes, although this is not always the case.

In a real-world context, the capability to perform dynamic risk assessment is a key skill exhibited and practised by those who work in emergency service type roles – for instance, within the fire service – where all visits and calls made by emergency first responders are potentially dangerous or life threatening. This contrasts with the type of work described here, where it's likely that the majority of visits made by these lone workers – particularly those of the kinds performed by Little Goat Tough and Middle Goat Tough – were routine and therefore did not require a switch to be made into 'dynamic mode'. Where the skill of operating in dynamic mode is not routinely called upon, there is a risk that even those initially trained in the approach will not be adept at applying it – brought about by so-called 'skill fade' – due to the rare occasions on which it's required.

Here, the goats all appeared unskilful at switching into dynamic mode. Anticipation is key in circumstances such as these, and worker readiness to alternate between routine and dynamic modes is vital if events escalate rapidly, as they did here. Lone workers need to regularly assess their situations and the risks to which they are exposed. The goats should have switched to dynamic mode, but their failure to do so meant they faced potentially greater risk. Where workers are competent to assess risk on a dynamic basis, this will be reflected in their effective performance of dynamic risk assessment, and in their being empowered to recognise when a safe situation has the potential (whether gradually or rapidly) to degrade into an unsafe one, and to respond accordingly. As has already been highlighted, emergency first responders are highly trained in this technique, due to the nature of the work situations they routinely face, but where the need for workers to act in this way is exceptional or non-routine, as looks to have been the case here, they still need to have the capability to switch into dynamic mode as dictated by circumstances. Such an approach applies equally to other categories of lone worker, including those referred to in this fable's *prologue*.

The circumstances in which some types of work are carried out are such that lone working is never likely to be an appropriate option. In these cases, the need for double handling of jobs is an ever-present one, which can often be fulfilled simply by enlisting the assistance of fellow workers. Let's consider in a little more detail each of the three activity types this tale describes. It's likely that the meter installation activity carried out by Little Goat Tough, as well as the meter reading and maintenance activity performed by Middle Goat Tough, would ordinarily have been viewed as types of work capable of being undertaken by lone workers, without their personal safety being compromised. By contrast, the nature of the debt recovery activity performed by Big Goat Tough would have routinely required assistance, due to this work type often being perceived as confrontational in nature. Given the scenario the fable sets out, had Little Goat Tough seen fit to report his troll encounter, it's probable that assistance would have been deemed an appropriate control measure for Middle Goat Tough's work visit too. Following the visit by Little Goat Tough, the opportunity could have been taken to send two workers to carry out the job as there was, by that stage, a known risk of violence. This would also have been the case if the workers had raised a concern, and of invaluable assistance to Big Goat Tough too, when he went to recover debt from the non-paying customer. Indeed, in his case, perhaps an arrangement could have been made for him to meet with the warrant officer before he passed by the bridge-based troll, meaning he wasn't unaccompanied at any point. There's a clear benefit to be gained from double handling jobs where there are known location issues, such as the threat of violence and aggression posed by specific individuals. In this instance, the need for these kinds of control measures should have been picked up at risk assessment stage, as would also be true of the arrangements made for other types of lone worker, such as those identified within the *prologue* to this fable.

Another task-related issue the fable highlights is the need for an organisation to know precisely where its lone workers are, at any given point in time. This can often be achieved through the deployment of monitoring and alert methodologies. In cases where organisations elect to proactively monitor worker whereabouts, there's a clear benefit to be had in achieving the right balance between safety and policing priorities. Knowing a worker's location undoubtedly has advantages from a safety perspective, often helping organisations to detect and address welfare concerns at an early stage. Over-monitoring, on the other hand, can be detrimental to manager/team member relationships, particularly where workers believe monitoring levels to be excessive. When used effectively, however, monitoring tools can be highly beneficial, allowing for the timely intervention and resolution of situations where lone workers are perceived to be under threat.

In an equivalent real-world scenario to that involving the three Goats Tough, arrangements to monitor this type of work would typically include periodic visits and observations of work activities, with regular contact being made at pre-agreed intervals, for instance by phone, radio, or email. In such cases, options also exist for the use of manually-operated or automatic warning devices, which can be activated where there is a failure to periodically receive specific expected signals from lone workers. A further control measure often used by organisations is the implementation of systems which verify the return of lone workers to base locations or home addresses, upon completion of their assigned tasks.

Monitoring is an important aspect, and one common to the safeguarding strategies adopted by many an organisation, for the work activities carried out by their lone workers. Putting in place some form of tracking system which enables an employer or fellow workers to know where lone workers are and who they are with – at all times – can be an invaluable control measure and is an indication of organisations taking their duty of care obligations towards employees seriously. Organisations have many different methods of monitoring employee whereabouts, ranging from diary entries and information boards to virtual tracking tools. Robust checking in and out arrangements – which can vary from simple to highly sophisticated means – help employers to know where their employees are, as well as enabling organisations to identify whether an alarm needs to be raised, in circumstances where employees fail to call or check back into base within a pre-agreed timeframe. Depending on the size of organisation, this might include a 24-hour reception with which workers can check-in, enabling their off-site movements to be monitored, or the establishment of a buddy system between colleagues, where they can text or call a fellow worker to let them know the address they are attending and the likely duration of their visit, supported by follow-up contact once they have safely left. This means that, in cases where no response to the follow-up contact is forthcoming, the organisation can make arrangements to swiftly despatch others to the location and/or report a potential situation to the emergency services. This might have been of potential use to the goats, but the absence of detail supplied by the fable would tend to suggest that no such method had been adopted here.

Technology can also be of invaluable assistance to any organisation wishing to know the location of its lone workers, an example being GPS trackers, which can be used to track their movements and highlight concerns relating to their perceived whereabouts, notwithstanding the potential issues with over-monitoring already highlighted. Other more advanced technologies, such as geofencing, might be considered too. This is location-based software, with a facility which enables alarms to be set. Achieved by setting up a virtual boundary around a geographical location, it functions by providing an 'alert' when a lone worker leaves an area in which they should be working, or if they enter a high-risk zone.

Organisations often need to make decisions about *how* to set up a system of alerts, a key aspect for them to think about being the basis on which these should operate. A common-sense approach to system design is needed in such cases. It might be that a warning to leave an area should be overt for those not in the immediate vicinity of danger, but that communications with those already inside a danger zone should operate on a discreet basis, so as not to heighten the risk to them. Mobile phones or communication devices can be useful tools for lone workers who need to call for help, where safe to do so, to let others know where and how they are. It's important to ensure phones are charged, in credit and in working order. Personal alarms are a popular device too. These help to give workers confidence about their personal safety, as do panic alarms, another commonly used method for alerting colleagues who work nearby or remote from the location in question. Where personal or panic alarms are issued, employees need to be trained and competent in their use. Each of these methods might have been beneficial in the circumstances outlined here, provided that the relevant access to the chosen solution was made available to workers. The types of solution commonly adopted by organisations seeking to fulfil their communication-based control measure requirements can include: mobile devices, in-vehicle technology, and computer-based 'apps', to name but a few possibilities.

A major benefit offered by the more sophisticated tracking methods is that many have in-built functions, which enable workers to send a signal if they are in jeopardy. In the majority of cases for the work-types the fable describes, the expectation would be that urgent help would not be required. But in circumstances where an alert *is* required, a clear advantage offered by technological options is that they have the functionality to send instant automatic alarm notifications, signalling the need for assistance to be provided. This helps to give lone workers confidence that support will be forthcoming, at their request, as long as those organisations choosing to use such systems have sufficiently resourced back-up and response arrangements, covering the full range of situations in which an alarm might need to be raised.

Whichever method is adopted, it's crucial for regular contact between organisations and workers to be maintained, both to satisfy organisational monitoring needs and to prevent workers from experiencing feelings of isolation. There should also be an onus placed upon employees to advise their 'line managers' in advance, when they know they are to be working alone, including emphasising the need for them to provide accurate details of their location. This enables discussions to take place, which should lead to a plan being agreed between workers and managers as to how task completion – and withdrawal from a lone working activity – is to be notified.

The fable makes no mention as to how knowledge of the whereabouts of the three Goats Tough was to be maintained. Nor does the tale give consideration to the potential use of alert methodologies. In this instance, the goats travelling to properties near the troll could have been warned not to enter the area via overt means, whilst communications with those already engaged in activities within the danger area around the bridge might have needed to be handled via more discreet methods. There's also no indication given here of the Goats Tough having looked out for each other, by monitoring each others' whereabouts, nor any suggestion made of them having been monitored from a central location.

The degree to which the directing or supervising of workers is required will very much depend upon the risks they face or are likely to face, and is a management decision, which should be risk-based. Here, decisions about the extent of supervision should not have been left to the three Goats Tough, with these instead being made at a more senior level. Particularly where inexperienced workers are involved – like the recently qualified Little Goat Tough in the fable – there is a clear rationale for increased supervision arrangements being put in place. Here, this could have been accomplished by arranging for a co-worker with the necessary level of 'competence' to accompany Little Goat Tough, both when he first took up the post and throughout the formative stages of his employment, until such time as he had attained the required knowledge, understanding and experience to perform his duties independently.

When considering the deployment of workers to work activities at given locations or assets, attention should be paid to those with specific needs – so called 'vulnerable workers' – who could conceivably be placed at greater risk than those who face no such issues. Whilst no mention is made here of any of the three Goats Tough having suffered from a medical condition, this is a further aspect which should be considered by employers when evaluating the lone working risks for particular individuals. For those deemed to be vulnerable, both routine work and foreseeable emergencies might impose greater physical or mental burdens upon them than would be true for other workers. This needs to be identified and robustly addressed and, in some cases, might include seeking and acting upon medical advice. In the circumstances described here, it would have been prudent to account for the potentially higher risk faced by the newly qualified

Little Goat Tough, given that his level of experience of the tasks he was required to perform was notably lower than that of the other two Goats Tough.

LOCATION RISKS

There's a clear need for lone workers to understand the risks inherent to the locations or environments within which they operate, and also for them to know the control measures they should apply and actions they can personally take to reduce any such risks to acceptable levels.

When organisations take the time and trouble to gain upfront insights about the challenges particular to any given location, this can be invaluable to those individuals who have cause to visit or work there, helping them to anticipate and reduce the risks to themselves and others. Some locations are inherently more hazardous than others, for instance, due to their physical layout or condition. It's important for workers to consider how they might get out in an emergency, by checking their escape routes before undertaking work and in advance of any such situation arising. This could require them to think about and check multiple routes, should their most obvious or convenient one be unavailable for any reason.

A key lesson from this fable concerns the need for an emergency response or evacuation plan to be in place, which was clearly lacking here. We learn that, one by one – on three separate occasions – the three Goats Tough had *tippetty-tapped* their way under the bridge and past the big troll to fulfil their responsibilities and perform various duties. Taking the fable at face value, it seems reasonable to assume that the three Goats Tough didn't go through any pre-planning or discussion about safe routes to and from the work location. It also appears that they gave no thought as to the possible means of escape, in advance of setting off to carry out their work activities. This is borne out by the part of the tale which speaks of there being no other obvious route available to them, an issue that might have been overcome, had they discussed the issues particular to the location they were required to visit on a successive basis, as lone workers. In circumstances where threats are perceived, workers should be instructed to make excuses and withdraw from the situation, ensuring they are able to make a swift exit, if required. This is made much more straightforward when organisations plan for, and provide workers with training in how to handle, such situations in advance rather than calling upon them to make impulsive decisions in the heat of the moment, as seems to have happened here.

A further important aspect for lone workers relates to the quality of information communicated internally by organisations, about any location-specific issues, which includes the sharing and transferring of knowledge between co-workers and colleagues. The effectiveness with which this takes place can make a real difference to organisational understanding and control of risk. From the scenario described, it was apparent that each of the three Goats Tough arrived with no knowledge of the difficulties encountered by those who had visited previously, including location-specific issues, such as the presence of trolls. This is particularly worrying, given that the fable reports '...Privately, Middle Goat Tough knew that Big Goat Tough would soon be visiting customers who had failed to settle their bills, that he was somewhat short-tempered and more than a match for any troll. But he did not let on about this, instead preferring to use these insights to his advantage, by simply implying that a bigger challenge lay in prospect for the troll...' We see Middle Goat Tough warning off the troll, but no mention is made of his having related details of his troll encounter back to Big Goat Tough, who was to face him next. *They might have been connected as a family, but the Goats Tough didn't appear to see the value in collectively discussing such matters!*

In the case of Little Goat Tough, who visited the location first, it's quite plausible that no prior knowledge was available to the organisation at that time, with no detail having been recorded at that stage about the specific troll risk, albeit that the area was noted as being one of the less desirable parts of town. But it's clear that for Middle and Big Goat Tough, records of the previous incidents – including that involving Little Goat Tough – would have added to their base-level knowledge of the risks and could have informed the onward development of control measures, appropriate to their own circumstances. Liaison with the police and the use of work diaries, information boards and GPS trackers can also be of assistance in real-world scenarios equivalent to the fictional events described here. When used effectively, insights built upon the internal sharing of experiences and concerns – including reporting and investigating incidents and discussing specific issues – can be a highly effective way of improving the control of risk and, with time, help to spread a learning culture across an organisation.

Another type of tool which can be considered for use in lone working circumstances is that of early-warning system alerts. Some computer-based systems allow for flagging, a function which operates by highlighting known threats linked to specific properties, assets or locations, and can support and facilitate the relaying of such information between workers. The implication from this fable seems to be that, even if such warning flags were provided here, these were ignored. In the case of Middle Goat Tough, it's possible he was unaware of such information, because he found activities involving inputting into and extracting from company systems to be 'long-winded and tiresome'[22]. The tale makes particular mention of the troll's previous issues with drugs and drink – which made him somewhat aggressive and his behaviour unpredictable – insights which would clearly have been invaluable to the Goats Tough. As has already been highlighted, risk assessments for lone working activities need to – where appropriate – document knowledge of any historical hazard information relevant to the premises or locations visited by lone workers. Here, this could have included issues related to drug or alcohol misuse and/or mental health conditions amongst those with whom lone workers had cause to interact, which had been shown to be 'contributory factors' in previous 'incidents' and 'near misses'. Of course, it's worth noting that this information not only needs to be captured in a way which fulfils employers' obligations to carry out risk assessments and address the outcomes, but also to be balanced with the meeting of the requirements of the *Data Protection Act 2018*[23], which controls how organisations and businesses use individuals' personal information. It requires that information is used fairly, lawfully and transparently, and that it is adequate, relevant and not excessive.

Whilst not specifically featured in this fable, the use of mobile technologies by frontline staff – including apps – can assist with safer and quicker decision-making, bringing the added benefits of streamlining processes and reducing reliance on paperwork. This clearly has potential merits, albeit that management teams need to

---

22. The tale does not shed any light as to how recently the system had been introduced, nor the reason why Middle Goat Tough found this activity to be frustrating. This is the kind of issue that a real-world organisation can overcome through having an effective consultation process in place. Employers are expected to consult employees or their representatives about the health and safety consequences of introducing new technology.
23. 2018 c. 12.

keep effective control of any associated systems and data repositories, whilst staff entering data into company systems have a corresponding need to be mindful of the data accuracy and protection issues already highlighted. It's important to remember that such technologies are merely tools and, in order for them to facilitate knowledge-sharing, they need to be well designed, properly used and effectively maintained – for instance, by keeping warning flag data up to date, where used – just as is true for any systems-based approach. A point which emerges from the fable is that the failures by Little Goat Tough and Middle Goat Tough to transfer across information about known safety risks – including their omissions relating to this specific location – would undoubtedly have made subsequent visits by the goats more perilous.

In addition to the internal sharing of knowledge, developing effective liaison arrangements which facilitate the transfer of information to and from external parties, in the outside world, can be a real help for organisations seeking to manage location-based lone working risks. For those seeking to build these insights into their management approach, this means establishing dialogue and formal mechanisms with external stakeholders – which might even include competitors – where it's in the mutual interest of the parties to do so. Whilst not always the case, it can also be beneficial for liaison to take place with the emergency services, including the police, as they might be able to advise on personal safety and related issues, particular to certain individuals, activities or locations, or simply be able to share incident data and knowledge, beyond that gathered by the organisation itself. This information might be of a general nature or could refer to particular addresses or assets. In this context, an asset could include infrastructure which, whilst not of obvious financial value, is of strategic importance to an organisation.

SOCIAL RISKS

The overriding message about social risks which emerges from this fable is the very clear need for lone workers to be on the lookout for difficult clients or members of the community, particularly where aspects of a job role could be perceived to be confrontational in nature.

Whilst it can be argued that it's not within an organisation's gift to eliminate social risks, there remains much that they can do to ensure that these are well managed and controlled. A view held by some is that effective monitoring and supervision regimes reduce, or even remove, the need for additional measures to be put in place. But things can still go wrong – including where there are 'emerging risks' – and organisations need to have arrangements in place to cater for just such scenarios. Here, it appeared that all three of the Goats Tough were unclear as to the actions they needed to take in response to an emergency situation, which ultimately meant they were each unwittingly exposed to a higher level of risk. In a real-world context, all lone workers need to be able to independently handle and have confidence about what to do in such situations. Risk assessments naturally require the identification of foreseeable events and, building upon these, emergency procedures should be established which identify and address potential scenarios. A key output that should follow the publication of such procedures is for employees to be trained in an agreed response to emergency situations, with essential information being provided to lone workers which appropriately considers their needs. Additionally, and in accordance with the requirements of *The Health and Safety (First-Aid) Regulations 1981*[24] (*'The First-Aid Regulations'*), risk assessments often indicate that lone workers should receive 'first-aid' training and/or carry first-aid kits; where these are identified as control measures, appropriate training must be deployed and equipment provided. Workers should also have access to adequate first-aid facilities, together with emergency contact details, so as to enable them to take appropriate action in the wake of any incident and allow injuries to be attended to, as soon as casualties have been identified. All employers are required to make provision for first-aid and to inform employees of their arrangements[25].

It's also vital to make sure that appropriate incident response arrangements are in place. These should not only focus on the provision of post-incident support to the workers involved, but also capture important data to help with incident identification and reporting. Ensuring that incidents are well-managed, both from a proactive and reactive perspective, can prove to be an effective way of minimising any potential negative impacts and long term consequences for lone workers' mental health and wellbeing.

---

24. S.I. 1981/917.
25. *The First-Aid Regulations* set out the requirements for employers to make provision for first-aid (regulation 3) and to inform employees of these arrangements (regulation 4).

The fable indicates that the three Goats Tough lacked the necessary understanding about how best to deal with difficult clients and members of the community. This was an oversight which rendered each of them ill-prepared to deal with bridge-based trolls. It culminated with Big Goat Tough responding to the troll's goading, by saying: 'No, no!...I want to beat YOU up!' Additionally, some earlier errors of judgment made by the goats would only have served to exacerbate the situation, antagonising the troll and making the visits by subsequent goats more perilous. In a bid to address these kinds of problems and to help foster a 'situational awareness' skill set amongst their workforces, many real-world organisations will deliver training packages, the primary objective of which is to empower workers not to enter situations where they feel they are at risk. Such training needs to have the backing of senior leaders, who should also clearly endorse workers' decisions to safely withdraw from circumstances which they sense may be about to escalate out of control. When accompanied by the ongoing coaching of workers to help them develop the appropriate skills, this type of approach can be highly effective, but it does require organisations to make a thorough evaluation of the risks they are likely to face, as a first step. Workers should also be equipped with the skills to exhibit non-confrontational behaviours, as well as being given an understanding of non-verbal cues and the importance of paying particular attention to good customer care, being polite, listening, and responding to clients' needs. Such behaviours can be instrumental in defusing potentially confrontational situations. Just as has been highlighted here, there are some individuals (and trolls!) who – if a thorough risk assessment is carried out – will be recognised as posing a greater threat than others. This might be due to them having a known history of violent behaviour, but could also simply be as a result of their current state of mind or condition being poor – with them perhaps being in a state of upset or intoxication.

Finally, it's important to consider whether lone workers know what they will face and, indeed, if it's possible for them to be suitably prepared for the range of circumstances they might encounter. Here, each of the Goats Tough displayed a pitiful level of situational awareness. They seemed largely oblivious as to what lay ahead of them and patently shared a lack of perception as to likely scenarios, including the potential for escalation. Employees should be mindful of the need to keep their wits about them, being aware of their particular situations and the impact of their own actions, including having an understanding of how these might be perceived by others. When used effectively, such techniques can help to defuse potential instances of violence and aggression, and swiftly restore risk to acceptable levels.

CLOSING THOUGHTS

In concluding the review of this fable it's important to reiterate that, in many cases, lone working is safe. But where such practices exist, organisational arrangements need to incorporate from the outset the desirable mindsets, behaviours and approaches to be adopted by the individuals involved, with the control measures they are expected to apply being clearly set out and communicated to them. This is vital both for those who undertake such roles and the organisations employing them[26]. It's disappointing to note that neither the right organisational mindset, nor the appropriate approach to assessing and controlling risk, were in evidence here, flaws which ultimately appeared to compromise the safety of all the goats involved.

For a summary of practical points to take away,
based upon the topics and subtopics handled by this fable,
see *How to...* Guide One.

A NOTE ON REPORTING REQUIREMENTS

The events portrayed in this fable were of a purely fictitious nature. See the *Epilogue* for indicative reporting requirements under *the Reporting of Injuries, Diseases and Dangerous Occurrences Regulations 2013*[27] *(RIDDOR)*, which could be triggered by equivalent real-world circumstances.

---

26. For further information on how to keep lone workers safe, see Health and Safety Executive Guidance (2020), *Protecting Lone Workers: How to manage the risks of working alone* (INDG73).
27. S.I. 2013/1471.

The Pest Control Piper, too many Rats,
and
an Outbreak of Weil's Disease:
A Tale of Two Risk Control Strategies

THE PIPER'S FABLE

'Unfortunately, it seemed as if the Pest Control Piper's music had also induced a trance-like state within the children. Of itself, this appeared harmless, but it left many of them temporarily unable to fight the urge to take an impulsive swim.'

PROLOGUE

This fable sees us join with the Pest Control Piper, a 'worker' who takes a somewhat questionable approach towards a rat problem, in a twist on the childhood tale of a man in a sparkly coat, charged with ridding a town of vermin. At a basic level, his actions might be viewed somewhat humorously, as those of a flamboyant musical maverick. More seriously, they seem to suggest a more sinister character, showing a flagrant disregard for the most basic of health risk control principles for dealing with hazardous substances. In reading this fable, you can judge for yourself which of these perspectives seems the more valid.

This is the second of four *workers' fables* in this collection which, just like the fable that preceded it, deals with some fundamental safety basics – in this case 'risk control strategies' – one for the control of 'hazardous substances' and another for the control of 'contractors'. The account of events it gives offers us an opportunity to explore the accompanying responsibilities for each of these strategies which, as we shall see, should have collectively addressed the Pest Control Piper's working arrangements. The first of these relates to the control of the hazardous substance *activity risk*, which the Pest Control Piper was engaged to undertake, the hazardous substance in this case being *Leptospira interrogans*. The second addresses the robustness of the approach taken towards managing the Pest Control Piper *contractor risk*, for which the mayor and his council should have taken responsibility, this being a relevant real-world consideration, given that pest control is an example of a type of activity commonly outsourced by organisations. It's therefore only natural that the fable should prompt our exploration of both employer/employee and contractor/client type relationships.

WHAT IS LEPTOSPIROSIS?

The tale recounted here concerns a fictitious outbreak of 'Weil's disease', one of the two types of 'leptospirosis' infection. Whilst rare in Great Britain, this is a serious, potentially fatal bacterial infection, transmissible to humans via direct or indirect contact with infected rat urine, most commonly through contaminated water[28]. A harmful 'bacteria', it can enter the human body via cuts, scratches, or the lining of the mouth, throat and eyes following contact with infected urine or contaminated water, as is sometimes found in sewers, ditches, ponds and slow-flowing rivers. The 'disease' initially presents as a flu-like illness, accompanied by a persistent and severe headache. It can lead to vomiting and muscle pains and ultimately to jaundice, meningitis and kidney failure. In rare cases, this can prove fatal, meaning urgent medical attention should be sought if any such symptoms are experienced, following activities which might give rise to exposure. Leptospirosis is treatable with antibiotics, which should be given without delay following onset of the disease, so as to reduce the duration of any possible fever and avoid a potential hospital admission. For more severe symptoms, intra-venous antibiotics may be required, with liver and kidney manifestations of the infection likely to require intensive medical care.

WHO'S AT RISK?

People at risk of contracting leptospirosis include anyone exposed to rats, rat or cattle urine, or the foetal fluids of cattle. This means veterinary surgeons, meat inspectors, butchers, abattoir and sewer workers fall within risk groups, as does anyone who comes into contact with canal or river water. Whilst cases are rare, pest controllers – as exemplified by this fable's central character – are in constant danger of contracting it, meaning 'control measures' need to be put in place to prevent the disease. Nevertheless, it's true to say that improved working practices and workplace controls have reduced the number of cases attributable to occupational exposure. On the flip side, the rise in popularity of

---

28. *Leptospira interrogans* is a bacterial species (germ) containing over 200 pathogenic serovars (variations between immune cells of different individuals). These pathogenic bacteria, commonly referred to as 'leptospires' are the infectious agents that cause the zoonotic disease, leptospirosis.

water sports – including windsurfing, paddleboarding and canoeing, where the risk of skin abrasions is high – is such that exposure is now more commonly associated with recreational activities[29].

Leptospirosis is just one example of an illness brought on by hazardous substance exposure and, whilst the subject matter of this fable might initially appear niche and of limited real-world relevance, the 'hierarchy of control' principle explored here is one which applies across the gamut of hazardous substances. Every year, thousands of workers suffer illnesses contracted through exposure to them, the effects of which can be 'acute' or 'chronic' in nature. Diseases include lung diseases, such as asthma and some forms of cancer, and skin disease, including dermatitis. The costs associated with these health conditions are widespread and significant, with 13,000 deaths each year estimated to be linked to previous occupational exposures[30]. Businesses face costs to replace workers. Society sees costs in terms of rising sickness benefits and disability allowances. And, arguably of greatest importance, from a human perspective, affected individuals face the costs of reduced personal 'wellbeing', potential loss of employment, and consequential weakened financial security, the significance of which should never be overlooked.

A TALE OF TWO RISK CONTROL STRATEGIES:
The 'Rat Risk' and the 'Piper Risk'

In order to contextualise this tale, let's start with a simple two-part question: *'What's the risk, and who carries responsibility for its control?'* As we shall shortly see played out in this fable, defining the 'risk' is particularly crucial here, as there are two distinct types on show, both of which need to be effectively managed: *first*, there's the *rat risk* or activity risk, which centres around the lead pest controller character

---

29. Leptospirosis is an extremely rare condition. There are approximately 40-50 cases reported annually in Great Britain, of which one or two are likely to prove fatal. Public attention was drawn to the condition in 2010, when Andy Holmes, a rower and medallist for Great Britain's Olympic team, tragically contracted the condition with fatal consequences. 30. The figure cited is according to the Labour Force Survey, (2021), as quoted in *Health and Safety at Work, Summary Statistics for Great Britain 2021*. Health and Safety Executive. It is suggested that 12,000 of these deaths are occupational lung diseases, linked to past exposures at work.

– the aptly named, Pest Control Piper – and his control of the rats, and *second*, there's the *piper risk* or contractor risk, which concerns the client council's control of the Pest Control Piper's work, headed up by the mayor. As will become clear in this fable, and as is equally true when considering the later tales in this collection, understanding *which* risk is being managed is key. *Why is this?* It's quite simply because thinking clearly about risk from the get-go, as is also true for real-world organisations, sets us on the right path to determine risk ownership, in turn bringing with it the need to clearly assign any associated actions, and for appropriate control measures and monitoring arrangements to be put in place accordingly, on a continuous basis.

Given that, in this tale, a presumption is made that the relationship the Pest Control Piper has with the mayor and his council is of a contractual nature, we shall look at the 'control strategy' for managing *the piper (contractor) risk*, in addition to that for the *rat (activity) risk*, before seeing whether these approaches were – to any extent – managed by the characters featured here. It's worth noting that both the activity risk control strategy and the contractors' risk control strategy on show here have broader applicability, being seen by many real-world organisations as aspects essential to effective health and safety and, indeed, wider business management.

THE THREE-STEP RAT RISK CONTROL STRATEGY

The first risk conjoured up by this tale arises from the health hazard. The health hazard at the centre of the fable is *Leptospira interrogans* (*the micro-organism with the potential to cause harm*), with the risk being the outbreak and spread of Weil's disease to the community (*loss of control of the hazard being manifested in the spread of the disease*). Where this kind of risk is identified, a control strategy needs to be developed for dealing with the harmful micro-organism, the focus of which should be upon the activity or risk giving rise to infection. It follows that the activity risk control strategy we're about to look at here would have needed to address 'the activity (*or rat*) risk', specifically the outbreak and spread of Weil's disease carried by the rats to the community, this being the strategy for which the Pest Control Piper, or his employer, should have assumed responsibility, as 'risk owner'.

The legal requirements applicable to the control of a hazardous substance risk, an example of which the fable describes, are primarily to be found within *the Control of Substances Hazardous to Health Regulations 2002*[31] ('*the COSHH Regulations*'), as amended, which are helpfully encompassed within the '*assess-control-review* model'[32] recommended by the Health and Safety Executive. The regulations and the control principles they articulate are additional to the 'general duty' imposed upon employers under *the Health and Safety at Work etc. Act 1974* ('*HSWA 1974*')[33] requiring them to put in place '...*arrangements for ensuring, so far as is reasonably practicable, safety and absence of risks to health in connection with the use, handling, storage and transport of articles and substances...*'[34] They cover a wide range of hazardous substances, including germs such as leptospirosis. As a human 'pathogen', leptospirosis falls within hazard group 2, in accordance with the classification of 'biological agents' by 'hazard group' given within *the COSHH Regulations*, and as shown in *Table 1*.

GROUP 1	Unlikely to cause human disease.
GROUP 2	Can cause human disease and may be a hazard to employees; it is unlikely to spread to the community and there is usually effective prophylaxis or treatment available.
GROUP 3	Can cause severe human disease and may be a serious hazard to employees; it may spread to the community and there is usually effective prophylaxis or treatment available.
GROUP 4	Causes severe human disease and is a serious hazard to employees; it is likely to spread to the community and there is usually no effective prophylaxis or treatment available.

Table 1: Classification of Biological Agents

---

31. S.I. 2002/2677.

32. This three-phase model is a tool which helps a judgment to be made about whether the requirements of *the COSHH regulations* have been fulfilled for a given activity. For further detail on this model, refer to https://www.hse.gov.uk/construction/healthrisks/managing-essentials/managing-essentials.htm [viewed 1 May 2021]. The requirements of *the COSHH regulations* are supplementary to the general requirements contained within regulation 3 of *the Management of Health and Safety at Work Regulations 1999*; S.I. 1999/3242, which sets out risk assessment principles for all work activities and workplaces.

33. 1974 c. 37.

34. This requirement is set out at section 2(2)(b) of *HSWA 1974*.

The COSHH Regulations have a broad scope, including hazardous substances which are both natural and artificial. The regulations apply to biological agents[35], as we'll see here. They cover any substance which has been assigned a 'workplace exposure limit' (WEL) too. And they also encompass substances which are very toxic, toxic, harmful, corrosive or irritant in nature, applying to all forms, including fumes, dusts, vapours and mists, gases and asphyxiating gases.

Let's take a look at the aspects of *the COSHH Regulations* of particular interest here. The regulations are helpful because they set out a structure for organisations to assess and control the risks from hazardous substances which, when followed, shapes an effective control strategy. Such a strategy needs to address the following requirements, as appropriate[36]: *first,* an employer is not to carry out work which is liable to expose employees to any substance which is hazardous to health, unless a 'suitable and sufficient' risk assessment ('COSHH assessment') has been made; *second,* exposure to hazardous substances is to be prevented or controlled; *third,* control measures are to be used; *fourth,* control measures are to be maintained, examined and tested; *fifth,* 'workplace exposure monitoring' is to be carried out; *sixth,* 'health surveillance' is to be put in place; *seventh,* information, instruction and training is to be delivered to those who could potentially be exposed, and *eighth,* and finally, arrangements are to be put in place for dealing with 'accidents', 'incidents' and emergencies.

---

35. The classification of biological agents is set out in *the COSHH regulations,* regulation 7(10), at Schedule 3, Part I, paragraph 2(2). *Leptospira interrogans* is classified within Group 2 as per the Health and Safety Executive's publication (2021); *The Approved List of Biological Agents (Advisory Committee on Dangerous Pathogens).* This list is applicable to those working with animals who are, or who are suspected of being, infected with such an agent, in addition to those who work with them in research, development, teaching or diagnostic laboratories and industrial processes.

36. These eight requirements are to be found within *the COSHH regulations,* regulations 6-13, the specifics of which are: regulation 6, which requires a COSHH assessment (an assessment of the risk to health created by work involving substances hazardous to health) to be carried out; regulation 7, which requires exposure to hazardous substances to be prevented or controlled; regulation 8, which deals with the use of control measures; regulation 9, which requires control measures to be maintained, examined and tested; regulation 10, which deals with the carrying out of workplace exposure monitoring; regulation 11, which deals with the putting in place of health surveillance; regulation 12, which requires the provision of information, instruction, training and supervision to those who might be exposed to hazardous substances, and regulation 13, which handles the arrangements to be put in place for dealing with accidents, incidents and emergencies.

The key control principles set out by the regulations apply to the leptospirosis risk, just as they do to risks arising from other substances hazardous to health[37]. The regulations require an assessment to be carried out for all activities where a risk of hazardous substance exposure exists. And upon completion of a COSHH assessment, employees need to be told about any risks and given instruction on how and when to use control measures including, for instance, any 'personal protective equipment' (PPE) and ventilation required, for the activity in question. The strategy for a rat-ridding activity of the type we'll observe here would be expected to address the following three steps, so as to meet the requirements of the regulations and apply the approach of the *assess-control-review* model, these steps being to: *first,* assess the health risk; *second,* control the health risk, and *third,* and finally, review the health risk. Checking the fable's activities off against each of these steps will allow us to look methodically at how the Pest Control Piper might have measured up to the expectations placed upon him.

Outlined here are the three steps to the strategy, which will be used to evaluate the events of the fable, to see the degree to which the requirements for control of the rat risk were met.

STEP #1
ASSESS THE HEALTH RISK

Managing a health risk, just like any other risk, calls for a clear plan which begins with assessment. When starting to manage any health risk – in this case, the rat control activity risk – this step requires the following four aspects to be addressed: *first,* planning the overall strategy for managing the risk; *second,* identifying the risk; *third,* assessing the risk, and finally, *fourth,* involving people in the assessment of the risk.

We'll look at whether an effective assessment of the health risk appears to have been carried out here, by or for the central Pest Control Piper character, given the events the fable describes.

---

37. For further guidance on the practical steps which can be taken to achieve control of a leptospirosis risk, the hazardous substance relevant to this fable – including what it is, how it might be caught, the ways of preventing it, and what can be done by those who contract the disease – see Health and Safety Executive Guidance document (2012); *Leptospirosis: Are you at risk?* (INDG84).

STEP #2
CONTROL THE HEALTH RISK

Having assessed a health risk and put a plan in place to address it at the first step, this second step looks at putting this plan into action to control it, and ultimately prevent cases of ill health – in this case, Weil's disease. As such, it involves the following aspects: *first,* preventing the risk before work begins; *second,* controlling any risk that cannot be fully prevented, and finally, *third,* training workers in what they can do to help control the risk of exposure. The requirements of this step, which are of a more practical nature than those identified for the first step, feed directly on from the plan developed there.

We'll consider whether appropriate control measures were applied to the health risk, given how the activities detailed in the fable play out. We'll also look at the key principles that need to be followed under the COSHH Regulations, to control hazardous substances and the diseases they cause, such as leptospirosis. And we'll take a look at the PPE requirements, making a judgment as to whether the attire donned by the Pest Control Piper was appropriate for the nature of the work activities he was called upon to carry out, and likely to have met the legal requirements.

STEP #3
REVIEW THE HEALTH RISK

With the health risk having been assessed and controlled, the focus of this third and final step to the activity risk control strategy is upon reviewing the risk, which checks that the controls put in place are actually working – albeit that the controls we shall see here were, of themselves, inherently flawed. This step involves the following aspects: *first,* supervising workers; *second,* maintaining control measures; *third,* monitoring control measure effectiveness, and finally, *fourth,* taking action, in circumstances where a need for additional control measures is identified. This step is just as critical as the first two steps that precede it – because the strategy not only needs to secure the implementation of the right control measures for the health risk in the first place, but also to check that they are still working effectively, so as to control the risk on an ongoing basis. The review step is the ideal point at which to take stock of a work activity, thinking about how well it has been executed and considering whether any additional action is necessary – as such, this is about resolving any problems identified, positively acting on lessons learnt, revisiting plans and risk assessments, and seeing if any of these are in need of update.

We'll look at whether the opportunity was taken to review the incident the fable portrays, which would have enabled the Pest Control Piper and his employer to learn and address the lessons from his approach towards controlling the health risk.

With the scene having been set for the leptospirosis (activity risk) control strategy – which, as we shall see, should have fallen to the Pest Control Piper to manage – it's here that the context for the piper (contractor risk) control strategy is provided, this being the aspect for which the mayor and his council would have carried ultimate responsibility.

THE FIVE-STEP PIPER RISK CONTROL STRATEGY

This fable also prompts exploration of a second risk, namely that which relates to a contractor-based hazard. We'll see that here this hazard arises due to the engagement of a contractor, the Pest Control Piper, to carry out pest control work (*the activity with the potential to cause harm*), with the accompanying risk being the failure to deliver against his contractual obligations towards the council, his client, specifically to eliminate the rats and the disease (*loss of control of the hazard in this case being a deviation from the contractual agreement*). As will soon become apparent, the responsibility which rested upon the mayor and his council would have been for managing the contract under which the Pest Control Piper's services were supplied – in a 'client' capacity – rather than for directly managing the Weil's disease risk. But whilst it's true to say that the emphasis of this type of strategy should be upon effective management of a contractor risk – with the contractor being called upon to manage the hazardous substance risk – both risks remain, meaning effective co-operation between all involved would have been required in order to address them. Fundamental to any client/contractor relationship is the need for there to be positive collaboration with a focus on, and engagement in, good health and safety practices, this being seen as integral to the roles the parties are expected to perform, rather than simply as an optional adjunct to them.

Where a risk of this kind is identified, a contractor risk control strategy needs to be developed, the emphasis of which is upon effectively

managing the person or organisation to whom the management of the
activity risk is formally delegated or contracted out. Essentially, this
tale is about controlling a pest control contractor undertaking short-
duration contracts, with the Pest Control Piper, in turn, being charged
with responsibility for controlling the activity or infection risk. In this
case, the assumption is made that he was employed by a contractor
organisation, rather than operating as a one man band. As such, it
follows that he would have been subject to direct supervision by his own
contractor organisation, rather than being managed as a member of the
council's own workforce. Approaching the scenario from this perspective
means that here he should have enjoyed a normal employee/employer
relationship with the contractor organisation. For this to have been
effective, however, the contractor risk control strategy here would have
needed to address the contractor (*or piper*) risk – in this case, managing
the delivery of the Pest Control Piper's contractual obligations – with the
responsibility for it being laid squarely at the door of the mayor and his
council colleagues, and the mayor regarded as risk owner. It's important to
note that, on the basis of the detail this fable contains, the works described
here would not have fallen within the scope of *the Construction (Design
and Management) Regulations 2015*[38] ('*the CDM Regulations*'), as they are
not deemed to have been 'construction work' but, for completeness, a
reference to them has been included, as a footnote[39].

Let's look in a bit more depth at what a contractual arrangement
would have meant in these circumstances. A 'contractor' refers to any
individual or organisation entering into an agreement – whether written
or oral – with another organisation to carry out services on its behalf, the
example we'll see sketched out here being the engagement, by the mayor
and his council, of a Pest Control Piper to perform rat catching and culling
services. Many activities, of which pest control is just one, are commonly
contracted out and, provided such arrangements are effectively managed
by a client, taking on a contractor can often prove to be the most sensible
and beneficial option all round. This is particularly so where the activities
undertaken by contractors don't form part of an organisation's core

38. S.I. 2015/51.

39. *The CDM regulations* apply to commercial clients who have construction work
carried out for them, the main duty being the one placed upon clients to make sure
that any project they carry out is suitably managed, being performed in such a way
as to ensure the health and safety of all who might be affected by the work, including
members of the public.

business, with them often possessing specialist expertise and skills that a client wouldn't routinely have cause to call upon. It is, however, right to point out that, even where organisations elect to use contractors, the health and safety responsibilities towards these individuals are no less onerous than those applied to their own employees – they are simply differently distributed. These legal duties – so-called general duties – are imposed upon all employers by section 2 of the *Health and Safety at Work etc. Act 1974*[40] ('*HSWA 1974*'), requiring them to take all 'reasonably practicable' steps to ensure the health and safety of their employees. But on top of this, organisations have obligations towards contractors and others working on site, and members of the public too, who might be affected by their activities, or more specifically: '*It shall be the duty of every employer to conduct his undertaking in such a way as to ensure, so far as is reasonably practicable, that persons not in his employment who may be affected thereby are not…exposed to risks to their health or safety.*'[41] The essential point to take from this is that the use of a contractor does not entitle organisations to delegate their health and safety responsibilities; they remain ultimately responsible for the risks generated by their activities, needing to take all reasonably practicable steps to control them. For a start this means that all employers are required to undertake a risk assessment[42] which, wherever necessary, needs to include contractors, in addition to employees and anyone else who might be impacted by the proposed work.

It's also appropriate to note that contractors have equivalent duties in their own right too – including the need to ensure the safety, health and welfare of their own employees and others, and to provide a safe place of work and 'safe systems of work' on clients' premises – just as they are obliged to at their own. They are subject to the same requirements as would apply to any employer which, in the context we'll see here, means they need to make an assessment of all activities where a risk of exposure to hazardous substances exists, advise their own employees about any associated risks, and inform them of the need to use control measures, including PPE and ventilation. And, just as is true for any organisation,

---

40. 1974 c. 37.

41. Section 3(1) of *HSWA 1974* sets out the general legal duties imposed upon employers to ensure the health and safety of persons other than their employees. Also, whilst not directly relevant to the scenario set out in this fable, section 3(2) imposes an equivalent duty upon those who are self-employed.

42. Regulation 3 of *the Management Regulations* sets out the requirement for employers to carry out a risk assessment.

other specific requirements to which contractors fall subject are shaped by the nature of the activities being undertaken, which will obviously vary on a case-by-case basis. Managing contractors requires strong leadership to be shown by those engaging them and there needs to be a common understanding upfront about any work the contractor is being taken on to complete, with the accompanying 'competence' requirements and standards they are required to meet being clearly set out and agreed.

Thought also needs to be applied to the contingency action to be taken on the occasions when, as can often be the case, things don't go to plan. It should be made clear to contractors that health and safety is paramount, with management support given to the halting of work in instances where serious concerns are raised. Where failings are highlighted, these need to be efficiently addressed, with actions backed by 'senior leaders', on both sides. Targets should be set right from the start, so as to drive performance levels – without inadvertently encouraging short cuts – and sufficient time and resource allocated to the agreed activities by all concerned. As we shall see in this fable, the use of a contractor should have been beneficial here. *Why?* It's because, had it been well-run, the contract would have removed the need for the council, as client, to maintain specialist in-house pest control expertise, thus saving them time and money. The flip side to this, of course, is that the outsourcing of an activity in this way naturally brings with it an additional need to interact, making effective co-operation and communication vital to ensuring all parties are clear on, and able to meet, their obligations right from the start – aspects which we shall see being poorly met here. Contractors who take a responsible approach will typically show this from the earliest stages of contractual negotiations, by willingly engaging in discussions with a potential client organisation, as the party with whom they are contemplating entering into a formal business relationship.

The strategy for managing contractors effectively can be broken down into five key steps, which are outlined here and align to those set out in Health and Safety Executive guidance[43]. Checking the fable's activities off against each of these steps will allow us to look methodically at how the mayor and the council might have measured up to the expectations placed upon them. In order to evaluate this risk control strategy, which

---

43. Guidance on the practical steps that can be taken to achieve safe working with contractors is to be found in Health and Safety Executive Guidance (2011) *Managing Contractors: A guide for employers* (HSG159); see also Health and Safety Executive Guidance (2013) *Using Contractors – A brief guide* (INDG368).

focuses on managing the contractor (*or piper*) risk – just as is to be done for the activity (*or rat*) risk – each step will fall to be considered, with the emphasis for the contractor risk control strategy shifting to how well the Pest Control Piper, with direct responsibility for managing the rat-culling activity, was managed from a contractual perspective. These steps are to: *first,* plan the job; *second,* pick the contractor; *third,* induct the contractor; *fourth,* check-in with the contractor, and *fifth,* and finally, review the work of the contractor. It's worth pointing out that these steps should be taken sequentially in the first instance but, in reality, it's often the case that something identified at one of the later steps will trigger an earlier step to be revisited. An example would be that *step four* – check-in with the contractor – could give rise to issues requiring some or all of the job to be replanned, calling for *step one* – plan the job – to be repeated, and so on.

In circumstances of the kind highlighted by this fable, it's particularly crucial for clients to ask the right questions at the right time, so as to help inform and drive the effective control of the contractor risk, and thus ensure that the requirements for managing it are being met collectively by the parties. To this end, indicative questions – of the kinds that also need to be asked by real-world organisations in relation to their potential contractors – have been included at the relevant points within *How to... Guide Two,* which accompanies this fable, these being the types of questions which would also have helped the mayor and his council to better manage *the piper risk.*

Let's now take a look at the steps that would be expected to feature within the piper risk control strategy. These are to be used to evaluate the events of the fable and help determine the degree to which the characters involved – specifically the mayor and his council colleagues – met the requirements for controlling the risk of taking on a contractor.

STEP #1
PLAN THE JOB

This first step is crucial, insofar as it lays the foundations for a contractor to be managed effectively by a client from the start and paves the way for the job to progress as intended. *Why?* Because it sets the scene, means all parties understand what the job involves, and enables decisions to be jointly made about how it can be performed safely. It also provides clarity as to the scope of the parties' respective roles and responsibilities – or *who needs to do what* – right from the outset.

Planning a job calls for the following aspects to be addressed: *first*, defining the job; *second*, identifying the hazards; *third*, assessing the risks; *fourth*, controlling the risks; *fifth*, specifying the health and safety conditions, and finally, *sixth*, discussing the job with the contractor.

We'll look at whether the job was planned effectively here.

STEP #2
PICK A CONTRACTOR

Having planned the job, the purpose of this next step is to reach a reasoned decision as to *who* should carry it out, via a selection process. Selecting the right contractor is a pivotal step in the forming of a positive working relationship between the parties involved, and one which – if well attended to – makes it far more likely that a contract will be effective, in the long run. This means it's not a step to be rushed or entered into lightly. As will become apparent from the tale, mistakes or rash decisions can easily be made when a contractor is taken on as a *quick fix* or in an emergency situation, where a need arises to arrange for work to be done in a hurry, an approach which can often lead to problems further down the line. Picking a contractor calls for the following aspects to be addressed: *first*, determining the safety and technical competence needed; *second*, asking questions; *third*, getting evidence; *fourth*, going through the job and site rules; *fifth*, asking to see a method statement, and finally, *sixth*, deciding whether sub-contracting is acceptable.

We'll look at whether the picking of the Pest Control Piper, as a contractor, took place in the right way here.

STEP #3
INDUCT THE CONTRACTOR

A suitable party having been chosen to perform the work, it's next that consideration needs to move to the provision of appropriate information to them. This is the opportune moment for the parties to exchange information, and allows the arrangements for the job to be formally checked in advance of work starting. The client organisation needs, however, to recognise that a job can change from day to day, and should accordingly arrange to check in regularly with the contractor, not only at the start of each day or shift, but also on an ongoing basis and particularly when there are alterations to site conditions, or if the job is modified in any way. Inducting a contractor calls for the following aspects to be addressed: *first*, setting the arrangements for contractors to sign in and out; *second*, naming a site contact; *third*, reinforcing health and safety information and site rules; *fourth*, checking the job and *fifth*, and finally, allowing work to begin.

We'll look at whether the Pest Control Piper was inducted to site in the right way.

STEP #4
CHECK-IN WITH THE CONTRACTOR

With work having started, this step's principal focus is upon making sure that things are progressing as intended. It's good to use this step of the process as an opportunity to make sure that the contractor's 'health and safety management system' and the client organisation's own are working effectively together, with checks being made that the required levels of supervision are in place and that responsibility has been assigned to stop the job or take action, should it become apparent that agreed standards are not being met. It's by proactively engaging at this point, with responsibilities between the parties being clearly defined, that problems can be averted before they become more serious or deep-seated, as can often be the case if they occur further down the line. Assuming that the three preceding steps have been followed, the contractor should have established themselves on site by this point and work should be progressing well. *But this isn't always the case!* Checking in with a contractor calls for the following aspects to be addressed: *first*, assessing the degree of contact needed; *second*, checking that work is going as planned; *third*, making sure that work is being carried out safely and as agreed; *fourth*, checking to see if any incidents have taken place and following them up, where required; *fifth*, identifying whether there has been any change to personnel, and finally, *sixth*, determining whether any special arrangements are needed.

In addressing this step, we'll look at whether sufficient ongoing checks were made on the contractor, in this instance.

STEP #5
STOP, TO REVIEW THE CONTRACTOR'S WORK

This fifth and final step is a really crucial one to get right, not least because it's the point at which an evaluation of the four steps which preceded it takes place. Fundamentally, the following of each aspect of this step should be a positive experience for all involved, bringing benefits to the client organisation and contractor alike, and helping both parties to learn from mistakes made at any point leading up to and including this review step. Reviewing the work of a contractor calls for the following aspects to be addressed: *first,* reviewing the job and the contractor; *second,* evaluating the effectiveness of the planning step; *third,* determining how the contractor performed; *fourth,* drawing conclusions and establishing how the job went overall, and *fifth* and finally, reviewing lessons learnt and working out how these can be applied in the future. Using this final step to draw conclusions about whether or not a job has been carried out satisfactorily and as agreed, as well as recording lessons about any shortfalls in contractual performance, provides invaluable data. It's this which makes it fundamental not to miss out the review step!

We'll look at whether the review step was well addressed in this case.

Having now set the scene for both the piper (contractor) risk control strategy and the rat (activity) risk control strategy – including the steps involved in each of them – it's now that attention turns to the fable and its accompanying *modern meaning,* which shows the relevance of the tale in a real-world context.

THE FOCUS OF THIS FABLE

This fable follows in the footsteps of a strange fluting fellow. By focusing on the Pest Control Piper's pest control efforts, it prompts some awkward questions about how a serious community outbreak of a 'zoonotic disease' could have been allowed to flow – apparently unchecked – from the seemingly happy origin of a merry town parade. In looking at both the control of activity and control of contractor risks, the fable invites judgments to be made about the degree to which the fictional characters involved met the expectations of each of the associated risk control strategies, and ultimately, the effectiveness of their arrangements for controlling both types of risk the fable portrays.

So, without further ado, let's join with the Pest Control Piper and some rodent rascals, before seeing what lessons might be learnt from the events of this tale...

THE FABLE

A long time ago, there was a town called Hammersmith, where the people had plenty of everything, including a gyratory, a flyover and an entertainment venue, known as the Apollo. The shops were high-end, cupboards were well stocked with food and life was idyllic. *Until, that is, the arrival of a few rats...*

In no time at all, huge families of rats were scurrying around everywhere, as bold as brass. They pillaged cheese from delicatessen counters. They drank soup from the artisan food stalls and stole meat from the plates laid out on the tables of local carveries. They made nests in hard hats left on local building sites and chewed up shoes and clothing at community recycling centres too. Frequently, the rats were so loud that people couldn't hear themselves talk, such was their tendency to interrupt commuters' conversations with their shrieks and squeaks, in a range of multiple sharp and flat notes. Even by night, there was no respite, as they shamelessly ran amok, their scratchy little feet drubbing relentlessly as they scuttled across wheelie bins and drain covers and shinnied up gate posts and shop frontages. Unsurprisingly, these habits made them highly unpopular with the townsfolk and local businesses.

The creatures showed no fear of anything. They antagonised dogs and chased the cats. They startled shoppers and pedestrians, as they innocently went about their daily lives. They caused extensive electrical damage too, as they nibbled their way through cables and wires in cavity structures. And they undermined building fabric and damaged drains and waste pipes, by burrowing their way in between joints in the surrounding earth and behind sewers. Some of the townsfolk even thought that the rodents' penchant for pipework gnawing might be causing flooding, and their delight in munching their way through electrical wiring, a fire risk. It was widely believed that it was all of this gnawing and munching which was keeping the rodents' incisors sharp and pointy and helping them to maintain their bite strength. No-one could say for certain exactly how the rat problem had started, although some of the townsfolk speculated that a reduced frequency of waste collections might have contributed to infestations. But no matter where the origins of the problem lay, on one point the townsfolk could all agree: they wanted the rat problem finished, once and for all!

Soon, the people had had enough.

In a fit of anger, the townsfolk marched to the mayor's office, to lobby him to find a suitable solution. 'DO SOMETHING!' they shouted. 'Our taxation funds your lavish meals and car and finery, Mr Mayor! Get rid of these rats, or else, leave yourself!'

The mayor paused for a moment and then turned to the window. And then he rubbed his eyes, as he couldn't quite believe the chaos of the rodent river scene being played out before him: 'Well, blow me down – I never saw, a *doggy-paddling rat* before…' he declared, before continuing on: '…it's as if they've cheated evolution – I need to find a swift solution!' The mayor needed some time to himself to work out what to do next and, not wishing to show he was flustered by the mischief of rats before him, pronounced to the assembled company: 'Fear not, my friends, here's what I'll do – *I'll hatch a clever plan for you!*' And then he pleaded with the townsfolk to return to their homes, so as to allow him a bit of breathing space. The angry crowd persisted with their protestations for some minutes, before reluctantly dispersing, but all the while continuing to demand action of the mayor. In all honesty, the mayor had no plan, and this worried him.

Some time later…

The mayor convened an emergency council session. If truth be told, he was a bit inept, his council little better, with not an iota of pest control knowledge nor common sense to rub together between them. Meetings, it seemed, were their answer to everything. Not so this time, it seemed, for this meeting had scarcely got underway and it was already painfully apparent that the council members were bereft of rat-ridding ideas. Then, quite out of the blue, and without canvassing the opinion of any of his fellow council officials, the mayor declared: 'We'll offer handsome payment to the person who frees us from this predicament!' The council members were momentarily dumbstruck and it was all they could do to nod in silent agreement. And then they moved on to *any other business*, before the mayor closed the meeting.

The very next day…

At around midday, the mayor left his office and nailed a poster up outside the town hall. His morning had largely been taken up with research into the possibility of advertising for a rat-ridding genius via more modern methods but, in the end, his love of all things traditional saw him press on with the use of his trusted paper, hammer and nail-based communication channels. In truth, the mayor remained utterly perplexed and bereft of ideas about what to do next, both to resolve the rat issue and to maintain the last shreds of his credibility. He spent the afternoon pondering his rodent control tactics.

The following morning...

Having endured a sleepless night, the mayor wasted little time in calling together some of his council friends for another day of talking. But no sooner had they arrived at the council offices and sat down at their big council table, than a knock was heard at the door. The mayor called out 'ENTER!', whereupon in stepped a tall fellow with sparkling eyes and an excited expression on his face, claiming to have secret charms and a curious sideline in pest control. 'Greetings, council people! Hello my mayoral man! I believe I am the tonic you've been looking for...the solution to your *ratty little problem*, if you will!' announced the surprise visitor, with unashamed confidence. He was quite a sight to behold, being dressed in a strange red and yellow garb, accessorised by a flute-type instrument hanging from his shoulder. But whilst his cloak was certainly eye-catching, it didn't appear to meet the specifications typically associated with the protective clothing needed for rat-ridding work. And, much as the mayor didn't like to admit it, the realisation was slowly dawning on him that it was going to take more than this funny flautist's fatuous claims to improve the lot of the council or his little town.

There was no doubting that this odd fellow's declarations were far-fetched. I say *far-fetched* because – had the mayor and his council colleagues thought to carry out even the most elementary of checks – they would have found that the contents of his curriculum vitae did little to validate the spurious claims to skills and experience made in the Pest Control Piper's verbal account. For a start, his proposed approach wasn't rooted in any of the mainstream pest control methodologies known to the council. His most outlandish boast was that any creature causing harm to humans – whether a mole, toad, newt or viper – could be controlled by his charms. This boast was supported by references of a dubious provenance. But the council failed to take the opportunity to verify his credentials, meaning that the Pest Control Piper was able to persist with his fanciful claims of ridding other towns of gnats and bats, without challenge. He recounted some quite unbelievable tales of previous rat-catching exploits which, curiously, went over the heads of the council members, with not one of them seeming to bat an eyelid. If only they had thought to look beyond the bounds of their big council table, it's likely that the signs of his cavalier approach to work would have been more readily detectable to the council members, given that in the outside world he appeared to be more widely known for his extravagant attire – a vision of crimson and gold touring the district – than for his rat-wooing allure, or culling capabilities. For the Pest Control Piper it seemed, in matters of *style* against *substance*, style won out every time, a flaw which – as the mayor and his council would soon learn – unfortunately pervaded his working methods too.

'Your honour...' he said, obviously keen to expand on his preamble whilst he had the attention of the mayor and his council, '...*I* am the Pest Control Piper! I have ridded castles of pests and plagues in distant lands. If you give me a thousand golden coins, I shall purge your town of rats!' The council members let out an audible gasp – an awkward expression of disbelief, tinged with a desperate hint of optimism. The Pest Control Piper's claim was indeed a spurious one; he was known to have paid occasional visits to industrial premises in Berkshire and Kent, but the notion of castles being involved seemed to be entirely the product of his own fertile imagination.

And yet, so euphoric was the mayor at the arrival of this vermin vanquisher – overwhelmingly impressed by the apparent speed with which his prayers and his job advert had been answered – that he saw no need to probe the Pest Control Piper any further on his outlandish claims, nor to dwell on what he viewed as trivial contractual details. He was – it was fair to say – less impressed by the Pest Control Piper's quoted price, but swiftly sought to allay the fears of his fellow council members. 'Do not fret. *I have a plan...*' whispered the mayor to his deputy. The mayor turned to the Pest Control Piper and smiled. '*A thousand?*' he declared grandly, punching his fist in the air. 'Free us of these wretched rats and I promise you'll have *one hundred thousand* golden coins. My word is my bond!' The mayor's deputy rolled his eyes and muttered under his breath: 'Another *artful* contractor, *I don't doubt...*', but of course the mayor was too wrapped up in his own blissful ignorance to listen to reason. Some of the slightly more meticulous council members looked on in horror – many of them perturbed by this curious character's preference to transact with golden coins, rather than via more modern card or contactless methods – but it was already too late! *The mayor had spoken!* The meeting having been drawn to a somewhat abrupt end, the Pest Control Piper nodded, gave a bow to the mayor, pivoted on his heels and, with a jaunty little skip in his stride, went out into the street.

The Pest Control Piper's eyes sparkled. Lifting his flute to his lips he blew five long, soft notes. And within moments, hundreds of rats appeared, seemingly responding to his call.

There were big rats...there were little rats...there were scrawny rats and chubby rats...there were black, grey and brown rats...there were elderly rats...and young whippersnapper rats...

Off skipped the Pest Control Piper, piping as he went, all the way through the town. Rats appeared from every crevice, as if the music would lead them to a place where there was all a rodent could wish for – a kind of ratty Utopia. Squeaking and scampering along the ground, the rats followed hot on the Pest Control Piper's heels, running faster and faster towards their dream. *For these rodent rascals, it had to be said, the event was assuming something of a festival feel!*

The Pest Control Piper soon reached the banks of the great river, whereupon he came to an abrupt halt. But such was his cunning nature, even though his feet had stopped, his frenetic flautist fingers continued playing on the tune's strangely hypnotic notes, seemingly urging the rats to sprint onwards! The rats followed the Pest Control Piper and his melodious music, streaming down the bank towards the deep cold river, into which it was initially believed they had plunged and perished. Within a matter of moments, every single rat was gone from view and it appeared as if, almost in an instant, the terrible plague had ended. The people of the town were so happy. And the rats' rapid disappearance was giving even the most cynical of townsfolk cause to question whether perhaps they'd been unnecessarily cautious in adopting the more conventional methods of pest control to date. They clapped and cheered and rang all the bells. Some even went for a swim, such was their state of euphoria. *It was quite the carnival atmosphere.*

The townsfolk rejoiced at the loss of the rats, but there had been just one tiny little oversight, which was to prematurely extinguish their joy. For, it wasn't only the rats that were seduced by the Pest Control Piper's tunes. No, bizarrely it seemed, the Pest Control Piper's piping had removed all trace of reason from the minds of even the most sensible of townsfolk. Not an iota of attention was paid to the most basic of hygiene control measures, and no-one saw fit to question the underpinning methodology to the approach proffered by this quirky flautist. Nevertheless, for the time being at least, it seemed all was well and with the rats having been sent into the water, the townsfolk set about the necessary remedial works, poking out nests and blocking up holes, and liaising with builders and carpenters as they went.

It wasn't long before the Pest Control Piper arrived back at the town hall, all keen and eager, and ready to collect his reward. The mayor smirked smugly because, in his mind, he had hatched what he believed to be a brilliant plan. 'Well done, Pest Control Piper!' he said. '...I hear the rats are well and truly gone.' 'As I promised,' replied the Pest Control Piper, '...*now give me my one hundred thousand golden coins please!*'

The mayor shrugged. '*Oh, dear fellow,* now this is slightly awkward...but I'm afraid if there are no rats in the town, we have no reason to pay you, do we?' The mayor threw some small coins at the Pest Control Piper. An ugly dispute ensued, with the mayor claiming it had been drowning, rather than piping, which had destroyed the rats – a technicality which he felt gave him just cause to revise his offer downwards – suggesting to the Pest Control Piper that a goodwill gesture of fifty golden coins was more than generous. 'Take these, you delusional fool...' said the mayor, '...*and be glad of what you get!*'

Within a matter of moments, and with an almost pantomime-like quality, a red mist appeared to descend upon the Pest Control Piper, his eyes suddenly bulging with rage. 'No, Mr Mayor! You are the foolish one...' he declared '...and you and your little town will grow to regret that you failed to keep your promise!' And unfortunately, as the mayor and his council colleagues would soon discover – the situation having already reached boiling point – there was nothing any of them could say to placate the now livid Pest Control Piper.

With his temper now inflamed beyond the point of no return, the Pest Control Piper resolved to exact his revenge...

THE RATS REAPPEAR

Assuming a facade of serenity, the Pest Control Piper stepped into the street, having – on the surface, at least – regained his composure, following his fit of fury. *He had a plan.* Lifting his flute-type instrument to his lips, he once again blew five long notes. As he set off, striding onwards through the town, infants appeared in every door and alleyway and started running towards the river, seemingly hypnotised by the Pest Control Piper's whimsical tunes. Brothers and sisters hurried along too, leading toddlers by the hand and carrying babies with them, as they went. More joined the Piper's parade at every street corner. Soon, every child in town was following the Pest Control

Piper's enchanting melody, faster and faster – keeping to the beat of his strange tune – and no amount of persuasion, nor parental chastising, it seemed, would make them see reason.

In a moment, the sky darkened, seeming aptly to reflect the mood of the assembled townsfolk. The children's parents froze like statues, unable to move. Soon sensing something was amiss however, they managed to shake themselves from their state of fear, with one shrieking in horror: *'Oh no! He's taking them to the river!'* Unfortunately, it seemed as if the Pest Control Piper's music had also induced a trance-like state within the children. Of itself, this appeared harmless, but it left many of them temporarily unable to fight the urge to take an impulsive swim. With the infants now surging towards the river, the Pest Control Piper sensed things might be about to turn ugly and so, spinning suddenly on his heels, he headed back towards his van, with the chaotic water-based antics continuing on apace behind him. On getting into his vehicle and turning the key, however, it quickly transpired that it wouldn't start. After a bit of a rant, during which his approach to van maintenance became clear for all to see – the immediate cause of his problem seemingly being a flat battery – the Pest Control Piper re-emerged from his vehicle, his cheeks now reddening with rage. His plan for a discreet exit now in tatters, he raised his arms to the heavens in despair and ran off along a path, leaving town in a flash. The only evidence of his having been there at all was his van, a document optimistically titled 'Risk Assessment', and a scene of utter chaos.

Why 'utter chaos', you may well ask? Well, it was only at this point that the parents noticed something strange for, whilst early indications were that the rats had been wiped out, some of them were clearly more resilient than had first appeared to be the case. Many hadn't perished after all and, as far as the eye could see, youngsters and vermin joined together side by side – seeming to bob along in unison in the water.

By this point, an angry mob of parents had gathered, shouting outside the mayor's office. *'DO SOMETHING!* Pay the Pest Control Piper all he was promised and more, if you have to...' they pleaded with the mayor, '...please don't let him leave our town in disarray!' One parent made a vain attempt at mediation, crying out to the Pest Control Piper, as he sprinted erratically towards the horizon. *Some speculated that this particular parent might be touting for future business, given that he was known to run a rival pest control firm along more conventional lines.*

The parent said:

'Look here, red-gold clad one, there's no need to be *ratty* –
You might be well meaning, but your methods are scatty!
You thought with your cloak and your fancy recorder
That ferrets would freeze and mice come to order.
But you're wrong, can't you see? Your plan had a flaw…
All the mainstream control measures you chose to ignore.
You might think you're a whizz and act all placatory,
But your ruse hasn't worked – the rats run our gyratory…
These verminous creatures seem to cheat evolution,
No amount of weird whistling should commend your solution.
With your battered old van and your wild whimsy tunes,
You – Piper – have shown up our council buffoons.
You can see we've a mayor on the brink of psychosis…
And all from a case of leptospirosis.
You've driven us mad, you're making us sick,
Less pest controller, more maverick!
We thought you a talented, clever rat slayer,
What we got – I'm afraid – was a phoney flute player!
The craziest aspect? Your tuneful coercion,
Of our townsfolk…some towards total immersion!
We don't rate your approach, see the rats are a-bobbin'
Next time *rat-man,* we'll call Batman and Robin…
Or, at least, check assessment of risk from the start
And manage contractors, so they play their part!'

'Don't worry! His shocking approach to vehicle maintenance left him with no option but to abandon his van in our town!' said the mayor, in a somewhat foolish bid to calm the situation and respond to the poetic parent's monologue. 'He's sure to be back soon to pick it up, what with parking costs being so high! You'll see…' *But how little the mayor knew!* The children continued to swim, splash and play in the river for some time and the Pest Control Piper never did return to his van, despite multiple parking enforcement charges being levied against him. The now wretched mayor wished he had kept his word, but by this point, of course, it was all far too late.

Some of the children had cuts and grazes, but still went swimming. Some swallowed water, such was their lack of swimming ability. Soon after, some

*of the youngsters suffered mild flu-like symptoms, whilst others presented
with more serious health issues and complaints. Others sadly died.*

With the passing of time, the townsfolk reflected that tuneful
melodies played on recorder and flute-like instruments might not be
the most effective means of pest control, after all. There was no denying
it, the Pest Control Piper's approach certainly seemed to fly in the face
of more mainstream risk control strategies, with this strange piping
fellow in fact having led more children into an area of heightened risk.
But no-one thought to report this occurrence, and so the opportunity
to fully understand what had happened was lost forever.

*Every street in the town was silent and every home filled with
sadness, and the Pest Control Piper was never to be seen again...*

Whether the Pest Control Piper was a fraudster, simply lacked
competence, or had met with a grisly end alongside the children due to
his own poor pest control practices, remained a matter of some debate.
There was some speculation locally that, alongside his unique melody-
based rat-ridding technique, the Pest Control Piper occasionally
defaulted to the more conventional pest control methodologies, but
always half-heartedly so. It was thought that the cavalier approach he
applied to controlling risk throughout the course of the activity had
probably resulted in his own undoing too – the most likely theory
being that he had succumbed to the same fate as that of the townsfolk –
given that pest controllers are at high risk of contracting leptospirosis.

Some time later, with the realisation having dawned on the mayor, his
council, and the townsfolk that the Pest Control Piper wasn't returning
for his van after all, it was opened up and there, in the back, what did they
discover but a box stuffed full of unworn personal protective equipment?
This rather flew in the face of the warning displayed on its rear, which
boldly stated: 'Nothing of value is left in this vehicle'. Unfortunately – so
it turned out – as well as being a remark about the absence of commercial
assets being stowed, this was also an ironic reflection on the lack of
importance the Pest Control Piper placed upon his personal protection
and the use of PPE as the last line of defence against zoonotic disease, of
which leptospirosis had been the one of concern here.

*Common to all fairy tales and fables is, of course, the hope that the 'ever
after' ending should be a happy one. Unfortunately, in this case, it appeared
unlikely that such an outcome would ever be more than a pipe dream...*

MODERN MEANING

It seems timely, at this point, to review the effectiveness with which the characters in this fable met the requirements of the two strategies outlined in the *prologue*. Remember that the *first* of these related to management of the *rat risk* (the hazardous substance risk – in this case, community spread of Weil's disease), and the *second*, to management of the *piper risk* (the contractor risk – which concerned the control of the Pest Control Piper, as the individual engaged to carry out the work). Much of what is noted here will undoubtedly appear to be common sense to many readers, but in the real world – just as is true of this fantastical example – it can be surprisingly easy to slip up on the basics, whether the concern is with the direct control of a physical risk, or the management of those assigned responsibility for controlling that risk, under contract.

We'll first consider the effectiveness with which the Pest Control Piper controlled the hazardous substance risk, by evaluating the degree to which he successfully delivered against the requirements of the three step rat risk control strategy outlined in the prologue, before second, reviewing the council's delivery against the five step contractor risk control strategy, to determine how effectively the piper risk was controlled here.

EVALUATING THE RAT RISK CONTROL STRATEGY

Remember, for control of the rat risk (the Weil's disease risk), the ownership of this strategy would have rested principally with the Pest Control Piper and those employing him, this being the risk he was contractually taken on to control.

STEP #1
WAS THE HEALTH RISK ASSESSED?

NO! *The Pest Control Piper did not assess the health risk in a structured manner.*

The focus of this step should have been upon making sure there was a structured approach in place for assessing the health risk and yet, the fable makes no reference to such an assessment having taken place. There was no clear strategy. There's no suggestion, either, of the Pest Control Piper having made a plan as to how he was to approach the work, nor even of efforts having been made by him to identify the potential hazards to health or to assess their significance. And there's no indication given of him having worked collaboratively with – or being involved with – others who would have had a shared interest in controlling the risk.

A pre-requisite for controlling any health risk is the need for clear plans. When planning any job, a strategy needs to be developed which identifies the health hazards present, in substances which are used or encountered, and assesses their significance, with involvement from workers who are actually managing the risk being sought right from the outset. This means that the Pest Control Piper or his employers should have made efforts to identify and assess the significance of the Weil's disease risk, including seeking the buy-in from anyone else with an interest in managing it. And yet, there's no suggestion here of dialogue taking place between the key parties involved in controlling it – amongst them, the Piper, the mayor, and the council – a flaw suggesting that there was no plan as to how the rat infestation was to be handled.

The next aspects of this step should involve the identification of the health risk – calling out potential hazards to health linked to the work tasks being undertaken – together with an assessment of the significance of these, thus allowing exposure risks to be evaluated, including any rated as *high*. Here, the Pest Control Piper, or those assessing the health risk on his behalf, would have needed to set out the potential hazards to health – and specifically, the Weil's disease health risk due to the presence of rats, associated with the treatment of rodent infestations – not just to him, but to others too. This should have seen him being upfront about the tasks he proposed to carry out to accomplish the rat-ridding activity, having applied clear thought to *who* might have been affected and *how*, in order to put himself in a better position to assess the significance of the risks associated with the activity. It's suggested that, had a thorough risk assessment been undertaken here, the flaws to the Pest Control Piper's method would have been highlighted which, far from keeping people away from the affected location, actually drew more of them towards it! The only reference the fable makes to risk assessment is of a document discarded in the vicinity of the Pest Control Piper's van, but this was possibly generic and, given the actions and outcomes the tale describes, it seems reasonable to conclude that it overlooked both the location-specific issues and the risks present there. This is a perceived deficiency which seems to be borne out by the disastrous outcome that ensued here, which reinforces why it would have been important to gauge, at this first step, the Pest Control Piper's level of understanding about the information the risk assessment contained, possibly asking him: *'Were you responsible for, or involved in, writing it?',* *'Is it valid, current, and in date?'* and *'Does it suitably cover the risks relevant to the location and on-site risks, or is it generic in nature, meaning it needs adaptation to cover this particular situation?'*

Had the Pest Control Piper and those managing him taken the time to adopt a more measured approach to risk assessment, completing it with the required level of detail, the likelihood of his being exposed to Weil's disease – and that of other river users being exposed to it too – would likely have been deemed to be *high*, given the evidence of rat activity, and with rivers being regarded as higher risk locations. *But of course, we never get to learn whether the risk assessment document discarded by his van contained this kind of detail!* Had the requirement for risk assessment been robustly addressed here however, the proposal to wade through water possibly contaminated with rat urine would have been recognised as placing him at high risk, the severity of the consequences would have become all too clear, and the tone set for a more effective control strategy. The apparent failure by the Pest Control Piper to identify and assess risk effectively undoubtedly gave him a poor basis from which to start to control the health risk, for which he had been assigned responsibility, and can be regarded as the root of many of the subsequent issues that arose in this somewhat macabre tale.

Involving people in the risk assessment is arguably the most crucial aspect to this first step of the process, basically requiring those who face the health risks to be actively engaged, with their inputs being sought as to how these might best be managed. It's these insights which should be used to inform the strategy for managing the specific risk. Here, the Pest Control Piper should have directly participated in any discussions about how the risk to him personally, and to others – including the children entering the water – was to be managed. Had he been actively involved in such a process, as a person facing the risk, this would have put him in a far better position to understand the risk itself, as well as giving him the opportunity to contribute to the development of additional control measures to protect all concerned[44]. And engaging others at this early stage would have paid

---

44. As outlined in this book's introduction, employers are required to have 'consultation' arrangements in place with those who carry out work, or their representatives. For this type of work, employers would be expected to provide employees with information on the risks and dangers associated with exposure to a biological agent, the measures put in place to get rid of or reduce these risks, and what they should do in the event of them being uncontrolled.

other dividends too. Had the Pest Control Piper talked with the mayor, his council and, if applicable, perhaps other council workers who worked alongside him – about how he proposed to tackle the rat-ridding activity – it's far more likely the health risks would have been better managed from the outset. It's even possible that this would have seen him buying into the council's own 'safety culture', to the undoubted benefit of all concerned!

Once the assess step has been addressed, it's at this point that a plan can start to be formed, detailing how those involved in the work are to approach it. It's vital that they should not only understand, but also buy into, the risk assessment process – both as individuals and as part of a team, where applicable – so that they have a clear appreciation of the risk itself and are given the opportunity to contribute to the development of control measures. As well as securing effective control of a risk, this is key to making sure workers feel part of an inclusive safety culture. It's by involving workers and gaining their input at this first step, that real-world organisations increase the likelihood of health risks being effectively managed, throughout the entire process.

STEP #2
WAS THE HEALTH RISK CONTROLLED?

NO! *There's no suggestion of the Pest Control Piper having put in place an effective strategy to control the health risk.*

There was seemingly little effort made by or for him to design out risk or to select appropriate control measures. Furthermore, no mention is made of training having been received, nor of 'competencies' held, by the Pest Control Piper and it appears he was ill-equipped to respond effectively when confronted, as here, with an emergency situation. The focus of this step needs to be upon preventing risks before work starts, as well as controlling any remaining risk, and ensuring workers are trained to an appropriate level.

The first aspect of this strategy, on prevention, is about taking action before work begins – which includes designing out risk through the use of different work methods – the rationale behind this being that it's better to prevent risks, rather than having to think about how to control them when work is already underway. Had moves been made to appropriately identify and assess the risk of Weil's disease by or for the Pest Control Piper at the previous step, this should have led to his implementing of robust control measures to address it. At the heart of any effective risk control strategy is the principle that it's better to prevent risks from occurring in the first place – or at least, before work starts – rather than efforts only being made to control them when work is already underway. Here, this should have seen attempts being made to control the rat population, the ultimate aim being to eliminate the risk or, failing that, at least achieve a significant reduction in the likely level of exposure.

So how might risk prevention have been achieved here? One way would have been to design out risk by looking at different methodologies for the Pest Control Piper to adopt, in preference to the questionable music-based approach he selected! For the circumstances described, it's right to recognise that fully preventing or designing out the risk would have proved challenging, given that control of the rat population – *the source of the health hazard* – was the very task the Pest Control Piper had been taken on to accomplish. But rather than simply seeking to control it, there would nonetheless have remained a very clear need for him to consider, or have suggested for him, other less hazardous methods, before moving on to select the most appropriate approach and starting work.

The fable makes mention of the rats having caused '...extensive electrical damage...as they nibbled their way through cables and wires in cavity structures...' and '...undermined building fabric and damaged drains and waste pipes, by burrowing between joints in the surrounding earth and behind sewers...' It also implicates them as having been behind flood and fire risks, reporting as it does upon their destructive 'gnawing of pipework' habit, and of them 'munching their way through electrical wiring'. Given these wide-ranging problems, there might well have been earlier opportunities to deploy more strategic tactics from the get-go, to eliminate and control the rat community at its source, perhaps with more beneficial outcomes. It might have been that CCTV surveys or other detection methods could have been used to help pinpoint where the rodents were most prolific, which in turn would have facilitated more proactive control efforts than those seen here. Other alternative control methods that might have been considered could have included the use of rodenticides, entrapment, or other forms of non-toxic monitoring and control.

The control aspect to this step focuses on the remaining risk, looking at how it is handled in situations where prevention is not possible. As such, this is about exploring a multitude of options, all with the purpose of preventing illness resulting from poorly controlled health risks. Here, simply asking the Pest Control Piper: '*What arrangements have you, or those you work for, put in place to control risk?*' would likely have given rise to an answer triggering alarm as to his proposed methods. Rather than logically selecting effective control measures however, the Pest Control Piper appeared hell-bent on pursuing his own unorthodox method – one which saw events quickly escalate to the point where modifying his approach was no longer an option. This underlines the point that it's better to do everything possible to proactively prevent health risks, rather than simply seeking to control them once an activity is already in progress. In scenarios of the kind described, options for more effective methods should always be explored, but the presence of rats here highlights that there would have been a need to look beyond prevention methods towards control of the remaining risk. This scenario was certainly one which should have seen the Pest Control Piper making better use of 'administrative controls' to limit the size of population potentially affected or exposed – restricting numbers near the work area, preventing people entering areas of known risk within the vicinity of the outbreak, and protecting social users from exposure to the contaminated water, either by barring their entry to the river, or setting up an 'exclusion zone' at the location. But he should also have thought about arranging an exodus of anyone already in the area away from the source of risk, with the social and domestic pleasure users, including swimmers, needing to be directed away from the area too. The Pest Control Piper's behaviour arguably went beyond a simple disregard for administrative controls here, tending towards recklessness, with his whimsical notes serving only to increase in the numbers exposed, by leading the children into an area where the extent and likelihood of exposure were, in fact, higher. *This encouragement of counter-intuitive behaviours, which would only have worsened the extent of the outbreak, is almost certainly the most alarming aspect of this fable!*

As well as thinking about the size of population affected, it's also important for any health risk control strategy to limit the level of exposure to which any particular individual or group is subject. If the Pest Control Piper was part of a wider team, thought should have been given to rotating the tasks involved in the activity – so-called 'task rotation' – in co-operation with other team members, so as to lessen his personal exposure. Another positive control measure would have been to ensure that he took regular breaks away from areas believed to be contaminated, this being both a simple means of reducing his exposure time, and helpful in lowering the risks associated with poor hygiene, as can occur during meal breaks or other rest break activities.

That the Pest Control Piper should have avoided wading through, or being fully submerged in, water to prevent exposure is not in doubt. If, however, avoidance wasn't possible, he should have been directed to the use of appropriate personal protective clothing – disposable overalls, gloves, and 'respiratory protective equipment' (RPE) too, if required, rather than a sparkly cloak – and to keeping this separate from personal clothing, all with the common aim of controlling personal exposure arising from contact with contaminated water[45].

Training is the final aspect to this second control step, which is about making sure workers do a job in the right way and is also concerned with securing their active involvement in aspects including: identifying risks and understanding how their health might be harmed by exposure to them; the use of control measures; maintenance of equipment, and the use and care of PPE, including RPE, together with what they need to do if something goes wrong. The fable leaves as something of a mystery what, if any, training the Pest Control Piper had personally received, but his response when things started to spiral out of control would tend to suggest he lacked the necessary competence. With hindsight, it would certainly have been beneficial for the mayor and the council to have enquired about his pest control qualifications, accreditations, and other credentials. But additionally, it would have

---

45. Given an equivalent real-world scenario to that involving the Pest Control Piper – where PPE is provided but not used – it's likely that this would constitute a breach of regulation 10(2) of *the Personal Protective Equipment at Work Regulations 1992* ('the PPE Regulations'); S.I. 1992/2966. This provision requires employees to use PPE in accordance with the instructions supplied by their employers, as long as they have been given adequate and appropriate information, instruction and training on its use, as set out by regulation 9. This should include information on the risk it will avoid or limit, together with its purpose and how it is to be used, as well as any action required by employees to help maintain it in good working order and repair. Furthermore, within the context of this fable, the Pest Control Piper would have been expected to report any loss or defect to his employer, as required by regulation 11. An employee's choice to don alternative clothing – as exemplified by the Pest Control Piper – can also be viewed as a breach of their duty to co-operate, a requirement which is placed on all employees, under section 7(b) of *HSWA 1974*.

been important for the Pest Control Piper to be trained in 'first-aid' and other emergency response arrangements, as this should have directly influenced his capability to effectively mitigate any consequences and therefore lessened the extent of any harm caused. In equivalent real-world circumstances to those the fable depicts, employees need to be made aware of the availability and benefits of hygiene and emergency measures too – which might include showering and the use of antibacterial wipes – as well as the added advantages won from immediate action being taken, following any suspected exposure.

There were training messages which either didn't reach the Pest Control Piper here or were, at best, poorly understood by him, given his very clear failure to take the right action when needed. For this type of work, the expectation would have been that the Pest Control Piper and anyone working with him or potentially exposed would have had an awareness of the types of micro-organism that might be encountered. Furthermore, any training given to workers should emphasise that the ability to identify symptoms of, and signs of exposure to, hazardous substances – in this case leptospirosis – is crucial. Arming workers with an awareness of the 'routes of exposure' is key to the effective control of a hazardous substance risk – including the possibility of infection entering the human body via cuts, scratches, and mucous membranes. Such training should also include instruction on how any PPE and RPE is to be correctly donned, in order that the full level of protection and effectiveness can be achieved – with any cuts and grazes being covered, so as to prevent infection from entering the body via these routes.

The fable is somewhat scant on the details of the prognosis for the characters involved here, but it seems likely that the odds were stacked against them, given that early-stage detection and treatment is seen as vital to recovery prospects. The fable does report that: *'Some of the children had cuts and grazes, but still went swimming. Some swallowed water, such was their lack of swimming ability. Soon after, some of the youngsters suffered mild flu-like symptoms, whilst others presented with more serious health issues and complaints...'*, suggesting that there might perhaps have been opportunities for a better outcome, had the Pest Control Piper and anyone else involved acted more swiftly. In real-world circumstances where exposure is confirmed, it's essential for reports to be submitted without delay – to managers, medical practitioners and other interested agencies, where appropriate –

so that wider societal implications can be identified, gauged and addressed, as necessary. Given his neglect of the most basic aspects of a control strategy however, it seems overly-optimistic to suggest that the Pest Control Piper would have attended to the essential reporting requirements here[46].

STEP #3
WAS THE HEALTH RISK REVIEWED?

NO! *It's clear that the Pest Control Piper did not review the health risk.*

The tale makes no suggestion of planned or actual reviews of the risk having taken place during the course of the work activity. This is a really crucial step, as the process of managing health risks isn't just about the right control measures being instituted at the start – the review step makes sure the controls put in place continue to work, for the full duration of the work activity. A review of the health risk would have needed to be carried out here, so as to confirm whether or not the control measures such as work methods, PPE and welfare arrangements were effective and being used. It's clear, however, that the initial risk assessment and applied control measures were poor, which would have somewhat limited the Pest Control Piper's capacity to review the risk throughout the job's lifecycle. This is also the reason why the review here is focused upon what *should* have been in place to control the health risk – as per *step two* of the rat risk control strategy – rather than being based solely upon the limited information the tale provides.

The supervision of workers is a crucial aspect to this step, this being key to making sure that they understand the risks and the part they play in applying the required control measures by following agreed methods – which includes checking that they are up to date, effective, used, maintained and monitored. But more than this, proper supervision is also about making sure workers are clear about how to raise any concerns they might have. It's particularly important to make sure that new, inexperienced, and young workers are adequately supervised, as they are likely to require a greater degree of support and guidance than is the case for more experienced workers. Without the

---

46. *Table 1* sets out the Classification of Biological Agents; the *Epilogue* gives an indication of the reporting and notifications likely to apply in real-world scenarios, equivalent to the fictional one depicted here.

back-up offered by good quality supervision, it's possible that some might be reluctant to ask questions, or even coerced by others into taking short cuts.

Here it's unclear who, if anyone, was supervising the Pest Control Piper's work, but there certainly didn't appear to have been any checks made to confirm whether or not he was following agreed methods. Had checks been made here, these would perhaps have brought to light the Pest Control Piper's fundamental lack of understanding as to the risks and the associated control measures applicable to the activity. And, whilst not excusing his unorthodox choice of working methods, this omission might go some way to explaining why he deemed it acceptable to plough on and continue to use them! It seems entirely possible that the quality of the Pest Control Piper's work was habitually poor, with his behaviours likely to have formed part of a wider pattern, but there were various ways in which such issues might have been identified and ironed out before they became problematic. Simply asking the Pest Control Piper to describe how he'd carried out previous jobs might have flagged concerns to his supervisors. Similarly, asking to see his risk assessments, certifications and other authorisations would likely have highlighted problems. And of course, it always pays to remember the basics of good supervision too – carrying out an inspection would have been one way of detecting issues with the physical quality of the Pest Control Piper's work, as well as allowing any underlying performance issues to be more readily detected and resolved.

It's important to remember that the requirement to supervise employees – and to provide them with information, instruction and training – is a legal one[47]. In the Pest Control Piper's case, the responsibility for training him and for ensuring his continued competence would have fallen upon his employers. This should have included checks being made as to his level of understanding about the risks he faced and the adequacy of measures in place to control them. Asking a range of questions here might have helped to gauge the effectiveness of the Pest Control Piper's review of the risk involved, which could have included: *'Were there any other control measures*

---

47. Section 2(2)(c) of *HSWA 1974* requires employers to provide employees with information, instruction, training and supervision, as key elements to ensuring their health, safety and welfare at work.

available to you, which you elected not to use?', 'What made you choose the control measures you used?', 'Were you aware of other possible control measures, which you might have been able to adopt in this instance?', and, 'If you were in any doubt about the control measures you should have used here, did you feel you had someone you could approach to discuss the possible options and raise any concerns?'

In reviewing the risk, it's also important to make sure control measures are maintained, the focus of which is upon checking that these are in order and that equipment remains in good shape, including ensuring that procedures are in place to report faulty or damaged pieces of kit. But maintaining controls goes further than this, because it's also about whether the personal skills, knowledge and experience of the workers who are expected to use them are kept up-to-date too. In some cases – as was possibly true here – someone may elect to use their own (*perhaps flute-based!*) equipment due to the more mainstream equipment provided to them having been or become unsuitable. This is why it's so important for effective procedures to be in place for reporting damaged or faulty equipment. A range of questions should have been asked here, to inform the review of the Pest Control Piper's handling of the risk and determine whether any shortcomings had arisen, which were in need of resolving, either by him directly or by his supervisors stepping in, which might have included: '*Did you choose this method because of your not having access to suitable equipment?', 'Were you made aware of the procedures for reporting damaged or faulty equipment and, if not, was it this which led you to use your own instead?', 'Did you feel your skill set, knowledge and experience equipped you to deal with the circumstances you faced here?', and, 'Were there any other reasons why you selected this particular method of pest control, as opposed to some of the more orthodox, or tried and tested methods?'* Being proactive in maintaining control measures is key to making sure they are still working and helps to give confidence that health risks continue to be well-controlled, throughout the lifecycle of a job.

The focus of the third aspect to this step is upon monitoring control measures, including welfare and PPE, the purpose being to check and verify that, together with the associated working methods, these are as effective as they should be – being used by workers, in the right ways and at the right times – and to help proactively identify and correct any weaknesses. This can be achieved through *ad hoc* checks or via formal audit processes, as well as from the use of exposure monitoring, and analysis of health surveillance outcomes and investigations into cases of ill health, related to the type of activity being undertaken and/or the location in question. When swift action is taken in response to negative findings uncovered through the proactive monitoring of control measures – including by the halting of poorly controlled activities – this can prove vital in restoring risk to acceptable levels, as well as helping with the development of longer term solutions too. From what is known of the events described here, no plan to provide health surveillance for or by the Pest Control Piper seems to have been put in place before work commenced, and there's certainly no mention made of any other forms of monitoring – whether workplace or personal – having been instituted at set points, as the work progressed.

The final aspect of this review step is to act to put any problems right. This means resolving issues without delay, taking action in response to any lessons learnt and revisiting plans and risk assessments, to see if these are in need of update. It's hard to believe the Pest Control Piper would have addressed this aspect here, given his clear failure to identify problems at the start, and his instinctive urge to flee the chaotic scene, rather than stopping to answer questions, seeking to put things right, or report pathogenic exposure, in the wake of these events. It's this failing, together with the foregoing issues identified, which unfortunately make it unsurprising that those involved or otherwise caught up in this unconventional and farcical effort at pest control were destined for an untimely demise!

EVALUATING THE PIPER RISK CONTROL STRATEGY

Here, consideration turns to the effectiveness with which the mayor and his council colleagues managed their contractual arrangement with the Pest Control Piper. Essentially, what follows is an evaluation of the control of the piper risk (the contractor risk) by the mayor and his council, against the five step contractor risk control strategy outlined in the prologue.

STEP #1
WAS THE JOB WELL PLANNED?

NO! *The mayor and his council failed to plan the job.*

There's little evidence of the mayor and his council having

identified the hazard of taking on a contractor, nor is anything said here that points to them having appropriately identified and addressed the risk of the Pest Control Piper, as a contractor, failing to deliver against his contractual obligations.

It's apparent from the fable that the nature of the situation which confronted the mayor and his council led to them rushing to get someone in to do the job quickly. *This was to be just the start of their troubles!* There's no mention of them having checked the Pest Control Piper's credentials, nor of them having raised appropriate questions with him or his own employers. But even where – as here – a client is pressed for time, the opportunity to plan a job properly is a step of the process which should never be undertaken in haste. Had a plan been developed, it's suggested that the mayor and his council would have been able to reach a more measured decision, which might have averted the catastrophic consequences that played out here.

When planning any job the focus should, first and foremost, be upon getting the basics right. Being clear about what a job involves paves the way for hazards to be readily identified, which tees up the risk assessment aspect of this step. In looking at the planning of the rat extermination job which was to be carried out here, we see no suggestion of any attempt having been made to calmly define the scope of work the Pest Control Piper was expected to do, nor of efforts made to identify the health and safety implications of the work in the job specification. Doing this upfront, in advance of work taking place, would have been helpful by both providing contractual certainty and avoiding doubt amongst all involved. The mayor's proclamation of: 'Well, blow me down – I never saw, a *doggy paddling rat* before...', followed swiftly by an impulsive offer of payment to anyone promising rat riddance, suggests that his efforts to pin down the detail about what needed to be done were woefully inadequate. Defining the scope of a job at this formative step of the process is an opportunity that should never be passed by and failing to be prescriptive about what is involved, as occurred here, is the root cause of many a real-world contractual problem, further down the line.

The next aspect of the planning step is for a risk assessment to be undertaken by the client organisation, but the contractor needs to undertake one too, which fits with the client's own and provides appropriate information to them. Having sight of a 'method statement' can be really helpful here – even if only for similar jobs at this stage, rather than the specific job in question – as it shows how work is proposed to be carried out, thus giving a clear picture of *how* the risks are to be managed, and a good insight into a contractor's general approach towards controlling risk too. It's quite clear that little, if any, effort was made here to consider the scale of the problem, the nature of the environment, or indeed the health and safety implications of the work – which should have included attending to the basics of hazard identification and risk assessment, elimination and reduction. This failure was undoubtedly rooted in the mayor's early stage failure to define the work he wanted the Pest Control Piper to carry out for him.

Having carried out a risk assessment, a strategy needs to be put in place to eliminate and reduce the risks identified, with health and safety conditions being clearly specified right from the start. Initial discussions between the parties involved are invaluable at this point, helping client organisations to detect those contractors or potential contractors who fail or are unwilling to satisfy even the most basic of requirements – requirements which are fundamental to making sure that work is safely carried out from the outset. It's the forming of a picture based upon factors such as these which should ultimately guide an organisation's decision about whether or not it wishes to transact with a particular contractor. It's abundantly clear that, on the basis that they were to enter into a contractual arrangement, the mayor should have provided the Pest Control Piper with details about the level of risk involved, of which the council was aware, including the nature and complexity of the work that lay ahead.

With the approach to controlling risk having been agreed between the parties, reaching consensus on how work is to be done is the next important aspect for discussion. Agreeing what is to be done needs to encompass not only the conditions for the activity – in this case, incorporating consideration of exposure to leptospirosis – but should also include any action to be taken in an emergency situation, detailing the appropriate procedures to be followed, when required. Asking to see copies of risk assessments and method statements for the type of work a contractor is to carry out is an entirely reasonable request at this point and if a contractor cannot provide these, this should set alarm bells ringing for the client organisation as to why this is not possible. For the scenario set out, starting discussions as to expected performance levels would also have proved invaluable here. It's quite true that the mayor promises: 'Free us of these wretched rats and I promise you'll have *one hundred thousand* golden coins. My word is my bond!' and yet, there is no thought given as to *how* success was to be measured. Attaching targets – including measurable ones – and addressing these kinds of questions would have gone at least partway to ensuring that both parties knew whether contractual success had been achieved further down the line. It would also have driven upfront expectations of performance levels – perhaps based upon the numbers of rats killed, or water monitoring and testing results – with likely health and safety benefits for all concerned, as well as being supportive of the principle of contractual certainty. It's quite clear that the opportunity to specify health and safety conditions at an early stage, and to discuss the job with the Pest Control Piper, was not one that should have been missed here.

Finally, in fulfilling the requirements of the planning step here, as is often the case in real-world scenarios, it's likely that carrying out a joint site visit to the location would have proved invaluable – it would have given both parties an insight into the scale of the problem, plus the chance for all involved to discuss how the job was to be tackled before work started, in addition to allowing the mayor and his council the opportunity to take on board any self-help advice the Pest Control Piper or his employers might have been able to offer them, by way of preparation for the work that he was to carry out. It would also have allowed the mayor and his council to give the Pest Control Piper an early stage heads-up about any health and safety issues they knew to exist on site.

STEP #2
WAS THE PIPER SELECTED EFFECTIVELY?

NO! *There's no evidence of the mayor and his council having taken on the Pest Control Piper via a robust contractor selection process.*

At the point of contractor selection it would seem that the mayor and his council fell prey to the temptation of a *quick fix* approach. This can be viewed as a hangover from the failure identified at the previous planning step, with the mayor and his council omitting to be vigilant about even the most basic of health and safety considerations, purely because they were in a hurry to get the job done.

Any contractor selection process should be founded upon defined safety and technical competence requirements. In starting to form a view as to whether or not a prospective contractor has the capacity and capability to perform the proposed work, checks should be made that the contractor has an appropriate health and safety management system in place. These checks are likely to focus on the policies, procedures and practices the contractor adopts or uses, but the client organisation also needs to have confidence that the contractor's workforce will be able to meet the standards it sets, together with any legislative requirements applicable to the tasks and activities in question. Contractor selection is not a process to be casually undertaken, as seems to have happened here, where the omission to define competence expectations looked to be a fundamental error. It was this which made the council vulnerable to engaging the wrong person, and ultimately led to them selecting someone unsuitable to carry out the work. In deciding to take on the Pest Control Piper, we see displayed here a total failure on the mayor's part to make an appropriate choice based upon defined safety and technical competencies, with him passing up the opportunity to consider other contractors perhaps better placed to resolve the rat problem. Rather than acting on the basis of set-down objective competence criteria, applying sound judgment, and taking the time to properly define the extent of the work he expected to be carried out however, we see him choosing instead to place his ill-judged faith in a passing chancer, and ultimately paying the price for so doing.

Structured safety and technical competence requirements are a fundamental pre-requisite for any contractor risk control strategy, but these can usefully be supplemented with questions being raised directly with the contractor and/or with contacts internal or external to the client organisation, who have prior experience of their work. The fable raises numerous questions about the Pest Control Piper's suitability to carry out the work – questions which the mayor and his council could have posed directly to him. With the Pest Control Piper having been identified as the person responsible for carrying out the work, it's clear that the parties should have reached agreement as to their expectations about what that would entail. Furthermore, it's suggested that it would have been a wise move for the mayor and his council to have delved a little deeper into some of the Pest Control Piper's more spurious claims to competence, most notably of his having cleared '...castles of pests and plagues in distant lands...'. It's likely that probing into the details behind these grand statements by asking simply *'Can you supply references in support of your statements about these previous jobs?'* would have started to raise alarm bells, highlighted gaps and perhaps have provided the necessary impetus the mayor and his council needed to begin their exploration of other more suitable options.

The inputs from professional networks – sometimes even those that are anecdotal in nature – are also invaluable, as they can serve to either substantiate or contradict information provided at any point in a contractor selection process. Finding out whether others in the same field of work use the same type of contractor, seeking their view on who they think adopts professional methods, and asking what they know about the health and safety competence of a particular contractor, all provide useful insights which can guide decisions about whether they should be engaged. Here, the council's own workers might have had direct knowledge of the Pest Control Piper's approach or that of his organisation, and there might also have been neighbouring councils with previous experience of this flamboyant character's portfolio of work. Workers on site might have had acquaintances with particular contractors too, or seen them at work in a different context. Given that they would have been closer to the action at the sharp end, it's far more likely they would have witnessed first-hand any poor or inappropriate practices, as well as perhaps being able to recommend other contractors known to take an exemplary approach. As well as providing background context, such opinions can be insightful and in this case it's likely that these alone would have given the mayor and his council just cause for turning down the Pest Control Piper's service offering! All of these sources – whether external or internal in origin – are invaluable in their own way, and it's important for organisations to be broad-minded, by thinking about the whole picture, before committing to what will hopefully be a long-term business relationship for them.

Furthermore, it's clear that the council members could have placed themselves in a far better situation to deal with emergency situations like the rat infestation one they encountered here, simply by acquiring some base-level knowledge about the services of other reputable contractors, upon whose services they could have drawn quickly and easily when an urgent need arose. In a bid to avoid negative outcomes of the kind the tale describes, organisations can find it beneficial to proactively build relationships, for instance, by the setting up of arrangements with so-called 'preferred contractors'. Taking such an approach means contractors' safety records can be checked from time to time and also provides an effective method by which contractors can be kept updated with the client organisation's expectations – together with any changes to its rules and standards – on an ongoing basis. It also makes it possible to have a contractor or multiple contractors waiting in the wings on an 'approved contractors' list' (with their considered and reliable arrangements for safe working already having been established), saving client organisations the effort of starting from scratch and needing to carry out a complete selection process, every time they want a job to be done. In a similar vein, another method can be to interview different contractors – requesting certain information from them about how they work, what they know about health and safety, and how they implement their own 'health and safety policies' – giving crucial insights into their overall approach, helping to determine whether or not the principles of the parties align, and ultimately steering the decision as to whether any particular contractor is a party with whom the organisation wishes to do business.

Going still further into the detail, looking at a risk assessment can prove invaluable when thinking logically about what a job involves in advance of it being carried out, helping to inform the decision about which contractor to select. Here, we learn that a copy of a risk assessment document was found discarded near to the Pest Control Piper's van, but this appears to have been generic and seemingly paid insufficient attention to the challenges of the job ahead and the issues particular to the location in question; had the mayor taken the time to look at this in advance, however, it would no doubt have set a hare running for him and his council. Indeed, it seems probable that even a cursory inspection of this document at a formative stage of the process would have given rise to answers or revealed gaps, which would have sparked alarm for the mayor and his council and possibly influenced their ultimate decision about who to select to carry out the work for them.

The failure to assess the risks involved in the work, together with the omission by the parties to agree upon the actions needed to control them, arguably lies at the heart of what went wrong here. Going methodically through the job should have been a collaborative exercise, and the mayor should also have supplied the Pest Control Piper with any reciprocal information about the risks, of which he was aware. In the circumstances outlined, the control of risk clearly failed, not only to the detriment of the Pest Control Piper, but to the wider public too. The health risks, of which leptospirosis exposure was the obvious one, should have been considered alongside safety risks, with the level of detail captured between the parties including actions agreed to control them, who was responsible for what, and when they were required to do it.

Had the mayor and his council set out upfront their health and safety requirements, alongside other contractual obligations, this would have sent out a clear message about their expectations, in terms of policy, performance and procedures, making it much more straightforward for them to select the contractor best able to meet them. In equivalent real-world scenarios, doing this early on in the process often helps to stave off disputes further down the line. Here, it would also have meant that important safety aspects weren't overlooked, by spelling out that these were equivalently weighted to concerns of a more commercial nature. Taking a close look at the activity being undertaken here and the accompanying site requirements in advance – including the basics such as the need for the Pest Control Piper to report any incidents, seeking confirmation from him about his willingness to abide by site rules, and stressing to him the importance of raising any problems without delay – would have provided the mayor and his council with the ideal opportunity to proactively set expectations including, perhaps, booking in interim visits throughout the job's lifecycle. This would have allowed the parties to reach agreement on what checks were expected to be carried out on a routine basis. It would also have paved the way for the development of a common approach for carrying out checks on a more *ad hoc* basis.

A method statement is another invaluable source of information, which could have been requested from the Pest Control Piper at the contractor selection step of the process. Here, it's likely that this too should have triggered cause for concern, as it would have revealed the unusual approach proposed for the work activity, as well as highlighting gaps! It would also have been useful to question the Pest Control Piper about his emergency procedures at this point – including the timings, points and methods of invocation involved – the answers to which would likely have sparked alarm about his somewhat bizarre methods of controlling risk.

A trait shared by effective contractor selection processes is that they tend to supplement questions asked of potential contractors with requests for supporting information to be supplied, to help verify claims made to competence. Seeking references, determining whether a contractor is a member of, or has affiliations with, reputable trade bodies and using an approved contractors' list can all help to provide the answers to these questions. Asking a potential contractor to run through a job, including site rules – ideally with the client organisation's own workers in attendance too – can support the making of an informed judgment as to whether they are likely to align with their requirements and ethos. A wide variety of evidence can be called upon within such processes, but here this might have included independent assessments of the Pest Control Piper's competence, details of his membership of relevant trade associations or professional bodies, such as the British Pest Control Association[48] for instance, or examples of safety method statements he had previously prepared. It seems likely that here both the answers to these enquiries and the lack of supporting evidence to back up the Pest Control Piper's claims would have given justifiable cause for concern. And, of course, in taking this approach, the mayor and his council would also have had the option of seeking clarification from the Pest Control Piper's own employer. Being satisfied that their chosen contractor could do the job safely and without risks to health would have best served the interests of the Pest Control Piper, the mayor and of course, the local population indulging in water-based activities. And asking some simple questions upfront would have either reassured the mayor of the Pest Control Piper's competence or, here, most likely highlighted him as being an unsuitable choice to carry out the work. Taking a little time early on to make sure the Pest Control Piper understood the health and safety standards he had to achieve – based upon objective competence criteria – would have likely paid dividends later. *Who knows?* It might even have prompted the Pest Control Piper to raise his game!

Finally for this second step, it's worth highlighting that even if the Pest Control Piper was acting as a 'sub-contractor', the relationship between the council, as client, and the main contractor would still have needed to be a strong one, requiring dialogue to take place between the parties before work started. In circumstances where sub-contractors are to be used, there needs to be a clear upfront agreement between the two parties that

---

48. The British Pest Control Association is a UK trade association representing organisations with a professional interest in the eradication and management of public health pests. Organisations wishing to join it have to prove their competence in pest control.

this is permissible. Furthermore, in cases where such arrangements exist, defining the client-contractor relationship is fundamental, as it helps the client to ensure that any choice of sub-contractor made by the contractor is consistent with their wishes. This is particularly important, given that sub-contractors are a further step removed from a client's direct control, meaning that the onus needs to be placed upon the main contractor to manage the sub-contractor. The purpose of this is to make sure that the sub-contractor has the required credentials and adheres just as tightly to site rules, working methods, and procedures as would be the case if the main contractor did the work directly, thus ensuring safety standards are preserved, at all times. Had this been the case here, this would have meant the mayor and his team needed to impose requirements via the main contractor to manage the Pest Control Piper, as well as making sure that all the necessary health and safety information he needed to do the work was passed across to him and that arrangements were put in place to check on his performance and remedy any identified shortcomings.

STEP #3
DID THE PIPER RECEIVE A SITE INDUCTION?

NO! *There's no suggestion of the mayor and his council having provided information to the Pest Control Piper, a process which should have started as soon as he arrived on site.*

The Pest Control Piper was seemingly recruited on the basis of little more than a casual conversation, and no mention is made of any information having been passed to the Pest Control Piper by the mayor and his council, either on his arrival or subsequent to it. At the point of setting a contractor to work on site, it's important for them to be made aware of the site safety rules that apply to them and any particular hazards they could encounter in the course of the job. Ostensibly, the action of signing in and out is a simple stage in the process of information-sharing with contractors but, when used to best effect, it's a vital practical arrangement which helps achieve buy-in to a client's own culture. As well as the comings and goings of contractors being tightly controlled at this point, with their entry on to and exit off site logged via a formal sign-in and sign-out process (often accompanied by the issuing and returning of site passes), this also provides a good opportunity for essential details to be formally supplied to contractors. It didn't appear that any such process existed here but, had this been the case, it would have provided the ideal moment for the exchange of particulars about the work to have taken place between the mayor and the Pest Control Piper – both at the start of the job and on each subsequent occasion he arrived on site to perform his rat-culling duties.

In addition to instituting sign-in/sign out processes, the name of a site contact should be provided to contractors at the point of their being inducted on to site, so that they know who to approach in the event of any query or difficulty arising during the job's lifecycle. The importance of designating a site contact cannot be overstated, and here it should have been made clear to the Pest Control Piper who was to perform this role. This would have given him someone to get in touch with on a routine basis, if there was any alteration to the job, or if he experienced uncertainty about what to do, as the work progressed. It's impossible to say whether the Pest Control Piper would have actually approached such a site contact when his method of rat culling started to escalate out of control, but furnishing him with these details would at least have given him the route for so doing. Furthermore, had the Pest Control Piper got in touch with a designated site contact at an earlier stage, it seems likely that at least some of the adverse consequences which flowed here would have been averted.

An effective 'site induction' is a vital part of the process, offering the mechanism via which to brief workers on site conditions, facilities, and safety rules, including the PPE they are expected to wear and the equipment they are to use, together with any safe working methods with which they must comply. Here, having engaged the Pest Control Piper, the mayor and his council should have furnished him with the right information when he commenced work on site and yet, there doesn't appear to have been any such arrangement in place here. Even when a contractor is, as here, taken on at short notice the need for a site induction remains, this being a key method through which to stress the importance of health and safety information and site rules. One particularly vital inclusion at this stage is the provision of emergency procedures and it's suggested that, had such procedures been swiftly invoked here, at the first sign of trouble, this might have led to a better outcome for all concerned, rather than to the untimely end met by some members of the community in this fable. Additionally, concerted efforts should have been made to engage in discussions with the mayor's employees about how the work involved might affect their health and safety, by providing them with information and training and also making sure they knew how to raise any concerns, as would inevitably have been brought on by the questionable working practices adopted by the Pest Control Piper!

The site induction is also the point in the process at which it's appropriate to check that all the necessary arrangements for the job are in place, paving the way for work to commence. Such arrangements will often include administrative arrangements, for instance, putting in place a timetable for formal and regular reviews of the contractors' safety management performance and defining the appropriate supporting monitoring mechanisms. There are many ways in which ongoing monitoring can be accomplished, and it's commonplace for organisations to adopt a combination of different approaches, as befits their needs. It might be through 'inspections' and 'audits'. It might be through safety meetings. Or simply by reporting against an agreed set of 'performance indicators'. Whilst the details of these various methods are to be set down at this point, preliminary discussions about checks will often have been discussed previously, at the stage of contractor selection. In this instance, it would have been reasonable for such arrangements to include checks on pest reproduction and the planning in of follow-up visits, in cases where remedial works were deemed not to have cured the pest problem. Unsurprisingly perhaps, this was a further area which neither party saw fit to raise in this case!

Once these arrangements have been put in place, it's at this point that work can be allowed to begin. In this instance, some readers will no doubt question whether the Pest Control Piper would have been receptive to and complied with information and any accompanying instructions provided to him, even if the mayor and his council had shown diligence at this step of the process. It's entirely fair to pose questions of this kind, particularly given the Pest Control Piper's propensity towards roguishness! But furnishing him with sufficient information would at least have ensured the mayor and his council fulfilled their responsibilities towards him, and shown their intent to forge an effective contractual relationship, before work was formally allowed to begin. That the Pest Control Piper had obligations which he breached is undeniable, but the mayor and his team had a reciprocal obligation to supply relevant details to him, a requirement which they appeared to disregard. They should have taken the lead on this and yet, it's clear that the mayor and his council fell some way short of the expectations of them here.

STEP #4
WERE THERE REGULAR SITE CHECK-INS WITH THE PIPER?

NO! *There's no evidence of the mayor and his council having kept a check on the Pest Control Piper, whilst he was working on site.*

It's clear from the fable that events quickly escalated out of control here, from children frolicking happily in the water one moment, to a chaotic situation with rats overrunning the town and an outbreak of Weil's disease the next. Nevertheless, there seems to have been an abject failure by the mayor and his team to put in place arrangements to manage the contract under which the Pest Control Piper was taken on, which would no doubt have hampered any subsequent efforts to co-ordinate and monitor his activities in accordance with a plan, consistent with the level of risk present. The scenario the fable describes seems to have escalated in a short period of time, but it's quite apparent that the problems arising at this point had their genesis at the previous step, with the failure to provide formal procedures upfront having been a notable omission when inducting him on to site. By providing information to the Pest Control Piper at that point, the council would have set the tone for positive engagement to take place, giving them legitimate cause to directly pursue him via ongoing checks if he went beyond his agreed remit at any stage, wasn't carrying out the work safely and as agreed, or was failing to meet the agreed timelines or deliver against the job's key milestones.

When putting in place arrangements to check that work is progressing as planned with contractors, decisions need to be made about the degree and frequency of contact. Unfortunately, it's quite clear that this didn't take place here, but taking the time to determine this upfront, based upon the risks and parties involved, paves the way for regular checks to be made that work is going as intended throughout the course of the job's lifecycle. Here, the mayor and his council should have worked out the required level of contractual supervision. Furthermore, it would have been sensible for the mayor to assign responsibilities to specific council colleagues to carry out routine checks on the Pest Control Piper's work at appropriate intervals, in order that they could be satisfied that he was meeting his contractual obligations. This should, of course, have involved the designated individuals verifying his work against the plan, the job specification and set down working methods, including method statements.

And importantly, the agreement reached earlier on in the process, concerning how the work was to be done and the control measures the Pest Control Piper intended to apply, would have provided much of the subject matter for these ongoing checks.

The carrying out of periodic checks is vital to ensuring effective oversight of contractors. Not only does it verify that the selected control measures are working and that work is going to plan, but it also provides chances to investigate things going wrong prior to more serious events occurring and to follow up any concerns, thereby helping to stave off accidents, 'near misses', occurrences of ill health, and other unwanted incidents. It's quite apparent that the situation here was a fast-evolving one – which quickly turned from a happy leisure scene to a chaotic health risk scenario – but had care been taken to form a closer contractual relationship during the foregoing steps of the process, the mayor and his council would likely have found earlier opportunities to intervene, including applying the lessons learnt from earlier, perhaps less serious, incident reports at this particular work location. Of course, hindsight tells us that – in light of the very clear concerns that subsequently arose with the Pest Control Piper's work – had the council formalised such arrangements from the outset, this would have given them a range of options for increasing the frequency and depth of checks applied at this point, to a level commensurate with the nature and scale of the prevailing circumstances. In terms of the details of such checks, there would undoubtedly have been earlier opportunities to set defined targets – for instance, the number of rats killed or a goal of *rat population zero*, or for the success of the Pest Control Piper to be judged on the basis of testing and monitoring results – which would then have served as the barometer to check his actual performance at this stage. In circumstances where arrangements with contractors are well managed, preliminary target setting discussions typically take place at the first step of the contractor risk control strategy.

Whilst not the course events took here, another possible way in which difficulties of the kind encountered by the mayor and his council can arise, is where changes to personnel are made. In a slight twist on this scenario, it could have been that the Pest Control Piper was an unauthorised substitution for an agreed named resource. Had this been the case, the switch could have been caught by monitoring and checking – covering what was being done, who was doing it, how it was being done, and whether the job was generally progressing as planned – which would have given clear opportunities to swiftly agree changes and resolve matters, in the wake of any identified problems. And had the Pest Control Piper arrived at a site where other workers hired under the same contract had previously been working, the mayor and his team should have been vigilant to this, either inducting him on to site or, if he was identified as an inappropriate substitution, by flagging this to the main contractor, to indicate reneging of the agreement in place. In any event the mayor and his council should, as a minimum, have checked-in with the Pest Control Piper at the start of each working day or shift, or more frequently, if – as was the case here – the need dictated it.

Another possibility was that the Pest Control Piper's lack of experience in pest control meant that special arrangements were required in his case, to ensure he carried out his work safely. In such circumstances, it would have been likely that supervision levels needed to be increased by his own employer, on a risk basis, with his activities closely monitored and overseen by someone with a suitable level of knowledge, understanding and experience – an arrangement with which the mayor and his council would have needed to agree, and on which they should have been fully sighted.

Other arrangements that needed to be considered for this step would have included determining the type of equipment – including PPE – the Pest Control Piper was going to use, and establishing the working procedures to be adopted, together with any permits required. Engaging in positive dialogue for this checking step would undoubtedly have been invaluable to the detection and weeding out of some of the Pest Control Piper's quirky working methods, and paved the way for concerns to be addressed, giving the mayor and his council options for barring work from starting, or halting it, when it became problematic. Here, there's little doubt that the lack of early-stage discussions would have hampered their ability to intervene as the situation started to escalate out of control. Had a programme of routine checks been put in place and followed, however, it seems likely that vital signs would have been picked up that the job wasn't going as planned, that the Pest Control Piper wasn't working safely and as agreed, and that his chosen method of pest control was, at best, ineffective, giving an opportunity for the mayor and his team to swiftly step in, so as to prevent, or at least limit, any adverse consequences.

STEP #5

WAS THE PIPER'S WORK REVIEWED?

NO! *The response to this question cannot be given with the same degree of certainty as those for the other steps, due to the fable ending so abruptly after the incident outcome!*

There's no suggestion, however, of any review of the rat control work undertaken by the Pest Control Piper having taken place, nor of one even having been scheduled by the mayor and his council. In the real world, after a job has been carried out there is, of course, much to be gained from calmly taking stock of the situation, including reviewing incident outcomes and learning any lessons, so as to drive up future levels of performance. As we know of course, the opportunity to carry out a formal review - or even to plan for one - wasn't taken here. Nevertheless, the gravity of the incident described should have made clear the acute need for this to be conducted as a priority, in order to avoid a recurrence, prevent surprises in the future and ensure that lessons were learnt, recorded and acted upon. And it's worth adding that, had such a review been carried out on the Pest Control Piper's work at a previous job, prior to the set of events which unfolded here, this whole sorry scenario might have been avoided - hopefully he wouldn't even have made it past the initial selection stage!

Carried out upon conclusion of the work, this final step comprises a comprehensive review of the job itself and the performance of the particular contractor - including consideration of the substantive health and safety performance elements - against what was agreed between the parties at the outset. It's important for a contractor to be provided with direct feedback on their performance at the point at which the job is reviewed. When carried out effectively, a critical evaluation of the job at this review stage can offer up crucial insights as to how future contracts might be improved. This is the right moment at which to determine the effectiveness of the planning step, recognise a contractor's achievements as well as any shortfalls, review the job outcomes, and for the parties to agree between themselves any learning points about what could be done better. It's sensible for the outcomes of such reviews to be formally recorded, in order to capture 'good practice' and document insights including, for instance, the possible amendment or revision of procedures and working practices for replication across similar contracts and jobs, to help drive up future contractual performance. The adequacy of the procedures put in place at the start of the job – and during it, if applicable – should also be verified at this point, with the overall performance of the contractor being recorded and rated against mutually agreed criteria.

It's worth noting that if either party fails to engage at this review step of the process – for instance, with matters being concluded simply by the sending and settlement of an invoice for the work – the opportunity to apply any learning to future jobs can easily be lost. Any further action deemed to be required should be taken at this point, including the making of a note on the contractor's record about the delivery of superior or sub-standard performance, as well as a record being made of any cautions for engaging in future contracts with them, or even blacklisting.

For *steps one* to *four*, it's been possible to make a reasonable attempt at evaluating the effectiveness of the arrangements the mayor and his council had in place for managing the contractor and the job itself. For *step five*, however, we can only make an educated guess as to how the level of contractual performance might have been viewed. *Why so?* Well, unlike the conventional contract reviews carried out within real-world workplaces, where the parties tend to sit down calmly over tea and biscuits, reflecting on how things have gone, no such opportunity is taken by the characters involved here. The ending to this fable appears to fall squarely at the Bedlam end of the *ever after* spectrum alluded to in this book's introduction – no doubt inducing a crushing sense of disappointment in those readers who drew comfort from the sunnier resolution enjoyed by the characters in *the goats' fable*. Here, instead, we are forced to accept the desertion of a central character – presumed dead or on the run – together with rumours of illness and fatalities aplenty, an abandoned vehicle, a hapless mayor and an inept council left in a quandary as to what to do next, against the backdrop of an emerging social discontent rippling throughout the town. *And still far too many rats running amok!* For those readers seeking some kind of closure, perhaps the only certainty here is an overriding sense of sadness – or even outrage – that things needlessly ended this way.

Being candid about the situation, there was every need for the mayor and the council to critically reflect upon the totality of their customer experience, following their engagement of the Pest Control Piper – it was quite apparent that their planning was negligible, the Pest Control Piper's performance abysmal, and the job unsuccessful. Had the expectations been clearly agreed from the start, however, there's a good chance that the sorry state of affairs which unfolded here might have been averted, or at least swiftly curtailed, at the first sign of trouble. Instead, we can only make an educated guess as to how such a review might have played out here, by considering: *first,* the choice of the Pest Control Piper as the contractor responsible for carrying out the work, *second,* the planning process and *third,* how the job went. Given an equivalent real-world scenario, the areas summarised here would undoubtedly merit further investigation – commonly achieved by carrying out a management system audit on contract and contractor management. Had the mayor and his council been pushed to review their management of the contractor, as is called for by this fifth step, it's likely they would have found little of merit, whether in how the job was performed overall, or in their management of the contract for the Pest Control Piper's services. These are not comprehensive listings, and there's inevitably an element of repetition here, given that the purpose of any such review – even in a real-world context – is to evaluate the effectiveness of the foregoing steps in the process.

So, let's think briefly about the issues that might have been picked up by such a review...

In relation to the chosen contractor, it's unlikely that, given their time again, the mayor and his council would make the same selection. Looking at their choice, in summary, the following points are worthy of note. *First,* no mention is made of any kind of pre-contract selection process having taken place – such as a request for the Pest Control Piper to complete a 'pre-qualification questionnaire' or a check made to see if his name featured on an approved contractors' list – nor even of efforts having been made to interrogate records documented within any kind of 'contract management system'. Neither is any suggestion made of engagement having taken place with formal or informal networks about the Pest Control Piper's record, nor even of a basic request made to view a copy of his health and safety policy or details of his safety performance, any or all of which might have highlighted to the mayor and his council the choice of the roguish Pest Control Piper as being an ill-judged one. *Second,* no sooner had work begun, than it became painfully apparent that there were multiple health and safety problems, confirming that the Pest Control Piper was indeed a poor choice. *Third,* given the nature of the events that unfolded here, there would have been every need for the council to take swift action. *Fourth,* it was apparent that there were multiple aspects on which the council would have wanted to take the

Pest Control Piper to task – three notable examples being his approach to risk assessment and control, his control of the work area, and his disregard for the more mainstream PPE choices. *Fifth,* with the Pest Control Piper having left site, were he to make any kind of bid to regain access in future, it seems highly likely that the mayor and his council would have wanted to bar his re-entry, with refusal needing to be made at the point of his attempting to sign in. And *sixth,* and finally, the very notion of the mayor and his council being prepared to provide the Pest Control Piper with a reference, or their being willing to add him to a preferred list, seems an entirely fanciful one; on the contrary, it's likely he would have been regarded as a candidate ripe for blacklisting!

Turning to the planning process, there's no suggestion of the job having been approached on a planned basis, with the mayor and his council failing to define the work beyond a desperate plea to rid their town of rats. There were multiple aspects which showed a failure to apply a robust planning process. *First,* there was a collective failure to identify hazards, which in turn meant that the risks were not assessed. This included the omission to identify the hazard of taking on a contractor, accompanied by the risk of non-delivery against contractual obligations. *Second,* this, in turn, meant that negligible effort was made towards controlling risks. *Third,* there was a failure to specify the health and safety conditions and upfront expectations. And *fourth* and finally, no mention is made of any meaningful discussions having taken place between the Pest Control Piper, the mayor and the council covering the basics of who was to do what, in advance of the job starting. In short, the planning process, which should have formed the very bedrock of the contractual relationship between the parties and paved the way for the effective performance of the work, could only be described as abysmal.

In looking at the job overall, including the effectiveness of the contact and supervision arrangements, it's impossible to cite an aspect that was well performed here, meaning that the question about how such shortfalls might be addressed in the future is answerable with a seemingly infinite list of possibilities! What is beyond doubt, however, is that, if confronted by an equivalent real-world scenario to that described here, a full overhaul of the council's approach to contract management would be in order. Numerous aspects – of which the following are just examples highlighting the ineffectiveness of the job overall – would need to be addressed. *First,* there was the failure to put in place systems for signing in and out and carrying out site inductions, and arrangements for hazard identification and risk assessment, which bordered on non-existent here. *Second,* there was the council's failure to set down the work expected from the Pest Control Piper in formal documents such as contracts and safety method statements, neither type having been mentioned – a flaw which would have hampered their ability to claim work wasn't done as agreed. *Third,* there was a failure to institute testing arrangements, which should have included the checking of the tests planned and performed, and results recorded by the Pest Control Piper. And *fourth,* and finally, there was an apparent failure to capture actions, achievements and shortfalls, which would have meant opportunities being lost to adjust working methods, adopt good practice, and address the gaps noted here.

It has to be hoped that events of the types described in this fable would motivate actions being taken by the mayor and his council to curb the possibility of a job being carried out in a similar fashion in the future. *Who knows?* Had the mayor and his council been privy to the outcomes of such precursor events, this might have seen them championing a better approach towards the scenario presented here. If a real-world organisation were to be faced with equivalent circumstances to those involving the Pest Control Piper, there's little doubt that the health and safety concerns raised would be of a type and magnitude justifying sanctions including the barring of re-entry to the work site and/or prevention of re-engagement to undertake similar work in the future (so-called blacklisting). In truth, on the basis of what's learnt here, it's difficult to see a review reaching any other conclusion. As it was, the failure by the mayor and his council to take action clearly contributed to the severity of the consequences that flowed from the events depicted by this fable. Any organisation with robust arrangements for contract management would expect to see structured reviews carried out as a matter of course, with the outputs from these, as well as from management system audits, being formally documented within an appropriate contract management system, helping to drive 'continual improvement' in the future. When they are well performed, activities such as audits and reviews are vital to the *check* and *act* steps of any 'risk management cycle'. In this case, they would have enabled the mayor and his council to apply the incident's learning points to improve their approach to the *plan* and *do* steps for the next round of the cycle. This would have been invaluable to them when they next sought to engage a contractor to carry out work, and is an approach which is readily transferable to any equivalent real-world scenario.

> **REMEMBER!**
>
> Contractual curiosity is a good thing! Questions to help check the five steps of an effective contractor risk control strategy have been included in *How to...* Guide Two, which accompanies this fable. These are indicative of the types of questions which, if asked, might have helped the mayor and his council to stave off difficulties at each stage of their contractual dealings with the Pest Control Piper.

CLOSING THOUGHTS

This fable's introduction to a quirky flautist brought to the fore the part played by two types of control strategy – one for the control of an activity (*rat culling*) risk and the other for the control of a contractor (*the wayward Pest Control Piper*) risk – together with some indications of the types of consequences that can flow when risks such as these are poorly managed. Understanding *who* is responsible for managing such strategies, as well as the key steps involved in giving effect to their accompanying arrangements, invariably leads to better outcomes for all concerned. When seeking to address an activity risk, the focus should be upon risk assessment, accompanied by the instituting of a strategy to control the risk, and arrangements for its review. In the case of managing a contractor risk, on the other hand, the aim should always be to achieve effective job planning, the adoption of a robust contractor selection process, the provision of good information, the use of appropriate checking methods, and the carrying out of a review upon completion of the work.

This has been a tale of two risk control strategies. When well-applied, such strategies enable risk to be controlled in a structured and coherent manner, paving the way for it to be managed to an acceptable level. Whether this relates to the control of a physical health risk such as leptospirosis, or a contractual risk such as the management of an errant Pest Control Piper engaged to carry out work, what matters most is that appropriate identification, assessment, management and control processes are in place to address risk, with lessons learnt and applied following review, both from what has gone well and what needs to be improved upon in the future.

For a summary of practical points to take away,
based upon the topics and subtopics handled by this fable,
see *How to...* Guide Two.

A NOTE ON REPORTING REQUIREMENTS

The events portrayed in this fable were of a purely fictitious nature. See the *Epilogue* for indicative reporting requirements under *the Reporting of Injuries, Diseases and Dangerous Occurrences Regulations 2013*[49] *(RIDDOR)*, as could be triggered by equivalent real-world circumstances.

STOP PRESS!

Within Great Britain, the longstanding position has been that an employer's duties in relation to PPE apply simply to employees. As this book goes to press however, following the outcome of a formal public consultation, new regulations are being introduced which extend this protection – correcting an anomaly identified with how aspects of European legislation were brought into domestic law via *the PPE regulations* – to include other workers who carry out work on a more casual basis too. In future, therefore, if the circumstances presented in this fable were to be real-world, rather than fictional, the mayor and his council would fall subject to certain duties towards the Pest Control Piper with regards to PPE – whether he was viewed as an employee, or merely a worker. These amended regulations, which broaden workers' rights in respect of PPE in the workplace, came into effect on 6 April 2022. They do not, however, change the more specific requirements for PPE that reduces risks such as those arising from workplace substances hazardous to health, noise, lead exposure, ionising radiation or asbestos, which continue to be covered by other regulations.

---

49. S.I. 2013/1471.

A Lad (Ian), a Poor Choice of Lamp, and Lessons in Lighting

IAN'S FABLE

'Deep down at the bottom of the deep dark mine, there was indeed a lamp, the likes of which Ian had never seen before. The mine walls glittered and sparkled, such was the power of light it emitted.
It had a strangely hypnotic quality. *The mine was very dusty.*'

PROLOGUE

This fable introduces a 'worker' – a lad called Ian – an encounter that naturally leads on to an exploration of some poor lighting choices, stemming from his use of an unsuitable lamp. As the third of four *workers' fables* in this collection, just like the two that preceded it, this tale highlights some fundamental safety basics – in this case, the need to use lamps and lighting which are appropriate, both for the activities being undertaken, and the environment within which they are to be used. It raises some interesting questions about the risks and potential consequences which might have flowed from Ian's decision to use a lamp under the direction of a – fortunately fictitious – rogue mine operator, with a particular focus on explosive atmospheres, as well as bringing to the fore some other activity and location-related risks. It also triggers the question as to what he was doing within a mining environment in the first place, given that he's portrayed as being green to the ways of 'confined space' working!

The tale also has elements of the *theatre* about it: a sparkly lamp *prop*; a moody mine *backdrop*; a *plot* about dangerous substances and explosive atmospheres (and a confined spaces *sub-plot*); some *cast* members with vital roles to play (not forgetting other *extras* or *bit-part players* performing procurement and waste management roles), and unwanted *special effects* seemingly avoided more by luck, than through the risks involved being well controlled!

At first sight the use of a sparkly lamp within a dusty mine might strike as a particularly niche scenario, but many of the general principles the fable espouses have relevance for any workplace where activities are carried out involving or using 'dangerous substances' which can cause an 'explosive atmosphere' to exist, whether on a permanent or temporary basis. The poor lamp choice at the heart of this fable marks the origin from which to explore the importance of selecting the right lighting – and other equipment – for use in 'potentially explosive atmospheres'. Real-world organisations are often faced with the need to make important decisions about equipment, which are typically informed by their responding to 'risk assessment' outcomes and through applying broader risk management principles to their particular operating circumstances.

THE ECONOMIC CONTRIBUTION OF MINING

Some readers might question why a twist on a childhood fable about a mine would be of interest. It's certainly true to say that the level of domestic coal production is now far below the heights seen in the 1950s, as borne out by data published by the Department for Business, Energy & Industrial Strategy (DBEIS), which records that it fell from a peak of 228 million tonnes in 1952 to just 2 million tonnes in 2020[50]. But whilst conventional mining, including for coal, has all but disappeared, Great Britain's mineral extraction industry remains significant. Given that minerals represent the largest flow of materials within the economy, their contribution to our financial wellbeing and way of life is not in doubt. Taking just a few examples, aggregates – including stone, gravel, sand and clay – are essential for highway construction and maintenance, and as a base material for concrete, whilst ballast is crucial for stabilising rolling stock within the rail industry, and dolomite, chalk and gypsum have applications within agricultural and other contexts. So whilst it's true to say that mining in the traditional sense does indeed belong to a bygone era, as the bringers of a range of significant risks, the extractive industries face a range of obligations to protect the workers involved.

A NOTE ON CONFINED SPACES

In common with the original tale upon which this one is based, the basic focus here is upon a poor choice of lamp for use in a dusty mine. But this updated version also looks into the location-related challenges posed

---

50. Department for Business, Energy and Industrial Strategy, (2021). *Historical Coal Data: Coal production, availability and consumption 1853 to 2020.* Published and available to view at www.gov.uk [Viewed 8 January 2022].

by the environment and the nature of work being undertaken within it, paying particular attention to the need to recognise when flammable and explosive atmospheric conditions are present, as a first step towards controlling dangerous substance and explosive atmosphere risks.

Delving a bit deeper, beneath the glitz of the sparkly lamp *prop* and behind the moody setting of the dusty mine *backdrop* against which this tale is set, the fable offers a useful reminder of the need to consider other significant risks associated with mining environments, including darkness and electricity and, perhaps most notably, confined spaces. Mines are, by definition, confined spaces, being places of an enclosed nature, where there is a risk of death or serious injury from hazardous substances or dangerous conditions[51]. And so, whilst not the main focus, it's for this reason that confined space working requirements (or *the sub-surface sub-plot!*) have also been considered, both as the subject matter of one of the principles in this fable's *modern meaning*, and within *How to...* Guide Three which accompanies the tale.

A PROP, A BACKDROP, AND A SCENE-SETTING QUESTION

Thus far, in setting the scene for this fable, mention has been made of a basic *prop* (lamp) and *backdrop* (mine), with a brief nod given as to why mining matters. There's undoubtedly a value to be gained through understanding the nature of the particular operating environment – which is relevant for considering the lighting requirements of mines, just as it would be for any other workplace where potentially explosive atmospheres exist. It's this which paves the way for lamps and lighting to be chosen which are appropriate for the mining location and environment in which they are to be used – not only should they be of robust construction, but they should also offer protection against dust ingress and ignition and, where relevant, be suitable for use within confined spaces and other harsh or hazardous conditions. But before getting into the detail of the risks involved in this tale, it's worth pondering for a moment the broader *scene-setting* question –

---

51. It's interesting to note that, unlike the majority of other confined space types and work situations seen in Great Britain, mines are covered by specific legislation, which is outlined later in the context of this fable.

'Why does light matter?' – as a helpful reminder of the basic, but wide-ranging benefits light has to offer.

It's key to remember that light is one of life's essential building blocks. It's one of the basics, like air and water. Our need for light pre-dates our *need* for computers and smartphones. It matters generally, just as it does specifically, for the type of scenario we'll see played out in this fable. Many of the reasons it matters are obvious. It helps people to see properly, assisting them with their hazard identification. It also illuminates the activities and tasks they are called upon or need to perform. It tells people when and where they can and cannot go – and where other people are going, too – by acting as a signal, in multiple traffic contexts. And it enables people to see their way ahead in emergency situations, when normal lighting might cease to function. At a fundamental level, natural light also supports human 'wellbeing', with the skin absorbing vitamin D, helping to keep bones strong and reducing the risk of heart disease, weight gain and various cancers.

The right sort of light matters too – for both safety and human health reasons – a point reflected(!) across much health and safety legislation, which specifically points out that, where possible, natural light is the preferred option[52]. It needs to be 'suitable and sufficient' for workplace occupants, so as to support their general health and help avoid health issues such as eyestrain. This same requirement applies to any places in which people use work equipment[53] for the tasks they need to perform, where it provides them with a clearer vision of their surroundings and heightens their workplace risk awareness too. Light also matters because it helps to achieve safe ways in and out of workplaces – a basic requirement of the *Health and Safety at Work etc. Act 1974*[54] (HSWA 1974). Specifically, this calls upon employers to 'so far as is reasonably practicable' maintain any workplace under their control '...*in a condition that is safe and without risks to health and the provision and maintenance of means of access to and egress from it that are safe and without such risks'.*[55]

---

52. Regulation 8 of *The Workplace (Health, Safety and Welfare) Regulations 1992;* S.I. 1992/3004, sets out the requirements for workplace lighting.
53. Regulation 21 of *The Provision and Use of Work Equipment Regulations 1998;* S.I. 1998/2306, sets out the requirement for lighting to be 'suitable and sufficient' where work equipment is being used.
54. 1974 c. 37.
55. Section 2(2)(d) of *HSWA 1974* sets out this requirement.

Light also needs to be of the right quality. But what does this mean? Well, in addition to being appropriate for the full range of tasks undertaken, good lighting assists the human visual system, by making it work less hard. This avoids immediate symptoms such as eyestrain, irritation of eyelids, breakdown of vision and blurred or double vision. It also helps to stave off or reduce referred symptoms, pain or discomfort, including headaches, fatigue, giddiness and other complaints, such as neck ache and backache. What this means for those who use 'display screen equipment' in offices – often including computer screens – is that environmental factors need to be appropriately considered. To take a basic example, computer workstations should be designed in such a way that *'direct glare'* and *'distracting reflections'* are avoided on screens, with windows being covered as necessary, so as to weaken any light which is too strong[56]. Looking to literature for a steer, it's a widely held view that Romeo was thinking only of Juliet, when he said: *'What light through yonder window breaks...?'*[57](Shakespeare, W), but things might have played out somewhat differently, had he continued the line on with *'...it is the east, and the early morning sun's playing havoc with my screen clarity. As a result, I'm left with blurry eyes, headaches and poor posture, what with all this leaning forward and squinting.'* The serious point here, of course, is to show just some of the health issues that sub-optimal lighting conditions can bring about.

Particular care should be taken to ensure lighting does not create undesirable effects, an example being that the use of stroboscopic lighting is to be avoided where epilepsy might be induced in photosensitive individuals. Recognising the diversity of workforce needs, and identifying circumstances which call for bespoke solutions, is just as important as meeting the requirements of workers who face no such challenges. Providing sufficient illumination is also generally important because it allows people to see clearly the tasks they are carrying out, which is helpful in reducing all manner of safety risks.

---

56. *The Health and Safety (Display Screen Equipment) Regulations 1992*; S.I. 1992/2792 cover these requirements, the Schedule to regulation 3 of which provides the minimum requirements for workstations, including lighting.
57. Shakespeare, W., *Romeo and Juliet.*(2.2.2), taken from *'The Arden Shakespeare Complete Works'* (Bloomsbury Publishing, 2019).

BALANCING INTERESTS & MANAGING RISK

Aside from the specific attention this fable pays to a mining environment, it also highlights the importance of adopting a broader outlook, so that attempts to manage one risk don't inadvertently introduce other – possibly unrelated and potentially greater – risks. This has particular significance in relation to restricted and confined spaces, which often receive insufficient natural lighting and hence, prompt the need for additional light sources to be introduced to workplaces. Safe light sources must be provided to enter and work in darkened confined spaces, where it might be unsafe to use regular types, particularly if the space contains flammable materials. Additionally, sparking from unsafe light sources can cause fires or explosions, ultimately leading to injuries or, worse still, fatalities. Tensions of this kind – between the need for light on the one hand, and the need to prevent risks associated with the type of lighting chosen on the other – make it crucially important to understand the work environment, work activities, and the actions and behaviours of workers. And it's only through recognising such tensions, and the dynamics that exist between these various factors, that informed decisions can be made about the right kind of light.

Different lighting challenges confront different industries too. The rail industry, for instance, illuminates station platforms so as to assist passengers boarding (*getting on*) and alighting (*getting off*) trains. Lighting aids the dispatch process, helping to make sure trains leave safely, and enhancing the safety and security of passengers carried by train operating companies. But of course any lighting introduced to control a boarding and alighting risk mustn't compromise a driver's view of signals and signage in any way, for obvious reasons. The aviation industry faces equivalent challenges, one being in relation to lighting near aerodromes. Street-lighting is essential to pedestrians and vehicle users on the ground, but this must be positioned so as to avoid potentially distracting pilots or confusing them by being mistaken for aeronautical ground lights. This is because pilots rely upon the particular pattern of these lights – principally approach and runway lights – to assist in their accurate alignment with the runway and critically, with landing at the correct point. The common thread that runs through these different industry examples, of course, is that whatever the setting, constant vigilance is needed so as to ensure that the control of one risk doesn't – even inadvertently – cause an uptick in other risks. This is also a tension which pervades this fable's mining example – in this case, it's between providing lighting for a dark mine on the one hand and, on the other, making sure an unwanted explosion risk isn't inadvertently introduced, which naturally leads to the question of *how* such issues can be avoided. In order to balance these competing considerations, and so as to ward off potential problems, there are three questions that organisations can usefully pose to help guide their control of risk. These are relevant to the fictional dangerous substance and explosive atmosphere example showcased in this fable, just as they are applicable across the whole gamut of real-world risks. The questions are, *first,* '*Who's involved in the work?*' – which is about choosing the right people; *second,* '*What work are they doing and where?*' – which is about understanding the work activities and location in which these take place, and *third* and finally, '*How are they doing the work?*' – which is about people doing things in the right way, including using the appropriate equipment and applying the relevant control measures. *Let's look at these in a bit more detail...*

First off, it's important to decide *who* is to carry out the work – or what might be colloquially referred to as *the cast list!* Understanding who is to be involved, the relationships between the different parties, and the functions and roles they are each to perform in an activity is key when seeking to control any risk – the particular focus of this fable being upon dangerous substances and explosive atmospheres. And for some workplaces and activities this is particularly crucial, because certain functions need to be performed by specific people – so-called 'duty holders'. This has relevance in the context of mining environments, with *The Mines Regulations 2014*[58] (*'the Mines Regulations'*) defining the roles to be performed for mining activities, most notably those of '(mine) owner' and 'mine operator'[59]. But it's key to note that because these regulations are 'goal-setting' they aren't prescriptive about exactly *what* these individuals are required to do, focusing instead on the important goal of controlling the risks from the major hazards involved in mining activities. They also remove areas of duplication, pointing to applicable general health and

---

58. S.I. 2014/3248.

59. Regulation 2 of *the Mines Regulations* defines these roles, together with other roles and key terms used within the regulations.

safety requirements, wherever relevant. Outlined here are the key roles (*or cast members!*) relevant to this fable, including that of mine operator, the principal duty holder in this scenario. And whilst these are roles taken by fictional characters in the fable they are, of course, vitally important roles to fill in equivalent real-world scenarios. *And so, to the cast list...*

A mine 'owner' is '*the person...entitled to work a mine*'[60], being a person who holds a licence to extract coal or permit to work other minerals – a role which can be fulfilled by an individual or an organisation. Where the mine owner chooses another person to be the mine operator, this appointment brings with it a requirement to furnish them with any information needed on how to work a mine safely. *In this fable, the magician's father is deemed to have been the mine owner – a role which would have brought with it obligations towards the magician, as the mine operator.*

A 'mine operator' is defined as the '*person...in control of the operation of a mine*'[61]. Where appointed by a mine owner – in all cases where they don't perform the role of mine operator themselves – they are the duty holder, with day-to-day control of mine operations, carrying responsibility for co-ordinating all measures relating to the health and safety of persons at work[62]. In cases where these roles are performed by different parties, the mine operator must satisfy the mine owner of their capability to operate a mine safely, including having competent staff and sufficient resource to lead, manage, supervise and work a mine. This requires a risk-based approach to be adopted, which typically comprises: identifying hazards; quantifying risks; examining available control options including 'human factors' aspects, and setting, implementing, monitoring and revising control measures. In particular, the mine operator needs to be able to show that the control measures they choose to adopt are adequate for all identified risks – often including fire, explosion and the release of toxic gases – and that they are able to identify the hazards present and assess and control the risks so that people can work safely. Where relevant, this encompasses the control of dangerous substance and explosive atmosphere risks. *In this fable, a presumption has been made that the magician acted as*

---

60. Regulation 5 of *the Mines Regulations* sets out the (mine) owner's duties.
61. Regulation 7 of *the Mines Regulations* sets out the mine operator's general duties. The mine operator is regarded as the principal duty holder.
62. Regulation 7(2) of *the Mines Regulations* sets out the mine operator's duty to co-ordinate health and safety measures.

mine operator. Having been appointed by his father (the mine owner) this role would have carried with it certain responsibilities towards Ian (a worker) – responsibilities which, as we shall see, the magician who assumed it was ill-equipped to fulfil.

A *'person at work' is the term the regulations give to a person working in a mine, a role performed by Ian in this fable.* The presumption made here is that the relationship between Ian and the magician (the mine operator) would have been of the employee/employer type although, as we are soon to learn, Ian should not have been set to work in a mine until such time as he knew what to do! *But more on that later...*

Second, it's important to understand the nature of work that needs to be undertaken and where it's to be carried out – or what, in the context of this tale, might be colloquially referred to as *the backdrop.* As is true for any type of risk assessment and control, this means assimilating all relevant details about the location and activities. Understanding the nature of the environment is key but, as we shall see, the fable lacks detail when it comes to the type of mine and what was being extracted from it. Of course, for any real-world scenario, it would be vital for anyone seeking to analyse and/or control the particular risks involved to have this kind of information available to them. But given that this level of detail is absent here, the primary focus will be upon consideration of the dust as the 'dangerous substance' – as covered by *the Dangerous Substances and Explosive Atmospheres Regulations 2002*[63]*('DSEAR'),* being *'...any dust, whether in the form of solid particles or fibrous materials or otherwise, which can form an explosive mixture with air or an explosive atmosphere...*[64] – together with the associated explosive atmosphere potential and the lamp itself. And on top of this, it's important to be aware that real-world mining environments can contain any number of other gases or vapours,

---

63. S.I. 2002/2776.

64. Regulation 2 of *DSEAR* defines the term 'dangerous substance', which includes *'...any dust...which can form an explosive mixture with air or an explosive atmosphere...',* dust being the dangerous substance specifically featured in this fable. See this book's *Glossary,* which also provides a further definition of a 'dangerous substance' as it applies in the context of *the COMAH regulations,* considered in relation to *the four little pigs' fable.* Furthermore, whilst the key issues arising from *Ian's fable* relate to the dangerous substance and explosive atmosphere risks, as well as to 'confined space' risks, the risks from hazardous substances used or encountered within any workplace also need to be controlled. A note about hazardous substance risks has been included at the end of the *modern meaning* to this fable.

including methane, ethane, butane, propane, and other contaminants. The fable might be somewhat short on details when it comes to the description of the work activities involved, but taking the time and trouble to understand these, as well as the environment in which they take place and the people involved, are the first vital steps towards securing the effective control of risk within any real-world setting. This paves the way for the introduction of any additional control measures required which, in the example here, would need to address the risks posed by any dangerous substances as might be present.

Third, having thought about who should carry out the work and the roles they perform, as well as the type of work and the location in which it's undertaken, the focus shifts to *how* best to carry it out, such that it's accomplished in the right (and safe) way. Of course, whatever the work activity, the method adopted to carry it out should always be informed by risk assessment outcomes. This naturally includes selecting and using the right equipment – being equipment which is right for the environment, right for the activities undertaken and right for the workers using it. The focus placed on the lamp *prop* in this fable underlines why equipment choices and usage are to be covered in some depth within its accompanying *modern meaning.*

MINES, SPARKS AND PRODUCT MARKS

Appreciating basic lighting concerns and how best to approach the control of risk are important considerations, but it's also vital that any relevant legal requirements are understood. In this instance, these legal expectations can be broadly divided into three types, covering location, activity and product-related aspects. As well as providing the legal context for the dangerous substance *plot* and the confined spaces *sub-plot,* as sit at the fable's heart, these also set the direction for any practical arrangements to be identified and put in place. These are the areas which need to be collectively addressed when seeking to control the use of lamps and lighting within a mining environment, which would no doubt resonate with the characters depicted in this tale, just as they are significant considerations for organisations seeking to institute equivalent arrangements within their real-world workplaces.

First, the *mines-related requirements* relevant to this fable are primarily to be found within *the Mines Regulations.* These gathered up all previous health and safety legislation specific to mining, by drawing into a single set of regulations the legal health and safety requirements related to major hazards present within the underground mining sector in Great Britain. Their relatively recent introduction underlines the point that the regulation of mines remains an area of national concern, bringing into being a comprehensive and easier to understand goal-setting legal framework – one which makes sure mine operators and other duty holders provide the necessary protection for mineworkers and others in the mineral extraction industries against the significant hazards inherent to mining. But it's important to note that they do not duplicate issues where these are already covered within the scope of general health and safety law.

Second, what have been colloquially referred to here as the *sparks requirements* (or, more accurately *non-sparks requirements!*) are the subject of *DSEAR*'s goal-setting focus, putting into effect as they did the 'ATEX Workplace Directive', a European Directive which stipulated minimum requirements for improving the health and safety protection of workers potentially at risk from explosive atmospheres. *The Mines Regulations* point specifically towards *DSEAR* for consideration of the particular dangerous substance and explosive atmosphere risks, because *DSEAR* have as their central concerns the control of risks and prevention and limitation of the effects of fire, explosion and similar events which can arise from the uncontrolled use or presence of dangerous substances within any workplace. Putting them in a nutshell, *DSEAR* set out minimum requirements to protect workers and others from fire and explosion risks related to dangerous substances and explosive atmospheres – applying to mines, as they also do elsewhere – and requiring employers to do all that they can to control them.

Explosive atmospheres can be caused by all manner of different substances – amongst them, flammable gases, mists or vapours, and combustible dusts (combustible dust being the type of substance featured in this fable's mining context) – and, where the control of risk fails, the consequences of explosions that follow can include loss of life, serious injuries and significant property damage. It's in order to ensure that these risks are addressed that *DSEAR* require any workplace where explosive atmospheres may occur to be classified, based upon the risk of an explosion occurring. In handling places where explosive atmospheres may occur, the regulations require a distinction to be made between 'hazardous places' and 'non-hazardous places', and for hazardous places to be further divided into 'zones'.[65] They also call for the protection from sources of ignition to be achieved by selecting the right equipment types and 'protective systems'.

Third, there is a whole gamut of regulations relating to how products (including equipment) are placed on the market in Great Britain, including *product marks*. There are requirements placed upon product manufacturers and those who represent them. There are others to which importers of products are subject. And there are certain requirements that product distributors have to meet too. This is an important area, and one which continues to evolve following our departure from the European Union, with a major change being that, going forward, a new UK Conformity Assessed Mark – the 'UKCA mark' – will be needed for products put on the GB market, substituting the EU 'CE mark'. There are long-standing requirements – so called 'Essential Health and Safety Requirements' – that have to be met before products are placed on the market, including those used within potentially explosive atmospheres[66]. A key principle is for equipment – which includes lighting and lamp products – to be suitable for the environment within which it is to be used. It was the *'ATEX Equipment Directive'* which set down the expectations for the equipment and protective systems suitable for use in potentially explosive atmospheres and, whilst Great Britain was part of the European Union, this meant that 'equipment category' requirements for so-called 'ATEX-certified' equipment types had to be met for equipment used within workplaces. The UK's leaving of the European Union has required adjustments to be made to ensure that *the EPS Regulations* – as just one example of sub-ordinate legislation – continue to function effectively[67]. It has also introduced a need for other gaps to be plugged, with fixes applied to resolve, for instance, outmoded references to EU institutions and the making of specific provisions for the GB market in their place.[68]

---

65. Regulation 7 of *DSEAR* sets out the classification and other requirements for places where explosive atmospheres may occur.

66. These requirements are set out in *the Equipment and Protective Systems Intended for Use in Potentially Explosive Atmospheres Regulations 2016; S.I. 2016/1107 ('the EPS regulations')*, Schedule 1 of which lists the Essential Health and Safety Requirements.

67. The *European Union (Withdrawal) Act 2018*, c. 16., as amended, preserved these regulations, together with many others.

68. *The Product Safety and Metrology (Amendment)(EU Exit) Regulations 2019; S.I. 2019/696* made these changes for equipment and protective systems to be used in potentially explosive atmospheres, just as they also made changes for other product types.

Amongst other changes, this means that equipment supplied for use in workplaces in Great Britain now has to be 'UKEX (UKCA 'Ex') approved', replacing the previous requirement for it to be ATEX-certified and CE marked. The marking of products supplied within or into Great Britain – including equipment and protective systems for use in potentially explosive atmospheres (the lamps in this tale being examples of equipment) – continues to be in a state of flux following European Union exit. As this book goes to press, this area continues to be subject to transitional arrangements, as are briefly explored in the *modern meaning* to this fable.

These 'mines, sparks and product marks' aspects give some legislative, historical and situational background to this fable. What follows next is an overview of the approach to risk assessment, as set out by DSEAR. Thinking about the requirements of the regulations in this structured way sets the context for the fable's events to be reviewed. This naturally includes the selection and proper use of lamps and lighting, but it also paves the way for the management of dangerous substances and explosive atmospheres to be more broadly considered. Keeping in mind the bigger picture is helpful, when seeking to address any kind of risk.

DANGEROUS SUBSTANCES, EXPLOSIVE ATMOSPHERES, AND THE SIX STAGES OF RISK CONTROL

In seeking to control dangerous substance and explosive atmosphere risks, there are six key stages that need to be followed. *Coincidentally, these stages also provide many of the criteria against which the events of the fable – the tale's plot – are to be reviewed!* In summary, they are to: *first,* conduct a risk assessment; *second,* put the necessary management measures in place; *third,* classify areas where potentially explosive atmospheres may exist into zones; *fourth,* mark 'classified areas'; *fifth,* select suitable equipment based on area classification, and finally, *sixth,* provide appropriate training. There's quite a bit of relevant legal detail here, and direction to the regulations has been added within footnotes, where this is felt to be helpful, or of potential reader interest. In reflecting back on the roles defined at the beginning of this fable's *prologue,* the responsibilities described here would fall largely to the magician mine operator to fulfil, with the magician's father, as mine owner, needing to check the suitability of the arrangements.

STAGE #1
CARRY OUT A RISK ASSESSMENT[69]

In common with the risk-based approaches used to consider the subject matter of some of the other fables, the start-point for ensuring the effective control of risk – in this case against fire and explosion within a mine – is the risk assessment. The general duty for employers to carry out a risk assessment is set out in *the Management of Health and Safety at Work Regulations 1999*[70] ('*the Management Regulations*'). But building upon this, the specific requirements for eliminating or reducing the particular risk of fire and explosion from substances connected with work activities are to be found within *DSEAR*, which helpfully set out what must be included in the risk assessment[71]. A *DSEAR* risk assessment covers some aspects also handled by other similar regulations, including the hazardous properties of the substance(s), the circumstances of the work and a focus on activities, such as maintenance, where there's a high level of risk. But it also needs to include other factors, specifically the likelihood of an explosive atmosphere occurring and its persistence, and the likelihood that 'ignition sources', including 'electrostatic discharges', will be present and become active and effective. Due consideration must be given to the effects of all measures to be taken to eliminate or control risks under *DSEAR*, which include: zoning and 'hazardous area classification'; the equipment used; coordination between employers; and the verification of overall explosion safety by a 'competent person'.

It's a well-established principle common to much health and safety legislation that getting the risk assessment right is the first vital stage in developing and implementing any necessary control measures. The basic expectations of *DSEAR* are no different – it's simply that their purpose, and the requirement for risk assessment they set out, is to address the fire and explosion risk. And, in order for the derived control measures to remain fully effective, they need to be regularly reviewed, together with any accompanying systems and the risk assessment itself.

We'll look at whether an effective risk assessment was carried out here.

---

69. Regulation 5 of *DSEAR* sets out the requirements for the risk assessment of workplaces where a dangerous substance is or might be present.

70. S.I. 1999/3242. Regulation 3 of *the Management Regulations* sets out the general requirement for risk assessment.

71. Regulation 5(2) of *DSEAR* sets out the aspects to be included within a risk assessment of dangerous substances in the workplace.

STAGE #2
ELIMINATE OR REDUCE THE RISK[72]

The focus of this stage is upon eliminating or reducing the risks to safety from the presence of dangerous substances, by removing or controlling risks and providing measures which limit or mitigate the consequences of any incidents which do occur. This is achieved by making sure the right management arrangements are in place. In circumstances where it's not 'reasonably practicable' to avoid or, failing that, eliminate the risk by replacement with alternative substances or processes[73], the regulations impose upon employers a responsibility so far as is reasonably practicable (SFAIRP) to control risks by the measures set out[74] and, where this is not possible, to mitigate the detrimental effects of a fire, explosion, or other harmful physical effects[75]. The regulations then go on to set out the hierarchy of control measures and the mitigation measures required to limit the detrimental effects of an incident. This 'hierarchy of control' principle is akin to that used when seeking to manage a 'hazardous substance' risk, an approach previously applied in this book, in the context of *the piper's fable.*

Applying the hierarchy of control principle to the dangerous substance explosive atmosphere risk, the steps involved can be summarised as follows: *first,* reduce the quantity of any dangerous substance to a minimum; *second,* avoid or minimise its release; *third,* control its release at source; *fourth,* if release is not preventable, prevent the formation of an explosive atmosphere, including by equipment

---

72. Regulation 6 of *DSEAR* sets out the measures to be taken by employers to eliminate or reduce the risks from dangerous substances. Schedule 1 to regulation 6 provides the list of 'general safety measures'.

73. Regulation 6(2) of *DSEAR* states that the preference is for employers to substitute a dangerous substance with a lower risk substance or process, so as to avoid its presence or use within the workplace. In so doing, employers fulfil the requirement imposed upon them by regulation 6(1), to ensure that the risks from dangerous substances are either eliminated or reduced so far as is reasonably practicable.

74. Regulation 6(3)(a) of *DSEAR* requires the risks from dangerous substances to be controlled, supported by regulation 6(4), which sets out the priority order in which control measures are to be applied (the hierarchy of control).

75. Regulation 6(3)(b) of *DSEAR* requires the fire, explosion and other risks arising from dangerous substances to be mitigated if they cannot be eliminated entirely, supported by regulation 6(5) which provides that control measures are to be applied, which are consistent with the risk assessment and appropriate to the nature of the activity or operation, in order for this to be achieved.

monitoring, detection and warning; *fifth*, if it's not possible to prevent the formation of an explosive atmosphere, collect, safely contain and remove any release of a dangerous substance which may give rise to risk to a safe place or otherwise render it safe, as appropriate; *sixth*, if this is still not possible, avoid ignition sources including electrostatic discharges and adverse conditions which could cause dangerous substances to give rise to harmful physical effects, and *seventh*, and finally, if this is not possible, segregate incompatible dangerous substances.

Once control measures have been considered, the next step is 'risk mitigation'. As the events of the fable will testify, it was fortuitous that, for the scenario it describes, the need to test the effectiveness of this step didn't arise. But in circumstances where incidents occur, with the hierarchy of control having essentially failed, the focus needs to move to the kinds of mitigation measures set out within the regulations. These measures call for employers to *first*, minimise the number of employees exposed and *second*, avoid the propagation of fires or explosions. Where these efforts are also unsuccessful, the provision of various equipment types is to be considered, *third*, through 'explosion pressure relief' arrangements and *fourth*, through 'explosion suppression equipment'. Should these further measures also fail, *fifth*, the aim is for equipment to be capable of withstanding the pressure likely to be produced by an explosion – achieved through a so-called 'explosion protection system' – and if this also fails, *sixth*, and finally, the provision and use of suitable 'personal protective equipment' is expected to reduce still further any residual risk. Employers have a duty to provide and maintain these measures – both technical and organisational – including making suitable provision for the handling of 'accidents', 'incidents' and emergencies, and embedding procedures which can be readily invoked, as the need arises.

The regulations also require the adoption of general safety measures[76], provided these are consistent with the risk assessment and appropriate to the nature of the work activity or operation. General safety measures include workplace measures – such as workplace design, work processes, work equipment and protective systems – and organisational measures, such as systems of work, including the

---

76. Regulation 6(8) of *DSEAR* requires the taking of general safety measures so far as is reasonably practicable, as are set out in Schedule 1, in order to control the dangerous substance risk.

issuing of written instructions for carrying out the work and a system of permits where work is carried out in hazardous places or involves hazardous activities.

We'll consider whether the hierarchy of control worked here, both to remove and/or control the risk, and by making available mitigation measures, to be adopted to limit or mitigate consequences, had an incident occurred.

STAGE #3
CLASSIFY AREAS INTO ZONES[77]

Once the risk assessment has been completed and the necessary control measures put in place to eliminate and/or reduce risk, as called for by the first two stages, it's at this point that zone classifications are assigned to the work location. Having already noted the requirement to classify the areas where potentially explosive atmospheres may exist into hazardous and non-hazardous places, the focus here is upon further classifying those designated as hazardous. This needs to be done before work starts, and verified by a competent person, to ensure the overall explosion safety measures have been confirmed to be safe. The most important aspect of this stage is to recognise the areas in which potentially explosive atmospheres may occur, as it's this which ultimately shapes the control measures, including the types of equipment to be used. In outline, the requirements set for areas – and more particularly, their sub-division into zones – are based around both the likelihood of an explosive atmosphere occurring and the duration for which it is expected to be present. The reason for designating areas as zones in this way is that they must be protected from effective sources of ignition, with the equipment and protective systems intended to be used within them required to meet the respective equipment category requirements. The classification of zones set out in the regulations – which covers both gases and vapours, and dusts – is summarised in *Table 2a* overleaf.

---

77. Regulation 7(1) of *DSEAR* sets out the requirement for employers to classify places where explosive atmospheres may occur into zones, in accordance with the definitions provided in Schedule 2.

ZONE DEFINITIONS				
ZONE		BROAD DEFINITIONS OF ZONES		
GASES & VAPOURS	DUSTS			
0	20	Explosive atmosphere is present continuously, for long periods or frequently.		
1	21	Explosive atmosphere is likely to occur under normal operation, occasionally.		
2	22	Explosive atmosphere is unlikely to occur in normal operation and, if it does, will persist for a short period only.		

Table 2a: Classification of Places where Explosive Atmospheres may occur[78]

It's at this point that the linkage between *the Mines Regulations* and *DSEAR* comes into play. *And why might this be?* It's simply because, in being classified as a hazardous place, the additional requirement for such locations to be further classified into zones brings into play two key concepts, *first,* keeping control of what's inside them and *second,* excluding anything which needs to be kept outside of them, namely ignition sources which present a fire or explosion risk.

So, what implications does the designation as a zone have for what goes on inside it? For a start, the hazardous workplace classification means that the explosive atmospheres provisions apply, with *the*

---

78. *Table 2a* summarises the requirements set out in Schedule 2 to regulation 7(1) of *DSEAR.*

Mines Regulations specifically signposting the reader to *DSEAR* at this point. This means mine operators need to put in place arrangements for the detection, monitoring and reduction of risks – including detecting the presence, monitoring the concentration, and reducing the level of flammable gases in any zone to a level which is 'as low as reasonably practicable (ALARP)'[79] – so as to control the area.

We'll look at whether arrangements for the detection, monitoring, and reduction of risk to an ALARP level were put in place here.

Next, the focus shifts to what needs to be kept outside designated zones. Put simply, this comprises anything which might cause an ignition risk. The 'ignition risks' provisions of *the Mines Regulations*[80] come into play here, with their accompanying guidance helping to clarify what's expected. Specifically, this guidance requires a mine operator to comply with *DSEAR* – in particular with the control measures hierarchy – which includes barring items that present an ignition risk from being introduced in an uncontrolled way[81]. And where the ignition of dangerous substances could affect safety, there are measures which must be taken, so as to prevent ignition sources occurring or being brought into areas where such a risk exists. This controls electrostatic discharge by banning from the area – in this case, a mine – anything which increases the risk. *DSEAR* set out clear requirements, covering how the risk of electrostatic discharge is to be avoided. The classification of an area as a zone introduces the particular need to exclude from it any items which could cause a thermite reaction, or which could generate or retain 'static charge'. Furthermore, some other items are specifically banned underground, notably tobacco and other smokers' materials, in addition to objects used to produce a flame for the purposes of smoking, such as lighters[82].

We'll look at what efforts, if any, were made by the characters in the fable to keep out items which presented an ignition risk.

---

79. Regulation 22 of *the Mines Regulations* sets out the mine operator's duties in respect of explosive atmospheres.

80. Regulation 23 of *the Mines Regulations* sets out the mine operator's duties in respect of ignition risks.

81. Regulation 6(4) of *DSEAR* sets out the hierarchy of control for eliminating or reducing the risk from dangerous substances.

82. Regulation 23(2) of *the Mines Regulations* sets out the items the mine operator is required to ban from being taken below ground.

The *DSEAR* 'Approved Code of Practice (ACOP)' provides multiple examples of ignition sources which are to be controlled or avoided. This document has been cited at relevant points here because, as was explained in this book's introduction, ACOPs give direction on how to comply with the law – in this case, *DSEAR* – providing advice on good practice, supported by appropriate examples. In respect of this fable, three principles have particular relevance[83], these being to: *first*, ensure that any portable or mobile equipment brought into hazardous places is either suitably protected or brought in under safe conditions, ensured by the implementation and control of a 'permit–to–work' scheme; *second*, implement control measures and procedures to prevent the occurrence of hazardous electrostatic discharges, and finally, *third*, avoid incompatible materials that could react together to produce heat or flames or give rise to incendive sparks, following frictional contact during impact, machining, grinding or polishing, which encompasses the dangerous substances being processed as well as the materials from which plant, equipment, process areas and tools are constructed. Alongside badly chosen lamps – of clear interest in the context of this fable – are numerous other examples of items typically excluded from zones in real-world workplaces, including battery operated electrical devices, digital watches, key fobs and mobile phones, to name just a few. Measures that can be taken to eliminate or reduce the risk of electrostatic discharge include the use of earth bonding and the selection of antistatic work clothing and footwear.

We'll consider whether appropriate zoning – including the setting up of zones and observance of the requirements relating to them – appears to have been carried out here.

---

83. As becomes apparent throughout the course of this fable, the characters show a disregard for the principles for controlling or avoiding ignition sources. Such principles are key to the elimination and reduction of dangerous substance risks, as is required by regulation 6 of *DSEAR*. The events of the tale highlight shortcomings in the measures adopted to avoid ignition sources occurring, as well as failures to stop them being brought into areas where the ignition of dangerous substances could affect safety. The fictional examples from the tale run counter to the practical advice on how to comply with *DSEAR*, notably being contrary to paragraphs 241(c), (e) and (h), at page 54 of the Health and Safety Executive's ACOP (2013) *Dangerous Substances and Explosive Atmospheres Regulations 2002* (L138), these being measures against which real-world employers' control arrangements can be found to fall short.

STAGE #4
MARK CLASSIFIED AREAS[84]

Once zones have been defined, classified areas need to be marked with appropriate 'warning signs'. Where necessary, the entry points to areas classified as zones have to be marked with a specified 'Ex sign', alerting people to the locations where an explosive atmosphere may exist. These signs also serve to make them aware of the need to take special precautions. An alternative to signage is to communicate via a different medium that these are locations where an explosive atmosphere may occur, including the requirement for special precautions to be followed for entry. Practically speaking, real-world organisations might choose to address this requirement by providing booklets, documents, site plans, briefings and the like.

We'll consider whether appropriate marking – or some other appropriate method of alerting people to such locations – was applied to classified areas in this instance.

It seems timely at this point to do a quick recap of these first four stages. The risk has been assessed. Steps have been taken to eliminate or reduce the risk. Areas have been classified into zones. And areas have been marked in accordance with zone classifications. It's only upon concluding these four stages that the important fifth stage can be addressed, which concerns the issue at the heart of this fable, namely how to select the right equipment.

STAGE #5
SELECT SUITABLE EQUIPMENT[85]

The choice of equipment, including lighting and lamps, needs to be based upon the assigned area classification. Remembering that *stage three* handled the classification of areas into defined zones and the assignment of

---

84. Regulation 7(3) of *DSEAR*, together with schedule 4, to which it refers, sets out the requirement for signs to mark the points of entry for places where explosive atmospheres may occur. The distinctive features of a warning sign expected to be displayed are a triangular shape and black letters on a yellow background with black edging (the yellow part to take up at least 50% of the area of the sign).
85. Regulation 46 of *the Mines Regulations* refers to lighting, whilst regulation 47 handles the requirements for personal lamps.

zone categories, it's at this point that the equipment category and associated 'equipment integrity requirements' need to be fulfilled, as shown in *Table 2b*, which supplements the information contained in *Table 2a*. Putting it in a nutshell, *Table 2b* shows that the lower the zone classification number, the higher the likelihood and duration of an explosive atmosphere occurring, and the more restrictive the choice of equipment will be.

ZONES & EQUIPMENT CATEGORIES				
ZONE		BROAD DEFINITIONS OF ZONES	ATEX EQUIPMENT CATEGORY	EQUIPMENT INTEGRITY REQUIREMENTS
GASES & VAPOURS	DUSTS			
0	20	Explosive atmosphere is present continuously, for long periods or frequently.	1 (most restrictive)	Equipment must be safe under normal operation, expected and rare malfunction.
1	21	Explosive atmosphere is likely to occur under normal operation, occasionally.	1 or 2	Equipment must be safe under normal operation, expected malfunction.
2	22	Explosive atmosphere is unlikely to occur in normal operation and, if it does, will persist for a short period only.	1, 2 or 3 (least restrictive)	Equipment must be safe under normal operation.

Table 2b: Criteria for the Selection of Equipment and Protective Systems[86].

There are a few important implications that zone categories bring with them but, as we shall see, the detail in this fable primarily leads to considerations about clothing and equipment. The basic requirements

---

86. *Table 2b* summarises the requirements set out in Schedule 3 to regulation 7(2) of *DSEAR*, which requires equipment and protective systems for all places in which explosive atmospheres may occur to be selected on the basis of the requirements set out in *the EPS Regulations*, unless the risk assessment finds otherwise.

are for any equipment brought into areas designated as hazardous to be suitably protected (or brought in under safe conditions), and for its use to be supported by appropriate permit-to-work arrangements. Additionally, control measures and procedures need to be in place to handle the risks associated with hazardous electrostatic discharges, commensurate with the zone classification. Further measures that can be taken to control the electrostatic discharge risk include restricting the personal items that can be brought into a zone, and ensuring that clothing worn is of a suitable material.

In making suitable clothing choices, it's important to note that some garments, including footwear, contain materials that can generate electrostatic discharges during use. Such discharges are capable of igniting certain types of explosive atmospheres, including gases or vapours and even some types of dust. This means that workers in zoned areas must be provided with appropriate clothing, including antistatic footwear, which doesn't introduce the risk of an electrostatic discharge igniting the explosive atmosphere. Antistatic footwear should be tested routinely and replaced if its antistatic properties are found to have deteriorated. And any clothing provided to them also needs to be appropriate to the level of risk identified by risk assessment. Furthermore, clothing should not be removed in places where an explosive atmosphere may occur; instead, a safe area needs to be established where workers are able to remove or change clothing. And, where necessary, arrangements should be made for visitors to be provided with appropriate antistatic clothing, with checks made to ensure that they follow the rules set out in management procedures[87]. Given that 'electrostatic risks' can also be created by personal items being brought into hazardous places, it's easy to understand why people need to be provided with clear instructions as to what they can and cannot take inside them.

---

87. The Health and Safety Executive's ACOP (2013) *Dangerous Substances and Explosive Atmospheres Regulations 2002* (L138) to regulation 6 lists out the likely ways that electrostatic discharge events presenting a risk of ignition may be generated, these being events which should be avoided. This includes personnel wearing clothing and/or footwear capable of generating a build-up of static electricity (paragraph 243(a), at page 54). Additionally, employers are required to ensure that visitors given access to hazardous areas are made aware of hazards prior to entering locations where potentially explosive atmospheres may exist, and to ensure that they are wearing appropriate antistatic clothing (paragraph 244, at page 54).

The suitability of personal lamps is important and, perhaps unsurprisingly, goes to the heart of this fable! *The Mines Regulations* impose a duty on mine operators to ensure that the lamps they provide for use are suitable or alternatively, if supplied by a person for their own use, to check the suitability of these. This naturally raises the question as to what constitutes a suitable lamp, the simple answer being that a lamp used below ground or at the surface must be certified as safe for use, adhering to the zone classifications set out under *DSEAR*[88], as looked at under *stage three*. Additionally, mine operators need to ensure that the battery life duration and illumination levels of personal lamps are sufficient. And a further consideration for mine operators concerns the 'ergonomics' of all such equipment – an aspect the guidance requires to be taken into account when selecting the most appropriate type of lamp. This includes – for instance – whether a cordless headpiece lamp would be better than a corded lamp with a belt-worn battery. As well as the specifics set out for lamps, there's also a more general requirement covering other lighting within mines, namely the need for '*suitable and sufficient artificial lighting to be provided at every part of the mine below ground, where persons work or pass.*'[89]

We'll look at whether due consideration was given to selecting the right equipment for the place where it was to be used – specifically, lamps suitable for mine use – including whether the requirements of DSEAR and the Mines Regulations were likely to have been met in this instance.

STAGE #6
TRAIN PEOPLE[90]

Where dangerous substances are present, employers are required to provide employees with information, instruction and training on the appropriate precautions and actions to be taken to protect themselves and others in the workplace, so as to ensure their safety. This includes not only significant risk assessment findings, but

---

88. Regulation 7(1) of *DSEAR* sets out the requirements for 'hazardous area classification'.
89. Regulation 46 of *the Mines Regulations* sets out the requirements for lighting within mines.
90. Regulation 9 of *DSEAR* sets out the requirement for employers to provide information, instruction and training to employees where a dangerous substance is present at the workplace.

also the arrangements for dealing with accidents, incidents and emergencies[91].

We'll consider whether sufficient training was likely to have been delivered by the magician mine operator, as based upon the activities he expected workers to undertake, the equipment issued for use, and the location featured in the tale.

THE FOCUS OF THIS FABLE

In order to avoid being distracted by the minutiae of mining safety, the learning points from this fable are – for the most part, at least – to be more broadly focused upon the principles for achieving the control of dangerous substances and explosive atmosphere risks wherever they arise, as are handled by *DSEAR*. This fable zooms in on the activities of the central character, Ian, looking at the importance of his using the right equipment for the location. But it's also used as the basis from which to consider risks more broadly – including explosion and confined spaces – these being risks that further amplify the need for stringent control measures to be put in place. And it touches upon 'procurement' and 'waste management' requirements too.

So, without further ado, let's join Ian...

THE FABLE

Once, there was a poor youth – a lad called Ian. He'd gained an apprenticeship some time back which, for reasons not fully explored here, hadn't turned out quite as well as he might have hoped. After much soul searching and some heart-to-heart discussions with his boss, he managed to leave this arrangement by mutual agreement, on reasonably amicable terms. He was even allowed to keep the boiler suit issued to him when he started the role. Unfortunately, for Ian, it wasn't long before he started to rue his rashness in leaving his apprenticeship, with a dip in the employment market meaning that

---

91. Regulation 8 of *DSEAR* sets out the requirement for employers to have arrangements in place to deal with accidents, incidents and emergencies.

similar opportunities in the short to medium term were few and far between.

Some time later...

One day, Ian donned his boiler suit and set out to visit a number of job agencies. He hoped the industrial nature of his attire might convince them of his readiness and willingness to commence work and get his hands dirty straight away. But, on emerging from the third agency he had visited that morning, he was starting to feel slightly dispirited, with no appropriate job openings being listed on their books. Suddenly, just as he was contemplating a return home to change into a pair of jeans and his favourite T-shirt to watch daytime television – as if from nowhere – a man appeared and said to him *'Greetings, young man! It's your lucky day!* Think of me as your uncle. I'm here to help you.' Of course, he wasn't really Ian's uncle – he was a magician! The magician's father just so happened to own a mine. Ian knew they weren't actually related, but had a funny feeling he recognised him from somewhere. Unfortunately, his offer was to prove too tempting for Ian to resist, in large part due to his need to start earning money again, a weakness which meant that he didn't like to ask too many questions. But Ian was old enough to have known better. 'You can work for my father's mineral extraction company and I will make you very rich – consider yourself hired!' the magician said. Now, little did Ian know that, in addition to being a magician, the man had a curious sideline as a mine operator, running the mine owned by his father. Ian nodded his approval at the magician's suggestion and made to shake his hand, but this funny fellow had already moved on to the next stage of his slightly bizarre 'onboarding' process, motioning him to walk towards a group of rocks which – as he was about to discover – formed the outer edge of a mine.

Eager not to waste any time, the magician quickly directed Ian towards one particular rock. It was only on closer inspection that Ian noticed it was quite different to all the other rocks, being situated next to a cover with a handle on it. 'Roll that rock and pull that handle!' said the magician, with a slightly mystical lilt to his voice. Ian felt a bit edgy about this, for even though he'd only completed the introductory module to his former apprenticeship, this had been enough to tell him that this kind of manual handling activity should be tackled by two people lifting the cover, with the use of manual lifting keys. And, in truth, Ian suspected that even the boulder-rolling aspect of the activity required more thought than the magician would have him believe. Ian was right to have misgivings, as there was a main entrance in, which would have made accessing the mine much easier and rendered all the *boulder-rolling cover-lifting sorcery*, advocated by the magician, somewhat superfluous.

Detecting the concern on Ian's face however, and being keen to continue with his introduction to all things mining, the magician wasted no time in pulling up his sleeves and stepping forward, rolling his eyes as he did so, with a look that spoke of his lack of faith in the physical toughness and staying power of the young. He muttered under his breath: 'You youngsters don't know you're born! We wouldn't have put up with such shilly-shallying in my day. I suppose I'll have to show you how it's done...*Step aside young man!*' With a slight grimace on his face – which Ian took as validation of his own misgivings – the magician pulled the handle and, eventually, the cover came up. Ian could see a black opening, revealing a mine entrance. Little did he know that it was a very big mine, with lots of ways in and out. 'If you want to be rich, go down there!' the magician said. 'You will see a lamp. Use it in the mine to light your way and then bring it back to me! This ring will help you.' Ian couldn't fathom why the magician had elected to leave the lamp deep down in the deep dark mine, rather than bringing it back to the surface so as to illuminate the way ahead of anyone needing to travel down into its murky depths. But such was his keenness to impress that, without giving it further thought, and with the jewel glistening on his finger, he put his gloves back on, left the magician and went down into the bottom of the deep dark mine.

Deep down at the bottom of the deep dark mine, there was indeed a lamp, the likes of which Ian had never seen before. The mine walls glittered and sparkled, such was the power of light it emitted. It had a strangely hypnotic quality. *The mine was very dusty.* Ian started work, using the mining pick he'd been given by the magician. Now he came to think of it, whilst his former role hadn't quite lived up to his expectations, early-stage indications suggested that this too wasn't a good opportunity. There hadn't been a site induction worthy of note. He hadn't been trained. Risk assessment of *boulder-rolling* and *mine-access cover lifting* activities was totally absent. And seemingly, there was no supervision. The list of issues went on endlessly and, in truth, although he was a generally happy-go-lucky individual, even Ian was struggling to think of a single positive point about the whole sorry experience. All of a sudden, from the mine entrance above him, the magician yelled down, 'Give me the lamp!' to which Ian replied, a little curtly: 'You'll have to help me out first!'

The magician was so angry – largely brought about by his panic that the lamp might not be returned to him – that he chose to ignore Ian's pleas. He closed the cover and rolled the rock back over the mine entrance, whilst pondering what to do next. Ian, meanwhile, was unable to get out, being unaware of the other entrances and exits. And being a whimsical individual, with just a smattering of knowledge having worked its way into his brain from what little he'd completed of his former apprenticeship, of course it hadn't occurred to him to think through how he'd get out of the mine before he got into it. Furthermore, the magician and magician's father – in their respective roles as mine operator and mine owner – had done precious little to ensure that those entering the mine were enlightened as to the tricky problems that spaces of a confined nature could pose, the requirements for entry, the applicable permit systems, or even the rescue plan for the unfortunate, albeit rare, times when things went wrong, let alone having accounted for the needs of enthusiastic youngsters like Ian. In truth, it was questionable whether such arrangements even existed.

It seemed as if – all of a sudden – things weren't looking so good for Ian. For one thing, any mine operating magician with a shred of decency, regard for legislative requirements, or respect for the expectations of regulators for that matter, certainly wouldn't have sent him down into the mine alone[92]. Ian was in the mine for what seemed like a long time. Time enough for him to rue his error in being so rash and believing the promises of the unscrupulous magician. Now he thought about it logically, there was merit in the idea of calmly reasoning things through in advance. Ian had ample time to reflect on the welcome presentation delivered to him by the nice – but oh so dull – chap from the safety team in his previous role. *He* would have known what to do. In fact, now Ian came to think about it, what he would have done would have been to avoid getting into this sorry predicament

---

92. Legal consequences aren't directly considered in the context of this fable, but this is a subject afforded attention in relation to *Zac's fable*.

in the first place. Poor Ian was cold. He took off his gloves and instinctively rubbed his hands together, before putting them straight back on again. But unbeknown to Ian, this had the unfortunate effect of abrading the ring too. A genie appeared from the ring in a puff of smoke and, after a bit of tutting, said... 'I don't wish to scaremonger or be over-dramatic, *but I can't help but feel that you're playing with static!*' to which Ian replied: 'What is this before me? Are you some kind of curse? *I have a sneaky suspicion, my day's about to get worse!*' Ian suddenly remembered the magician's promise that the ring would help him but, on first impressions, it struck Ian that the ring genie was an individual who was indifferent as to whether or not he pleased others.

It was fast becoming apparent to Ian that the angry little genie had no wish to be released from the ring, on this particular day. But Ian hadn't intended to create static build-up, nor had he foreseen the consequential electrostatic discharge which had unfortunately resulted, of which the genie appeared to be an integral part. *How was he to have known the ring was capable of holding static charge?* 'And *who*, might I ask, are *you*?' said Ian, on regaining his composure, to which the angry little genie replied: 'I thought you'd never ask, young man! *I* am the genie of the ring – Genie Junior! I'm always granting wishes, but no-one ever asks for mine. If you genuinely want my opinion – my greatest wish would be for you to be a bit more mindful of the risks of static build-up – the polishing, rubbing and shining of that ring are highly dangerous pursuits, let me tell you, young man. *But please, do go on though...*what is *your* wish?' Genie Junior was a slightly disgruntled sprite, as he spent much of his time granting wishes but, as far as he could recall, no-one had ever taken the time to ask him about his aspirations. As was fast becoming apparent to Ian, it wasn't just the release from the ring, but also this persistent wish-granting which was grating on the ring-genie. 'I know, *I know* – you're probably right, but my wish is to go home! *Please help me, as the magician said you would!*' said Ian, sounding increasingly distressed. In truth, Ian's most fervent wish was to get a better grasp on mining safety.

Fortunately for Ian, in an instant he found himself transported back to his home, with the lamp tucked under his arm, thus avoiding the wrath of the angry magician. He wasted no time at all in declaring to his mother: 'I must have some dinner, so I will sell this lamp!' Being of a naturally inquisitive nature and unable to let anything lie, Ian's mother responded to this announcement with a barrage of questions, scarcely pausing for breath, including: *'Where have you been?'*, *'What on earth is this?'*, *'Who gave it to you?'* and *'Is it yours to sell?'*, but, on picking it up, she quickly changed tack, saying: 'This lamp looks *so* old. *Antique, perhaps...*' Her sudden recall of daytime television programmes, in which enthusiastic amateur antique hunters bought unimpressive looking items for around the five pound mark before going on to make their fortunes, had given her cause to swiftly revise her line of questioning. She mused that maybe, just maybe, this time it was her turn to be lucky in life. She rubbed the lamp in a bid to make it look nice and shiny, because she liked shiny things, whereupon there was a puff of smoke, and a different genie appeared. *'Oh, tut tut!* What is it now? What is *your* wish?' said the genie of the lamp, Genie Senior, with a slightly condescending tone, before continuing on '...although before you answer, what *is* it with this family's constant desire to create sparks? Is it some kind of genetic trait as, by my reckoning, barely ten minutes has passed since your son Ian was rubbing my little ring genie relative up the wrong way?' Now of course, Ian couldn't be sure as to the exact nature of their relationship, but it was fast becoming clear to him that the two genies were closely connected, it being obvious that Genie Junior had already related his experience to Genie Senior. Genie Junior's name and smaller size – as well as his attitude and slightly uppity nature – had given Ian cause to think that he was most probably sub-ordinate to the larger Genie Senior who now appeared before them. 'Who on earth are *you*? If you must know, we wish for some dinner!' Ian and his mother said to Genie Senior in unison, for once appearing to find some common ground.

Their question went unanswered by Genie Senior, but barely a minute had passed and there was a knock at the door. In an instant, Ian and his mother had dinner, courtesy of a local food delivery service, which was strange given that neither of them had placed an order. Ian felt as if all of his dreams were coming true at once – a magic lamp complete with genie *and* enough food to sustain them, without so much as a call being made to a local takeaway. *It was almost too good to be believed!* And he wouldn't need to sell the lamp either, as all the food-based wish-granting meant that they didn't need to buy any. Eventually, with Genie Senior's anger having subsided and his mother having calmed down a little, Ian seized the moment to get a word in edgeways: 'I got a new job, Mum!' said Ian, sounding as pleased as punch. '*About time too!*' replied his mother. It had to be said, she wasn't a natural when it came to giving warm words of encouragement to her only son, and Ian sensed it wouldn't be long before she suggested reopening negotiations about the amount of housekeeping he should pay her. In a bid to avoid awkward conversations about money just before bedtime, he swiftly changed the subject, wished her goodnight and made his way hurriedly up to bed.

Time went by...

Ian was fast becoming a rich young man. Every time he rubbed the lamp, Genie Senior came to him. And sometimes the temperamental Genie Junior would respond to the rubbing of the ring too, if he was having a good day. It felt as if, after a decidedly rocky period, things might just be on the up for Ian and his mother.

Some time later...

One day, quite by chance, Ian passed by a princess on his way to the mine and he fell instantly in love with her. He had no time to stop, being – as was unfortunately typical for him – late for work. In truth, she harboured reciprocal feelings for Ian, but was unable to reach him in time, as her princess slippers were impeding her usually swift running technique. It just so happened she was a safety advisor, with a little knowledge of the expectations of regulators and a quirky interest in the suitability of workplace lighting. She had no wish to rely on family wealth, having a good personal work ethic and seeing the safety profession as offering a worthy, low risk, existence. Over recent weeks, the princess had often seen Ian in the vicinity of the mine but, much to her sadness, their paths just never seemed to coincide. Too numerous to mention were the occasions on which she'd waited at the mine's main entrance for him, her hands tightly clutching a hard hat with integrated LED lamp, which she considered to be a far more suitable lighting option for this particular work environment than could be said to be true of the old lamp. In all honesty, the princess feared that the signs didn't look good for Ian – including those next to the main entrance by which she waited! Of greatest concern to her was the Ex sign she'd seen prominently displayed by this particular entrance into the mine. It was this that had confirmed her belief that the location was one where an explosive atmosphere might occur. And such was the depth of the princess's devotion to Ian, together with her heartfelt concern that he lacked the essential knowledge of the requirements for equipment integrity, that still she waited, in the hope that he might see the error of his ways and offer up the old lamp in exchange for the new one. *Alas, it seemed this wasn't to be!* And every time the princess got word that he was in the mine, she winced at his disregard for basic safety requirements, a pain which she took to confirm her affection for Ian. In truth, much as she believed her gesture to be a generous one, she did wonder whether he possessed the necessary nous or even cursory background knowledge of the requirements that work in spaces of a confined nature demanded.

The princess had two handsome brothers – Procurement Prince Paul was good at buying things, whilst Disposal Duke Dave was a heavyweight waste management industry professional. Not for her a couple of disagreeable sisters, but two siblings who were fine young men, motivated by strong ethics and ever keen to do the right thing. They were oblivious to the magician's sinister motives and the *magical* qualities of the lamp. Like their little sister, they worked hard too. They also loved her dearly and would do anything within their power to see to it that she did well in life.

A few weeks previously...

Knowing of his sister's concerns over Ian's personal safety, Procurement Prince Paul had arranged to acquire the hard hat with integrated LED lamp, ensuring it met all the necessary requirements. And with Procurement Prince Paul having got hold of one for her, it was a source of much sadness to the princess that her path never seemed to cross with Ian's at the right time, so as to be able to present her gift to him. *Fate could be cruel like that.* If only she could engineer a meeting, she felt sure he'd be delighted with it and happily forsake his old lamp for one which conformed to legal requirements. As for the new lamp, what it lacked in magical qualities, it more than made up for in terms of intrinsic safety. 'Thanks Procurement Prince Paul...' said the princess to her brother, before continuing on excitedly '...a new lamp for Ian...*he's sure to love it!*' thinking to herself it was exactly what he needed. It was unusual for a princess to do the wooing, but then, she was a modern young lady and was happy to pursue Ian, if only for the good of his safety and welfare. And being, as she was, of a naturally cautious nature and one to cover all the angles, the princess knew it was only right that arrangements should be made to get rid of the old one in the correct way too.

Back in the present...

It was late in the evening and Ian had returned home, scarcely able to contain his excitement at the day's events, and being keen as mustard to recount tales of his serendipitous royal encounter to his mother.

'I saw the most beautiful princess in the world today, Mum. *I want to marry her!*' said Ian, the lamp tucked under his arm, as usual. He hardly ever let the lamp out of his sight. His mother was initially unimpressed, being as she was in the middle of tidying up and somewhat used to her son's ill-conceived plans. After having listened to Ian's latest anecdote about his day at work, however, she reflected that this chance royal sighting might just represent her hapless son's best hope of securing a better future for them both and, not wishing to waste a moment, said to him: 'We must go to see the king – *this could be the making of us!*' A touch of make-up for Ian's mother and a quick change of clothing for them both and they were in the car and heading on their way to see the king. And so as not to arrive empty-handed, they stopped off *en route* to buy a bunch of petrol station flowers, as well as topping up on fuel. The retail assistant had to advise Ian to stop shining the lamp, due to the presence of flammable atmospheres, muttering to herself about the pair's stupidity and pointing angrily towards the signage on the petrol pumps. Across the tannoy, the retail assistant could be heard making a metallic-sounding announcement. '*Attention! Attention! Pump number three! Pump number three! Stop rubbing that lamp RIGHT NOW! Can't you read the signage?*' Not wishing to cause a scene, Ian and his mother hastily paid for the fuel and petrol station flowers, taking advantage of a promotional offer for free coffee as they went, before getting back into the car, and heading on their way again.

On their arrival, Ian and his mother were met by the king, and they wasted no time in presenting him with the petrol station flowers for the princess. She was out but, in her absence, the king – being of a generally easy-going nature – said Ian could marry her, as he felt sure his only daughter would be happy with him. Unbeknown to the king, however, the princess had some significant reservations – notwithstanding her affections for Ian – misgivings which went far deeper than the fact of his flower gift being of petrol station provenance. The doubts about Ian's poor lighting choices had become something of a sticking point for her over recent weeks. Knowing of her concerns, and being aware of Procurement Prince Paul's recent purchase on the princess's behalf, the king handed over the hard hat with integrated LED lamp and related his daughter's wishes to Ian and his mother. Not wishing to appear ungrateful, and in a bid to continue on with his campaign to woo the princess, Ian reluctantly accepted her gift, but kept a firm grip on the old lamp too. The power of its allure and mystical aura made him curiously unwilling to part with it. As soon as he reached home, Ian once again rubbed the old lamp, now sensing the impending pressure of his future life as a member of the royal household. 'Genie Senior, I wish for a really big house!' he said. Ian married the princess and they lived in a big house.

Time went by and word soon reached the mine operator magician that Ian had become a very wealthy man. 'The magic lamp has made him rich, and royal too…' he said to himself, continuing: '…I must have that lamp back!' and he started hatching plans as to how he might make that so.

One day, just a few weeks into her marriage to Ian, the princess was feeling a little bored and thought that she would like him to become better acquainted with her relatives. 'I've been thinking…I don't feel you know my family…*and you really should*, so why don't I invite my brothers over?' said the princess to Ian. Ian couldn't really see her point and didn't particularly want to miss an afternoon's football on television, just for the sake of polite familial conversation over cheese straws but, being eager to keep the princess happy, and knowing deep down that her question wasn't really a question, he agreed and they invited her brothers over for afternoon tea. Despite Ian's initial misgivings, it was a relaxed affair, with some shop-bought sandwiches cut into triangles arranged on big plates, a few cherry tomatoes, a quiche, potato salad and coleslaw, cheese straws and some fancy little cakes. Things were just so, from the princess's perspective and, as far as Ian was concerned, if she was happy, then he was too.

Towards the end of the afternoon, whilst Ian was upstairs taking a quick shower to wash the day off following a tough stint at the mine (something the princess privately wished he'd thought to do prior to the arrival of her siblings), Disposal Duke Dave caught sight of the old lamp sitting on the table. Detecting that it was of low value and knowing his sister to be a stickler for decluttering, he said that he would see to it that the old lamp was disposed of correctly. The princess paused thoughtfully for a moment, recognising that she was a little out of her depth when it came to matters of waste, but Disposal Duke Dave sought to swiftly allay her fears, saying 'Don't worry sis' – this is all in a day's work for a heavyweight waste management industry professional like me! I'll see to it all for you, including the 'duty of care' requirements – *consider it sorted!*' The princess was delighted at Disposal Duke Dave's suggestion. She always drew reassurance from his sage words and – what with the old lamp being of dubious provenance and of questionable market value – she couldn't have wished for a better outcome. No sooner had the princess handed the old lamp over to him, than Disposal Duke Dave suddenly had to leave to deal with a problem that had arisen at work[93].

Once out of the shower, dressed and back downstairs, Ian immediately noticed that the old lamp wasn't where it should be and a look of blind panic spread across his face, his expression much like that of a toddler parted from its security blanket. He frantically questioned the princess about what had happened and she explained that he was not to worry, because Disposal Duke Dave was dealing with it. *Ian was not happy.* 'What on earth did you give it to *him* for?' he said. 'What do you mean Disposal Duke Dave's *dealing with it?*' The princess replied, somewhat defensively: 'We had no use for it…You've got a new one… I don't see your issue! I've got the relevant documentation!' By now clearly flustered, Ian protested *'But the old lamp is magic…*we must get it back! How else do you think I support you, and fund this beautiful house and your family teas?' Deep down, he was a little annoyed that his beloved had seen fit to part with the lamp, seemingly without a second thought.

By this stage, the princess felt she had no option but to come clean, her tone becoming notably defensive as she said: 'Oh, now that *is* unfortunate! But hear me out…because it might be *magic* according to you, but I think the new lamp's a much better option. I can see now that the old lamp brought you fortune, but by no stretch of the imagination is it a safe light source, and I'd rather protect people and the environment from harm, in addition to preventing plant damage, than see you using dubious work equipment, which falls short of every regulatory requirement known to humanity! And another thing, Ian – I *do* wish you'd make a bit more effort with my brothers – *they're good lads, you know!*' The princess had made sure the new hard hat with integrated LED lamp was certified as safe for

---

93. It's not entirely clear in what capacity Disposal Duke Dave was operating, as this isn't fully explored by the fable, but it's possible he was acting as a 'waste carrier', a 'waste dealer' or a 'waste broker', all of which are vital roles which support businesses that produce or handle hazardous waste, and are terms defined in this book's *Glossary*.

use below ground and at the surface in the classified zones. Unfortunately, the same couldn't be said for the old lamp, which, she was keen to point out to Ian, failed to comply with the equipment group and category requirements in terms of certification – the lack of suitable marks and labels having alerted her to this shortcoming. Ian was a bit peeved, not least because he believed it was the lamp and its associated magic he had to thank for winning him acceptance into the royal household and the lifestyle that went with it. Still, he was committed to a future with the princess, notwithstanding that he occasionally found her conventional safety wisdom a little tiresome. Following enforcement action – and reluctance on the part of the mine owner, the magician's father, to remedy the significant failings identified – the mine was shut and Ian was, once again, forced to contemplate a lifestyle founded on more realistic ambitions.

Ian explained to the princess that it was the magic lamp that had enabled him to acquire their nice home but by then, of course, it was too late anyway. House repossession was, unfortunately, on the cards. This sorry turn of events played into the hands of the magician. And being, as he was, of a slightly sneaky disposition, he intercepted the lamp and proudly declared to anyone who'd listen that he'd diverted waste away from landfill. This was the spin he put on the story he sold to the press too. With the lamp back in his grasp once more, the magician wasted no time in rubbing it enthusiastically, saying: 'Genie Senior, make Ian's house go away!' as he did so. The house disappeared in an instant. Unfortunately, much to Ian's dismay, so too did the princess! He'd foreseen the loss of his house as a possibility, but the departure of his beloved had been an unexpected and upsetting turn of events.

On hearing news of his lost princess daughter, the usually easy-going king became very angry and immediately telephoned Ian. He was cross because, as he saw it, the princess had married beneath herself – Ian being of no aristocratic lineage – and now he was without a house and a constant supply of free food, it seemed he had precious little else to offer his daughter. The king was also concerned that his princess daughter was now a missing person. 'Ian!' he said, 'Get the princess back, right this minute!' Now Ian might have lost their marital home but, in the circumstances, he felt that retrieving his lost princess wife was the very least he could do! In the desperate hope of one last wish, and in a frantic bid to make amends, Ian rubbed the magic ring on his finger, pleading 'Genie Junior, take me to the princess!' as he did so. On this occasion Ian struck it lucky, catching Genie Junior in an unusually reasonable mood and being returned to the princess's side in an instant. He had to admit that he'd found this whole affair somewhat stressful and reflected on the events that had taken place, including the part he'd played in them, resigning himself to a less exciting – albeit safer – future.

Local reports summarised the situation thus:

'Ian liked all the sparkle and the princess's affection,
It wasn't much of a courtship, more a safety inspection;
It was abundantly clear, in winning her heart,
Getting rid of old lighting would be a good start.
She had quite a fixation and let it be known,
That equipment must fit with the rules of the zone!
This was no trifling matter, these risks called for assessing,
In time, Ian too, would see they needed addressing.
Her message was simple: assess and comply!
Ian knew if he didn't, sparks were likely to fly.
With his safety at stake, the princess wouldn't be moved,
His lamp choice must be of a type she approved.

And as the tale moved on, the two they were married,
But she called the shots on the light Ian carried!
It was true he'd made errors, that he'd sometimes not listened,
His eye drawn, like a magpie, to a lamp that had glistened.
It was a pity, the lamp had seemed to offer all he was craving
No need to work hard, nor for scrimping and saving.
Life wasn't without glitches or free of trouble
The loss of all grandeur had burst Ian's bubble.
They still had each other, some say that's what matters,
But it still hit Ian hard, his first-home dream in tatters.
It was a tough time for him, he'd been bursting with pride,
That first day the royal household thought to bring him inside.
And though Ian was good-natured, it was a bit much to take,
That much trouble should flow from his simple mistake.
Hassle visited him too, when the King came a-knocking,
Ian could hardly escape family ribbing and mocking!
This also led to his blocking of incoming calls
From Disposal Duke Dave and Procurement Prince Paul.

And last, to a sub-plot of genie in-fighting
Born of a row about a poor choice in lighting –
We've looked at the risks, hot, dusty and sparky
But even genies, it seems, have a control hierarchy!
They do like to gripe, to whinge and to moan –
Of the room in the ring – confined space of its own!
'When it comes to lamp sprites, there's nobody meaner…',
Said young Genie Junior to old Genie Senior
'…There's no space in this ring for a sprite who's aerobic,
I need to stay out, it's so claustrophobic!'
Genie Senior replied 'One day, young sprite, this will be yours,
But for now, the lamp's mine, unless the mortgage rate soars!'

Genie Junior eventually got a peripatetic role (a fancy term for a job which allowed him to get out and about) meaning he no longer felt trapped, whilst the princess continued to go from strength to strength as a safety professional, and Ian set up a small-scale independent lighting business. For the most part, they all lived happily ever after. The princess, in particular, was content to live a life perceived as dull (with slightly lower lux levels than those to which she'd become accustomed) rather than one which showed a flagrant disregard for the basic principles of intrinsic safety. And Ian resigned himself to living with his princess wife at his in-laws' house on a temporary basis, in a bid to put aside enough money for a deposit on a home he could actually afford.

Locally, there was some speculation that the spark might have gone out of their relationship, but the princess thought that – at least as far as lighting choice was concerned – that was probably no bad thing…

MODERN MEANING

There are many aspects to be addressed here – the most notable of which concerns the suitability of the lamp (the *prop*) used by Ian. The main focus here is on the old lamp, but exploring this tale also gives an opportunity to reflect more broadly upon the general principles for good lighting, as well as the confined space concerns and other points the story raises. Applying the six-stage assessment process outlined in the *prologue* will show the points at which potential failures to control the dangerous substance and explosive atmosphere risk occurred. It will also highlight where the actions of the central character, Ian, as well as his interactions with others (the *cast*), fell short of the expectations for the control of work activities within this kind of environment, including those relating to the use of work equipment. Had the requirements of the six stages reviewed here been met, it's arguable that the fable's events might have been averted, or at least more tightly managed. In a real-world context, following the various stages to this approach enables lighting to be selected which is suitable for its intended use, conforms to zone classifications and satisfies equipment integrity requirements to boot. *So, with this in mind, let's take a look at this and the other principles arising from this tale...*

PRINCIPLE #1
UNDERSTAND THE BASICS OF GOOD LIGHTING

This clearly wasn't a principle universally observed here.

The *magic lamp* might have provided a means of illumination, but was of a type which introduced other risks to the process and people involved. The basics of good lighting were not met for the occupational setting the fable described. Specific risks are covered within the other principles set out here, and a summary of basic lighting requirements is provided in *How to...* Guide Three, which accompanies this fable.

PRINCIPLE #2
RESPECT CONFINED SPACES

Whilst not the central thrust of the fable, it would be remiss not to address this principle.

Confined spaces can be regarded as the sub-plot to the dangerous substances explosive atmospheres' central plot. And whilst it might, at first, appear counter-intuitive to handle a sub-plot before a central plot, there is a very good reason for doing so here. This is because it's quite clear that Ian should never have encountered the dangerous substance explosive atmosphere risk, given that his entry to the location within which it existed should have been barred, being as it was a confined space, and that he was an inexperienced worker.

The lamp and lighting considerations sit at the tale's heart but, when it comes to looking at control of the confined spaces' risk present here, the story is unfortunately somewhat sparse on detail. This said, the importance of this type of risk makes it right to provide an overview of the arrangements which need to be in place to address and control it, wherever it exists. A 'confined space' is described by the Health and Safety Executive as *a place which is substantially enclosed (though not always entirely) and where serious injury can occur from hazardous substances or conditions within the space or nearby, for instance, due to lack of oxygen.*[94] But, whilst this definition is drawn from *the Confined Spaces Regulations 1997 ('the Confined Spaces Regulations'),* the mine within which Ian was working is one of just a few examples of workplaces covered by their own regulations – this being a case where *the Mines Regulations* would have applied.

As is a basic requirement of safety legislation, the circumstances the tale describes would have called for a risk assessment to be carried out[95], with such assessments typically including: the tasks, the work environment, work equipment, materials and tools, the individual's suitability to carry out the tasks, and emergency rescue arrangements. Here however, the mine operator needed to be conversant with the requirements of *the Mines Regulations.* And had this been the case, this would have compelled him to take a co-ordinated proactive approach, so as to meet the goal-setting requirements they set out and ensure that workers and others were protected from the hazards inherent to mining – confined spaces being an example of circumstances where it's paramount to achieve control.

It's clear that Ian's lack of experience was such that his safety within a confined space could not be ensured. Given his obvious lack of competence he should not have entered the mine. Competence is essential and anyone working within a confined space must be adequately trained and made fully aware of all associated procedures. It seems likely that the absence of risk assessment would have marked the genesis of this failure. Had the mine operating magician delivered on the requirement to carry out a risk assessment, Ian's lack of experience

---

94. S.I. 1997/1713. The definition of a 'confined space' provided within regulation 1(2) of *the Confined Spaces Regulations,* is a broad one, being: '...*any place, including any chamber, tank, vat, silo, pit, trench, pipe, sewer, flue, well or other similar space in which, by virtue of its enclosed nature, there arises a reasonably foreseeable specified risk.*'
95. As is true for other types of risk, the requirement to risk assess confined spaces is set out under regulation 3 of *the Management Regulations.*

would have been recognised, due attention would have been paid to the major hazards (of which confined spaces was a prominent example), and he would have been barred from the mining environment – this being the only fitting control measure to put in place to satisfactorily address the risk, until such time as he attained the required level of competence.

The Mines Regulations and their accompanying guidance set out a plethora of requirements, but it's worth calling out three particular points which highlight how they would have practically applied in respect of any confined spaces risk here. *First,* confined spaces would have needed to feature within a 'safety management system', as one of the significant risks that the mine operator magician needed to show as being under control[96]. *Second,* the control measures to address the confined space risk, together with those for other risks, should also have been captured within a 'health and safety document', being derived from robust risk assessment and supported by practical information in a form easily understandable by anyone to whom they applied[97]. *Third,* there would have been an expectation that the mine operator magician would have instituted an appropriate management structure. This should have, amongst other things, ensured the competence of those in overall charge of the mine to address mining hazards – amongst them confined spaces – as well as the roles, responsibilities and competence of all levels of personnel working within it[98].

Confined spaces present levels of risk over which zero tolerance must be exercised. This means that if there is the potential for a restricted workspace to become a confined space, by virtue of the existence of a defined hazard, it must be treated as such, with strict control measures being put in place and rigorously applied. Globally, confined spaces remain the cause of a number of fatalities and serious injuries each year – including in Great Britain – with incidents seen across wide ranging industries, from those involving simple storage

---

96. The purpose of such a safety management system is to enable a mine operator to demonstrate that significant risks have been addressed, this being key to showing that the general duties under regulation 7 of *the Mines Regulations* have been satisfied.

97. A health and safety document is the document which a mine owner produces to show that all significant risks – which would include confined spaces – have been identified and assessed, and control measures put in place, so as to satisfy the requirements of regulation 9 of *the Mines Regulations.*

98. The requirement for a management structure to be put in place is set out in regulation 10 of *the Mines Regulations.*

vessels, through to others involving complex plant. In addition to these incidents affecting those who work in confined spaces, others who attempt rescues can become victims themselves, often due to training or equipment failures. Here, the magician's encouragement of Ian to enter into the mine – coupled with his eagerness to do so – would unquestionably have placed him in grave danger, not least because it would have been regarded as a confined space, on top of the other risks involved. Ian's inability to get out of the mine and his clear lack of awareness of other ways in and out of it were symptomatic of the weak arrangements for eliminating or reducing risk here, as was apparent right from the outset. On top of the need for competence requirements to be met, it would have been a basic expectation that the entry requirements, the permit system, and a 'rescue plan' covering circumstances when things didn't go to plan, would have been set out for anyone entering a confined space. *As has been said, Ian should not have been left to go it alone, down into the bottom of the deep dark mine.*

These multiple concerns – and more besides – help to explain why there is an acute need for competence requirements to be addressed throughout any management structure. We've looked at the general principles for lighting to be considered within any workplace. But importantly, where confined spaces are involved, there are some basic rules which need to be understood, including how to be best prepared for any work within them. These are high-risk work situations, requiring robust control measures to be agreed and put in place before work starts, and rigorously followed throughout. Whilst not claiming to be exhaustive, *How to...* Guide Three which accompanies this fable contains some key precautions to be incorporated within a 'safe system of work' based upon risk assessment for any work environments which are deemed to be – or have the potential to become – confined spaces, to reduce the risk of injury.

It's clear that Ian should <u>not</u> have been permitted to enter a confined space, until such time as he had attained the required level of competence.

But even if he had been deemed competent to work in confined spaces, there were also notable failures in relation to controlling dangerous substances and explosive atmospheres' risks, as are considered next under the third principle.

PRINCIPLE #3
CONTROL ALL DANGEROUS SUBSTANCE
& EXPLOSIVE ATMOSPHERE RISKS

Relating, as it does, to the central plot of this fable, it's quite clear that the requirements of this principle weren't fulfilled.

What follows here is a review of the contents of the fable against the six-stage approach for controlling the risks of dangerous substances and explosive atmospheres – as set out in the *prologue* – with the noteworthy points from the tale highlighted. The focus here is upon *where* the control of the dangerous substances and explosive atmospheres risks fell short, rather than with calling out failures by the mine owner and mine operator, at any given point. On the face of it, there appear to have been multiple shortcomings in the performance of both roles and, as would also be true of any such real-world scenario, further information would be needed, in order to be able to say precisely where the errors, omissions and oversights – and even 'violations' – might have occurred here.

STAGE #1
WAS A RISK ASSESSMENT CARRIED OUT?

NO! *There's no evidence of a risk assessment having been carried out to assess the risks of dangerous substances and explosive atmospheres and identify the associated control measures, for the activities performed by Ian. This lies at the heart of many of the other failings observed here.*

The shortfalls in the assessment and control of the dangerous substance and explosive atmosphere risks are unfortunately unsurprising, given the pitiful approach taken towards other risks. A flawed approach had already been seen in relation to the assessment of the manual handling risk even before Ian had reached the mine's interior, as shown by the magician's barked instruction to '...*pull that handle!*' – commanding him to lift the cover and gain access to it, with no account given to his lack of experience. There's no suggestion of the magician's instruction having been accompanied by any guidance as to the hazards associated with the activity, nor by any advice as to the control measures to be applied to reduce risks, such as the adoption of safe lifting techniques or the use of 'lifting and handling aids'[99]. And mention has also been made of weaknesses in relation to the approach to risk assessing confined spaces, a risk clearly presented by the mine. Yet, from what the fable reveals, it appeared that the magician was content to send Ian down into the depths of the deep dark mine with no more than a hastily hollered command.

But even setting aside the concerns in relation to how Ian got into the mine, and the point that he shouldn't have been there at all, the risk assessment for dangerous substances and explosive atmospheres seems to have been equally flawed. It's quite apparent that no thought was given to the fire and explosion risk associated with the mine here. The lamp was of an inappropriate type for use at the location and insufficient attention was paid to the clothing worn by workers, which in Ian's case might have carried with it the risk of electrostatic discharges being present and these becoming active and effective. A risk assessment which focused on the basic principles of the fire triangle – together with any applicable dust confinement and dust dispersion aspects – would have been a positive first step towards shaping an effective 'control strategy' for managing the fire and explosion risk within the mine. And had such a strategy been in place and effective here, this would then have paved the way for possible ignition sources to be recognised, together with the presence of fuel and oxygen. An ignition source is anything with the potential to get hot enough to ignite a material, substance or atmosphere in the workplace; *here, this would have been the lamp.* Anything that can burn is a potential fuel for a fire or explosion; *in this scenario, this would have been the dust within the mine.* Finally, oxygen is required; *the source of oxygen in this case would have been the general body of air within the mine.*

STAGE #2
WAS THE RISK ELIMINATED OR, IF NOT, REDUCED?

NO! *There was a dearth of management arrangements put in place here, to eliminate or reduce the dangerous substance and explosive atmosphere risk, aligned to the hierarchy of control. The absence of such arrangements is plain to see throughout this fable, with the origins of this failure most likely to have been rooted in the omission to carry out a risk assessment at the start.*

---

99. *The swede fable* (fable four) considers the use of 'lifting and handling aids' in the context of manual handling operations.

In terms of the expectations for controlling risks in accordance with the control hierarchy for dangerous substances and explosive atmospheres – as covered by *DSEAR* – the attempts made here seem to have been negligible, if indeed they were made at all. There's no mention of efforts to reduce the quantity of dust to a minimum, to avoiding or minimising its release, or to controlling it at source. Neither is there any suggestion made of endeavours to prevent the formation of an explosive atmosphere, nor to the containment of any such release. The use of an uncertified lamp, together with questionable clothing choices, are just two indications of an inadequate approach to controlling ignition sources, which are particularly concerning given the clear potential that would have existed for electrostatic discharges to be generated. The lack of risk assessment evident in the fable – as was called out at *stage one* – means it's unfortunately unsurprising that the accompanying management arrangements fell short of expectations, as it's this which should form the basis of control measure selection.

STAGE #3
WERE AREAS CLASSIFIED INTO ZONES?

NO! *There were no efforts made here to identify and classify into zones the areas of the work location where potentially explosive atmospheres might have existed. This suggests that the tale's backdrop – the mining environment – was poorly understood by many of the characters involved.*

Ian's behaviour, and that of the magician, would tend to indicate that neither had an understanding of zoning requirements, which always need to be observed where dusts, gases and vapours are present. The magician makes no reference to zoning and his behaviour in placing a lamp of an unsuitable type within the mine shows his ignorance of zones or, worse still, is suggestive of a flagrant disregard for the requirements attaching to them. Any areas in which potentially explosive atmospheres existed should have been identified as such. On a more positive note, the actions of the princess later on in the fable – including her procurement of a suitable hard hat with integrated LED lamp – indicate that she was *au fait* with requirements of this kind and showed her to possess a diligence that Ian lacked, when it came to understanding the importance of selecting an equipment type appropriate to the zone within which it was to be used.

STAGE #4
WERE CLASSIFIED AREAS MARKED?

YES! *But only in part! It's suggested that classified area marking had taken place at some point, although this most probably related to a previous effort at zone classification, with no reference made to the carrying out of such an exercise during the fable.*

Even if this had been done historically, it would seem that these arrangements were not maintained. The placement of a sign at the mine's main entrance lends support to the idea that area classification might have previously taken place, but it's clear that classified area requirements were not being enforced – with the taking of an unsuitable type of lamp inside suggestive of a breach having occurred here. Furthermore, whilst a sign was visible at the main entrance, there doesn't appear to have been any signage near to the entrance via which Ian gained access, making it reasonable to conclude that this was a shortcoming in the arrangements, given the requirement for it to be in place at each entry point. Additionally, there's no reference made to information, instruction and training having been provided to workers on the meaning of the signage displayed, nor of the actions to be taken by them in accordance with it, as is the subject of *stage six* of this principle.

STAGE #5
WAS SUITABLE EQUIPMENT SELECTED?

NO! *There's no suggestion that the rusty old 'magic' lamp (the tale's prop) supplied by the magician was selected based upon area classifications for zones nor, indeed, upon any other relevant requirements.*

The lamp used by Ian was plainly unsuitable, but it's clear that the princess had a better grasp of equipment expectations. Ensuring special tools and lighting are selected and provided requires verification that they are both certified for use at the location in question, and in good condition, before work begins. For circumstances of the type described in this tale, lamps need to be classified as being safe for use underground and the requirements of *DSEAR* must be observed, with the right type of equipment selected, which is appropriate to the zone where it is to be used. This clearly wasn't the case here, but classification is a vital stage, as it's the first step to avoiding sources of static electricity and preventing static build-up – an important lesson to draw from the fable. Specially protected lighting and non-sparking equipment are essential where flammable or potentially explosive atmospheres are likely, requiring the earthing or grounding of static-generating devices, so as to prevent static accumulation. Explosion-proof electrical equipment presents no explosion hazard, if properly maintained, being designed to withstand the pressure created by an internal explosion and to cool hot gases below ignition temperature, before they reach the outside of the explosion-proof housing. And equipment certified for use in potentially explosive atmospheres must be suitably labelled with the 'equipment group', including denoting the equipment category. It appears that the old lamp was devoid of labels, but the suggestion is that the new hard hat with integrated LED lamp was of a suitable type.

The concern regarding equipment – in this case the magic lamp – being suitable for the zone within which it is to be used or taken, is analogous to the real-world concern about mobile phone use or handling in the vicinity of petrol pumps. Taking the petrol pump example, in that context the fear is that electromagnetic radiation from a mobile phone could impart enough energy to ignite petrol vapour directly, or that it could induce currents in nearby metal objects and trigger a spark with the same effect. Whilst the risk of incendive sparking from mobile phones is low, they are not 'intrinsically safe' devices and should not be used in hazardous places, such as those that exist on petrol station forecourts. Of course, there were other concerns of a similar ilk raised by the tale, most notably the shining of the lamp on the petrol station forecourt, when Ian and his mother stopped off to buy garage flowers, as well as Ian's rubbing of the ring within the environs of the mine, with neither the lamp nor the ring said to have been intrinsically safe.

The specific failing in relation to the use of the magic lamp within the mine again appears to have been rooted in inadequate risk assessment, which was in turn compounded by the failures to classify areas into zones and enforce the requirements attaching to them. The fable is non-specific as to what zone definition applied to the mine, but the enforcement of zones and marking of classified areas should have prompted the supply of a lamp of a type commensurate with the level of risk, which complied with the applicable restrictions[100]. The

---

100. A summary of the requirements to help work out the appropriate lighting type (and other equipment types) for a given zone is provided within *Table 2a* and *Table 2b*, in the *prologue* to this fable.

fable makes plain that the rusty old lamp provided by the magician was of an unsuitable type. By contrast, the hard hat with integrated LED lamp that the princess presented to Ian for his use in the mine – whilst lacking the *magic* qualities of the rusty old lamp – appears to have met the requirements for lamps used below ground or at the surface in zones classified by *DSEAR*, being certified as safe for use there. The lamp the princess acquired for Ian appears to have been better from an ergonomic perspective too, being as it was of a headpiece-type design.

Items that are capable of generating or retaining static charge would be deemed inappropriate for the kind of environment depicted by this tale. The events it sets out suggest that the restriction on such items being brought into controlled zones was ineffective, with the 'administrative controls' seemingly weak here. Notwithstanding the point that Ian shouldn't have gained entry to the mine in the first place, checks on workers' clothing and footwear should always be made in advance of them entering such locations, so as to verify that they have antistatic properties. Furthermore, if workers are changing garments, this needs to take place in an area outside of the classified zones, thereby avoiding the sparking risk from clothing features, such as fastenings. It seems likely that similar concerns would have applied in relation to the magic ring from which Genie Junior appeared; the wearing of such items should be banned within the environs of a mine – and equivalent work areas – with workers instructed to remove them prior to entry, and their being stowed outside.

STAGE #6
WERE PEOPLE SUITABLY TRAINED?

NO! *There's nothing to suggest that Ian had received suitable training – an observation that might equally have applied to other 'cast' members featured in the fable, given their questionable 'performances', with the magician particularly weak in the role of mine operator.*

Appropriate information, training and instruction should have been given to workers – whether they were employees or 'contractors' – on the dangerous substances present, together with information on the hazards, risks, precautions and any actions they personally needed to take, in order to keep themselves and others safe. This would have included the details of any significant risk assessment findings.[101]

From the fable, it's apparent that no information, training or instruction – not even a basic 'site induction' – was provided to Ian, prior to his gaining entry into the mine. But on top of Ian's lack of competence for confined space work, it's clear that there were shortfalls in relation to his grasp of dangerous substances and explosive atmosphere risks too. For anyone to be deemed competent in relation to the control of dangerous substances and explosive atmospheres risks, as applies to all risks, it's essential that they possess the necessary knowledge, understanding and experience of the work they are to carry out. For the type of activity the fable describes, such training would need to include: dusts, explosion risks, zones, the provision of suitable equipment types, emergency measures (including any emergency equipment required for rescue), and breathing apparatus. It would also need to include a description of the types of foreseeable risk as could occur, together with the accompanying accident, emergency, and incident procedures. And for such training to have been deemed sufficient here, it would have needed to describe the types of things banned from use in the mine, including not only the sparkly ring, the lamp, and clothing which carried with them a clear electrostatic risk, but also other things such as cigarettes and lighters (albeit that there's no mention made of these having been an issue here). Additionally, it should have included a description of the types of dusts present, with any associated 'personal protective equipment' (PPE) – including 'respiratory protective equipment' (RPE) – requirements being met, and supported by the provision of user instructions.

Ian's behaviour gives cause for concern on a number of occasions within the fable – calling into question his level of competence and general level of risk awareness – and it seems likely, given what we are told in the tale, that many of these issues would have been rooted in the lack of training he received. These concerns have already been noted in relation to his competence to work within confined spaces, but it's clear that the shortfalls in his knowledge extended into the realms of controlling the risks of dangerous substances and explosive atmospheres too. Given that Ian had to be warned about his lamp-rubbing and shining

---

101. In addition to the need for competence in relation to the control of dangerous substance and explosive atmosphere risks, a range of other requirements is applicable to other mining environment risks, notably including confined spaces. See principle two of this fable's *modern meaning* and *How to... Guide* Three.

preoccupation within the vicinity of petrol pumps – which rightly sparked alarm with the petrol station assistant – it's questionable whether he possessed even a rudimentary understanding of the rules attaching to classified areas. Also, from what the ring genie had to say, it was apparent that the ring – just like the lamp itself – carried the potential to generate static charges. Where workers are undertaking work in circumstances involving dangerous substances and explosive atmospheres, of which a mining environment is just one example, they need to comply with any requirements imposed for such items to be excluded. In this case, it would have fallen to the mine operator magician to ensure such requirements were properly understood and effectively policed.

It appeared that Ian lacked experience in relation to controlling risks of any kind, which should have been addressed through the taking of a structured approach to his training. Such a training programme would have needed to include a focus on dangerous substances and explosive atmospheres – alongside other risks – with due recognition given to his 'risk perception' skills most probably being lower than those of regular employees. With the added context of a generally poor approach to the control of other risk types seen elsewhere in the tale – most notably in relation to manual handling and confined spaces – it's unfortunately no surprise that this also extended to the core activity Ian was required to undertake inside the mine. An approach which saw the types of activities performed within the mine being broken down into appropriate tasks, with control measures developed for each and every stage, would have been a positive step towards addressing this gap for anyone engaged to carry out this kind of work.

This brings us to the last two principles for this fable, which cover the activities of the extras – the princess's brothers in the tale – incorporating the role Procurement Prince Paul would have played in buying the new lamp (procurement) and the responsibilities Disposal Duke Dave would have held for getting rid of the old one, at the right point in time (waste management).

PRINCIPLE #4
BUY THINGS PROPERLY

The focus of this principle is upon putting in place appropriate procurement processes and making sure people follow them, which would have been the concern of Procurement Prince Paul here.

This wasn't a principle which was universally well-applied by the characters in this fable – but the making of *bad buying* or poor procurement decisions in a real-world context is a potentially perilous pursuit. With the first mention made of the old lamp being the instruction issued to Ian to see to its retrieval from the bottom of the deep dark mine, the tale leaves unclear exactly how it might have been acquired. On the basis of the limited details it gives however, it seems optimistic to think that the magician mine operator might have followed a robust procurement process – and questionable whether thoughts of such a process even entered his head – in the lead-up to his getting hold of the old lamp.

On a more positive note, much like his brother Disposal Duke Dave (whose activities are considered under the fifth and final principle, here), Procurement Prince Paul may have initially appeared as something of an *extra* or a *bit-part player,* but closer inspection shows the role he played in acquiring the new lamp to have been that of a gatekeeper to safe products. Furthermore, the kinds of action taken by Procurement Prince Paul, together with those of anyone else involved in the product supply chain – whether as manufacturers (or their authorised representatives), importers, or distributors – are crucial, whether in the realms of lamp-based fiction, or in the wider world of reality.

It's worth pausing for a moment here to think about the processes that should have led up to the sourcing and acquiring of the lamps – both old and new. It's invaluable for organisations to institute and follow robust procurement arrangements, not least because these help them to ensure that any equipment they obtain meets certain safety requirements, as well as fulfilling other strategic objectives, including economic and efficiency goals. Given what we learn here, it seems likely that Procurement Prince Paul would have had these in mind, when he went about acquiring the new lamp – the hard hat with integrated light – by making sure it was certified as safe for use, and appropriate to the classification of the place in which it was to be used[102]. Alas, it seems no such rigorous process was followed by the magician, in initially getting hold of the old lamp, with the princess having made plain to Ian her dissatisfaction that it '...failed to comply with the equipment group and category requirements in terms of certification, the lack of suitable

---

102. As noted previously, the requirement for 'hazardous area classification' is set out under regulation 7(1) of *DSEAR*.

marks and labels having alerted her to this shortcoming.' And it's likely that this failure would have been the tip of the iceberg, as just one of a range of issues which should have been caught and addressed by a well-managed procurement approach.

In life, it's often said that *opposites attract* and the interactions that take place between the princess and Ian throughout the course of this fable would appear to support this claim. The princess's desire for safe lighting, appropriate to the zone within which it was to be used, was commendable with there being little doubt that she would have asked the right questions of Procurement Prince Paul at the procurement stage, in her bid to acquire the hard hat with integrated LED lamp. Ian, by contrast – at least in the tale's early stages – appeared ignorant of even the most basic of requirements, behaving in a way which would have risked electrostatic discharge, by his shining of the lamp in the environs of the mine and at the petrol station, not to mention his rubbing of the ring too!

Advance checks with suppliers are vitally important to ensuring that the appropriate equipment is selected and procured – making sure it will meet all expected needs – which can only be achieved by buyers explaining the nature of work activities and environments to them. Here, this would likely have involved Procurement Prince Paul, who was said to have been 'good at buying things', raising a specific enquiry with the supplier, so as to ensure the suitability of the new lamp (the hard hat with integral light) for the zone within which it was to be used. This would have meant a check needed to be made that it was UKEX (UKCA 'Ex') approved – *formerly ATEX (Ex)-certified* – for mining activities[103]. The marking of products is an interesting and evolving area, and it's relevant to revisit the subject of European Union exit at this point, as one of the themes touched upon in this book's introduction and picked up by this fable's *prologue* too. The fable is non-specific on dates but, with effect from 1 January 2021, the way in which equipment and systems for use in potentially explosive atmospheres are supplied within, or into, Great Britain has changed, which includes product marking. Essentially, with only limited exceptions, a product – of which a lamp is an example – placed on the market by a business in Great Britain (England, Wales and Scotland)

---

103. Whilst within the EU, the expectation was for such products to be CE marked following ATEX approval, a requirement which continues to apply to EU member states.

will now be expected to bear a UKCA mark[104]. This mark replaces the CE mark used previously, whilst the UK was a member country of the EU, and is applied either as a result of a 'conformity assessment' by a 'United Kingdom Approved Body (UKAB)' or, where allowable, for certain categories of goods, as the result of 'self-declaration'.[105]

But whilst these new requirements, including the use of the UKCA mark, came into effect on 1 January 2021, in most cases use of the CE mark is permissible until 31 December 2022, so as to allow time for organisations to adjust to the changes. This means that the required use of the UKCA mark is subject to two caveats: *first*, a product placed on the market, if fully manufactured in the 'European Economic Area' or the UK market prior to 1 January 2021, demands no further action, with it being permitted to circulate on either market until reaching its end user (not needing to comply with the changes that took effect on that date), and *second*, a product deemed to be existing CE marked stock, which is placed on the GB market up until 31 December 2022, and which is approved by an EU 'Notified Body' or is the subject of self-declaration, will be able to continue to circulate on the GB market with a CE mark after that date. These two caveats form part of transitional arrangements, being examples of the types of adjustment to regulations often needed to ensure they continue to function effectively, in the wake of a change to the prevailing legislative regime. Furthermore, it should be noted that, at the time of this book going to press, the assessment criteria for GB Essential Health and Safety Requirements (against which products for the GB market are assessed by approved bodies) are ostensibly the same as those for goods originating from the EU. Whether, and to what degree, these two approaches will part ways in future however, and indeed how any such divergence might need to be addressed, remains to be seen.

Whilst the fable is not forthcoming on equipment dates, it seems improbable that marking requirements would have been met for the old lamp. As for the new lamp, it would be beneficial to know a little more about when it was manufactured and supplied, so as to guide expectations about how it should have been marked. Speaking in general terms about

104. Different conformity marking rules apply for goods placed on the market in Northern Ireland, including the use of a new 'UKNI mark', as defined in this book's *Glossary*.
105. See The Office for Product Safety & Standards Guidance document, (2021). *Equipment and Protective Systems Intended for Use in Potentially Explosive Atmospheres Regulations 2016*, version 2. [Viewed 3 January 2022].

both lamps, as has been indicated, there are some technicalities which would need to be understood before determining whether a CE mark continued to be acceptable, or whether the new UKCA mark would have been required. Practically speaking, in real-world terms, following a limited period of time which will see the coexistence of these marks, the UKCA mark will be the expected badge for products to display on the GB market. Furthermore, a little more would need to be known about how a lamp was classified in order to know whether it would be a product for which a self-declaration of conformity would be allowable. On the basis of how it is described in the fable however, this seems unlikely given that, insofar as self-declaration is possible for products subject to *the EPS Regulations,* it applies only to those from equipment group II, equipment category 3, for use where there is a low likelihood of an explosive atmosphere being present (readers will recall that *Table 2b* gave the full list of criteria for the selection of equipment and protective systems).

PRINCIPLE #5
DISPOSE OF THINGS PROPERLY

The need to responsibly dispose of equipment at the end of its useful life was one which was neither universally understood, nor followed by many of the characters in this fable.

Much like the other fables in this collection, the focus of this tale is primarily upon safety but, given the involvement of Disposal Duke Dave (*another extra!*) and the old lamp here, it would be wrong not to make brief mention of the potential waste management concerns it raises too. In essence, good waste management is observable when waste is handled in the right way, by the right people, and supported by the right documentation, with checks being made that the journey it takes is as expected, for the given circumstances.

A fundamental tenet of environmental management is for the people or businesses that transport, buy, sell or dispose of waste, or arrange for someone else to do so – including 'waste brokers', 'waste carriers' and 'waste dealers' – to be suitably authorised and appropriately registered[106]. These are responsibilities which, in respect of this tale's

---

106. In England and Wales, the registration of waste brokers, carriers and dealers is to be made with the Environment Agency.

old lamp, would have been shared between the mine owner, the mine operator and Disposal Duke Dave, as well as others involved in its disposal. It's clear that Disposal Duke Dave did indeed set in train plans for the lamp's appropriate disposal – plans which were then thwarted by an unscrupulous magician claiming that his snatching back of the lamp had been motivated by a benevolent desire to divert waste away from landfill. That seems to have been a falsehood here, but whenever the point of disposal came – most likely once the lamp ceased to have *magical* properties – the need for this to have been done responsibly would have kicked in. These responsibilities are referred to as the 'duty of care'[107], encompassing several aspects, including: keeping waste to a minimum through its prevention, reuse, recycling or recovery; sorting and storing it securely; completing waste documentation with accurate waste descriptions for each load of waste that leaves the premises; checking that the waste carrier used is registered to dispose of waste and, following its disposal, checking to see that the waste carrier hasn't disposed of it illegally. These responsibilities are of importance in relation to all types of waste, but are particularly stringent in relation to dealing with 'hazardous waste' of which the old lamp could have been an example. Had the lamp been categorised as such, this would have meant making sure that its handling as hazardous waste was done in such a way as to prevent any harm or damage being caused to the environment, checking that all those involved in its handling or disposal were appropriately registered, ascertaining which of the materials it contained were hazardous, and classifying it accordingly.

The fable suggests the princess trusted her brother as a heavyweight waste management professional but, given her keenness to adhere to safety rules, it seems likely that she would have wanted to satisfy herself that her brother showed the same level of diligence in complying with equivalent environmental obligations!

CLOSING THOUGHTS

This fable has – with an element of *theatre* – focused upon the approach that needs to be taken for assessing and managing the risks associated with dangerous substances and explosive atmospheres,

---

107. Section 34 of the *Environmental Protection Act 1990*, c. 43. sets out the duty of care.

with specific emphasis placed upon the suitability of equipment used in such locations[108]. Additionally, it has provided some insights into other aspects associated with the use of lamps and lighting, including relevant considerations at the procurement stage of the product lifecycle (with a focus on marking expectations), and at the point of its ultimate disposal. It has also shown the importance of addressing confined space risks, alongside core lighting concerns, as well as having recognised some of the basic fundamental benefits conferred by light – whether natural or artificial – which, of course, should never be overlooked.

And finally, given this tale's theatrical tendencies, it's perhaps appropriate to consider how closing thoughts might be expressed from the perspective of a theatre critic...

A THEATRICAL ENDING

This production saw a mine worker, Ian, punching above his weight in the lead role, unfortunately outshone by a couple of extras in the forms of Disposal Duke Dave and Procurement Prince Paul – two bit-part players who took pride in demonstrating proficiency in the fields of waste management and procurement, respectively. There's little doubt that Ian's was a role which should have been differently cast. Set against the backdrop of a deep dark mine, what inevitably followed was an uncomfortable performance by an inexperienced individual, who allowed rapture at a sparkly lamp prop of unknown provenance to overwhelm any inkling he might have had of the need for basic risk control. Whilst Ian's youthfulness brought an endearing quality to the piece, greater levels of competence are rightly demanded from those who take on real-world performances within confined spaces or indeed, any work involving dangerous substances and explosive atmospheres.

But the flaws seen here weren't restricted to the casting alone. The intention behind the lighting chosen for a theatrical production is often to create an eerie atmosphere that puts an audience on the edge

---

108. Guidance, advice and direction on how to comply with the requirements of *the Mines Regulations* is to be found within Health and Safety Executive Guidance document (2015). *The Mines Regulations 2014: Guidance on Regulations* (L149).

of its seats, but this was an approach which had no place in this setting! The purpose of workplace lighting adopted here, as is true across all settings, should have been to support safety and avoid real-world jeopardy. As for the script, if this was intended to be about effective risk control, the plots and sub-plots were either ill-conceived or went unrehearsed by the actors involved. This was a production which raised some awkward questions, as well as provoking in the audience a broader desire for all the characters operating in real-world hazardous workplaces to work safely. Overall, this was a piece poorly directed by an unscrupulous magician mine operator, appointed to the role by his father, the mine owner, with catastrophic special effects and final curtain calls avoided more by luck than sound safety judgment.

For all involved in this production, this seems to have been a classic case of 'could do better'...

For a summary of practical points to take away,
based upon the topics and subtopics handled by this fable,
see *How to...* Guide Three.

A NOTE ON REPORTING REQUIREMENTS

The events portrayed in this fable were of a purely fictitious nature. See the *Epilogue* for indicative reporting requirements under *the Reporting of Injuries, Diseases and Dangerous Occurrences Regulations 2013*[109] *(RIDDOR)*, as could be triggered by equivalent real-world circumstances.

POST SCRIPT:
A FEW WORDS ON
HAZARDOUS SUBSTANCE RISKS

As the *prologue* to this tale identified, the key focus here was upon dangerous substance and explosive atmosphere risks. But it's important to remember that the risks from hazardous substances used or encountered within any workplace also have to be controlled, and

---

109. S.I. 2013/1471.

these aspects would need to be considered by applying the '*assess-control-review* model', as outlined in the context of *the piper's fable*. *Ian's fable* makes particular mention of the mine being very dusty. Dusts of any kind can be deemed substances hazardous to health and therefore fall subject to *the Control of Substances Hazardous to Health Regulations 2002*[110] if people are exposed to certain concentrations in the air, above defined limits – so-called 'workplace exposure limits (WELs)' – expressed as a 'time weighted average' for both 'inhalable dust' and 'respirable dust'. These limits are listed within the accompanying environmental hygiene guidance document for workplace exposure limits.[111] Where present, exposure levels must fall within the limits set out by this guidance document. There are two types of WELs – 'Long Term Exposure Limits (LTELs)' which apply over 8-hour time periods, and 'Short Term Exposure Limits (STELs)' which apply over 15 minute reference periods and are set to help prevent effects which may occur following exposure over a short period of time.

Also, whilst the fable is non-specific on the type of dust Ian encountered, some dusts have specific WELs assigned. This includes, for instance, respirable crystalline silica, as is found in coal mines, and other workplaces. Silica is a natural substance found in most rocks, sand and clay, as well as in products such as bricks and concrete, and its dusts can be released in the course of materials being cut, sanded down or mined. Following minor amendments made to *the Mines Regulations*, by the *Carcinogens and Mutagens (Miscellaneous Amendments) Regulations 2020*[112], the WEL for respirable crystalline silica has been reduced, it now being subject to a new binding limit of $0.1mg/m^3$, thus bringing coal mines into line with other workplaces. It was previously subject to a higher limit of $0.3mg/m^3$, but the effect of aligning the limits is to extend the same level of protection to coal miners, as to other workers.

---

110. S.I. 2002/2677.

111. See Health and Safety Executive Guidance document (2020); *Workplace Exposure Limits* (EH40/2005).

112. S.I. 2020/40.

A Super-Sized Swede,
some Big Manual Handling Errors,
and
Addressing Push and Pull Risks

THE SWEDE FABLE

'The rueful dog looked miffed, the aloof cat pretended not to care, and the smug little mouse read a book on *Push & Pull Risks*, feeling a little judgmental about the chaotic human enterprise unfolding in front of his eyes, and slightly superior, thinking to himself that their whole approach to the activity was far from best practice.'

PROLOGUE

This fable sees a motley crew at work within an agricultural setting – a group of 'workers' arranging the seemingly *ad hoc* extraction of a large vegetable from *terra firma* – with their activities drawing some criticism from a slightly supercilious mouse commentator. In common with the first three *workers' fables*, this tale deals with some fundamental safety basics – in this case, the manual handling risk assessment and control obligations organisations have towards workers. The various personal traits of the super-sized swede-shifters, the antics they get up to in the tale, and the generally ill thought out nature of their endeavours, present us with ample opportunities to explore the requirements for the assessment and control of 'manual handling' activities. We'll use this fable to look in some detail at one type of assessment tool – the 'Risk Assessment of Pushing and Pulling (RAPP) tool'[113] – within the broader context of manual handling risk assessment. This tool helps to both identify high-risk pushing and pulling operations, and check the effectiveness of any 'risk reduction measures' put in place to address them. And whilst, as we'll see, the RAPP tool is the natural choice here, it's just one of many manual handling assessment tool types which might merit exploration, depending upon exactly what's involved in any given activity requiring manual effort.

In its consideration of a particular manual handling activity, this fable focuses on several key areas. It looks at the approach to 'risk assessment'. It touches upon relevant 'psychosocial factors'. And it considers the characteristics of the individuals carrying it out including, amongst them, some 'vulnerable workers'.

But first, let's set the fable in some context...

---

113. The 'RAPP tool' was introduced by the Health and Safety Executive in 2016 and forms part of their 'Toolkit for Musculoskeletal Disorders (MSDs)'.

THE MANY FORMS OF MANUAL HANDLING

A 'Manual Handling Operation' is defined in *The Manual Handling Operations Regulations 1992*[114] (*'the Manual Handling Regulations'*) as: *'...any transporting or supporting of a load (including the lifting, putting down, pushing, pulling, carrying or moving thereof) by hand or by bodily force.'*[115] Breaking down this definition highlights that – far from being a single activity type – manual handling can be seen as an umbrella term for what is a rather diverse activity set. Its scope includes pushing and pulling movements, alongside other more commonly thought of types, such as the lifting, lowering, and carrying of loads. The activities this fable describes make the *push* and *pull* aspects of the definition the natural focus of attention here – with a 'pull' referring to a 'drag', 'haul' or 'slide' force being applied, and a 'push' denoting the 'roll' of a load. But it's also worth noting that the general approach to be taken towards this fable's events can be readily applied across the full spectrum of manual handling activity types included within the definition. At the risk of spoiling the story that follows here, the operations performed by the characters involved can be broken down into two basic elements – *first, pull* the super-sized swede from the ground and *second, push* the super-sized swede towards the smallholding cottage. Taking an ostensibly simple approach of this kind is never wasted effort. Irrespective of the type or complexity of the manual handling operation being considered, it's always time well spent to seek to understand *how* it's to be tackled before it starts, because a subtle change in the way workers approach an operation can make a significant difference to the effort required from them, as the activity progresses[116].

---

114. S.I. 1992/2793.

115. This term is defined at regulation 2(1), together with other terms used throughout the regulations.

116. Note that the action of 'pulling' referred to within this fable has been deemed to be of the 'drag' or 'haul' type (rather than a 'slide' motion), whilst the action of 'pushing' a load aligns to a 'roll' force being applied. Also mentioned within the guidance is a 'churn' movement, but this is not directly considered here, given that the actions of the characters in the fable did not involve this type of motion. Each of these terms is referred to – although not specifically defined – within Health and Safety Executive Guidance document (2016) *Risk Assessment of Pushing and Pulling (RAPP) tool*: (INDG478), at page 10. For completeness, brief definitions of these terms have been included within this book's *Glossary*.

As a cause of injury, manual handling falls under a broader set called 'musculoskeletal disorders' (MSDs), a category which comprises any injury, damage, disorder of the joints or other tissues in the upper limbs, lower limbs or back. In addition to manual handling, other risk factors which make people more likely to develop these conditions include where heavy manual labour or the adoption of awkward postures is demanded from them, or where they have suffered any recent or pre-existing injuries. Whilst the movement of loads by pushing and pulling avoids the more strenuous efforts involved in manual lifting and carrying, the manual handling definition makes clear that these methods of moving objects are included too. Moving loads by pushing and pulling requires less effort by people, but it still doesn't entirely remove the risk of musculoskeletal disorders, meaning the need remains for the assessment and control of these activities to be treated seriously.

THE SCALE OF GREAT BRITAIN'S MANUAL HANDLING PROBLEM

Before looking at the scale of the manual handling problem, it's worth pausing for a moment to ponder the question: *'Why should we be worried about a simple 'risk' like manual handling?'* There's no denying it, the safety consequences of a poorly controlled manual handling activity are typically lower than those associated with some of the risks contemplated by other fables in this collection. We've already considered 'confined spaces' and 'explosive atmospheres' in the context of *Ian's fable*, and will see further examples when we look at the risk of 'loss of containment' in relation to *the porridge pot fable*, and the 'dropped object' and 'fall from height' risks at the heart of *Zac's fable*. But, whilst accepting that most manual handling risk sits towards the lower end of the severity scale, there are other compelling reasons why it should concern us as a risk type. *And why might this be?* It's simply because, in addition to the injuries attributable to unsafe manual handling practices, the health impacts on individuals can be considerable, meaning organisations need to be mindful of these too. Pain and discomfort are concerns for many, in addition to the consequences which follow in the wake of an incident, including lost productivity and income, and the loss of enjoyment of social activities. This means that, whilst it's true to say that manual handling doesn't cause a significant number of workplace fatalities or catastrophic injuries, in thinking more broadly about adverse health effects, we see that it still leads to a multitude of 'chronic' conditions, having a detrimental impact upon quality of life and general 'wellbeing' for a high proportion of the population, often for a protracted period of time. In order to validate this assertion, we only need look at some basic statistics; whilst the trend for self-reported work-related musculoskeletal disorders and working days lost per worker is generally downward in Great Britain, the numbers of people affected and working days involved are such that the challenge to address them remains a seismic one.

As a category, musculoskeletal disorders accounts for 28% of new and long-standing cases of work-related ill health, with 18% of non-fatal injuries to employees attributable to handling, lifting or carrying. An estimate based on self-reports suggested that in 2020/21 there were 470,000 'work-related musculoskeletal disorder' cases (new or long-standing), amongst people who had worked in the previous 12 months. But the incentives to address manual handling as a cause aren't limited to those of a legal or humane nature, with lost productivity being a further concern for many an organisation. An estimated 8.9 million working days were lost due to work-related musculoskeletal disorders in 2019/20.[117] In the face of such startling statistical data, the argument for addressing manual handling, as a risk, is simply incontrovertible.

MANUAL HANDLING CHALLENGES IN AGRICULTURE

Many industries face manual handling challenges, but this injury type is a specific focus area for the agricultural sector, as lies at the heart of this fable. *Farming is hazardous.* The nature of many farm work activities – including those of the type to be considered here – is physically demanding and repetitive, causing a range of workforce musculoskeletal

---

117. Figures cited are according to the Labour Force Survey (2021), and are as quoted in *Health and Safety at Work, Summary Statistics for Great Britain 2021.* Health and Safety Executive. This is with the exception of data on working days lost, the figures for which were only available from the previous year's report at the time of going to press (Labour Force Survey (2020), as quoted in *Health and Safety at Work, Summary Statistics for Great Britain 2020*), due to statistics for the year 2020/21 having been impacted by the Coronavirus (COVID-19) pandemic.

conditions. But risk also arises from numerous other aspects associated with these activities and work environments, including: dangerous machinery, difficult access, vehicles, crop types, chemicals, livestock, working at height, and working near pits and silos, in addition to environmental factors such as weather, noise and dust. Agricultural employees make up just 1% of Great Britain's workforce, and yet the sector accounts for around one in five work-related fatalities reported each year, making it a priority within the Health and Safety Executive's workplan. 'RIDDOR' statistics for 2020/21 showed the sector's fatal injury rate of 8.47 per 100,000 workers to be around 20 times the all-industry rate, with 34 fatal injuries recorded across agriculture, forestry and fishing for that year[118]. Additionally, the agricultural industry has a very poor record for non-fatal injury and occupational health performance[119]. Understanding the considerable challenges faced by the sector is key, especially when seeking to evaluate the risks and decide on the right 'control measures' to put in place to protect people. Achieving high crop yields is naturally a prime concern, but these can become unattainable or severely compromised due to sometimes challenging environmental conditions. The nature of crop cycles has a part to play too, with seasonal harvests calling for periods of intense activity by agricultural workers, followed by fallow times, during which little or no work is required from them. This has clear implications for the physical strain imposed upon them as individuals, due to fluctuating goals and productivity pressures.

THE HIERARCHY OF CONTROL

Having dwelt briefly upon the scale of the manual handling problem in Great Britain, and the challenges particular to the agricultural sector, it's natural to want to know how best to go about managing the

---

118. Figures cited are annual statistics from (2021) 'Agriculture, forestry and fishing statistics in Great Britain, 2021', data up to March 2021. Health and Safety Executive. The recording of 34 fatal injuries to workers in 2020/21 compares to an annual average of 28 fatalities for 2016/17-2020/21.

119. *ibid.* By way of example, and of relevance in the context of this fable, at the time of going to press figures suggest that across agriculture, forestry and fishing, 11,000 work-related ill health cases (new or long-standing) occur annually, with a staggering 44% of these being musculoskeletal disorders (source: Labour Force Survey, estimated annual average 2018/19-2020/21).

risk, a question which is best answered by looking at the 'hierarchy of control'. The hierarchy of control is an oft-used principle found throughout our domestic safety legislation. We've seen it already with rats and the hazardous substance risk in *the piper's fable*. We saw it in *Ian's fable* too, with his bad lamp choice and poor approach to explosive atmosphere risks. In common with the regulations for the 'hazardous substance' and 'confined space' risks considered by these previous fables, *the Manual Handling Regulations* also set out a hierarchy of control, which needs to be followed for any manual handling activity[120]. The requirements of the hierarchy of control for this risk are to: *first,* avoid the need for manual handling 'so far as is reasonably practicable (SFAIRP)'[121]; *second,* carry out a 'suitable and sufficient' assessment of the risk of injury from any hazardous manual handling which cannot be avoided, and *third,* reduce the risk of injury from hazardous manual handling, to the lowest level reasonably practicable. The SFAIRP principle requires a balance to be struck between the level of risk and the measures required to control it, in terms of money, time or trouble. Action does not need to be taken, if it would be grossly disproportionate to the reduction in risk level achieved. Additionally, where circumstances are such that manual handling operations cannot be avoided, there's a requirement to provide employees with details of the load[122].

Putting the hierarchy of control principle and the need to reduce risks SFAIRP in simple terms, in the context of manual handling, the expectations placed upon employers make perfect sense. Things shouldn't be moved if they don't need to be moved – *avoid the risk*. If they do have to be moved, thought needs to be given as to how they are going to be moved first – *assess the risk*. And, before they start to be moved, the right equipment and information needs to be made

---

120. Regulation 4(1) of *the Manual Handling Regulations* sets out the duties of employers, as regards manual handling, which follow a 'hierarchy of control' approach. These duties are supplementary to the general requirement for a suitable and sufficient risk assessment to be carried out, as set out in regulation 3 of *the Management of Health and Safety at Work Regulations 1999 ('the Management Regulations')*.

121. As explained in the introduction to this book, the principle of reducing risks SFAIRP is equivalent to the principle for them to be reduced to a level which is ALARP.

122. Regulation 4(1)(b)(iii) of *the Manual Handling Regulations* sets out the requirement for employers to provide employees with information on the load, specifically, the weight of each load, and the heaviest side of any load, where the centre of gravity is not positioned centrally.

available to the workers involved, to cut down the risk to them as much as possible – *reduce the risk*.

Needless to say, the carrying out of effective task identification is a prerequisite for applying the hierarchy of control. This means understanding the jobs people do and, more particularly, those that they don't like doing. By sitting down and talking with their workforces, organisations are better able to pick out high risk tasks, as well as those that people find tricky or irksome. Observing people involved in operational activity within a shift, day or week is one way of picking out such tasks, but talking with them to gain their perspectives is arguably the best way of gauging which jobs are hardest for them to complete and which, therefore, require priority attention. It's only once these tasks and their connected risks have been identified, that an organisation can start to work out how to avoid them.

For the first *avoid* level of the hierarchy, it's often the case that entirely bypassing manual handling is difficult, or simply isn't feasible. Whilst the old man and his fellow super-sized swede shifters featured in the fable that follows here give little, if any, thought as to how the removal of vegetables by strenuous manual methods might have been avoided, many real-world workplaces will already have made their processes as smart as possible, including through the use of mechanisation and automation. But in some contexts, effective design and 'procurement' strategies offer further opportunities for risks to be engineered out. Thinking more broadly about how manual handling principles might apply in agricultural settings, a simple design example relevant in the context of harvesting vegetables could be to produce bags which only allow quantities to be carried which fall within safe load limits, or at least make it less likely that weight limits will be exceeded. A procurement solution, on the other hand, might be to stipulate at contract stage that vegetables yielded from the seed varieties supplied should only be capable of reaching a certain maximum weight. This reduces the likelihood that excessive loads will result, due to the smaller size achieved by any given vegetable within a particular crop. In reality, of course, these kinds of options are only available at the design or contract stages, and they might give rights of recourse in the event of a contractual breach, but they don't take away the practical problem of how to physically remove a swede of the magnitude we'll see presented here! As is all too often the case, such options are not easily influenced by frontline workers – who directly face the risk at a far later stage of the process – a common problem, which touches all manner of work settings. If it's not possible to design out risk at an early stage, another method which can help to avoid or reduce risk is to use a 'lifting and handling aid'[123]; this isn't necessarily complicated and might mean providing workers with something as basic as a wheelbarrow or trolley, if required!

In circumstances where it is decided that avoidance of manual handling of a type listed in *the Manual Handling Regulations* definition is not possible – whether by management or technical means – and where options for an activity to be automated or mechanised have been exhausted, the focus of the next *assess* stage shifts to the carrying out of a suitable and sufficient risk assessment. It's the risk assessing of activities, and their component tasks, that enables organisations to determine the level of risk and prioritise where interventions are needed. And, having decided that a risk assessment *is* necessary, the thoughts of those completing assessments need to turn to which type is most appropriate. The principal driver for any kind of risk assessment should always be to reduce the injury risk. As such, any manual handling risk assessment needs to account for the nature of the task, the capabilities of the individuals carrying it out, the features of the load, and the environment within which the load is being moved, with the actions arising from the assessment being focused upon how to reduce any remaining risk. A range of assessment types is considered here, within the context of the activities the fable describes but, irrespective of the type chosen, it's the assessment stage of the process which paves the way for the key risk factors to be better understood and in turn reduced, whether through their elimination or, failing that, by risk reduction.

RISK FACTORS

The weight of a load is one of the contributing factors to the level of manual handling risk, but there will often be many other factors

---

123. The purpose of a lifting and handling aid is to help remove or reduce the risk of back injuries, caused by frequent and heavy lifting and handling. For an overview of the range of lifting and handling aid options available, refer to the Health and Safety Executive's Guidance document (2013) *Making the best use of Lifting and Handling Aids* (INDG398).

involved. As is true of any assessment process, it's always helpful to pose a few questions to gather background information, as the answers to these provide useful insights and form a good basis from which to start it, by ensuring consideration is given to the totality of the circumstances. Within the context of any manual handling activity, general early-stage questions to ask would typically include: *'How many times does the load have to be picked up and carried?', 'How far does it need to be carried or moved?', 'From where is it to be picked up, and where is it to be taken?', 'Is it to be moved from down low to up high, or along a tricky route?'* And, *'Does the manoeuvring of the load require those moving it to get into tricky positions to accomplish the task, for instance, twisting, bending, stretching, or the adoption of awkward postures?'* The answers to these questions all provide valuable inputs to the assessment process. Not only are they to be used here to help flag up issues faced by the swede-shifters at the heart of this fable, but they are also the types of question it's appropriate to ask when considering the challenges that confront those involved in equivalent real-world scenarios.

VULNERABLE WORKERS

It will shortly become apparent that, as well as the work activity factors, this fable also prompts some questions about the involvement of vulnerable workers in manual handling activities. The needs of these workers give rise to issues which organisations are expected to address across the full spectrum of their activities. These are acutely felt in relation to manual handling, however, due to the often physical nature of the work type, which can be more problematic for some individuals and groups than is true for the rest of the population. The Health and Safety Executive defines 'vulnerable workers' as *'those who are at risk of having their workplace entitlements denied, or who lack the capacity or means to secure them.'*[124] It's clear, however, that health and safety is not to be used as a basis upon which to discriminate against particular individuals or groups of workers, and that it should instead be used to afford vulnerable workers specific

---

124. Definition as stated at https://www.hse.gov.uk/vulnerable-workers/ [viewed 1 May 2021].

protection. This fable sees a range of these individuals represented, each of whom might require some form of adjustment to be made for them in a real-world context, including 'young workers', someone with a pre-existing condition, a 'migrant worker', and a 'new and expectant mother'. These are workers with particular needs, which employers must take into account, given the additional challenges that any work activity might present to them.

Of further concern, and potentially relevant when considering the protection afforded to vulnerable workers of the types this fable showcases, is modern slavery, a societal problem which poses significant issues for the agricultural sector. Whilst it might be presumed that slavery had been abolished around two centuries ago[125], pockets of exploitation and worker abuse still persist within modern-day workforces, with farm workers a group particularly susceptible to being subjected to horrific conditions. A number of factors conspire to make slavery a prominent problem within agriculture. In addition to the high reliance the sector places upon the use of low-skilled seasonal labour, workers are called upon to work some of the longest hours and lack job security, due to the ease with which they can be replaced. When taken in combination with pressures from food retailers to keep consumer prices low, it's perhaps unsurprising that this creates the perfect storm for the exploitation of agricultural workers.

The relatively recent enactment of the *Modern Slavery Act 2015*[126] serves as recognition in itself that the eradication of slavery remains a challenge to this day. In the UK, the number of modern slavery cases rose by more than a half between 2018 and 2019, with labour exploitation being the most common type, amongst adults and minors alike[127]. This means that the farming industry – alongside other sectors – faces mounting pressure to improve standards. The offences that fall within the scope of the legislation include: slavery, servitude, forced or compulsory labour, and human trafficking. And, whilst many would argue that this new legislation does not go far

---

125. The *Slavery Abolition Act 1833*, later repealed, abolished slavery in most British colonies. This has been replaced by subsequent anti-slavery legislation in the UK.
126. 2015 c. 30.
127. There were 10,613 referrals of potential victims submitted to the National Referral Mechanism – the UK's national helpline – in 2020, showing little change on the previous year, when 10,616 referrals were received. (Home Office (2021) *National Referral Mechanism and Duty to Notify Statistics, UK, End of Year Summary, 2020*).

enough, it has raised the profile for businesses – particularly large organisations – to ensure their supply chains, as well as their own operations, are purged of slavery and human trafficking practices. For larger companies, this includes a requirement to report publicly their performance, in addition to producing 'modern slavery statements', which document what they are doing to end labour exploitation in their workforces. Within the agricultural sector, even smaller firms and organisations are expected to be vigilant in identifying and eradicating slavery practices.

The scale of the manual handling problem and the types of challenges facing those working within agriculture having been outlined – and the needs of vulnerable workers highlighted – it seems timely, at this point, for attention to turn to the scale of the vegetable, which sits at the heart of this fable...

THE SCALE OF THE SWEDE:
A Vegetable of Super-Sized Proportions

A criticism often levelled against fables and fairy tales is that they simply don't resonate in real life. Or that the scale of the events they seek to portray is simply ridiculous or far-fetched. At face value, this fable will do nothing to quash such beliefs – it being fair to challenge the gargantuan proportions of the swede it describes, as being a touch unrealistic!

In recognition of this concern, and in a bid to try to tackle it head-on, here's some real-world data. For the purposes of this fable, the awkward vegetable at its heart is assumed to have been a 54 kilogram swede, comparable to that grown by Ian Neale (UK), the current record holder. This was recorded by the Guinness Book of World Records at the UK National Giant Vegetable Championships, held at the Malvern Autumn Show in Worcestershire in 2013[128]. Applying some scale to the large lump of starch that sits at the centre of this tale should help to build an understanding of the challenges faced by the super-sized swede-shifters. The data on Ian Neale's record-

---

128. Guinness Book of World Records., (2020) [online]. Guinness World Records. [Viewed 1 May 2021]. Available from: http://www.guinnessworldrecords.com This was recorded on 29 October 2013.

breaking swede, together with the description of the characters' activities, are to be used as inputs to the RAPP tool, thus bringing a touch of realism to this fictional episode and allowing some example push and pull risk assessments to be generated. This should, in turn, pave the way for the events the tale describes to be considered in a structured manner and give some insights as to just how effectively the super-sized swede-shifters controlled the risks showcased here. Moreover, consideration of the outputs from the RAPP tool should also highlight the multitude of factors – besides weight alone – which can affect the level of injury risk faced by those involved in pushing and pulling activities. The outputs from this tool – in common with those of tools used for the other types of manual handling operation – form a key part of the wider three stage risk assessment process, which applies to all manual handling activities.

THE THREE-STAGE RISK ASSESSMENT PROCESS

Understanding the challenges posed by manual handling activities – as well as those particular to the workers involved – provides a good foundation from which to begin the risk assessment process. The process outlined here follows that set out in guidance published by the Health and Safety Executive. This guidance supports both the intent of *the Health and Safety at Work etc. Act 1974*[129] *(HSWA 1974)* and the more detailed requirements contained within *the Manual Handling Regulations,* and reference has been made to it at the relevant points here. This is useful because, as outlined in this book's introduction, guidance helps to flesh out some of the questions raised by regulations, and more particularly steers organisations towards the practical steps they need to take to control risk. As such, the process overview that follows here takes each stage in turn, highlighting what needs to be done to work out the appropriate level and type of manual handling risk assessment for the circumstances. The assessment process will be used to help evaluate the risks involved in this fable, this being the same approach that would be taken towards equivalent real-world scenarios. It is comprised of three stages, these being: *stage one* – carry out a manual handling

129. 1974 c. 37.

risk assessment; *stage two* – consider psychosocial factors, and *stage three* – consider individual workers.

The way the process operates is to be demonstrated by its application to this tale's events, with these theoretical assessment outputs being reviewed in the accompanying modern meaning which follows it.

STAGE #1
PERFORM A MANUAL HANDLING RISK ASSESSMENT

When faced with the need to risk assess any manual handling activity, the crucial first stage of the process involves working out the level of risk assessment and type of manual handling assessment tool to use. This first stage includes three levels of detail, and the complete process is outlined here, even though it's likely certain factors involved in this fable's scenario (most notably, the participation of a number of vulnerable workers) would tend to support the case for carrying out a full risk assessment, as called for by its third level. The Health and Safety Executive guidance recognises that some circumstances will call for those making an assessment to proceed straight to the third assessment level, stating: '...*you may not need to complete all three levels. For high-risk tasks you can go straight to a detailed full risk assessment.*'

Approaching the process chronologically, however, means this stage can be summarised as follows: the *first level* is the application of 'simple filters' – basic criteria, which distinguish low risk tasks from those tasks needing a more detailed assessment – the relevant one here being the 'pushing and pulling risk filter'; the *second level* is the use of 'risk assessment tools' – in this case the RAPP tool – a tool for assessing the most common manual handling risk factors of push and pull tasks, and the *third* and *final level* is full risk assessment – for use where a decision is made that the RAPP tool does not sufficiently cover the factors required by *the Manual Handling Regulations*. But of course, whilst the events of this fable make it a natural choice to focus upon the push and pull types of manual handling risk, an equivalent approach would need to be taken for the other types – requiring use of the relevant filter, assessment tool and full risk assessment – as appropriate to the circumstances.

There follows here an overview of each of the assessment levels, against which the practical scenario the fable sets out is to be evaluated[130].

LEVEL #1
APPLY THE SIMPLE FILTERS[131]

In starting to work through this process, an obvious – and sensible – question to ask about this first assessment level is: *'What exactly is a simple filter?'* The basic answer is that the filters are useful pointers – risk evaluation tools, developed by the Health and Safety Executive – which help assessors to reach a decision as to whether a given manual handling operation is of low risk, hence *filtering* out the need for more complex assessment. In most cases, this level can be addressed through direct observation of the activity in question. In this instance, reference is to be made to the filter applicable to *push and pull* activities, as the one clearly relevant to the swede pushing and pulling circumstances the tale portrays. Nevertheless, it's worth keeping in mind that other filter types are available – also provided by the Health and Safety Executive – which span the different types of manual handling activities, including lifting and lowering, carrying up to 10 metres, and handling whilst seated, any or all of which might need to be drawn upon, depending upon the specific context of any given scenario.

The guidance to the regulations helpfully sets out the parameters for the pushing and pulling risk filter. It explains that all four filters need to be satisfied for the task of moving of a load by pushing and pulling to be designated as low risk. These filters are: *first,* the force is applied with the hands; *second,* the torso is largely upright and not twisted; *third,* the hands are between hip and shoulder level, and finally, *fourth,* the distance involved without a pause or break is no

130. Guidance on the three assessment levels, the linkages between them, and the instruction to proceed directly to detailed full risk assessment for high-risk tasks, is to be found within the Health and Safety Executive's document (2016), *Manual handling – Manual Handling (Operations) Regulations 1992, Guidance on Regulations* (L23), Appendix, at page 51, paragraph 3 – *'How to choose the right level of detail for your manual handling risk assessments'.* See also Health and Safety Executive Guidance document (2020) *Manual Handling at Work – A brief guide* (INDG143).
131. Guidance document L23 describes the first assessment level 'simple filters' available for the four types of manual handling operations (Appendix, page 52, paragraphs 4-22). Given the nature of the events portrayed in this fable, the filter of particular interest here is the 'pushing and pulling risk filter' (Appendix, page 56, paragraphs 18-20).

more than about 20 metres. Also, whilst not a filter as such, a further indication that a push and pull activity is of low risk is where the load can be moved and controlled with only one hand.

When we come to reflect on the events of this fable, we'll consider whether some or all of the filter limits were likely to have been met here and, consequently, whether the activity was of 'low risk'. It's the use of these filters that informs the decision as to whether the use of a tool – in this case, the RAPP tool – is necessary, as is set out in the next level of this first stage of the process.

LEVEL #2
CHOOSE AND USE THE RIGHT TOOL[132]

Where *level one* of this first stage of the assessment process leads an assessor to conclude that an activity is not low risk, this second level sees them move onwards, to selecting the appropriate manual handling risk tool. There are lots of tools available for carrying out manual handling risk assessment, which are to be found within the Health and Safety Executive's 'Toolkit for Musculoskeletal Disorders (MSDs)', and in this case, the push and pull filter outputs will point towards the need to use the RAPP tool. *Why should this be?* It's because, as we shall see, this fable highlights the challenges involved in *pulling* a super-sized swede from the ground, and *pushing* it towards a cottage at the top of a smallholding. This makes the RAPP tool the natural choice – as the tool which specifically handles push and pull risk types. An assessor should always use the nature of the scenario to guide their decision as to which is the most appropriate tool to use, with this ultimately depending upon the features of the activity and the tasks of which it's comprised. To put this in some context here, had the farm workers who feature in this fable been confronted by a glut of swedes in need of harvesting, for instance – or, indeed, other objects needing to be removed on a repetitive basis within a fixed time period involving the upper limbs – the 'Assessment of Repetitive Tasks (ART)

---

132. Guidance document L23 describes the second assessment level, which involves the use of the HSE's tools – part of the MSD toolkit for assessing the most common manual handling risk factors of these tasks – these being tools which help to prioritise action to control the risks involved (Appendix, page 57, paragraphs 23-29), including particular guidance on how to use the RAPP tool (Appendix, page 58, paragraph 28); further detail on this tool, as selected for the circumstances described here, is to be found in Health and Safety Executive Guidance document INDG478.

tool' would have been the best option. If, on the other hand, their activities had involved lifting, lowering, carrying and team manual handling, the 'Manual Handling Assessment Charts (MAC) tool' would have been the right choice. Finally, had the activity to be considered here involved multiple swedes of differing size – or any other objects for that matter – the 'Variable Manual Handling Assessment Chart (V-MAC) tool' would have been the most appropriate one, because this tool can be used to assess manual handling operations where there is load weight variability.

But, as will soon become apparent, these would not have been the best options for this particular super-sized swede-shifting activity, so let's look at the tool of choice here – in this case, it's the RAPP!

Once a decision is made that the RAPP tool is the appropriate one to use, it's at this point of the process that consideration shifts to how to apply it, for the given circumstances. The assessment guide, shown in *Appendix A* of this book, summarises the assessment criteria defined by the Health and Safety Executive and forms the basis upon which activities of the types described in this fable can be evaluated. Just like the MAC tool, which has been around for some time now – and is another of the tools within the Toolkit for MSDs – the RAPP tool uses colour-coding and numeric scoring, helping to identify high-risk pushing and pulling activities, before leading to an evaluation of the effectiveness of any risk reduction measures. The guidance to the regulations provides assistance in how to complete a RAPP assessment, through the use of the tool.

There are two types of pushing and pulling operations that the RAPP tool can be used to assess – loads moved without wheels, as we'll see applies here, and loads moved with wheels – but common to both types is the need to progress through the following steps[133]. *First*, take time to observe the task; *second*, select the appropriate type of assessment; *third*, follow the appropriate assessment guide and flow chart, to determine the level of risk for each risk factor; *fourth*, enter the colour band and corresponding numeric score for each risk factor on to

---

133. The approach adopted here summarises the key elements of Guidance document INDG478, in particular the contents of the flowchart it contains for 'pushing or pulling loads without wheels' (page 9, section B of the Guidance document). The accompanying assessment guide from the Guidance document has been summarised in chart form at *Appendix A* of this book. The full assessment guide is to be found in INDG478, at pages 10-13. Although not considered here, the guidance also provides an equivalent flowchart and assessment guide for 'pushing or pulling loads on wheeled equipment'.

the correct score sheet, using the colour band to help determine which elements of the task require attention, and *fifth* and finally, consider individual characteristics and psychosocial factors, as well as completing the task description and considering the indications of a high-risk task. The scores derived from the RAPP tool can be used to help prioritise actions according to the scores awarded, both between factors in a single task, and between multiple tasks, where these need to be carried out. The pushing and pulling operations need to be separately considered however, with the approach also differing depending upon whether loads are to be moved with or without wheels, the examples completed within the *modern meaning* attached to this fable being for loads without wheels, based upon the description of events given[134]. There follows here a brief outline of the different stages involved in completing the tool.

This fable's modern meaning showcases the tool's use, being based upon the events it depicts, in combination with the weight data for Ian Neale's real-world swede – the scale of this particular vegetable having been described earlier in the prologue.

Looking at the assessment guide in *Appendix A* in a little more detail, this highlights the tool's key features and gives the parameters by which any given push and pull without wheels activity can be assessed. It shows that the RAPP tool requires consideration of eight factors affecting the risk, which are: *first*, activity/load weight (*B-1*); *second*, posture (*B-2*); *third*, hand grip (*B-3*); *fourth*, work pattern (*B-4*); *fifth*, travel distance (*B-5*); *sixth*, floor surface (*B-6*); *seventh*, obstacles along the route (*B-7*), and finally, *eighth*, other factors (*B-8*). The (*B-*) references denote the factors listed on the score sheets. The RAPP tool takes the scores awarded for each factor, and interprets these by applying different colour ratings and risk levels to them, together with accompanying actions, as shown in *Table 3* overleaf.

Once we've looked at the key elements of the scenario the fable describes, we'll use the insights it offers, together with the accompanying assessment guide, to determine the inputs to be entered against each

---

134. Pushing and pulling can be considered on the same score sheet for moving loads without wheels but, as will become apparent, the author has adapted the score sheet example template provided within the Guidance document for illustrative purposes, with the push' and 'pull' operations being evaluated on separate score sheets and additional notes recorded in support of the colour band rating awarded for each factor, based upon the events the fable describes.

of these factors on the score sheets, using the tool in the same way as it would be applied for equivalent real-world activities[135].

RATING	RISK LEVEL	ACTION REQUIRED
G = Green	Low level of risk	Although the risk is low, consider the effect on vulnerable groups such as pregnant women or young workers, where appropriate.
A = Amber	Medium level of risk	Examine tasks closely.
R = Red	High or very high level of risk	Prompt action needed. This may expose a significant proportion of the working population to risk of injury.

Table 3: RAPP Tool Risk Rating Classifications[136]

The use of the RAPP tool requires the colour band rating and corresponding numeric score awarded to each factor to be entered on to the score sheet[137]. In a real-world context, organisations can use these total figures and colour bands to help them work out which risk factors of any given operation demand their most urgent attention, as well as to support them in checking the effectiveness of any risk reduction measures. The scores can also be used for comparison purposes – helping to prioritise the action required to address a factor, relative to other factors on the one score sheet *or* between score sheets – but it should be noted that they do not relate to specific 'action levels'.

Once the RAPP score sheets have been completed, the focus next shifts to working out what the scores produced by the RAPP tool mean, with particular emphasis being placed upon those scores that are not green-rated. It's by using the relevant assessment guide (*Appendix A*), and completing and reviewing separate score sheets for the pull

---

135. The example score sheets have been completed on the basis of the events described, and are to be found at *Appendix B* and *C* of this book, with the outputs from them being reviewed in the *modern meaning* that accompanies this fable.

136. Source of information within *Table 3*: INDG478, page 2. Note that for transporting loads with wheels, the guidance also specifies a higher rating level of P = Purple, but this is not listed here, given that the operation described in the fable involves the transporting of a load without wheels, to which this rating level is not applicable.

137. For the example used here, supporting task information has been entered in the comments boxes on the score sheets.

and push activities that outcomes based upon the data entered can be derived. The reason why non-green-rated scores are of greatest interest is that it's these which call for appropriate remedial action to be taken, to help bring about acceptable risk levels. Adopting this approach here will allow us to look through the respective ratings for the pulling and pushing activities carried out by the characters, with the assessment outputs for both activities being reviewed simultaneously against each factor, for simplicity, within the fable's accompanying *modern meaning*. As *Table 3* shows, it's important to remember that even where a factor is green-rated – and hence, deemed to be of low risk – the assessment process still calls for specific consideration to be given to the effects of the activity on vulnerable workers, including pregnant women and young workers, as well as to any psychosocial issues, and a space at the bottom of the score sheet allows these details to be specifically recorded.

The use and interpretation of the RAPP tool places an assessor in a position to understand the risk *as is*. And having used the tool, the assessor's attention next needs to shift to looking at the gap between risk *as is* and risk *as desired*, with the assessment moving on a stage, to consider *how* to reduce the risk. The focus of any assessment stage should always be on reducing risk to a level which is 'as low as reasonably practicable (ALARP)' and, where this is not already the case, it's important to work out how risk reduction to this level might be achieved. Real-world organisations need to be ever-mindful of this point, thinking about where to focus their efforts – and more specifically, their time, money and resource – so as to achieve the biggest risk reduction. Practically speaking, this means that it's necessary to look through the different factors as addressed on each of the score sheets, and to put in place additional control measures, in particular where factors fall into non-green-rated colour bands. It's also key to note that the same load weight can have different implications, depending on whether the activity type involves pushing or pulling. This is simply down to physics – because pulling demands more effort than pushing.

As we shall see, the use of the RAPP tool provides some insights about how to address the key factors involved in an activity, which is to be applied to the fable's example of a super-sized swede being removed from the ground and rolled across a smallholding! But there's also a need to consider whether there are any additional risk factors – as listed within *the Manual Handling Regulations* – which point to the need for a full risk assessment to be carried out, the one of particular relevance we shall see here being that the activity calls for unusual strength or height[138].

The approach to be adopted here – which considers how the risk factors would be rated in the context of the fable's fictional events – is consistent with that which would be taken towards any equivalent real-world scenario. These are important factors for those assessing the activity to think about, helping them to ensure that any risk assessment is a suitable and sufficient one.

LEVEL #3
IF REQUIRED, CONDUCT A FULL RISK ASSESSMENT[139]

A full risk assessment is not going to be undertaken here, given that the fable is anecdotal and hence, as is unfortunately typical of the fairy tale genre, somewhat scant on detail! That said, it would be remiss not to outline what the process would involve in a real-world context. Just as is true for any risk assessment it is, of course, crucial for workers to be observed carrying out their various tasks, over a sufficient period of time, so as to provide the necessary level of information and build up a full picture of what's involved. As already noted, talking to workers is vital too – it gives additional insights into the difficulties they face and also allows those assessing the risk to take on board their suggestions as to how they feel their activities might be made easier. Working collaboratively in this way makes it much more likely that the risk assessment and any control measures applied as a result will fully reflect and address the risks present.

---

138. Guidance document L23 sets out the information to be considered in addition to the tool, to ensure that the factors required by the regulations have been adequately covered, and that the risk assessment is 'suitable and sufficient'. Aside from unusual strength or height being required from workers, other additional risk factors which require consideration are: large vertical movements; the risk of sudden movement of loads; a rate of work imposed by a process; a load which is unstable or with contents which are likely to shift; a load which is sharp, hot or otherwise potentially damaging; an activity which requires special information or training for its safe performance, and circumstances in which the movement or posture of those carrying out the activity is hindered by PPE or by clothing (Appendix to L23, page 59, paragraphs 32, 33).

139. Guidance document L23 states that a standalone full risk assessment is to be carried out – the third assessment level – if required (Appendix to L23, page 59, paragraphs 34-36). This can either be performed right from the start or be driven by the outcomes of the previous assessment levels outlined here. The factors pointing to the need to carry out a full risk assessment are to be found in the Appendix to L23, at page 58, paragraph 30.

This third assessment level sees a decision being reached about whether a full risk assessment is needed, before this is undertaken in appropriate circumstances. In the real world, it's here that the information gathered about the capabilities of the individuals carrying out the activities would be used to further develop the risk assessment. But individual capability is also a factor which, of itself, is instrumental in steering the decision as to whether a full risk assessment is required. The participation of a number of vulnerable workers here – any of whom could potentially be at significant risk due to their temporarily reduced or low capability to do physical work – is a factor which would prompt the carrying out of a full risk assessment, a requirement which is reflected within the regulations and supporting guidance. The involvement of a pregnant worker, a migrant worker, an apprentice new to the job, and an older worker with a pre-existing medical condition would – even individually – point towards this being the right decision. The risk factors and questions to be included within a full suitable and sufficient risk assessment are specifically set out in *the Manual Handling Regulations*[140], this being the level of assessment required where manual handling operations involving a risk of injury to employees cannot be avoided. These factors include: the tasks, the loads, the environment, and the individuals involved, together with other issues such as the hindrance of movement or posture by personal protective equipment or clothing.

As the process is an iterative one, in cases where a full risk assessment is undertaken, there remains a need to, once again, consider whether the risk has been reduced SFAIRP, in exactly the same way as was described under *level two* of *stage one*; this applies to real-world scenarios, just as would be the case for the fictional scenario this fable sets out. There may be control measures identified through full risk assessment which need to be adopted in order to sufficiently reduce the risk.

The completion of this third level ends the assessment of the manual handling activity itself, but this only finishes the first stage of the assessment process. In addition to looking at the aspects inherent to the activity, it's also important to consider psychosocial factors and any needs particular to the individual workers involved. A brief outline of these two subsequent stages follows here.

---

140. See regulation 4(1)(b)(i), together with Schedule 1, which sets out the factors and questions employers are to consider when making assessments of their own manual handling operations.

STAGE #2
CONSIDER PSYCHOSOCIAL FACTORS

In addition to carrying out a risk assessment and putting in place control measures, those in charge of activities need to think about psychosocial factors and how work is organised too, which is the focus of this second stage. These are factors which – if inadequately managed – can affect workers' psychological reactions to work and the environment, including high 'workload' demands, short deadlines and a general feeling amongst the workforce that they lack control over their working methods. Another factor which can have a detrimental impact is that of poor communication between managers and employees – as well as any form of harassment – leading to low workforce morale which can, in turn, give rise to adverse consequences for levels of work output. Conflicting demands and poorly managed organisational change can also impact negatively upon workforce motivation, as can task-related aspects. A further point is that repetitive pushing and pulling – when performed without sufficient recovery time being taken in between bursts of activity – can cause unnecessary impact or strain on the human body.

Brief attention is to be paid to the types of psychosocial factors that might have applied here, in light of the description given by the fable.

STAGE #3
TACKLE RISKS TO INDIVIDUAL WORKERS[141]

This final stage of the assessment process considers the risks to individual workers. Where there are deemed to be risks to individuals who could have temporarily reduced or low capability to carry out physical work, this should be highlighted at *stage one,* which calls for a full risk assessment to be undertaken in such circumstances. But it's worth making brief mention of the risks that any worker might face, as these require consideration too. Examples of individual 'anthropometric' factors are relevant here – a tall worker may have to

---

141. Guidance for regulation 4(3)(e), provided in Guidance document L23 at page 19, paragraphs 74-83, sets out the considerations for 'employees especially at risk' with respect to their involvement in manual handling operations.

stoop or adopt an awkward posture, whilst a shorter worker may find it difficult to see over a load, an issue we'll see the old farmer facing in this fable. Workers have different characteristics and capabilities and it's important to recognise and account for these, rather than presuming that a *one size fits all* approach will suffice. Also, some individuals might be temporarily impacted by conditions which reduce the amount of force that can safely be handled by them. Young people – whose joints and muscles may not be fully developed, or whose 'risk perception' skills might be less advanced than those with more experience – also need to be considered, with adjustments being made accordingly. And it's always important to account for the needs of individuals who could be placed at increased risk, where the tasks involved call for an unusual level of capability. Such circumstances need to be handled on a case-by-case basis, with due thought given to *who* is to carry out a task and *how* it is to be safely accomplished, without compromising the safety of the employees or that of their co-workers, and with specialist training or instruction being required in some cases.

An overview of the risks to individual workers, and how to go about evaluating and addressing these, is to be provided in the modern meaning that accompanies this fable, once a little more is known about the particular characteristics of the super-sized swede-shifters involved!

THE FOCUS OF THIS FABLE

As we shall soon discover, this fable prompts consideration of the risk assessment of manual handling *push and pull* activities – including the use of filters, assessment tools and full risk assessment – as well as the corresponding control measures that need to be put in place to ease the burden on those carrying them out, in order to reduce risk as part of an holistic risk management approach. But we shall also see that it goes beyond simply looking at activities, with the tale raising wider questions about the challenges and needs of particular individuals (some of whom may have conditions or traits which make it potentially higher risk for them than would be the case for others), together with psychosocial factors, both being aspects of relevance within broader workplace contexts.

So, without further ado, let's head off to the smallholding...

THE FABLE

There once was an old farmer, who worked for a big farming business. The old farmer had some swede seeds. An old woman who worked alongside him had sourced them from a well-known supplier, but they hadn't come with much in the way of growing instructions. *Still, he reasoned, at least they hadn't been an expensive purchase...*

The old farmer planted the seeds. He watered the seeds. The swede seeds grew. One swede in particular grew and grew AND GREW! *It was super-sized!*

One windy and blustery day, the old farmer said: 'I want to pull up my super-sized swede!' He went to pull up the super-sized swede. It was the biggest of its kind he'd ever seen and, even with his hands above his head, he could barely reach its leaves.

He pulled and he dragged, and he pulled and he hauled but, try as he might, he couldn't pull up the super-sized swede.

He was leaning back and straining to pull out the difficult vegetable with all the strength he could muster. It was awkward to gain a grip on the monstrous vegetable, with it being by turns, scratchy and slippery. The ground was rutted in places following recent heavy rain too, and the field was littered with random objects, debris and general detritus, as he and his co-workers weren't the tidiest of folk, nor their employers the most diligent, when it came to matters of smallholding housekeeping. The old farmer was pivoting back on his heels and he had quite some distance to travel, in order to accomplish his half-baked plan.

The old farmer called out to the old woman. 'Come and help me to pull up this super-sized swede!' he said. He wasn't in the best of moods, what with his hands being muddied from his efforts, and it having dawned on him that the task ahead was going to be a little more arduous than he had first anticipated.

The old woman complained, but it wasn't long before she relented and followed him out to the area of the smallholding devoted to swede growing. She held him around the waist. *It was the closest the pair of them had been in years.*

The old woman pulled the old farmer and the old farmer pulled the super-sized swede. After a while, however, the old woman let go with one hand and rubbed her lower back, as all the tugging was causing her discomfort and she was prone to lumbago, having suffered a previous injury. But being of a steely nature and not wishing to be beaten, she was swift to resume her efforts…

They pulled and they dragged, and they pulled and they hauled, but they couldn't pull up the super-sized swede.

A migrant worker had been employed for some time at the smallholding and the old woman decided his help was just what they needed. *He was a hard worker.* The old woman called out to the migrant worker. 'Come and help us to pull up this super-sized swede!' she said, gesturing frantically towards him.

Without giving the old woman's request a moment's thought, the migrant worker ran over to the super-sized swede-shifters and the super-sized swede. With his hands gripping her waist, the migrant worker pulled the old woman. And the old woman pulled the old farmer. And the old farmer pulled the super-sized swede.

They pulled and they dragged and they pulled and they hauled, but they couldn't pull up the super-sized swede.

The migrant worker signalled to a young lad apprentice to join them. The young lad apprentice needed little by way of encouragement, being constantly keen to impress others and, on seeing the growing group of super-sized swede-shifters before him, headed straight on over to join them, to support their efforts.

The young lad apprentice pulled the migrant worker and the migrant worker pulled the old woman and the old woman pulled the old farmer and the old farmer pulled the super-sized swede.

They pulled and they dragged, and they pulled and they hauled, but they couldn't pull up the super-sized swede.

The young lad apprentice called out to a young lady. 'Come and help us to pull up this super-sized swede!' he said.

The young lady was a little reluctant to join in, on the whim of the young lad apprentice. For one thing, she'd moisturised her hands barely ten minutes beforehand, meaning she wasn't best pleased at the idea of getting her hands dirty. For another, she'd recently advised the owner of the big farming business which employed them that she was expecting a baby. But despite having slight reservations, she didn't want to miss out on the activity, and so headed on over to join the other super-sized swede-shifters.

The young lady pulled the young lad apprentice, and the young lad apprentice pulled the migrant worker, and the migrant worker pulled the old woman, and the old woman pulled the old farmer, and the old farmer pulled the super-sized swede.

They pulled and they dragged, and they pulled and they hauled, but they couldn't pull up the super-sized swede.

The young lady saw a little dog nearby and, thinking he might be able to support their efforts, called out to him. 'Here boy! Here boy! *There's a good boy!* Come here and help us!' she said. The little dog wagged his tail enthusiastically. But before he had chance to scamper across to join them, the young lady's request was rudely interrupted by the young lad apprentice, who made no bones about telling her that, even with his limited level of experience, he could see that seeking the involvement of this little hound was a ridiculous idea. The little dog looked on ruefully, as it occurred to him that the super-sized swede-shifting activity might be rather fun. It wasn't long before the rueful-looking dog was joined by an aloof-looking cat and a smug-looking little mouse, both of whom had also been out looking for some afternoon escapades, to break up what they saw as the monotony of arable farm life. The three of them skulked off to the margins of the smallholding, in truth being slightly irked by the unwillingness of these humans to involve their animal counterparts in their efforts. The rueful dog looked miffed, the aloof cat pretended not to care, and the smug little mouse read a book on *Push & Pull Risks*, feeling a little judgmental about the chaotic human enterprise unfolding in front of his eyes, and slightly superior, thinking to himself that their whole approach to the activity was far from best practice.

There followed a considerable period of tugging and huffing by the human participants. And much pulling, dragging and hauling. And quite a bit of '*ooohhhing*' and '*aaaggghhhing*' from those involved too. And then eventually, just as the super-sized swede-shifters were starting to contemplate giving up on the whole sorry charade, all of a sudden – UP CAME THE SUPER-SIZED SWEDE!

After several minutes in disarray, during which various mumbles and grumbles could be heard coming from the group on the ground, they dusted themselves off and contemplated their next move. They still faced the prospect of having to roll the super-sized swede some thirty or so metres back to the cottage at the top of the smallholding, in itself not to be sniffed at, given the vastness of the vegetable that lay before them.

The super-sized swede-shifters all helped to roll the super-sized swede across the smallholding and up the slope towards the cottage, where one of the other workers from the smallholding was waiting for them. It wasn't easy and it took all of their efforts to get it there.

They pushed and they rolled, and they pushed and they rolled, and they pushed and they rolled the super-sized swede.

And, with the movement of the vast vegetable having been accomplished, the super-sized swede-shifters retired to the smallholding cottage to recover from their efforts. All that was, with the exception of the old farmer, who had remembered he needed to tend to one of his other crops in an adjacent field.

Having taken a bit of a lie down to rest her aching bones, the old woman quickly set to work on the super-sized swede. She scrubbed the super-sized swede. She chopped the super-sized swede. She diced the super-sized swede. And she boiled and simmered the super-sized swede in her biggest pot, until it was reduced to some malodorous mush.

The old farmer soon returned and, the super-sized swede preparation having been completed by the old woman, without further ado they all sat down to a hearty, *but horrible*, meal. All that was, except for the rueful dog, the aloof cat and the smug little mouse, who loitered around outside hoping that, just maybe, some non-swede-based leftovers might find their way across to them some time soon.

Then, just as the old farmer, the old woman, the migrant worker, the young lad apprentice and the young lady were finishing their super-sized swede supper, the smug little mouse had an idea. He scurried quickly across the smallholding, right up to the cottage window, and on to the ledge as fast as his little mouse feet would carry him. And, when all of the humans were busying themselves with the washing up in the kitchen, he tapped on the window with the book he'd been reading earlier.

Tap! Tap! TAP! TAP! went the smug little mouse, with his little mouse feet and his *Push & Pull Risks* book on the cottage window.

The young lady looked up with a start from washing her bowl and, on seeing the smug little mouse, headed outside. By now, the smug little mouse was frantically waving his little mouse feet, seemingly agitated by something. And just as the young lady was starting to rue her decision in succumbing so easily to the gesturing of this imperious little rodent, she noticed a piece of paper which had been marking a page in his book. Suddenly, and quite unexpectedly, it was picked up by a gust of wind and floated out on the breeze. The smug little mouse gestured to her to catch it, which the young lady did. He nodded – in what appeared to be a fairly passive-aggressive fashion – which she took to mean he was anticipating some kind of recital of its contents. It didn't take the young lady long to deduce that the smug little mouse had authored the work...

'I thought this would happen, I knew there'd be trouble...
A group scrabbling through dirt and tripping on rubble.
Led by a farmer – stretching – to reach a swede's top,
Who seemed not to plan, nor to pause, think or stop!
Had he gone off his rocker? Was he out of his mind?
His torso was twisted, body badly inclined.
I'm just not convinced there's a spine here worth busting
For a limited diet, for a swede so disgusting.
For what petty reward? Humble vegetable soup,
Just not worth the pain...or the stagger...or stoop,
Or the groans of a farmer, a would-be prize winner,
Who unwittingly ate up his best hope, for dinner!
There's no reason apparent, nor compelling need,
For this level of toil, for the sake of a swede!
A vegetable, not to my taste, all slippery and scratchy,
And the approach to risk here – seems, at best, to be patchy!
So please, huddle around, for a moment of order,
For there lurk challenges here, from furrow to border.
In all of my travels – from meadow to farm,
Ne'er did I see such potential for harm!
It should be no surprise, you have failed to impress,
And some points come to mind I just have to express...

Never let it be said that things got out of kilter,
By a failure to start with a basic risk filter,
Or next, selecting a risk tool – there's *RAPP,* for a start,
And if not, there's *MAC,* or *V-MAC,* or *ART.*
But in my estimation, here, it would have been best,
All factors considered – these tasks to be full risk assessed.

> You should have watched for those too, with particular needs,
> As you dragged, as you hauled, pulled and tugged at this swede.
> As for pushing and rolling of turnips or marrows,
> If it's super-sized veg', next time, consider trolleys and barrows.
> I'm not trying to be smug, but there's little that's clever,
> About your hapless, ill-thought out, swede-shifting endeavour.
> If you think through the risk, then you'll move things with ease
> And harvest a future that's injury free!'

The old farmer looked angry. The young lady, meanwhile, was slightly perplexed at having happened upon a little mouse with such a niche interest in manual handling risk tools, who seemed to fancy himself as some kind of roving rodent risk reporter (and who, despite his protestations, did strike her as a touch smug). And, whilst the young lady didn't doubt his experience, she did detect a whiff of hypocrisy, feeling that the carrying of such a big book by such a little mouse – smug or otherwise – was pushing the boundaries of his lifting capabilities, to say the least. Still, it transpired that the smug little mouse had been minded to complete the RAPP tool, as the basis of a push and pull risk assessment, using the information he'd derived from observing all the super-sized swede-tugging and shoving that had been going on[142]. She could well believe he'd acquired this skill from scampering around the different farms in the locality, as he appeared a little fickle, seeming to show no loyalty to this particular smallholding. But however he'd arrived at his conclusions, she had to concede, he had a point and it had raised in her mind the need for them all to adopt a more measured approach to this kind of activity in the future.

Returning to the washing up once again, the young lady suggested to the young lad apprentice that perhaps a step-change in the control of manual handling risk would be beneficial for them, as well as for other workers involved in big farming business activities. He said he agreed with her in principle, but that – rather than worrying about their approach to vegetable harvesting – he'd prefer to telephone for a takeaway pizza in future, thus avoiding a repeat of the whole sorry super-sized swede-based fiasco and associated catering issues, and removing the need for any of them to go to bed hungry. And the more the pair chatted, the more the realisation was dawning that they

---

142. See *Appendix B* and *Appendix C* of this book, which provide two completed examples of RAPP score sheets, as based upon the events described in this fable.

shared much common ground. Not only did they recognise the need to avoid the weighty problems that they, and the rest of the group, had encountered in shifting the sizeable vegetable, but they also questioned whether this beige produce was deserving of their efforts at all. When contrasted with say, the tree-like beauty of a head of broccoli, or the glorious orange glow of a carrot, the young lady took the view that this pale vegetable had far less to offer than the abundant harvest boasted by other crops at the smallholding. And the young lad apprentice had begun to wonder whether his speedy consumption of their super-sized swede supper might be behind his feeling a touch bilious, too.

The young lady and young lad apprentice suddenly became aware of raised voices, which gave them cause to break away from their discussion on the merits and demerits of different vegetable types. Some terse comments were exchanged between the old farmer and the old woman, followed by a stony silence as the last of their bowls were cleared away. The young lady questioned the young lad apprentice as to what had been going on whilst she'd been away speaking with the smug little mouse. He told her that – as it turned out – the old farmer hadn't wanted the group to eat the super-sized swede after all, as he'd hoped to profit from its size. But, having been out surveying another crop, of course he'd been unaware of the old woman's scrubbing, chopping, dicing, boiling and simmering of his prized vegetable. It was only upon finishing his meal – and through the surprisingly sage words of the smug little mouse – that the awful truth had been revealed to him. Added to this, the old woman had forgotten to get dessert in, which did little to lift the group's mood and so, after a few minutes' conversation over a pot of tea, they all made their sorry way up to bed.

On rising from their slumber the next day, many of the super-sized swede-shifters reported muscular twinges and niggles, in varying degrees and forms. Although annoying, these were fortunately nothing too serious. Serious enough though for the smug little mouse to feel even more smug, from his window ledge vantage point. And for the young lady to petition the old farmer to speak to their employers about the need to update their approach to the range of manual handling activities carried out across the smallholding.

Although fortunately only temporary, the various twinges and niggles experienced by the super-sized swede-shifters – together with their limited knowledge of suitably scrumptious super-sized swede-based recipes – had given the young lady cause to reflect on where things might have started to go wrong for them all. She perceived the old woman and the old farmer to be a somewhat unfortunate combination. The old woman had an apparent magpie instinct to source seeds from popular suppliers, without reference to reviews from other buyers. The old farmer, on the other hand, appeared over-zealous in applying well-known growing aids – mulch, fertiliser, and the like – and harboured an unchecked desire to compete with fellow vast vegetable growers at the local county shows.

The super-sized swede-shifters reviewed the range of vegetables grown at the smallholding, together with their cultivation and harvesting methods. An audit was also carried out on their suppliers to check that what was being sold to them was as described on the seed packets. And the old farmer tactfully suggested to the old woman that in future, if she was procuring seeds, it might be worth her taking a moment to check the growing instructions in a little more detail, before she committed to buying them, feedback which she grudgingly accepted. Finally, the owners of the big farming business took the lessons learnt from this unfortunate super-sized swede-based experience as an opportunity to review their overall approach to manual handling, not only at this smallholding but also at the others within their agricultural portfolio, paying particular attention to push and pull operations.

And the super-sized swede-shifters couldn't face the prospect of eating that particular root vegetable for quite some time...

MODERN MEANING

This fable depicted a bunch of super-sized swede-shifters grappling with the challenges presented by an awkward and heavy load. The tale offered a window on a group displaying a multitude of characteristics, affording us an insight into their various struggles with poor postures and tricky hand grip, some with pre-existing ailments, others simply breaking out in a sweat from their efforts. And it also showcased their bid to manoeuvre a big vegetable along a less than ideal route, over rough ground littered with obstacles. Having just digested the contents of the fable – although fortunately for us, not the swede – it's here that we revisit the three key stages introduced in this tale's *prologue*: *first*, the manual handling activity undertaken; *second*, psychosocial factors, and *third,* individual workers, including those classed as vulnerable workers. Much of the focus here will be upon the old farmer, as it was he who had the task of directly tugging at the vegetable, albeit that consideration is also given to the others involved, whenever appropriate to do so. With manual handling activities, it's important to bear in mind the specific context of the particular operating environment which, as we've seen here, can create issues that raise risk levels, if suitable control measures aren't put in place. Turning to some real-world examples for a moment, someone who has to manoeuvre themselves, whilst carrying flow-stopping equipment alongside utility pipes within an excavation, or who has to navigate their way through a narrow tunnel moving tunnel-boring equipment, will likely face greater challenges than a worker tasked with transporting boxes containing paper through a modern purpose-built office space, with observable good housekeeping standards in place, as well as trolleys and goods lifts being available for them to use and the option of removing reams of paper from boxes on reaching their destination, so as to reduce the weight of any given load. But the issues faced by any of them are likely to be driven by a range of factors, including time, cost pressures, and productivity demands, to name but a few.

So then, let's see what can be learnt from this fable...

In beginning to look at the endeavours of this hapless bunch of super-sized swede-shifters, it's concerning to note that there's no hint of a risk assessment having been carried out by the pullers and pushers before the activity got underway. Had a risk assessment been undertaken, it's likely this would have led to some kind of discussion taking place about the tasks involved, the size of the swede, how much effort was thought to be required to shift it, the physical suitability of the participants involved for the task at hand, or even whether an entirely different approach might have been possible[143]. It would have been natural for this to include seeking the views of the old farmer, and anyone else in the group, about

---

143. As outlined in this book's introduction, employers are required to have 'consultation' arrangements in place with those who carry out work or their representatives. For this type of work, employers would be expected to provide employees with information on the risks and dangers associated with manual handling, the measures put in place to get rid of or reduce these risks, and what they should do in the event of them being uncontrolled.

ways in which the sizeable vegetable's removal and transfer might have been avoided. And, even if avoidance wasn't deemed possible, an effective risk assessment would at least have paved the way for an alternative method of working to be adopted, perhaps including the use of some form of powered assistance, rather than exclusive reliance being placed upon human effort to achieve super-sized swede extraction. This is important, because it's a legal requirement to avoid operations which involve the risk of injury and, where this isn't feasible, to assess them and reduce the associated injury risk to the lowest level reasonably practicable. Carrying out an effective suitable and sufficient risk assessment would have pointed the group towards a range of options for improving upon their chosen working methods, as well as highlighting to them other small changes that might have been needed, perhaps including the wearing of more appropriate clothing for the tasks involved.

It's quite true to say that pushing and pulling generally reduces the effort associated with other types of manual handling but, whilst such activities do usually allow larger loads to be handled safely, they can still be harmful. Furthermore, items that don't have wheels, such as the super-sized swede described here, are likely to place greater demands on the human body than are wheeled items. Having decided that they were going to remove and transfer the swede with manual effort however, the group's attention should have turned to the working methods they were to adopt to achieve this safely. Each assessment level has been considered here, with reference also being made to the choice of the appropriate tool, and examples of the RAPP tool completed for both pulling and pushing aspects, based upon the observations of the smug little mouse.

What follows here is a consideration of the requirements for each assessment stage, with the assessment process being used to guide an evaluation of the super-sized swede-shifting activity, using the description given in the fable. Just as would hold true for any real-world scenario of course, the choice of tool(s) needs to be based upon the perceived level of risk, which is determined by responding to a series of questions for each assessment level – as articulated in the prologue – the answers here being provided on the basis of the fable's commentary on the activities carried out and the characteristics of those involved in undertaking them.

STAGE #1
PERFORM THE MANUAL HANDLING
RISK ASSESSMENT

For this first stage, a theoretical assessment of the manual handling activity is outlined, in the context of the fable's events. This comprises an application of the simple filters, an evaluation of the RAPP tool outcomes, and a consideration of the need for full risk assessment, based upon the super-sized swede-shifting shenanigans described.

LEVEL #1
APPLY THE SIMPLE FILTERS
Was this a low risk activity?

NO! *This was not a low risk activity.*

This question is addressed by working out whether the tasks performed met the simple filter assumptions, which is answerable by seeing if they fell within the filter values. Had this been the case, the activity would have been designated as *low risk*, with the requirement for further assessment then being removed. By applying the simple 'manual handling risk filter' here, however, it's relatively straightforward to conclude that this was not a low risk activity. With the exception of the application of force by the hands, none of the other criteria were met. We note from the description given that at least one of the pushers and pullers – namely, the old farmer – had their hands above shoulder level, the use of both hands was required, and the distance involved was in excess of 20 metres. The old farmer, we are told, had to reach above his head, the old lady was twisting, and the distance the super-sized vegetable needed to be moved was around 30 metres. Remember though, that here we've only looked at filters for a push and pull-type activity and, just as would hold true for any equivalent real-life scenario, there might be a need to apply other filters, depending upon the particular type of manual handling operation being contemplated. Had the tasks being evaluated met the assumptions of the simple risk filter and fallen within the filter values, this would have rendered the assessment process complete at this point, albeit that efforts would still have needed to be made to avoid these operations or make them less demanding for the super-sized swede-shifters, if 'reasonably practicable' to do so.

Here, however, the tasks did not meet the assumptions of the relevant simple filters. Given that the 'pushing and pulling risk filter' tells us that this was not low risk and all the indications are that significant forces were required for pushing and pulling, the next step is to look at the RAPP tool outcomes.

LEVEL #2
EVALUATE THE RAPP TOOL OUTCOMES
Were all the factors green-rated?

NO! *The factors were not all green-rated.*

It's at this point that attention turns to the completed RAPP assessment score sheets for pushing or pulling loads without wheels, to see what the RAPP scores reveal, as based upon the assessment criteria, shown at *Appendix A*. The first completed score sheet is to be found at *Appendix B*, for the pulling of the super-sized swede from the ground – which involved it being dragged/hauled. A second completed score sheet is to be found at *Appendix C*, for the pushing of the super-sized swede back to the cottage at the top of the smallholding – which involved it being rolled. The scores noted against each factor, together with the comments entered for both the pulling and pushing operations are reviewed and discussed here[144]. Recalling for a moment the information given in the *prologue*, the assumption made for both the pulling and the pushing operations is that this is based upon a swede weighing 54 kilograms – Ian Neale's swede – with the RAPP assessments having been completed in accordance with the criteria in the assessment guide.

It's worth stressing that, had this been a real-world scenario, some time would have needed to be spent in observing the activity and the various tasks carried out by the super-sized swede-shifters, so that what has been taken as a snapshot here could be said to be reflective of normal working practice. With assessments of this kind, it's particularly important to have a sound grasp of the working practices employed, together with the challenges faced by workers, which is invariably best achieved by talking to them about what they do and the problems they

---

144. The format adopted for the completed score sheets used in *Appendix B* of this book (for the 'pull' or 'drag'/'haul' action) and *Appendix C* of this book (for the 'push' or 'roll' action) has been based upon the *score sheet: pushing or pulling loads without wheels* template provided within publication INDG478, at page 14.

face, as well as taking on board their comments as to how things might be done better. It's in so doing that an assessor is able to build up a clear picture of what's involved, including gaining the different perspectives of those participating in the work activity. The data provided about the fable's scenario has made it possible for some basic details to be recorded at the top of the score sheets in *Appendices B* and *C*, with notes also entered at the bottom of each of them, reflecting the points made that the operations involved were known to be hard or high-risk work, and that there were indications of workers showing signs of finding the work hard, for instance, by some of them breaking out in a sweat.

As just one of the tools in the Health and Safety Executive's Toolkit for MSDs, the RAPP tool is designed to help assess the key risks in manual pushing and pulling operations involving whole-body effort, including by dragging/hauling, sliding or rolling loads. This is important because, although pushing and pulling usually allows larger loads to be handled safely, this type of manual handling operation can still be harmful, if not carried out correctly. In this fable, we are *first* told of the removal of the super-sized swede from the ground, involving dragging/hauling, and *second* of the rolling of the super-sized swede towards the cottage at the top of the smallholding. The key point to note is that these are two separate operations, which is the reason why it's important to assess them discretely, and why a RAPP score sheet has been completed for each of them. The RAPP tool is designed to take assessors methodically through the factors needing to be evaluated when pushing and pulling. Such tasks can sometimes be ignored because they are viewed as solutions, but even in these circumstances, there remain issues of distances, uneven surfaces, obstructions, and slopes which still need to be considered[145].

A further organisational benefit that can be gained from carrying out multiple assessments, where required, is that it enables actions and resources to be prioritised on the basis of scores awarded. So, whilst here just two RAPP assessments have been completed with – as we shall see – little difference between the total scores awarded to the push

---

145. Other assessment tools could be considered alongside the RAPP tool given this, or another similar, real-world scenario. For instance, had a large number of smaller crops needed pulling out in quick succession, this would have pointed towards the ART tool as being the natural option. Here, however, the focus has been restricted to the pulling and pushing of the large vegetable at the heart of the tale, based upon the level of detail supplied, making the RAPP tool the logical choice.

and pull activities, this still gives a slight justification for prioritising the actions arising from the pulling activity assessment (*Appendix B*) above those identified for the pushing activity (*Appendix C*). This is because, in drawing a comparison between the score sheets, we see that the pulling activity gives a total score which is one point higher than that for the pushing activity. Here then, the difference between assessment scores is minimal but, where multiple assessments are carried out in real-world circumstances, the differences seen between the respective RAPP scores can steer organisations to prioritise their efforts towards the highest scoring activities, or at least influence the order in which they should address them. And of course, it's often the case that several risk factors are present in a single manual handling operation, which can interact in complex ways, affecting both an individual's capability to perform the task and the associated injury risk.

Let's now look at each of the eight factors included within the RAPP assessment tool in a little more detail, considering the RAPP ratings awarded on the score sheets for this scenario. When carrying out such assessments in a real-world context, it's important to take the outputs from the score sheets, in conjunction with any supporting comments noted which highlight issues requiring correction, making sure that any identified actions are addressed. The *B*– references within the headings here relate to the corresponding factors on the RAPP score sheets, whilst the two numeric scores and ratings – together with colour bands for the *push* and *pull* activities – denote the score and rating awarded to that factor for the given operation on the relevant score sheet.

B-1 – LOAD WEIGHT
Pull – Red 4 (High); Push – Green 0 (Low)

It is said that the super-sized swede '...*was the biggest of its kind...*' the old farmer had ever seen. Taking the fable to be true on this point, the weight of the super-sized swede has been assumed to be 54 kilograms, this being the weight of Ian Neale's record-breaking swede, as cited in the fable's *prologue*. It's quite apparent that the failure to consider the use of lifting and handling aids – probably some form of powered assistance – was an oversight here. It's also worth noting that the pulling of a load places a greater strain on the body than does pushing a load of the same weight, hence why the pull aspect for the load weight was rated *high* and red, whilst the push aspect was *low* and green-rated[146]. Reducing load weight is the vital first step, making a key difference to the level of manual effort required and hence, the strain borne by those tasked with applying it. But, as is so often the case in fables, the characters depicted here appear to have been predisposed to act on a whim, rather than taking the time to carry out a careful evaluation of the risk posed by the weight involved first!

B-2 – POSTURE
Pull – Red 6 (Poor); Push – Red 6 (Poor)

There are signs of the group having struggled to move with ease, as shown by their postures. For the pulling aspect of the activity, the old farmer's posture was rated as *poor*. We are told he had his hands above head height, tugging at the super-sized swede stalk and that '...even with his hands above his head, he could barely reach its leaves'. *Hardly ideal.* The fable also makes mention of other super-sized swede-shifters, for whom severe bending or twisting of the torso was clearly an issue. Posture was rated as *poor* for the activity of rolling the super-sized swede back to the smallholding cottage too, given that the old farmer's body was severely inclined in order to push the load and again, as for the pull activity, his hands were above shoulder height.

B-3 – HAND GRIP
Pull – Red 2 (Poor); Push – Red 2 (Poor)

The fable records that the slippery and scratchy nature of the super-sized swede made getting a grip of the vegetable problematic, for a number of reasons. The hand grip for both the pulling action to remove it from the ground and the pushing action as it was rolled across the smallholding was deemed to be *poor*. The features of the super-sized swede load being large, rounded, smooth, wet and greasy, with no natural handles or handholds upon which the super-sized swede-shifters could gain

---

146. The prologue to this tale draws a distinction between the dragging/hauling or sliding of a load, these being different types of 'pull' motion. Whilst gaining this level of understanding about any activity being undertaken is helpful, the scoring of load weight by the RAPP tool only differentiates between 'pushing' (rolling) and 'pulling' (dragging/hauling or sliding) types.

purchase, would have made it difficult for them to grasp the vegetable, with a consequence being that additional strength would have been needed to grip it, as it was dragged/hauled from the ground. This would, of itself, have been tiring for them, making it seem likely they would have needed to alter their grip at various points. We know that the old farmer, in particular, found it '…awkward to gain a grip on the monstrous vegetable, with it being by turns, scratchy and slippery…' and that contact with the vegetable was uncomfortable, with his hands muddied by his endeavours. These same difficulties are likely to have applied, albeit probably to a lesser extent, to any of the super-sized swede-shifters at one point or another, during the rolling aspect of the activity.

B-4 – WORK PATTERN
Pull – Green 0 (Good); Push – Green 0 (Good)

On the face of it, working pattern didn't appear to have been a particular concern here, given the circumstances described. All the indications are that the group seemed to move at a pace that was comfortable for them. Both the push and pull aspects were green-rated and *good* for this factor. Positive features to note are that the work pattern lacked repetition (as far as we know there was only one super-sized swede) and that the workers were allowed to dictate the pace for themselves, rather than them being under pressure to accomplish the activity within any given timeframe. The *ad hoc* nature of the activity, together with the super-sized swede-shifters' improvisation as the tasks and associated level of difficulty progressed, indicates no particular productivity pressures that would have needed addressing, albeit that the randomness of their approach certainly pointed towards poor planning here. Within a commercial agricultural context, however, work pattern *is* of greater concern, as is seen, for instance where workers are involved in large-scale, high-intensity, repetitive crop harvesting. The only way in which it could have been determined whether work pattern was, in fact, problematic in the given scenario would have been by directly observing the work activity concerned, over a sustained period of time.

B-5 – TRAVEL DISTANCE
Pull – Green 0 (Short); Push – Red 3 (Long)

For this factor, it's important to consider whether the route was thought through in advance, paying particular attention to the distance which needed to be covered. It seems unlikely that this took place here – there was no apparent pre-discussion and in most cases it took no more than a casual gesture or a few words to encourage the super-sized swede-shifters to join the endeavour. The travel distance for the super-sized swede's removal from the ground – *the pull* – was fairly short (and deemed *short* and green-rated by the tool too), whilst that which needed to be covered to roll the swede towards the smallholding cottage – *the push* – was around 30 metres, which would have made this aspect of the activity harder to sustain, being on a more prolonged basis (the travel distance was deemed to be *long* and red-rated, as it was over ten metres, this being the threshold set out in the tool). One reason for this factor's importance is that the force a person can apply is influenced by how far an object is to be pushed, with the amount sustainable by a person decreasing as the distance travelled increases. A positive point for the distance travelled in this instance – both for pulling and pushing – is that neither aspect was repetitive, but the aim with this sort of task should always be to minimise any such distance, irrespective of how frequently the activity takes place.

B-6 – FLOOR SURFACE
Pull – Red 4 (Poor); Push – Red 4 (Poor)

It will come as little surprise to learn that this factor was rated as *poor*, against both pulling and pushing aspects. The fable makes clear that surface condition was poor – a problem for both pushing and pulling – with crops, soil, mud and generally rough ground which was '...rutted in places, following recent heavy rain...' making it unstable under foot for all those involved. Uneven surfaces can dramatically increase the forces required to start and keep loads moving, which increases the injury risk. This makes it concerning to note that the super-sized swede-shifters seemingly lacked awareness of the need to check their footing. Recent rainfall would undoubtedly have played a part in increasing the slips risk too, by undermining the foothold achievable by the super-sized swede pullers and pushers, resulting in them failing to achieve a good grip. Finally, on this factor, assuming the gradient up the slope towards the smallholding cottage to have been over 5°, this alone would have justified the floor surface being rated as *poor* for the pushing aspect.

B-7 – OBSTACLES ON ROUTE
Pull – Red 3 (Poor); Push – Red 3 (Poor)

No indication is given of any of the super-sized swede-shifters having checked their route in advance for obvious obstacles – the reason why this factor has been rated as *poor* for both pulling and pushing. It's apparent from the fable that there were obstacles encountered in the course of the pulling and pushing activities. The work area was said to have been '...littered with random objects, debris and general detritus...', suggesting that site housekeeping was poor. And the fact of the super-sized swede-shifters having had to roll the load up a slope is listed as a relevant consideration under this factor too. A further complication in this instance would have been that the load itself posed an obstruction to the workers' vision – of particular importance for the aspect of the activity requiring the pushing of the load towards the smallholding cottage, where the group needed to have a clear view of their way ahead.

B-8 – OTHER FACTORS
Pull – Red 2 (2+ factors); Push – Red 2 (2+ factors)

There were other notable factors at play here, which should have given the super-sized swede-shifters – and certainly those managing them – cause for concern. The fable makes mention of a number of aspects which would have made the activity harder than it needed to be. Factors can be manifold, but in this instance would have included: the instability of the load; the large size of the load, which, in the case of the push aspect of the activity, obstructed the workers' view of the direction in which they were moving; the need to face away from the direction of travel for the pull aspect of the activity, which meant the super-sized swede-shifters were unable to see any hazards that lay ahead of them, and the weather conditions – strong gusts of wind having been noted in the description of the activity.

Had all the RAPP scores been green-rated, the only thing remaining to be done at this point would have been to consider any additional factors not listed in the RAPP. But this wasn't the case here, so thought also needs to be given as to how the risks to the group might have been reduced to a level which was ALARP, before considering any additional risk factors that might have been at play.

WAS THE RISK ALARP?
(and if not, how might this have been achieved?)

NO! *The risk was not ALARP.*

An employer's duty to avoid manual handling or reduce the risk of injury requires the balancing of the level of risk against the measures to control it, in terms of the money, time or trouble involved. Here, in order to be sure that the risk to the super-sized swede-shifters from push and pull activities had been reduced to an ALARP level, each of the risk factors would need to be revisited, as covered by the respective score sheets (*Appendices B* and *C*), with any additional control measures put in place to address them, and particular attention being paid to any red-rated ones. This was a fictional scenario, but ensuring that risk has been reduced to a level which is ALARP is a crucial stage for those seeking to control risk in real-world circumstances. Indeed, effective real-world risk reduction is achieved as the result of organisations focusing on key risk factors, by applying their time, money and effort to the aspects of the risk assessment which will see them achieving most impact in terms of overall risk levels. This underlines why the initial risk assessment is so important and explains why its consideration occupies a large proportion of this fable's review.

Next, each factor is briefly revisited – whether red-rated or better – with some potential areas for improvement highlighted. It's important to remember that the assessment score can differ as between pulling and pushing activities, even though the factor is identical in both cases, an example being that the same load weight carries with it different implications, depending upon whether the operation involved is of a push or pull type.

So, keeping all of this in mind, let's think about how it might have been possible to improve upon each of the factors, for those involved in the super-sized swede-shifting activity...

B-1 – LOAD WEIGHT

In considering load weight, both the weight of the load itself and that of any equipment need to be taken into account. Here, there was no equipment involved but, where this is provided, it needs to suit both the task and purpose. Taking the super-sized swede weight to have been 54 kilograms, it's worth noting that for the pulling activity, the risk rating for this factor was red (*high*), whilst for the pushing activity, the risk rating came out as green (*low*). This neatly makes the point that rolling requires less effort than the dragging, hauling or sliding of a load of equivalent weight.

In order to be satisfied that the level of risk achieved for an activity is ALARP, it always pays to keep in mind the longer term options, as well as those that can be pursued in the short and medium term. Here, a reduction in the load weight risk factor score might have been achieved by growing crops of a smaller size or by harvesting this variety sooner. An important part of the process in this case would have been to understand whether the farmer in the fable *knew* his vegetable to be of super-sized proportions. Thinking even earlier in the process, it would be helpful to know whether some or all of the risk could have been designed out at the point of seed purchase, with the end of the fable recording that this was advice passed on by the old farmer to the old woman. It also might have been pertinent to have approached the supplier if the giant vegetable supplied was not *as per sample*. This need to obtain sufficient information from manufacturers and suppliers is particularly important for organisations seeking to buy large quantities of products, and here it would have been entirely reasonable to ask whether the product met the sample specification, especially given that the remainder of the crop seemed to be of normal size. But this is, of course, mere conjecture and we can only go on the limited detail presented here.

We learn from the fable that, when confronted by a super-sized swede, the group elected to pull the giant vegetable out by using manual strength, before rolling it towards the smallholding cottage using team effort. Whilst accepting that the first aspect in addressing assessment outcomes should always be to look at reducing load weights, here it would have been difficult to see how the super-sized swede weight could have been reduced, unless it had perhaps been chopped up *in situ* and transported by the making of multiple wheelbarrow trips – albeit that no such equipment was mentioned here – rather than in one demanding journey. Adopting this kind of approach is, however, not always the preferred option, as it increases the handling frequency, which can in turn add to levels of worker 'fatigue' – not to mention diminishing the chances of any vegetable growers involved securing a giant vegetable competition win, as was said to have been an aspiration held by the old farmer depicted here!

B-2 – POSTURE

For the posture factor, there are a few different features to bear in mind. Here, this was rated as red (*poor*) for both pushing and pulling, but for different reasons. With respect to the pulling out of the super-sized swede from the ground, posture was adjudged to be *poor* due to the old farmer's hands being above his shoulders and other super-sized swede-shifters experiencing severe bending or torso twisting. For the rolling of the super-sized swede towards the smallholding cottage, however, it was *poor* due to the old farmer's body being severely inclined from the effort required by him to push the load. This is likely to have been a relevant concern for the rest of the group too, albeit in varying degrees.

Where a task is such that a worker has to move suddenly or twist so as to manoeuvre a load, this can create unnecessary stresses and strains on the body. There's little doubt that this could have been the case for the rolling aspect of the task seen here, with the rutted ground perhaps causing the super-sized swede to veer unpredictably off course. Where a task requires a large amount of effort to start or stop a load from moving, or to keep it moving, this adds to the strain placed upon the human body. Other risk factors to look out for include where a worker has to push or pull a load with one hand, or where a lack of space forces them into adopting an awkward posture.

The positioning of the hands on a load needs to be comfortable for a worker and they are best positioned between hip and shoulder height for the task, rather than above shoulder height, as was said to have been the case here. This avoids additional stress being placed upon the arms and back and improves the control of the load, which becomes more difficult when reaching upwards, above shoulder level. If it wasn't possible for the old farmer to adopt an appropriate posture in this case, efforts should have been put into re-designing the task, so as to avoid his exposure to unnecessary risk. Where loads need to be held or supported above shoulder height, it becomes necessary to consider providing some kind of lifting and handling aid.

B-3 – HAND GRIP

There are a few different features to bear in mind, when considering hand grip. Here, this was red-rated (*poor*) for both pushing and pulling. In terms of reducing risk, it's certainly true that good handholds would have helped the old farmer to gain purchase on the vegetable, thereby assisting him in applying force and allowing him to better control the load; achieving a firm hand-grip would have helped with both the pulling activity and the pushing of the super-sized swede back towards the property. To a lesser degree, this would have applied to all of the other super-sized swede-shifters too, as they rolled the vegetable back across the smallholding, towards the cottage.

It's quite clear that no thought was given to the effectiveness of the old farmer's grip on the super-sized swede and it's certainly true to say that suitable 'personal protective equipment' (PPE) – gloves – should have been considered here, together with any other devices that might have made it easier to achieve a good hand grip. This would have been particularly important to the old farmer for the pull aspect of the activity, given that it was he who had direct hand contact with the vegetable during the course of its removal from the ground. Additionally, it would have been a relevant consideration for all of the super-sized swede-shifters in varying degrees, as they embarked on the task of rolling it back towards the smallholding cottage. It's important to note that a careful selection of PPE should have been made here, as in some cases gloves can also make it more difficult to manoeuvre a load; this neatly underlines a key general principle, which is that the use of PPE should always serve to reduce any residual risk associated with an activity.

B-4 – WORK PATTERN

The best approach to work pattern tends to be one which allows workers to self-pace tasks and which trains them to adjust their work rate, so as to optimise safety and productivity. The description of the activity given here, as a one-off episode, suggests that it was not repetitive; there were fewer than five transfers per minute, and the workers were also able to set the pace for themselves. This was, therefore, a green-rated (*good*) factor for both the pull and push aspects and not directly concerning on the basis of the scene the fable sets out, but it might have become an issue, had there been a requirement for the group to undertake the removal of swedes of super-sized proportions – or indeed other vegetables – on a repeat or more sustained basis. Had the operation involved differed slightly from that depicted in the fable, the use of the MAC or V-MAC tools might have proved insightful for assessing and putting in place control measures for this factor. Where, for instance, regular frequent lifting is required, the MAC tool can be used, and where the pattern is variable or irregular, the V-MAC tool can be of assistance[147].

A further aspect related to setting the right pace concerns whether the design of a task allows the workers involved to have sufficient rest or recovery periods. Proactively taking steps to reduce fatigue, as can be brought on by physically demanding work, invariably lessens the occurrences of ill health and maintains output; for instance, where mild fatigue is experienced, relieving this through short breaks can be an effective control measure. It's unclear what the arrangements were for taking breaks or recovery here, but opportunities for rest are essential. It can sometimes be the case that simply switching between tasks – for instance, here between pulling and pushing – can reduce fatigue, by working different sets of muscles. The pattern of work, as described, should not have given rise to any particular issues, with the *ad hoc* nature of the activity and the improvisation required from the super-sized swede-shifters as the difficulty of the task grew suggesting they weren't subject to pressures of a repetitive kind. But whilst the fable doesn't instantly generate concerns about working pattern, this is an area which needs constantly reviewing in any given case, so as to ensure that the work involved doesn't have a detrimental effect upon workers. This is because what might begin as an easy, low effort activity can sometimes develop into a more complex and strenuous scenario. Had more frequent or prolonged physical effort been demanded of the super-sized swede-shifters, this would have triggered a need for the risk assessment to be revisited, revised and updated. Whilst this doesn't appear to have been a significant concern here, in cases where workers are unable to change their work rate, this might result in their being exposed to increased, and possibly unacceptable, levels of risk. As has already been called out, this could have been relevant had the activity in question differed slightly from that described, for instance, involving the pulling up of lots of smaller crops within a short time period.

B-5 – TRAVEL DISTANCE

Risk increases where tasks involve travelling longer distances or moving at high speed. The distance of the *pull* aspect of the task was green-rated (*short*), with the route travelled for removing the super-

---

147. For brief definitions of the MAC and V-MAC tool types, refer to this book's *Glossary*.

sized swede from the ground being estimated at less than two metres. The *push* aspect, on the other hand, was red-rated (*long*), given the distance of 30 metres that the super-sized swede-shifters were required to travel, to roll the super-sized swede back to the cottage at the top of the smallholding.

Efforts should always be made to reduce any travel distances involved as much as possible, so as to lessen the impact on individuals and lower the likelihood of an incident occurring or an injury being sustained by any of them. According to the criteria applied by the tool, here the risk rating was higher for pushing, primarily due to the distance the super-sized swede-shifters were required to travel. For the rolling of the super-sized swede towards the smallholding cottage, an alternative approach might have been to designate a specific storage area part way along the route, thus rendering it unnecessary to manoeuvre the whole vegetable back and so minimising the distance travelled. It does, however, need to be understood that any decision to chop up the super-sized swede and place it within a storage area for onward transportation would have brought with it the need to increase the handling frequency and, had this been the method adopted, the concerns noted against the B-1 – LOAD WEIGHT factor, would also have been relevant here.

B-6 – FLOOR SURFACE

It is known that the manual handling risk is higher where the environment in which an activity takes place has steep slopes and rough surfaces, as these can increase the amount of force required to push or pull a load. For both the pulling and pushing activities, this factor was red-rated (*poor*). The fable records that the ground was rutted and slippery in places, creating instability under foot and increasing the force required to move the super-sized swede. The reverse is also true – environments where floor or ground surfaces are clean and dry can help to reduce the force needed to move a load.

In order to counteract the slips and trips risk here, the route for both the pulling and pushing operations should have been checked in advance, with any obvious ground condition hazards being resolved. This is because the risk of injury can be raised by uneven surfaces which increase the forces required to start and keep loads moving. For permanent outdoor sites of this kind, surfaces should be checked to ensure they are firm, stable, well-maintained and properly drained. In agricultural environments – including those of the type described here, where manual handling takes place on unmade ground or temporary surfaces – preparing the ground and keeping it even and firm with suitable coverings, where appropriate, can be a real help in keeping the injury risk in check. Pushing and pulling activities are safest when performed on floor or ground surfaces which are level, clean, dry and unbroken. Slip-resistant surfaces, including matting, and the wearing of suitable slip-resistant footwear might further reduce the risk of manual handling-related slips. In circumstances such as those described here, appropriate PPE – specifically footwear – should be worn, which is suitable for the conditions and reduces any residual risk, for instance, if the ground slopes, or if it is wet or contaminated. Equivalent considerations would apply to indoor locations too. And where there are slopes, as was said to have been the case here, they should not be so steep as to make retaining control of the load difficult. It appeared that the pulling activity was not conducted on a slope, but in travelling along the route towards the smallholding cottage – for the pushing activity – the party appears to have been required to negotiate an incline, which would have increased the push force involved. In any case, the increase in force needed will depend upon the degree of incline.

This was a factor of the activity which would have pointed to the use of powered assistance – for instance, a forklift truck – being of potential benefit and, as such, was an option which should have been considered by the super-sized swede-shifters or, more specifically, their employers. But, whilst it's true to say that the effective use of such trucks can reduce the burden of manual effort required from workers, if used improperly, they too can introduce additional risks, which in turn need to be carefully controlled so as to prevent the replacement of a musculoskeletal risk with, say, a forklift truck overturn risk. Forklift trucks used on uneven ground – the ground having been described as such here – need to be suitable for such a use. And if they are to be used, one particular point to stress is that no attempt should be made to turn them on a slope, as this raises the overturn risk[148]. Without knowing more about whether the use of a forklift truck might have

---

148. Where it is proposed that adjustments are to be made to the way in which an activity is performed by employees – for instance, the introduction of new equipment or changes to the pace at which it is carried out – with the potential to substantially impact their health and safety, their employer would be expected to consult with them or their representatives in advance.

been an option here, it's not possible to analyse this point any further, but in circumstances where one is to be used, three aspects of the activity need to be looked at – namely the driver, the vehicle (including due consideration of rollover protection), and the location.

B-7 – OBSTACLES ON ROUTE

It is clear that there were obstacles present on the route travelled here, which would have created a range of different risks, hence why this factor was red-rated (*poor*) for both the pulling and pushing activities. In terms of the task, the rutted ground and other crops created risks as the workers tried to avoid colliding with them. The same would have been true of the angle of the slope for the rolling of the super-sized swede towards the smallholding cottage. In terms of the load, it needed to be sufficiently stable for negotiating any slopes, corners or rough surfaces, and the route should have been planned so as to ensure the workers involved could see safely over the super-sized swede.

The fable tells us that the workers were unable to see over the super-sized swede and, as it would seem that obstacles on the route could not be avoided – such as other smaller vegetables protruding above the ground surface, and the angle of the slope – account should have been taken of the increased risk of them slipping, tripping, falling, or colliding with obstructions. It follows that efforts should have been made to check and clear crops, soil, and rubble from the route – in advance of both the pull and push activities taking place – so as to reduce the risk to the workers. It's possible that the super-sized swede-shifters might have counteracted this issue by splitting up, with one person facing the direction of travel and warning of any difficulties ahead, including obstructions, by guiding and telling the rest of the group how to avoid them. Where a load blocks a person's view, this kind of team handling can be invaluable, with the person at the other end having a clear line of sight. The guidance specifically points out '...*if any dimension of the load exceeds about 75 centimetres, handling it is likely to pose an increased risk of injury, especially if this size is exceeded in more than one dimension. The risk is further increased if the load does not provide convenient handholds.*'[149] This is likely to have applied here, meaning that appropriate handling aids should have been considered.

---

149. Guidance document L23 covers how to assess and reduce manual handling risks when dealing with loads of large dimensions (see Part 3, page 38, paragraph 155).

B-8 - OTHER FACTORS

Given that at least two extra factors were present for both pushing and pulling activities, this was red-rated (*poor*) here. Of the other factors present in this scenario, a key additional concern was that of the obscuration of the old farmer's view when pulling up the super-sized swede, and the impaired view of all the super-sized swede-shifters, in the course of rolling it towards the cottage at the top of the smallholding. The unstable and unwieldy nature of the load would have created difficulties for the workers, as would the clothing worn by some of them. Additionally, the individual characteristics of the pullers and pushers (including some classed as vulnerable workers) were clearly relevant, as are considered at *stage two* here, together with other psychosocial factors at *stage three*. Also in need of addressing would have been environmental factors such as temperature, lighting and air currents, any or all of which could have increased the push and pull risks, together with the physical forces demanded of those involved.

Efforts needed to be made to deal with each of these other factors, but the nature of the difficulties they presented, together with the observations made in relation to the seven specific factors, all suggest that full risk assessment would have been the most appropriate choice for assessing the events described in the fable. Given an equivalent real-world scenario to that seen here, therefore, it would be expected that full risk assessment would be the best means by which to specifically consider and address each of these factors.

Having looked at the possible actions required to address those RAPP scores giving cause for concern from the details of the fable, it's at this point that the focus moves to the next level of the process.

LEVEL #3
GAUGE THE NEED FOR A FULL RISK ASSESSMENT
Was this required here?

YES! *It would have been.*

There were risk factors involved – not covered by the RAPP – which would have pointed to the need for full risk assessment in this case. Of the additional risk factors involved, one of particular note and relevant here – as would equally be true for many real-world circumstances – is the excessive pushing or pulling of loads[150]. The individual characteristics of those attempting the activity, together with psychosocial factors, are other aspects indicating that full risk assessment would have been appropriate, over and above the use of the RAPP tool alone. Given that the fable reports that the old farmer could not see over the top of the super-sized swede[151], the feature of the activity requiring unusual height was clearly a relevant risk factor here. But, in addition to the activity calling for unusual height, it also created potential hazards for those with health problems – a factor which must be taken into account when considering the capabilities of individuals[152]. The full risk assessment has not been completed here, given that additional detail – over and above that which the fable supplies – would be required in order to progress the assessment of the activity to this stage. In an equivalent real-world scenario however, this extra information would best be gained through observing and discussing the site activities with those involved over an extended period of time, particularly noting the distances pushed and/or pulled, as well as the weights of objects being moved.

Remember that, just as was required for *level two* of this stage, at the end of *level three* there's also a need to check to see that the risk has been reduced to ALARP levels, following completion of the full risk assessment. Whilst it's not possible to reach a conclusion on this here, it's likely that a full risk assessment would have identified further control measures which needed to be implemented, in order to reduce the risk to those involved to an acceptable level.

This ends the substantive review of the events of this fable – consideration having been given to the nature of the manual handling activity involved and associated risk filters, the relevant risk tool – in this case, the RAPP – and full risk assessment requirements. But it's worth briefly focusing upon the relevant psychosocial factors and vulnerable workers too, as

---

150. The risk factors are listed within Schedule 1 of *The Manual Handling Regulations*.

151. This was an aspect previously considered under both *B-2* – Posture and *B-8* – Other factors, for the second level of the first stage of the RAPP assessment.

152. The general requirement for risk assessment is contained within regulation 3 of *the Management Regulations*. These regulations also require specific consideration to be given to particular groups of workers (as highlighted by the *prologue* to the fable), some examples of which are provided under the review of the third stage – Tackle Risks to Individual Workers – within the fable's attached *modern meaning*.

would also need to be done for the assessment of any real-world scenario, points which are covered by stages two and three, that follow here.

STAGE #2
ACCOUNT FOR PSYCHOSOCIAL FACTORS

Psychosocial factors are important, but there is unfortunately insufficient information given within the fable so as to be able to fully determine the relevance or respective contribution of particular factors here.

Given that the tale is about an isolated operation, rather than a typical day, shift or week, we'd need to know more about both the people and the factors involved, before being able to evaluate the psychosocial impact upon the individuals concerned. Psychosocial factors are factors which have the potential to negatively impact upon workers which are, in turn, likely to affect the quality and/or quantity of their outputs. In order to gauge the effects of these here, the types of questions to put to the participants involved at the point of completing the assessment might have included: *'Do you feel you have sufficient control over your work or working methods, including shift patterns?', 'Do you feel involved in making decisions which affect you?', 'Do you feel able to make full use of your skills?',* and, *'Do you feel that the tasks you are expected to carry out are of sufficient interest and variety, not being too repetitive or monotonous in nature?'* If the response to any of these questions was *'no'*, then measures would have needed to be put in place, so as to satisfactorily alter the balance of the workload for those involved.

Other issues which can sometimes have a detrimental impact upon workers include the direct or indirect checking of their outputs, as can occur where work is machine or system-paced and monitored inappropriately, or where payment systems are – whether intentionally or unintentionally – geared towards workers working too quickly or without breaks. It might simply be that work demands are perceived by workers as excessive, or that high levels of effort don't appear to be balanced by sufficient reward – whether in terms of resources, remuneration, self-esteem or status. A further negative impact, as can be relevant in a psychosocial context, is seen where work systems limit opportunities for social interaction. And there's always a need to be mindful of negative underlying cultural issues too, including whether those involved are being subjected to any form of harassment. From what little information the fable offers on these aspects, it's impossible to pinpoint which negative psychosocial factors might have been at play for the group here. Certainly, superficially at least, there didn't appear to be any obvious concerns of this ilk, but if the super-sized swede-shifters were under excessive pressure, unable to set their own pace, or if they simply felt that they were inadequately rewarded, this would have tended to suggest that a review of the working methods and approach applied would have been advantageous for them. A comment about psychosocial factors, based on the scenario presented here, has been recorded on the score sheets completed at *Appendices B* and *C* of this book.

STAGE #3
TACKLE RISKS TO INDIVIDUAL WORKERS

Here, the risks to individual workers are briefly considered, including how the different types of vulnerable worker represented in the fable could have been impacted by their participation in the swede-shifting activity.

Clearly, even on its own, the involvement of any vulnerable workers offers sufficient justification for the carrying out of a full risk assessment. This said, it's been considered beneficial to have run through all three stages here, so as to give an overview of the approach, in totality – from filter stage, through to the RAPP tool, and ultimately to full risk assessment. In so doing, the review of this fable has provided an insight as to the full extent of the risk assessment process that would apply to any type of manual handling operation.

It's true to say that vulnerable workers – as is the case for other employees – have a 'general duty' to take care of their own health and safety and that of others who may be affected by their actions[153]. But, from an employer's perspective, it's vitally important for particular consideration to be given to those classified as vulnerable, and it's here that brief attention is paid to the challenges faced by these different types of workers. A comment recognising the needs of individual workers, as based upon the scenario presented, has been added to the score sheets completed at *Appendices B* and *C* of this book.

Just like equivalent real-world workers, the super-sized swede-shifters would undoubtedly have brought personal qualities and strengths

---

153. Section 7(a) of *HSWA 1974* requires all employees to take care of their own health and safety, as well as that of others, whilst at work.

to their work activities, but it's equally clear that some of them had specific needs too. This being the case, brief attention is paid to each of the workers here, so as to showcase any particular challenges they might have faced, together with the accompanying requirements that would need to be satisfied to address these, in a real-world context. All cases are different but, where applicable, direction has been given in footnotes, signposting useful supplementary information and guidance relevant to these types of workers.

THE OLD FARMER

There's little doubt that the activities and tasks described here could have been better designed for all concerned. But in looking at the old farmer in particular, whilst it's true that physical capability varies with age and that there is a tendency for this to decline with the ageing process, variability between individuals is such that it should not be taken as a given that certain jobs are physically too demanding for older workers. In relation to the old farmer, there were no specific issues identified for him as an individual, but it would no doubt have been beneficial to engage with him to gather his insights, given that it's likely he had a good level of judgment, prior experience and knowledge of vegetable growing and harvesting.

THE OLD WOMAN

Just as was true for the old farmer, the old woman's age would not, of itself, have presented an issue here. But in the old woman's case, her capability should have been specifically considered, given that she was noted to have been suffering from lumbago, a pre-existing back condition. It's important for employers to be made aware of such conditions, so as to enable them to make a decision as to whether this impairs the ability of affected workers to carry out an activity safely. Given that there would have been good reason to suspect her state of health might significantly increase her risk of injury from manual handling operations, it's suggested that medical advice should have been sought in advance of the old woman's involvement in the activity, with any recommendations made by her medical practitioners followed up and action taken accordingly.

THE MIGRANT WORKER[154]

It's possible that the migrant worker would have lacked experience in the job and that language barriers may have prevented him from being able to complete tasks quickly, safely and effectively. But health and safety should never be used as the basis for discriminating against a certain person or group, as everyone has different qualities to bring to activities and it might be that certain tasks simply need adjustment, by adapting the work to suit the worker.

Before migrant workers start work, it's important for employers to be clear on the nature of their engagement. To this end, it's worth asking the question: '*Are they employed directly or through a labour provider?*' There needs to be clarity about who has day-to-day control over their work and, just as is true for other workers, thought needs to be given as to whether any special qualifications are required, with checks also made on qualifications gained elsewhere. It's essential for sufficient research to take place into the equivalence of basic 'competencies' and the compatibility of vocational qualifications, as might have been acquired through their previous periods of employment. And it's also important to account for the effects of attitudes and assumptions of workers new to work in Great Britain, with risks being judged accordingly and appropriately controlled.

It's invaluable for organisations to adopt a proactive approach as soon as any new workers, including migrant workers, join them. Well planned 'inductions', which can include photographs of hazards and good quality information being provided in plain simple language, together with verification of the suitability of supervision arrangements, can pay dividends when seeking to safeguard the welfare of migrant workers in particular, in the long term. Time might be well spent by translating materials, instituting buddy or mentor systems, providing visual tools or signs, giving clear explanations for signs (including hand signals) and training supervisors in how to communicate clearly. This type of approach can be particularly valuable for those migrant workers for whom English is not their

---

154. For information on how to identify problems and control risks to migrant workers, additional to that supplied here, see Health and Safety Executive. (2010). *Protecting Migrant Workers*. Guidance leaflet; see also Health and Safety Executive (2008). *Working in the UK from Overseas? Your health and safety at work in agriculture and food processing*. (INDG410).

first language, who might need written instructions to be translated, or who could require consideration to be given to providing pictorial instructions to clearly show them what's expected. Without being sympathetic to the linguistic and communication challenges faced by some migrant workers, key messages from health and safety training and instructions might not be received, safety critical communications could be misunderstood and routine exchanges with supervisors hampered, ultimately compromising their safety and wellbeing and that of their fellow workers, with whom they could be required to have crucial interactions. This is particularly important for those tasks which are safety critical in nature.

Every effort should be made to draw migrant workers into an organisation's 'safety culture'. The approach taken to achieve this needs to encompass many elements, but key features would typically include: stressing the importance of reporting 'accidents' and 'near misses'; investigating accidents with a specific emphasis placed upon ensuring that 'underlying causes' are picked up; clearly explaining the responsibilities for risk assessment and control measures, together with workers' responsibilities for their own health and safety; providing guidance to supervisors on cultural differences that could affect working relationships, and encouraging workers who are less confident at communicating in English to refer their concerns to a colleague who can help to represent them. Carrying out workplace tours with new workers to highlight areas of potential risk can also be invaluable, as a means of making sure that new starters are fully engaged and buy into their organisation's culture and ethos from the outset.

THE YOUNG WORKERS[155]

Potentially greater risk exists for young workers, who can be considered vulnerable due to their lack of experience, knowledge and maturity. Specifically relevant to manual handling activities is the fact that young workers may be put at higher risk of injury due to their muscular strength not being fully developed and their being

---

155. For further information on how the health and safety of young people can be ensured in the workplace, refer to Health and Safety Executive. (2013). *Young People and Work Experience – A brief guide to health and safety for employers* (INDG364).

less skilled in handling techniques and pacing work to match their ability. Whilst there's no absolute requirement to conduct a separate risk assessment specifically for a young person, particular factors *do* need to be considered for young persons under health and safety law[156]. Risk levels are often higher for those new to jobs, because of their lack of experience, or unfamiliarity with the workplace. As has already been highlighted, agricultural environments and activities are considered higher risk, and the work to be undertaken – including the associated risks and how these can best be managed – needs to be thought through before the activities begin. Satisfactory instruction, training and supervisory arrangements should have been planned and tested in advance here, so as to give the employer confidence that these would work in practice, for the young workers. This would have included consideration of cultural factors, if these might have adversely impacted upon the risk levels to which the young workers were subject – for instance, if it had been identified that a macho culture was pervasive. In appropriate circumstances, an explanation should also be provided to the parents or carers of young persons about any significant risks involved, together with the accompanying control measures that have been put in place, to protect their health and safety.

EXTRA CONSIDERATIONS FOR FEMALE WORKERS

Many of the considerations relevant to the young lad apprentice would apply equally to the female worker featured in this fable, being a fellow young worker. A point of differentiation for a female worker, however, is that, in the case of new and expectant mothers, thought needs to be given as to whether a given task creates a hazard to those who might reasonably be considered to be pregnant[157]. Given the suggestion that a pregnant worker was involved in the activities described here, it would have been important to recognise this, as well as the potential

---

156. Regulation 19 of *the Management Regulations* requires employers to protect young persons from risks to their health and safety whilst at work, taking due account of their lack of experience and risk awareness.

157. For additional guidance on the action an employer should take to protect the health and safety of a new and expectant mother who works, and that of her baby, refer to Health and Safety Executive guidance leaflet. (2013) *New and Expectant Mothers who Work: A brief guide to your health and safety* (INDG373).

implications for her health and that of her foetus. Being pregnant or a new mother does not preclude these individuals from working, but it does require their employers to consider the risks from processes, working conditions and physical, biological and chemical agents, some of which place new and expectant mothers (and their unborn children) at potentially greater risk than other workers. Relevant risk examples in environments of the kind portrayed here would typically include lifting or carrying heavy loads, exposure to lead or toxic chemicals, and long working hours. Some evidence suggests that physically demanding work might cause premature birth, especially where job roles require long periods of standing and/or walking. In particular, during the last three months of pregnancy there is an increased risk of musculoskeletal symptoms, where heavy or repeated lifting is undertaken. This is due to hormonal changes affecting the ligaments which support the joints. Good postures may also become more difficult to achieve and maintain, particularly as the pregnancy progresses, further reducing manual handling capability. Shifting the centre of gravity can increase the risk of back pain for pregnant women, too. Finally, it's important to note that the risk assessment for a new and expectant mother who works should be regularly reviewed, as her pregnancy progresses[158].

CLOSING THOUGHTS

The review of this fable has usefully helped to highlight an approach that can be taken for assessing and managing the risks involved in pushing and pulling operations – just one type of manual handling – and the types of tool that can be used to support decision-making and the implementation of specific control measures for these activities. As the relative *new kid on the block* within the Toolkit for MSDs, the RAPP tool has usefully plugged a gap in the manual handling guidance, providing an increased level of detail on the particular factors that need to be considered by organisations in relation to their push and pull-type activities. Furthermore, the inclusion of the RAPP tool within the all-in-one digital Toolkit for

---

158. Employers need to include consideration of the risks to new and expectant mothers within their general risk assessment, carried out under regulation 3 of *the Management Regulations*. This requirement is specifically set out in regulation 16 ('Risk Assessment in respect of New or Expectant Mothers'), on receipt of notification of the fact of pregnancy under regulation 18 ('Notification by New or Expectant Mothers').

MSDs, released in 2021, suggest it has achieved parity with its elder sibling manual handling tools, sitting alongside MAC and ART, within this Health and Safety Executive-developed resource. It's worth noting that the rating criteria and other contents of the RAPP tool incorporated within this digital version are identical to those of the conventional paper-based version, which remains a valid assessment format. The digital version does, however, bring additional benefits, most notably by setting out a simplified step-by-step approach for completing assessments, and through providing an additional output on the overall level of risk.

It's recognised that a very specific super-sized swede-shifting scenario has been under the spotlight here! But the process of progressing through the assessment levels – from filters, to the use of the Toolkit for MSDs (which includes the RAPP tool), and ultimately, to full risk assessment – is the key point to take away, this being an approach which is readily transferrable to other types of manual handling activity. No matter how good organisations believe their efforts at risk reduction to be, it's likely that they will be left with some residual musculoskeletal disorder risk. There's no question that getting the risk assessment stage right is vital, being widely seen as the cornerstone of risk management – and the tools outlined here are invaluable in this regard – but this must be accompanied by the right elements being in place which both address the assessment findings and work to reduce risk. It's also essential for organisations to grow workforce understanding about the risks which cannot be reduced or eliminated, supported by training where required, and for it to be made clear to workers the part they can personally play in adopting good practice and behaviours which help to bring risk exposure down to an acceptable level.

The fable has also highlighted the need to consider the range of individuals who may be called upon to carry out manual handling activities, together with their varied needs – whether transient or permanent in nature – and has touched upon psychosocial factors too. Finally, it's important to stress that taking an 'ergonomic' approach in which manual handling is looked at as a whole, including the task, load and environmental aspects – when married with considerations of worker participation and input – can often prove to be invaluable.

For a summary of practical points to take away,
based upon the topics and subtopics handled by this fable,
see *How to...* Guide Four.

A NOTE ON REPORTING REQUIREMENTS

The events portrayed in this fable were of a purely fictitious nature. See the *Epilogue* for indicative reporting requirements under *the Reporting of Injuries, Diseases and Dangerous Occurrences Regulations 2013*[159] *(RIDDOR)*, as could be triggered by equivalent real-world circumstances.

---

159. S.I. 2013/1471.

Pixie-Locks
and
the Ergonomic Endeavours of Three Bears

PIXIE-LOCKS' FABLE

' '*Who* has been sitting in my Small Bear chair *and broken it?*' he asked in a very small voice. 'I *loved* that chair. It was set up in line with the guidance to *the DSE Regulations*. To others it might have looked like any generic office chair…but, *to me*…before, my Small Bear paws couldn't touch the floor and I was getting aches and pains everywhere. Now look at me! *Just look at me!* I've got a spring back in my step. *That chair's been the making of me!*' '

PROLOGUE

At its most basic level, *Pixie-Locks' fable* allows us to observe the behaviours of three bears, focusing on their ergonomic endeavours in choosing cutlery, chairs and beds to suit their needs. It also gives an insight into the antics of Pixie, a slightly irksome little lady, who appears hell-bent on undermining the bears' labours and seemingly thinks nothing of eating their porridge too. But set amidst what might appear to be one of the more simplistic – even superficial – fables in this collection are some important learning points about the two-way interaction between 'products', 'systems' and 'processes' on the one hand, and 'users', being those who need or want to use them, on the other. In essence, this fable's purpose is to highlight the benefits that can be derived from taking the time to understand and apply basic ergonomic principles, not only in the workplace, but in the wider world too. In order to show this broader focus, *Pixie-Locks' fable* sees a deliberate shift in language, away from that of 'worker' which was common to the first four tales, towards the concept of a 'user' – a subtle difference, but one which goes to the heart of the ergonomist's endeavour and which is also reflected within the legislation in this area. Keeping this user concept in mind helps to set the context for this fable – *the users' fable* – prompting, as it does, an exploration of how individuals can both *affect*, and *be affected by*, the products, systems and processes they use, and the environments within which they operate.

WHAT IS ERGONOMICS?

'Ergonomics' is defined as *'the scientific discipline concerned with the understanding of interactions among humans and other elements of a system, and the profession that applies theory, principles, data and methods to design in order to optimise human wellbeing and overall system performance'* (International Ergonomics Association)[160]. It's typically credited with solving physical problems, such as the positioning of emergency stop buttons, but also importantly deals with the psychosocial and social aspects of a person and their work, which can be summed up as the fit between the user, their equipment and the environment.

In order to help organisations meet their ergonomic goals, ergonomic specialists – so-called 'ergonomists' – seek to understand how products, systems, processes and workplaces can be designed to suit those who use them. The ergonomics field draws together specialists from multiple disciplines – anatomy, physiology, psychology, statistics and engineering, to name but a few – with a shared goal of ensuring that designs complement the abilities of those who use products, systems and processes, and operate within workplaces and other environments, whilst minimising the effects of any limitations they might have. It accounts for users' capabilities by seeking to ensure that tasks, functions, information and environments suit them, which carries benefits for their health and 'wellbeing'. It also aids the 'reliability' with which 'safety critical tasks' are carried out by users, by seeking to minimise the risk of 'human error' and support the delivery of 'reliable human performance'. Arguably, it's this which makes the discipline of particular interest to those in charge of 'high-hazard organisations'.

THE ERGONOMIST'S ENDEAVOUR:
A Mission of Two Parts

The ergonomist's endeavour is a two-part mission, namely *first*, to achieve 'user comfort' within environments, which should reduce the numbers of cases of long-term ill health, and *second*, to support the achievement of reliable human performance, thereby preventing operational incidents. Each of these aspects makes a very different – but vital – contribution to health, safety and wellbeing.

The *first aspect* can be regarded as *protecting the user from the system*, which fails in circumstances where users aren't protected from the products, systems, processes they use or the environments within

---

160. Definition as provided at https://iea.cc/what-is-ergonomics/ [viewed 01 May 2021].

which they operate, for example, where they are provided with screens with inadequate resolution, or ill-fitting chairs. When this aspect is properly addressed, however, the potential for ill-health at work is reduced, with fewer instances of aches and pains being reported, and the avoidance of longer term damage to users' wrists, shoulders and backs too. But even though the ill-health aspects associated with poor ergonomics are undeniably important, such instances tend to cluster as high frequency, low severity events, when looked at from an organisational 'risk' perspective. Simply put, this means that, whilst from the health angle poor ergonomics can affect many users, this is primarily seen in a small way, as is evidenced by them presenting with what are ostensibly minor ailments. For anyone affected, the severity of symptoms might be viewed as *high* – ranging from annoying to very painful and debilitating – but from an organisational perspective, the overall risk is, in most cases, perceived to be *low*. Within a workplace context, the addressing of ill-health – and defence of this aspect – tends to be overseen by occupational health specialists, often as part of an occupational health and wellbeing strategy.

Contrasting this first aspect with the *second aspect* – the instances in which *protection of the system from the user* fails – shows a very different picture, with events which are low in frequency, but potentially catastrophic, whenever they happen. Despite the tendency for these to be low likelihood events, such outcomes provide the primary drivers for high-hazard organisations to ensure that they have the required measures in place. The focus of this aspect is upon applying ergonomics and 'human factors' insights to reduce the likelihood of operational incidents occurring, which typically falls within the domain of a process safety specialist, as part of a process safety strategy. Where such issues are inadequately addressed, the results are observable in (and felt through!) poorly designed workplaces, control rooms and control panels, which can *make* users make bad decisions or take the wrong actions. In the context explored by this fable, it's worth picking out 'control panel and control room design', and the use and interpretation of instrumentation panels, as being vital to these *protection of the system from the user* instances. To help illustrate the big impact a seemingly small oversight can have in this context, let's pause for a moment to look at a well-known and tragic example – the Kegworth air disaster – which shows the catastrophic consequences that can flow from basic shortcomings in ergonomic design.

In the *Kegworth disaster* (*Great Britain, 1989*), a Boeing 737-400 aircraft came down just short of the runway at East Midlands Airport, to where it had diverted. The flight from Heathrow to Belfast suffered a blade detachment in the port side (left) engine, producing noise, vibration and smoke in the cabin. The pilots shut down what they believed to be the failed engine, but in fact they had chosen the wrong one, due to confusion over the aircraft's redesign. The 737-400 aircraft – to which they had recently converted – had a new digital primary instrument display, with which they were unfamiliar. This led to the pilots experiencing 'mode confusion' – due to variance from the instrument display they were used to seeing – resulting in their misdiagnosis of the fault. *The outcome was devastating.* 126 people were on board at the time. A total of 47 passengers were killed – 39 instantly – and 74 others suffered serious injuries.

The 'Kegworth report' highlighted that the instrumentation which would have enabled the pilots to identify the correct engine to shut down was small, worked in a different way to that which they routinely used, and was habitually ignored because of its previous unreliability. There were also contrary cues due to the fact that the cabin smoke stopped when the pilots took the incorrect action. The incident investigation found that – amongst other factors – it was a seemingly small error based on the pilots' understanding of the instrumentation panel in front of them, in the heat of the moment, which led to a disastrous outcome, with the report noting one of the factors which contributed to the flight crew's incorrect response as having been that '...*they did not assimilate the indications on the engine instrument display before they throttled back...*'[161]. Kegworth highlights the crucial importance of getting ergonomics right – even apparently small details.

Events of the kind seen in the Kegworth incident support the argument that this second *protection of the system from the user* aspect is the more important of the two, and in terms of high consequences at a single point in time, this position is irrefutable. But there is another viewpoint which says they both matter – for very different reasons. One concerns an apparently simple failure, where flicking a switch in the wrong direction can create catastrophic consequences in an instant. The other is about a repeated motion which can – over time

---

161. 'The Kegworth report', at page 2.

– be attritional on a user's physical, and possibly mental, wellbeing. *But make no mistake!* The long latency associated with the *protection of the user from the system* instances isn't just cause for organisations to rest on their laurels. The numbers of people affected – even in a small way – when viewed across a population highlights the size of the problem. In order to expand upon this, let's return to think a little more about the effects a system can have on a user, or user population. When taken at face value, the previously cited example of one user of 'display screen equipment' presenting with what are, on the face of it, mild symptoms (aches and pains) attributable to their work activity could be said to be of minimal interest to an organisation, but this can still set in motion a range of consequences. Perhaps a diagnosis of a 'work related musculoskeletal disorder'. Possibly a report to the Health and Safety Executive. Maybe even an increase in organisational claims exposure. And, with time, perhaps the tarnishing of corporate reputation too. *And where might the roots of this failure lie?* It could be in a lack of 'risk assessment'. Or a failure to consider sufficiently the needs of users. And it might be that users, as a result, develop poor technique. Or that a failure to identify symptoms at early-stage onset means that the resulting conditions are more serious than they might otherwise have been. Or even that the organisation fails to recognise and manage its higher risk users. And that's without even considering the consequential lowering of workforce morale. This shows how something which initially presents as a low likelihood-low severity event can also become a significant organisational concern, when left unchecked.

The examples cited here offer some insights as to how both *protection of the user from the system* and *protection of the system from the user* perspectives matter – for very different reasons. Within organisations, occupational health specialists are rightly concerned about high numbers of workers – or users – reporting even low levels of discomfort, particularly as over the longer term such complaints can lead to serious conditions, with reduced wellbeing, rising absences and threats to an organisation from a claims and reputational perspective, just some of the potential problems. Taking a longer term view is important here. Conditions which take a long time to develop – of which, in a different context, 'Hand Arm Vibration Syndrome (HAVS)' is another example – can be marked by significantly increased organisational claims exposure if 'control measures' aren't put in place, or are insufficiently robust, to manage the risk to those with high potential to develop them. The priority focus for the high-hazard organisation and its 'process safety' specialists, however, must always be upon high-severity incidents – of which Kegworth is just one example – no matter how low in frequency these may be.

Keeping both 'protection of the user from the system' and 'protection of the system from the user' aspects in mind, let's now turn to the fable...

THE FOCUS OF THIS FABLE:
It's all about the User

At a basic level, this fable features what, for many, will be the most familiar example of ergonomics – workstation set-up (in this case, 'display screen equipment (DSE) assessment') – which concerns a user's comfort with a computer, together with other aspects such as their chair, desk, screen, keyboard, mouse and working environment. For detail as to the practical requirements here, reference should be made to *the Health and Safety (Display Screen Equipment) Regulations 1992*[162] *('the DSE Regulations').* Workstation set-up will most likely be the area of ergonomics best known to those readers whose work is office-based, but to assume that this is where it starts and ends is to miss out on the far broader perspective the field has to offer, hence the reason why this fable's main purpose is to highlight the wide reach of the ergonomics' discipline. Central to the ergonomic mission is the desire to ensure a positive 'user experience', which calls for organisations to think beyond safety standards and 'usability' to the enjoyment, fulfilment and pleasure that can be derived from operating within comfortable environments and interacting with products, systems and processes which are satisfying, rather than frustrating, to use. As we shall see, in addition to a positive user experience being good for workforce wellbeing, it has the potential to deliver benefits on a much wider scale.

This fable takes three fictional bears and their use of spoons, chairs and beds, as the focus for exploring user comfort and usability principles. It also examines the potential for users' activities and actions to impact

---

162. S.I. 1992/2792. The requirements for workstations are specifically set out in the Schedule to regulation 3.

upon the systems they operate and the products they use. So, with this in mind, let's join the three bears to see what light their tale sheds on the practical benefits that can be enjoyed, when ergonomic principles are positively applied.

THE FABLE

Once upon a time there were three bears, who had roles which allowed them to undertake some of their work at home. There was Large Bear. There was Medium Bear. And there was Small Bear.

The work of the three bears had primarily involved desk-based computer tasks, in recent times. But some time back, Small Bear had set his sights on a career in air traffic control or, failing that, a job which required the monitoring of porridge levels in a porridge production plant, because porridge was his favourite food. And whether his future career path was to take a porridge plant or aviation-based direction, he knew he was going to need to prove he had the right mindset and temperament to look at screens and make quick and accurate decisions in line with procedures, based upon what he saw in front of him. That's not to say it was all plain sailing – Small Bear had initially struggled with some of the software – an issue which had prompted Medium Bear and Large Bear to upgrade the computer programs he used. But happily, things were looking up, with clearly observable improvements in Small Bear's performance having been noted, since the upgrade had taken place. It was thought that this was due, at least in part, to Small Bear having been involved in recent trials to improve the bears' software.

One morning, before they settled down to their day's work activities, Medium Bear cooked the three bears some porridge for breakfast. She put it into three bowls, which she placed down neatly on the kitchen table. There was a large bowl for Large Bear, a medium bowl for Medium Bear and a small bowl for Small Bear. She also laid out three spoons, of a size commensurate with both bears and bowls. The porridge was a bit hot, so Large Bear, Medium Bear and Small Bear decided to go for a short walk in the adjacent woods whilst it cooled.

Now at the edge of the woods, in another little house, there lived a little lady. Her father owned a long-established business as a locksmith, with an enviable reputation for making and repairing locks and key cutting. She was called Pixie-Locks. Pixie had always taken an interest in her father's business and, as his only child, was the logical choice to succeed him as owner. There was no denying it – she lacked some of his integrity when it came to the orthodox methods of lock repair and accessing premises – but more than made up for this shortcoming with her boundless enthusiasm and natural business acumen.

On that very same morning, having already eaten her own breakfast, as chance would have it Pixie had also decided to go for a walk in the woods. Soon, Pixie came to the little house where the three bears lived and worked. The door was shut but, being as she was of a naturally inquisitive nature, Pixie couldn't resist the urge to sneak a peek in through the window. On seeing there was no-one there – the bears being out on their walk to allow for porridge cooling time – she deployed her trademark *lock-sorcery* skills and, without a moment's hesitation, marched straight on in, as if she owned the place.

Pixie saw the three bowls of porridge and the three spoons neatly laid out on the table. The porridge smelt good and Pixie was hungry and, being a slightly dizzy teenager, had already forgotten that she'd eaten a good breakfast less than an hour beforehand. Still, she was at that fortunate stage in life where she didn't need to worry too much about watching what she ate, with her metabolism seeming to work very much in her favour.

Pixie picked up the very large spoon and tasted the porridge in the very large bowl. *It was too hot!* And the spoon was so large, it was a struggle to fit it in her mouth at all. Then she picked up the medium spoon and tasted the porridge in the medium bowl. *It was too lumpy!* And the spoon was still of a size which slightly grazed the corners of her mouth as she put it in. Then she picked up the very small spoon and tasted the porridge in the very small bowl. The porridge was just right for her, as was the spoon, which appeared to glide into and out of her mouth with comfortable ease. *Soon she had eaten it all up!* In her haste, she neglected to load the bowls and spoons into the dishwasher, such was her eagerness to know what curiosities might lay hidden in the rest of the house.

Then Pixie went to the room set up with the three bears' workstations and saw three chairs, positioned in front of three computer screens: a very large chair for Large Bear, a medium chair for Medium Bear, and a very small chair for Small Bear. She sat in Large Bear's chair. *It was too high!* But just right for Large Bear. She sat in Medium Bear's chair. *It was too soft!* But just right for Medium Bear.

Then her eyes alighted upon Small Bear's chair.

Small Bear's chair had been properly set up for him. Medium Bear and Large Bear had helped him when it had been delivered and it displayed a sign saying 'DO NOT ADJUST', making clear to others it was set up just how he liked it. He had a footrest too, and a nice little stand for his papers, which helped him to view his documents with a neutral neck position. Small Bear had lowered his screen and brought it closer towards him, so as to avoid leaning forward when viewing it. And he'd positioned his equipment exactly how he wanted it, in relation to how he needed to use it, which meant he didn't have to stretch or hunch. Added to this, in order to make his workspace even more homely, he had placed a few photographs of close friends near to his computer screen, so that they were never far from his thoughts. He also took regular breaks from his keyboard work and always used these opportunities wisely, moving around and changing his posture, during the time spent away from his desk. In fact, sometimes Small Bear enjoyed these breaks so much that Large Bear had to ask Medium Bear to politely suggest that he should get back to work. This was something which Medium Bear did gladly, as she had recently completed courses on *tact and diplomacy, managing employee performance,* and *using teamwork to make the dream work* to help develop her management style, and she relished any opportunity to put her newly-acquired skills to the test.

Pixie sat in Small Bear's chair.

She twiddled the knobs. She flicked a lever. She adjusted the seat height and depth. *And Small Bear's chair was just right.* Or so she thought. *Was Small Bear's chair just right?* No! On the contrary, Pixie was rather too heavy for it. Within moments, and to the soundtrack of some rather unpleasant creaking and cracking noises, a couple of wheels had fallen off, followed swiftly by Pixie. Both Pixie and Small Bear's chair lay on their sides, on the floor. Fortunately, Pixie was unharmed, but there was no hiding the fact – she had been very much mistaken in the belief that Small Bear's chair was the perfect fit for her!

Oh dear! Pixie-Locks had broken Small Bear's chair and she was very sorry. I say *'very sorry'*, but given her dubious method of entry into the three bears' living and work accommodation, consumption of food that wasn't hers, and clumsy ways with office furniture and equipment, her level of remorse was perhaps questionable. In truth, she bore many of the traits of the archetypal inconsiderate 'hot-desker', such was her habit of leaving things not quite as she found them.

Apparently unflustered by the unfortunate chair-breaking incident, Pixie went upstairs into the bedroom.

There she saw three beds: a large bed, a medium bed and a very small bed. She felt tired and thought she would like to sleep. So Pixie climbed up on to Large Bear's bed. *It was too hard!* But Large Bear found it comfortable, because it allowed his bones to absorb most of the pressure, thereby placing less stress on his muscles, veins and arteries and improving his circulation. Then she climbed up on to Medium Bear's bed. *It was too soft!* But it was just right for Medium Bear, whose reasoning was a little less scientific than that of Large Bear. She said it made her feel as if she was sleeping on a cloud.

Then, in an instant, Pixie's eyes fixated upon Small Bear's bed.

Pixie had a lie down on Small Bear's bed. *It was just right!* Soon she was fast asleep.

Before long, the three bears returned home for breakfast.

They went straight to the table which had been set neatly – with crockery, cutlery, care and love – by Medium Bear, before their pre-porridge perambulation. But little did the bears know that events were about to take a dark and upsetting turn.

Large Bear looked at his very large bowl and said in a very loud voice: '*Who* has been eating my porridge?'

Medium Bear looked at her medium porridge bowl and said in a medium voice, '*Who* has been eating my porridge?'

Small Bear looked forlornly at his very small porridge bowl and said in a small voice, '*Who* has been eating my porridge with my favourite Small Bear spoon and *eaten it all up*?'

Next, the three bears walked towards the area set aside for their work.

Large Bear looked at his very large chair. '*Who* has been sitting in my chair?' he asked in a very loud voice.

Then Medium Bear looked at her medium chair. '*Who* has been sitting in my chair?' she asked in a medium voice.

Then Small Bear looked at his very small chair, which he quickly realised wasn't where it should be and was instead lying on its side on the floor, exactly where Pixie-Locks had left it. '*Who* has been sitting in my Small Bear chair *and broken it*?' he asked in a very small voice. 'I *loved* that chair. It was set up in line with the guidance to *the DSE Regulations*. To others it might have looked like any generic office chair...but, *to me...*' Small Bear's voice faltered with the emotion of it all, but he continued on, stoically: '...before, my Small Bear paws couldn't touch the floor and I was getting aches and pains everywhere. Now look at me! *Just look at me!* I've got a spring back in my step. *That chair's been the making of me!*'

Large Bear looked affectionately across at Small Bear, as he somewhat clumsily attempted a pirouette across the floor. He took Small Bear's point and was pleasantly surprised by his knowledge of the relevant regulatory requirements, but did wonder whether his melodramatic tendencies might perhaps make some of his job aspirations unwise ones. If a career in air traffic control or a porridge production plant didn't work out, he mused, there was always the possibility of him treading the boards, when the time came for him to look for his next role. As for Medium Bear, her naturally more cautious nature gave her cause to wince slightly at Small Bear's balletic efforts, as she reasoned to herself that were he to sustain a sprained ankle or similar, in the course of performing what was a chiefly desk-based job, it would not look good for them.

Next, the three bears went upstairs into the bedroom.

Large Bear looked across at his very large bed. 'Who has been lying on *my* bed?' he asked in a very loud voice.

Medium Bear looked across at her medium bed. 'Who has been lying on *my* bed?' she asked in a medium voice.

Small Bear looked at his very small bed. '*Here she is!*' he cried, making his very small voice as loud as he possibly could and waving one of his Small Bear paws towards his very small bed. 'Here is the vexatious little lady, who's eaten my porridge, broken my chair and tried out all of our beds for size! *Here she is!*'

At the sounds of their voices, Pixie-Locks woke up with a start. When she saw the three bears and their six beady eyes glaring back at her, she jumped off the bed in fright. She rushed back down the stairs. She burst out through the front door of the three bears' little house. And she disappeared off into the woods. In fact, by the time the three bears reached their front door, Pixie had vanished from sight. The three bears never saw her again – a change in fortunes which gave them cause to thank their lucky stars.

Shortly after Pixie had left, Large Bear called Medium Bear and Small Bear across to where he was standing and, collectively, the three of them agreed on a plan of action. They got Small Bear's chair mended as a priority and engaged an ergonomist to look at other areas for improvement. The ergonomist spent a few days observing the bears' practices and some time talking to them about their work environment. This provided her with some useful insights, helped to build up a picture of issues where action was needed, and gave her some other ideas she could offer the bears, including sourcing keyboards better suited to bear paw pads, rather than human digits. She hoped that this, together with her other good practice suggestions, might help them to ward off any future problems.

The ergonomist summarised her findings, which not only recognised the bears' present circumstances, but also took into account Small Bear's career aspirations:

'My report here reveals human behaviour at worst –
Reminding all bears – security first!
A girl – *Pixie-Locks* – sneaks inside their abode,
Showing none of the features of a good moral code.

The bears' day started out well, things just felt so right.
Porridge served. Ramble done. A dose of early sunlight.
But there was trouble ahead, as the bears were to learn,
And question *'What's Pixie been up to?'* upon their return…
No sooner had Medium Bear set paw through the door,
Than – with alarm – she saw oats scattered all over the floor!
Large Bear wasn't happy, he too disliked clutter,
'I've only just vacuumed!' Medium Bear heard him mutter!
Small Bear, bright and breezy, said *'I'm sure things could be worse…'*
But soon, even he would have good cause to curse!

Small Bear's supposition was that life was unfair!
She'd eaten his porridge and broken his chair.

The photos on his desk of his ursine relations,
Knocked down, just one of his many frustrations!
He was baffled by those who made such a mockery,
Ergonomics wasn't just chairs and different sized crockery!
Though a bear small in size, he had unlimited vision,
The future he saw was jam-packed with ambition.
As he gazed at the sky, filled with hope and elation,
His career plan – just three words: 'all things aviation!'
But whilst Small Bear's big plans seem all cute and endearing,
His control of air traffic is a prospect worth fearing.
You'll need early on, to plant in his brain,
On the runway to competence, he'll have long to train.
Though the runway is long, there's reward in the end,
And the thanks of air passengers, who on him will depend!
So listen up! Make sure he learns what a bear needs to know,
About displays, and all that control panels show.
It'll be worth it, you see, for when put to the test,
You need to be sure bears perform at their best.
He'll have lots to consider, but it's not too much to ask
Of a bear, when assigned safety critical tasks.
As for user trials, truth be told, it astonished the bears
That Pixie sat without asking, and then came the repairs!

In time, this was resolved, with not much more to say,
About a porridge-based break-in and a girl's meddlesome ways.
Save from Ursa Major to Minor, please let it be known,
There's nothing as fine as a chair of one's own…
…so, remember the basics of workstation assessing,
And stow your porridge away, to save you from stressing!'

The three bears read the ergonomist's report and put in place measures to address the findings she had raised. They also formulated a development plan to help Small Bear reach his goals and achieve his ambition. And life was good again. They got the locks to their little house changed as a priority too, and found a secret place in which to store their porridge oats, so as to prevent a recurrence of these deeply upsetting events.

And they all lived *comfortably* ever after…

MODERN MEANING

At a simplistic level, this fable is about bowls, chairs and beds being appropriately sized for their respective users. But looking at the tale on a slightly deeper level shows it to have a bigger purpose, both in its highlighting of ergonomics as a broad and enlightening field, and through its bringing to light the wider societal benefits that can flow when good ergonomic principles are applied. More than just being about spoons, seating and sleeping arrangements, there is much of broader ergonomic relevance, on which to pass comment here. Some organisations separate out this discipline – often achieved by enlisting the help of ergonomists, or establishing a human factors team – but regardless of exactly how they choose to address such concerns, organisations have much to gain from instilling good ergonomic design principles and practice, wherever this can be accomplished in combination with other, often commercial and sometimes competing, considerations. And when ergonomics is taken seriously, there are clear benefits to be had – seen in outcomes including improved reliability, increased speed, more intuitive behaviours, and raised levels of satisfaction amongst user populations. *Why should this be?* It's simple really. If users find products, systems, processes and workplaces to be reliable, quick, easy and even fun(!) to use or navigate their way around, this is likely to see them adopting behaviours which aid system and product reliability, as well as protecting their health, safety and wellbeing and that of others too. This applies in both occupational and leisure-related contexts. So whether the challenge is one of a passenger boarding a train to get to work, an engineer filling in an on-line form for a meter work job, a holiday-maker following directional signs to an aircraft through a busy airport, or – as here – a fictional bear using a workstation, the ultimate goal differs little: the aim should be to create an ultimately positive and satisfying user experience which is more edifying for them, whilst fulfilling broader safety, economic and efficiency goals too.

Here, on the one level, we learn of workstation ergonomics having been taken seriously, with the appropriate sizing, positioning and adjustment of computer chairs and desks. At another level, it's quite clear that the bears took broader ergonomic principles to their hearts. It's important to appreciate just how extensively these principles apply, because they have as much relevance in the wider world, as they do for workplaces. For a practical example, one only has to look at the issue of leg-room on various forms of transport to see that designing to the *average* person is an ineffective principle to apply to all. In transport settings ergonomics can be helpful by, for instance, ensuring that design briefs require anthropometric data to be considered, which means that the tallest and widest of passengers can be accommodated, in comfort. For another example, when thinking about the principles to be applied in deciding where to position alarm buttons within industrial plants, the challenges are quite different in nature. In that type of scenario, it's likely that the ergonomist's goal would be to land on a design which puts the buttons within the easy reach of even those with the shortest limbs, so that in an emergency situation, all users are able to activate them, without difficulty.

Whilst the fable reports that the bears regarded Pixie-Locks as vexatious, and understandably so, the insights we can draw from her behaviour are, nonetheless, valuable. This is because, in seeking to reap practical benefits from ergonomic principles, it's imperative that due consideration is given to 'user-centred design', with the involvement of users in 'user testing' during the design test phase invariably leading to the best outcomes being achieved. Ideally, of course, these will be planned activities, but useful information can also be derived in circumstances where – as seen here with Pixie-Locks – a product is tested to its limits or to the point of destruction. And regardless of whether such issues become apparent from test data in the course of 'user trials' or emerge later, when a product is in live use, these outcomes are invaluable in pinpointing where enhancements might be required. The tale suggests that Small Bear's chair was set up exclusively for him, but other benefits might have been yielded by factoring into the design the differences in weights, heights and limb lengths of multiple users, or even their variable methods and patterns of use.

There will, of course, be circumstances in which satisfying the range of different user goals simultaneously proves challenging – and times when the realisation of ideas doesn't work out as hoped, or where improvements to user experience cannot be justified – sometimes simply on the basis of the costs involved being too prohibitive. The cost consideration is an important one, because however brilliant a product might be from an ergonomic angle, it can still be doomed never to reach its intended market, if manufacturing costs are prohibitive to production. *This benefits no-one!* It also highlights a constant challenge which confronts ergonomists, who view usability considerations as vital, but know that the solutions they see as optimal are unlikely to be pursued at any cost. Their aim must therefore be to look for outcomes which are as inclusive as possible, whilst also being commercially viable. In practical terms this means, wherever possible, seeking the inclusion of ergonomic principles from the get-go in any project, rather than trying to retro-fit solutions at the end. *Why is this?* Well, it's only by thinking about these principles in parallel with commercial considerations, right from the start – from project initiation, through to planning, execution, and ultimately, at the review and monitoring stages – that organisations will be able to fully realise the benefits of any ergonomic endeavours.

Here, there's no doubting that the bears' interest in products (spoons, chairs and beds) and systems (Small Bear's software) to suit users was commendable. But the fable says little about the thought they applied to protecting systems from the user. Were Small Bear to follow through with his plans to pursue a career in air traffic control, or even the monitoring of a porridge production plant, the optimisation of systems would clearly be an area of vital importance. As such, the fable raises several key questions, which are pertinent in a real-world context, just as they are of interest in relation to this fairy-tale scenario. *'What does the user need to do?'* We saw this in the description of Small Bear's tasks. *'What makes the user happy?'* We observed this through the description of Small Bear and his chair, which had been adjusted to suit his needs. And, *'What improvements to user experience might make the system work most effectively?'* It would seem that the bears had started to address this last question through Small Bear's software upgrade, but there were clearly other actions they might have taken. Further improvements could have been achieved by making any number of small adjustments for him as a user, adding to the quality of his user experience and vitally, making it more likely he would succeed rather than fail – crucially important for a career of the kind he had in mind! In a real-world context, it's here that the ergonomic discipline comes into its own. Because as well as attending to straightforward user requirements, ergonomics challenges us to think about the benefits the user sees at the interface with the equipment they use, and importantly towards the multitude of small enhancements which make it more likely that they will succeed, rather than fail, at any given task, ultimately driving improved reliability.

The outline of ergonomic issues provided here is not intended to trivialise what is a broad and complex area, nor does it set out to be a comprehensive study. It is, however, worth calling out some of the fable's noteworthy points, together with the corresponding concerns organisations need to address in a real-world context, when seeking to ensure that the tri-partite relationship between the user, their work equipment and the work environment is a harmonious one. The key aspects the fable brings to mind are: *first:* usability; *second:* user experience; *third:* user interface – control panel and control room design, and finally, *fourth:* workstation assessment.

USABILITY

The fable suggests the bears' paw pads were perhaps too big for the keys on their keyboards, which had most probably been designed to accommodate human digits. But the tale also makes positive mention of 'anthropometric' considerations, in its reference to body dimensions, with Small Bear exclaiming delightedly: '...before, my Small Bear paws couldn't touch the floor and I was getting aches and pains everywhere. Now look at me! *Just look at me!* I've got a spring back in my step. *That chair's been the making of me!*' Small Bear's chair having been set for his personal use can be regarded as an example of ergonomic principles being applied to good effect, with the tale touching as it does upon relevant physical usability concerns, including his flexibility, dexterity and reach.

'Usability' is the aspect of ergonomics which defines the extent to which something can successfully be used by a target audience, to achieve certain goals, encompassing physical, sensory and cognitive aspects. It follows that successful application of the usability principle is observable where things are, for example: easy to reach, rather than inaccessible; clearly visible rather than being difficult to perceive, and clear and understandable, rather than incomprehensible to the user. Usability goes hand in hand with user testing. Testing is seen as the most effective way of measuring the level of success achieved in applying usability considerations, as it highlights the design aspects which work well for users, together with those in need of further modification. Where needed, making adaptations early on invariably paves the way for a more satisfying user experience, as well as leading to time and cost savings in the long run.

So how is usability relevant in a real-world context? It's important for products and services to suit the user and even better if they suit the multiple needs and desires of different users. This means, for example, making PIN machine numbers sufficiently large so that partially-sighted people can see them, and positioning cash machines so as to make them just as accessible for wheelchair users, as they are for able-bodied users. These examples highlight the value of adopting 'inclusive design' principles, which allow more users to access products and services, by reducing the capability demands – whether physical, sensory or cognitive – placed upon those who use them. These principles also apply to situations where a device needs to be made usable for someone wearing gloves, which might be of particular importance where these are required for some other purpose, for instance as a vital piece of 'personal protective equipment'(PPE). Even these few examples highlight why usability matters in broader society, just as it does within a workplace context. Returning to this tale's bear-based example, it's said that the trio had addressed the ease with which their software could be used, as an issue, but no mention is made of usability having been considered when it came to the design or sourcing of suitable keyboards, by factoring paw pad size requirements into their procurement processes.

Usability can also feed reliability. *And why is this?* It's simply because, if a device is made easier to use, this lowers the likelihood of mistakes being made. Something which is straightforward to use is also more likely to be pleasurable to use, and is consequently less likely to frustrate or anger a user, than something which is not; this improves the chance of them engaging positively with it. It follows that it's beneficial to adopt a design approach which combines user experience, considered next here, with usability; products should be designed which are both useful and usable. To take a real-world scenario, incorporating usability concerns is vital to the design of a pilot's cockpit and, more particularly, its instrumentation panels, where the positioning of controls should support quick and accurate decision-making. Such concerns also need to be addressed for mobile engineers inputting data into on-line forms. *And perhaps for lone working goats carrying out jobs within a defined geographic area too!* In seeking to satisfy their usability needs, the keys on the keyboard they use should be appropriate to the size of their digits, because this makes data inputting easier and tends to mean unintended error rates are low. And in addition to the more mundane examples, such concerns also exist in relation to high-end technology markets, where usability is inextricably linked to brand and experience. We see these principles being positively applied for real-world products including smart phones, personal fitness devices, and home heating controls, where design approaches integrate satisfaction and usability factors, alongside engineering considerations.

In seeking to comprehensively address usability concerns, it's important to make sure user testing is conducted to reveal the aspects of designs which work well and those in need of adjustment. Carrying out user testing improves the chances of a product, system or process being successfully used, expertly navigated or diligently followed by a target audience (in this case, the bears). *Perhaps a keyboard's keys need to be bigger, for someone with larger than average hands (or paws). Maybe a touch-screen needs to work for a person wearing gloves. It's possible that a device needs to work for someone who is less dextrous than the person who designed it. Or it might be that there needs to be a dimple on an entry key pad, so as to allow a partially-sighted person to navigate it without assistance.* Effective testing regimes help to pick up on these kinds of usability considerations – and many more besides – which can then be addressed by an inclusive approach being taken throughout the course of design and re-design processes.

USER EXPERIENCE (UX)

Reflecting back on the events of the fable, it might have been that generic cutlery, bedroom furniture and seating options would have sufficed for these bears, but it was evident that the three of them derived some satisfaction, pleasure – and ultimately a better user experience – from having the right sized spoons, beds, and chairs. This is made apparent through Small Bear's delighted cry of '*Just look at me!* I've got a spring back in my step...' in response to the set-up of his chair, and from Medium Bear's 'sleeping on a cloud' description of the comfort offered by her bed. And of course, there's a serious point to these seemingly light-hearted asides, because they serve as recognition that the ergonomist's mission isn't a purely utilitarian one. *Some of it's about pleasure too!* The pleasure aspect might not be viewed as the top priority in a safety critical setting – where safety and efficiency goals are often, understandably, prioritised above aesthetics and desirability – but it certainly has relevance elsewhere, as can be seen in the automotive sector, when someone wishes to buy a high-end vehicle, rather than a cheap '*just want it to get me from A to B*' model. This goes to the heart of the user experience (UX) principle, which is regarded as the process of simplifying a user's encounter with a product or service, by looking at it in totality. It's the field concerned with the methods and processes which design for and assess total user experience – including usability, user feelings, motivations and values – with respect to products and services.

User experience can be regarded as a blend of both usability and utility considerations. And, whilst it's arguable that experiential aspects are secondary, the incorporation of aesthetics and the evoking of emotional responses within users clearly have a place within any holistic ergonomics and human factors approach. Designing products, systems and processes which are both usable and pleasurable, giving satisfaction to the user, facilitates a move beyond the *form versus function* argument, towards a situation in which form and function positively coexist and interact. This would have been relevant to the software upgrade mentioned in relation to Small Bear's activities, with the noted improvements in his performance likely to have been attributable, at least in part, to him being better satisfied. Small Bear's inclusion within user trials, which should have seen his involvement in 'user acceptance testing', would likely have seen him enjoying a higher quality user experience, not only benefitting him as a user, but also supporting his reliable use of the system. Returning to the real-world example of mobile engineers, when designing systems for their use, efforts should be made to ensure that the sequence of job task steps, questions and prompts within the on-line forms they need to use follow a logical path, because this leads to a better user experience.

Challenges undoubtedly exist in designing for wide-ranging populations, with their often complex and diverse needs and desires, but the early integration of ergonomics and human factors principles, alongside commercial considerations – particularly at the design phase of a project – ensures that broad-ranging capabilities are accounted for in the design and user testing stages. Ultimately this can lead to highly usable devices, products, systems and processes, which fit their intended purposes and result in a higher quality of user experience. Practical testing in the field can be far more effective than endless classroom-style debate, enabling the identification and resolution of issues beyond those which might be uncovered through laboratory tests and trials alone. In the context of *Pixie-Locks' fable*, this might have applied to the software used by Small Bear but, as has been noted, it could just as easily apply to on-line forms, risk assessments or inspection forms, such as those completed by real-world mobile engineers. Where elements of feedback are incorporated during the course of the design phase, this is often rewarded by improved engagement with products, systems and processes, and ultimately leads to a more positive outcome in terms of 'user satisfaction' and experience, in the long run.

Curiously, the relevance of a high quality user experience spills over into the domain of safety critical tasks too. *Why is this?* Well, if something's enjoyable to do, there's a far better chance that someone will engage positively in doing it. If, on the other hand, it's annoying to do, reluctant users are likely to find this to be a further reason for doing it badly or half-heartedly, or even not to do it at all. So, in essence, this means that a high quality of user experience can indeed raise compliance levels as a side benefit – particularly where emotional, cognitive and experiential factors improve acceptance levels throughout a user population.

DESIGNING THE USER INTERFACE (UI): CONTROL PANELS & CONTROL ROOMS

Early on in the fable it was suggested that Small Bear had designs on becoming an air traffic controller or securing a safety critical role in a porridge production plant. Of course, we can only speculate as to whether these dreams might have become a reality for him, with Small Bear's future career plans fortunately being some way off, so as not to trigger immediate concerns about the compromising of safety systems within such workplace environments! Casting our minds back to the serious real-world matters addressed in this fable's *prologue*, however – and specifically, to the Kegworth incident – provides us with a sobering reminder of the importance that should be attached to user interface considerations. This incident highlighted the significance of control panel understanding and its close connection with safety critical control – of particular concern where users are required to switch between different types – as well as it having shown the tragic and stark consequences which can flow in circumstances where organisations fail to effectively address such issues.

The 'user interface' can be regarded as a sub-set of user experience, being essentially about what the user sees, which organisations should always seek to make attractive and engaging. Those who speak of user experience (UX), tend to refer to the aspects of control panel and control room design as the user interface (UI). 'User interface design' concerns the design of user interfaces for machines and computer software, including task menus, with a focus on maximising usability and user experience. Revisiting the example of mobile engineers, in designing task menus, effort should be put into making these attractive and intuitive for them as users, with steps being taken to ensure opposite responses are not located adjacent to each other, so as to prevent unintentional data input errors being made.

Operating environments vary widely, but those found within high-hazard organisations can be particularly challenging and complex, often containing an array of displays. This makes it crucial to get the design of control panels and control rooms right, such that overall system states can be clearly and universally understood by a range of different users completing a multitude of often difficult tasks. As such, key considerations when configuring control rooms include the analysis of layouts and sight-lines to equipment, screens and other team members. Layouts should enable the right number of people with the right skills and authority levels to communicate effectively with each other in all circumstances. Adopting user-centred design methods in this way ensures user requirements are both better understood and met – whether for normal or abnormal 'operating conditions', or emergency situations – thus ensuring that appropriate numbers of skilled people are able to oversee activities in all types of situations. When user-centred design is effectively applied, this invariably leads to improved job design and control. At a basic fictional level, we've seen that designing workstations to suit those who use them helps to keep users (like Small Bear) happy but, in the real world, user-centred design has a big part to play in safety critical settings. More than simply just facilitating task execution, it's a far-sighted approach, which can produce observable increases in user output as well as feeding operative reliability, making it the right thing to do on all counts. It also improves the comfort of tasks, reduces the numbers of reports of user discomfort and supports workforce wellbeing too.

Across a diverse range of operational settings – within transport, manufacturing and energy management locations, to name but a few – control panels and control rooms are vital tools which give users oversight of, and allow them to monitor, 'safety critical systems'. But of course, it's a pre-requisite for all those with responsibilities in such environments to have the ability to understand the system states involved and to react quickly to intervene, whenever required. Whilst the four aspects highlighted here arguably have importance in their own right, this control panel and control room aspect is widely viewed as being the most significant. *And why is this?* It's because this affects not just the safety, health and satisfaction of the user – in this fable, Small Bear – but also the reliability and effectiveness with which safety critical tasks are performed, a topic revisited in the context of *the porridge pot fable*. Factors affecting user reliability, referred to as 'performance influencing factors' by the Health and Safety Executive, also come into play here. These factors can be multiple and complex, and they form the central theme of the final fable in this collection – *Not-Quite's fable* – to which reference is advised.

WORKSTATION ASSESSMENT

Early on in the fable, we learn that the three bears '...had roles which allowed them to undertake some of their work at home'. As a direct result of the 'Coronavirus disease (COVID-19)' outbreak of 2020, the practice of 'homeworking' has become prevalent across Great Britain, with a marked increase in the number of 'home workers' seen in real-world workforces. It's important to note that employers have the same responsibilities for the health, safety and welfare of home workers as for other workers, which includes aspects such as: the tasks they are required to perform; their levels of stress and mental wellbeing, and working with display screen equipment. The focus here is upon working with display screen equipment and, more particularly, workstation set-up and assessments. It is generally well understood that such assessments should be undertaken within office environments but, where work with display screen equipment takes place in domestic settings, the guidance from the Health and Safety Executive is that risks are to be assessed and controlled in the home too[163].

The fable makes mention of efforts having been made to set up Small Bear's chair specifically for him, with thought also having been

---

163. For guidance on how to protect home workers, see https://www.hse.gov.uk/toolbox/workers/home.htm [viewed 01 May 2021].

given to other aspects of his workstation and work environment. From the description given to Small Bear's workstation set-up, the three bears certainly seemed to take the basics of workstation assessment seriously. This is, of course, positive because when workstation assessments are carried out effectively – with their outcomes being well addressed – this tends to feed through into improved user experience, working conditions and workforce wellbeing, and often brings about increases in workforce productivity and engagement levels too.

It's in the context of workstation assessment that the concept of a worker as a user, referred to in the *prologue* to this fable, has direct relevance, this being the term used in the legislation. The need to carry out workstation assessment is linked to 'users' in *the DSE Regulations*, being those who '...*habitually use display screen equipment as a significant part of...normal work.*'[164] A 'workstation assessment' is a thorough analysis of a user's tasks, environment and workstation, including the desk, chair and any associated equipment, its two-fold purpose being to establish whether the workstation equipment and practices are likely to harm the user, and to proactively identify the associated steps that can be taken to increase workstation safety and comfort.

Whilst noting the positive steps the bears had taken in relation to workstation assessment, it's probable that they still had a little further to go in order to fully meet Small Bear's user requirements. We know from the tale that Small Bear had a chair suited to his needs, together with a footrest and document holder, and that the positioning of his screen meant he adopted a good neutral neck position. What is perhaps less clear is whether the keyboard was suitable for his bear paw pads. Even for Small Bear, as the smallest of the bears, it seems entirely probable that his ursine paws were larger than the human hands for which the keyboard was designed, meaning they should have looked to source a better alternative.

Many advantages can be seen from the effective carrying out of workstation assessments[165]. They help to ensure that working

---

164. 'User' is defined within regulation 1 of *the DSE Regulations*, together with other terms.

165. As outlined in this book's introduction, employers are required to have 'consultation' arrangements in place with those who carry out work, or their representatives. For this type of work, employers would be expected to provide employees with information on the risks and dangers associated with the use of display screen equipment, the measures put in place to get rid of or reduce these risks, and what they should do in the event of them being uncontrolled.

environments are suitable for those who use them. They can also save money by identifying the factors affecting user comfort and providing cost-effective solutions to help prevent any reduced productivity or a rise in illness and absenteeism, which might otherwise result amongst their user populations. Furthermore, they are vital to making sure that those with health problems or mobility needs are appropriately accommodated and enabled to participate fully in workplace activities. Assessments also have a key part to play in identifying a range of control measures which, when adopted, can help to secure the safe and comfortable return to work of those who have been absent for health reasons.

Finally, it's worth noting that, in modern office environments the now commonplace practice of 'hot-desking' presents additional challenges for the carrying out of workstation assessment with the activity needing to be performed, and adjustments made, on a more dynamic basis. Where organisations allow their workers to hot-desk, they need to be particularly mindful of individual concerns, requiring the taking of a more intuitive approach towards assessment. A culture of consideration should also be fostered amongst users when vacating workstations after use, such that they are left in a fit and hygienic state for subsequent occupants.

CLOSING THOUGHTS

A slight twist on a time-worn tale's naïve description of three bears provided the origin from which to explore some of the fundamentals of the ergonomics discipline. This modern version emphasised the importance of *the user*, recognising the need to account for both *protection of the user from the system* and *protection of the system from the user* perspectives. It led to the consideration of concepts including usability, user experience, and the user interface. It also touched upon broader issues, such as user-centred and inclusive design, and underlined the significant part the discipline plays in ensuring that users are appropriately equipped with products, systems and processes which are useful and usable, being meaningful and evoking positive reactions amongst them. By highlighting the complexities involved in control panel and control room design alongside the basic elements of workstation assessment, the fable has offered a glimpse into the diverse nature of the challenges ergonomics seeks to address.

Who would have thought the ostensibly simple tale of three bears would lead to a meaning so profound in nature? The range and scale of the ergonomist's endeavour is breathtaking. As well as the field attending to the important aspects of user comfort and wellbeing, it makes an invaluable contribution towards achieving the reliable performance of safety critical tasks, making it of crucial interest to high-hazard organisations.

For a summary of practical points to take away,
based upon the topics and subtopics handled by this fable,
see *How to...* Guide Five.

A NOTE ON REPORTING REQUIREMENTS

The events portrayed in this fable were of a purely fictitious nature. See the *Epilogue* for indicative reporting requirements under *the Reporting of Injuries, Diseases and Dangerous Occurrences Regulations 2013*[166] *(RIDDOR),* as could be triggered by equivalent real-world circumstances.

---

166. S.I. 2013/1471.

The Perilous Porridge Pot,
Preventing Loss of Containment,
and
some Risk Modelling Insights

THE PORRIDGE POT FABLE

' When the little girl returned home from her day at school, she was shocked at the scene of chaos and devastation unfolding before her eyes, shrieking at her mother: 'What *have* you done?' to which the terse reply came back: 'What have I done? What have *I* done? That's rich, coming from you, dear! What have *you* done, more like?... I never asked for a full-scale process plant to be set up in my kitchen.' '

PROLOGUE

At a superficial level, this fable portrays what could be simplistically described as a *too much porridge* kitchen-based cookery failure, naturally prompting consideration about what might happen if a preoccupied breakfast chef were to take their eye off a peculiar – *and ultimately perilous* – porridge pot. More seriously, the fable provides a step-by-step walk through a basic 'loss of containment' risk example. Aided by a 'risk model', the analysis of this tale will reveal how putting in place 'risk controls' ('barriers') can – when accompanied by actions which ensure they remain effective ('barrier maintenance') – prevent the 'risk', or limit the consequences of an overflow scenario, should one occur. This is the first of a pair of *operatives' fables* in this collection, the common intention of which is to highlight how the things 'workers' do to make systems and processes work are vital to achieving the effective control of risk.

PORRIDGE POTS AND PRINCIPLES

As well as providing the impetus to build a basic risk model, the contents of this fable – most notably, its overflowing porridge pot – are to be used to show the crucial part operatives play in performing 'safety critical tasks' to ensure risk is robustly controlled. This is a theme further developed later on in this book, in *Not-Quite's fable*, where an overview of the 'safety critical task analysis (SCTA)' technique is given and the crucial importance of 'reliable human performance' being delivered by operatives highlighted, again in the context of a loss of containment risk scenario.

It's worth highlighting that, whilst undeniably capable of beneficial use within other domains, the 'bow tie modelling' technique considered here – as well as that of safety critical task analysis explored later in *Not-Quite's fable* – tend to be best suited and most naturally applied within 'high-hazard organisation' settings. This is borne out by the fact that such organisations typically reserve their use of such methods for modelling circumstances where fires, explosions, toxic releases or other serious outcomes could result, if their control of so-called 'major accident hazards' is unsuccessful. These organisations tend to deal with substances of a more hazardous nature than the oaty sludge featured within this fable – and there is arguably far more to be gained by applying risk modelling to, say, a real-world fuel-in-tank scenario than a fictional porridge-in-pot based one – but the tale's scenario does at least highlight the basic benefits that such techniques have to offer, even if not the finer points of detail they are capable of representing.

In order to support the aim of outlining basic risk principles, this tale presents some oat-based action, as the backdrop against which to set out an overview of 'barrier modelling' and 'barrier thinking'. In so doing, it sets the context for showcasing a specific type of risk model called a 'bow tie model', with the value of the methodology and its related concepts being highlighted through their application to the loss of containment risk at the fable's heart. As such, the fable can be viewed as an introduction to the broader perspective offered by 'risk-based thinking' often adopted by organisations seeking to establish control processes to improve upon their existing risk management arrangements. Additionally, it affords us a look at a type of 'assurance' activity known as 'barrier-based risk management', a valuable approach now widely accepted by those high-hazard organisations choosing to use 'barrier models' as part of their 'risk management strategies'. *But more on this later...*

I accept that some readers will view the terms 'loss of containment' and 'risk models' as classic examples of the *impenetrable jargon* cautioned against in this book's introduction and so, in a bid to allay any such concerns, let me offer these words of comfort. Until my mid-thirties, I too had no notion of what these concepts involved but, believe me, they are accessible, valuable, and insightful for anyone curious to learn about them. And for those directly involved in controlling risk (of which something escaping from where it's supposed to be contained is just an example) – from those who actually monitor 'gauges', respond to 'alarms' and shut 'valves', right up to an organisation's Chief Executive Officer (CEO) who needs to be confident that these activities are carried out effectively – risk models are a powerful tool for good. I've put the *gauge-watchers*, *alarm-responders* and *valve-shutters* first for sound reason here because, whilst

CEOs ultimately own the risk generated by their organisations, it's to these other people that they look to control risk – at the sharp end – on a frequent basis. This is where the 'risk modelling' approach set out in the context of this fable can achieve its greatest effect, in a visually powerful way. It enables everyone with a role in controlling risk to see where they fit in, the value they add, and the gap that might be left if they don't do what they are called upon to do – *brilliantly* – every time it's required.

KEY THEMES

I do acknowledge that the analytical concepts introduced here – which will be used to support the explanation of the fable and assist in its review – might be new to some readers[167]. *If this is true for you, please don't allow it to put you off!* Some themes covered by this *prologue* might seem a little abstract on first reading, but the fable and its connected *modern meaning* should help to show and explain how these concepts can be practically applied, to great effect. In approaching the development of a risk model, we'll start off simply, by looking at the identification of a risk (a so-called 'top event'). We'll then look at ways of stopping the risk in the first place, by blocking off the causes (or 'threats') that could lead to it. We'll also look at ways of blocking the outcomes (or 'consequences') which flow from the top event, if efforts to stop it are unsuccessful. And we'll look at the value of having multiple risk controls ('barriers') available – both 'prevention barriers' which block threats from leading to the top event and, if it materialises, 'mitigation barriers' which stop the top event from leading to adverse consequences – including how these are chosen ('barrier selection'). Finally, the fable seeks to highlight the benefits organisations stand to gain by checking that the tools they think they have to hand will be available to them at their point of need, and actually work, whenever they reach for them. This checking process is where the role of an assurance team can come into its own, particularly where an organisation chooses to champion a pro-active approach such

---

167. The description given in the *prologue* to this fable includes some key terms in wide use amongst those who build risk models, and which it's important to understand when seeking to apply the technique to real-world scenarios. The terminology used here includes just some of the terms in common usage for building bow tie models and forms part of the lexicon adopted and applied within this fable's *modern meaning*, with the relevant definitions provided within this book's *Glossary*.

as 'barrier-based risk management', which is outlined later in the *modern meaning* to this fable.

Keeping in mind these themes, let's look at four key stages which put the building of risk models in context, with the last stage setting up the modelling approach to be practically applied to the scenario described in this fable. It's worth noting that here, the value of bow tie modelling is to be highlighted by applying the approach to retrospectively analyse a fictional incident (or a failure to control risk). In the real world, the benefits of using such techniques for this purpose are widely recognised, but organisations that fully embrace methodologies of this kind will, above all, seek to institute them to proactively determine what would best prevent their risks from being realised in the first place. *Colloquially expressed, and as the events of this fable will testify, it's far better to stop porridge spilling in the first place, than to have to scurry around post-spillage and fathom out in haste what didn't work!*

BUILDING SUCCESSFUL RISK MODELS: A FOUR-STAGE APPROACH

Simply expressed, the stages involved in risk model development are to: *first,* work out what risk needs to be stopped or managed; *second,* work out why stopping or managing the particular risk matters; *third,* work out how to go about stopping or managing the risk, and finally, *fourth,* work out what the risk model – in this case the bow tie model – looks like, which here has been framed around a fictional overflowing porridge pot scenario!

So, without further ado, let's begin...

STAGE #1
IDENTIFY THE RISK THAT NEEDS TO BE STOPPED OR MANAGED

The principal aim of this stage is to precisely identify the risk that needs to be managed.

This might sound obvious, but it's a really vital stage to get right, as any well-constructed risk model needs to have at its heart a clearly defined risk, this being the foundation upon which all of its constituent parts are subsequently built. Defining the risk is important because it clearly marks a specific point in time. *It's the bad thing that we don't want to happen.* It represents a shift in circumstances, from the potential for a loss of control to a state in which control has already been lost. In the context of this particular fable, we'll see that understanding a loss of containment risk is a prerequisite for determining how to control it – both in terms of the requirements for preventing the escape of substances in the first place, and those which limit the effects in circumstances where they have already escaped. Material which is contained is a good thing. Material which leaves containment when we don't want it to is a bad thing. A loss of containment incident occurs when there is an unplanned or uncontrolled release of any material or – expressed more simply – when stuff unexpectedly comes out of a container which was supposed to contain it. Materials can possess all manner of properties, including toxicity, flammability and volatility – which introduce additional risks – but the need for containment is a basic concern common to them all. Examples of substances requiring containment range from steam, hot condensate and nitrogen, through to compressed carbon dioxide and compressed air. Loss of containment incidents have received increased scrutiny in recent times, due to a number of high-profile occurrences across the chemical and petrochemical industries. Even if the term loss of containment has, until now, been alien, the well-known incidents that can flow from such events are unlikely to have escaped your notice. And, whilst thankfully rare, the consequences of failure when these incidents do occur tend to be significant. Defining the risk, then – whatever it might be – is the important first stage in the process of working out how to control it.

In terms of the *'What's the risk?'* question, in this particular instance we'll be looking at an oat-based problem, with the substance at the centre of the fable being porridge spilling out of a peculiar porridge pot. Here, we're going to focus exclusively on physical containment and the subsequent loss of containment aspect – the *too much stuff for the container intended to contain it* problem. For the purposes of modelling this scenario, we'll be looking at the simple physical risk of an excessive amount of porridge sludge being produced in a porridge pot, within a domestic kitchen setting, rather than any more inherently hazardous substance or vulnerable environment. But in a real-world scenario the hazardous or other properties of a given substance, together with where it ends up, must concern us too. *Why is this?* It's because the gravity of potential consequences is such that, in a workplace context, alongside the obvious moral and economic reasons, there are regulations which impose upon organisations a range of requirements which control or limit *what* they release into the environment. And, whilst here we are simply looking at the principle of blocking the unintended escape of a substance – the physical loss of containment – those in charge of high-hazard organisations must also pay particular attention to the intrinsic properties of *what* is released. *Why should this be?* Well, depending on what it is, the additional risks seen through so-called 'domino effect' can include chemical reactions, fires, explosions and spillages – linked to the nature of the substances stored and processes operated by the organisations involved – which rightly mean they fall subject to other more stringent regulatory requirements. *The Control of Substances Hazardous to Health Regulations 2002*[168] *('the COSHH Regulations'),* for instance, require the application of 'control measures' which address the hazardous nature of substances. *The Control of Major Accident Hazards Regulations 2015*[169] *('the COMAH Regulations'),* on the other hand, impose requirements on sites which handle or store certain substances in excess of specified tonnage thresholds, of particular relevance where substances leave site and cause trouble for others. Real-world high-hazard organisations have a responsibility to address the off-site impacts generated by their activities, a topic which is briefly considered in relation to *the four little pigs' fable,* which immediately follows this one.

So, having understood the basic nature of the problem at hand and identified a risk that needs managing – in this case, loss of containment – the next stage of the process is to give some thought as to why managing a particular risk matters.

STAGE #2
UNDERSTAND WHY THE RISK NEEDS TO BE STOPPED OR MANAGED

The focus of this stage is upon developing a rationale as to why a particular risk needs to be stopped or managed, which will likely draw upon a few different factors.

---

168. S.I. 2002/2677.
169. S.I. 2015/483.

One common – and of course, compelling – reason for needing to stop or manage a risk in any given situation is the range of applicable legal requirements, some examples of which were highlighted at *stage one*. Another is the magnitude of the consequences which might flow from a failure to manage the risk, in circumstances where things go wrong. A key point to note is that low probability of a risk materialising doesn't remove the need to control it. Indeed, it's particularly crucial for risks to be well controlled where the consequences of failure are *high*, even where the likelihood of their occurrence is regarded as *low*. Taking the time to analyse and comprehend the full range of potential consequences is a vital stage of the process for organisations serious about managing their risks. *And why is this?* It's simply because when organisations appreciate the gravity of consequences which could flow from their failure to manage a risk for which they are responsible, this should give them the necessary impetus to remove or control it, which in turn builds their understanding about what they are required to do, by way of resource allocation and prioritisation. Historically, even high-hazard organisations have tended to focus on personal injury rates, often to the detriment of monitoring significant process safety issues but, left unchecked, seemingly small failures in process safety monitoring can have catastrophic consequences – both in terms of threats to 'personal safety' and for the 'reliability' of plant and equipment performance – which is particularly important where 'safety critical systems' are involved. It's for this reason that process safety has rightly moved further up the priority list on many a corporate agenda. And of course, these aren't the only drivers.

If further justification were needed as to *why* a risk needs to be managed, we only have to consider for a moment some real-world failed containment incidents, which starkly show what can happen when things do go wrong. The insights from these are helpful because they highlight dramatic effects – things that go *'CRACKLE!'*, *'POP!'*, or *'SQUELCH!'* – which result from small, sometimes seemingly innocuous, failings or oversights at site level. And whilst these events are viewed as failures themselves, they often, in turn, reveal another layer of big failings elsewhere. This might be due to shortcomings in the performance of tasks by 'functional managers', 'process managers', or 'operatives', but can equally be rooted in failings on the part of 'senior leaders' too. There are many well-documented cases – seen across multiple industries – where little gaps or weaknesses in management system controls have led to big problems, by either creating or permitting catastrophic outcomes – to the detriment of people, process plant, and the environment. This is an area to be considered in more detail later, supported by the context of the fable, but first, here are some real-world examples of failures to manage a loss of containment risk.

Buncefield (Great Britain, 2005) was a noteworthy case of so-called 'barrier (or risk control) failure'. There, the overfilling of a tank resulted in the spillage of 250,000 litres of fuel. *The cause?* A stuck gauge and an inoperable switch. Digging a little deeper shows that there, an independent overflow would have solved the problem – avoiding the extensive damage to plant and the environment that resulted – the absence of this feature being picked out as an 'underlying cause' within the 'Buncefield report' that followed. Another notable example was that of *Associated Octel (Great Britain, 1994).* There, a major pool fire plus secondary fires resulted, when there was a leak between fixed pipework and the discharge port of a pump recirculating liquids to a reactor. *The cause in that case?* The 'Associated Octel report' found that this was either the failure of pipework due to a corroded flange working loose, or the failure of a flexible connection, connecting a pump discharge port to a pipe.

Now of course, in both of these cases, just as is true of other well-known high-consequence incidents, it would be naïve to suggest that a mended switch, a new flange, or a replaced flexible connection would have entirely abated the problems that followed. *But the point is that few big incidents start off as big things.* And of course, the need to attend to the small things that stop these big incidents, which we'll explore shortly, isn't unique to loss of containment scenarios. These small things are simple shortfalls – in plant or equipment not performing as it should, or humans not carrying out tasks as intended – which result in failures to control risk to the standard which is required and expected. For a further example, we only need look to the rail sector and the redundant bare wire left dangling and connected in the *Clapham Junction* incident. It was to be this dangling wire which would ultimately lead to inadvertent contact being made with a terminal, an incorrect signal being given, the devastating loss of 35 human lives, and injury of nearly 500 others, 69 seriously.

A point the *Clapham Junction* incident poignantly makes is that 'vigilance' at critical points always matters. It matters when putting in place barriers (or closing gaps in safety management). It also matters when designing and developing 'permit-to-work' systems and 'independent verification' activities, as well as processes for reporting – even minor – incidents. It matters at times of job handover or managing business change too. Such vigilance is, to a large extent, about ensuring the delivery of basic risk controls (barriers), as well as having the required level of confidence that they will work on demand, every time they are needed. Crucially, this includes being sure that the vital roles played by people in making barriers work – through the performance of their safety critical tasks – are carried out without them being tired, distracted, or having their performance impaired for any other reason. This issue was noted in the report that followed Clapham Junction – the 'Hidden Report' – which identified that, alongside the supervisory and management failings, the technician's 'fatigue' had '...*blunted his working edge, his freshness and his concentration*'[170], a significant 'contributory factor' which undermined the risk controls the organisation thought it had in place to manage the risk.

The common theme to the incidents referred to here – together with many others besides – is that, even in complex industrial settings, it's often the alignment of apparently simple failings, rather than one big thing, which culminates in an unwanted catastrophic outcome. And however unlikely such alignment, or rare the consequential outcomes might be, wherever such risks are identified, they must be robustly assessed and addressed; this is why the goal of controlling risk needs to be pursued the whole way along the barrier management process – from the point of barrier selection, through to barrier modelling and ultimately by barrier-based risk management – a theme we'll see highlighted throughout the course of this fable and in the *modern meaning* that follows it. Ultimately, it's having an understanding of these types of events that enables organisations to determine which are the right risk controls – the barriers – to put in place for a given risk or group of risks, by providing them with the necessary impetus to reduce them to levels which are 'as low as reasonably practicable (ALARP)'. These barriers are the required things and/or actions which stop the bad things from happening. And, in working out why a risk needs to be stopped or managed, organisations must concern themselves not only with using barriers to stop the risk, but also with addressing situations in which the

---

170. '*The Hidden Report*', at page 148, paragraph 16.11.

barriers themselves don't work. A term coined to describe this type of occurrence is a 'barrier failure', which describes circumstances in which the barriers – the things and/or actions organisations use to block something from happening – fail. Organisations don't want their processes, equipment or people to fail – these are bad things. But nor do they want the things or actions they put in place to stop these failures, to fail themselves. This undermines their capability to control risk. It's bad from a resource point of view. It's negative from an incident consequence perspective. And it's detrimental for personal health and safety. It destroys stakeholder confidence in organisations too. This is why it's important not only to understand why a given risk is of concern, but also to appreciate why the failure of things and/or people intended to stop or control that risk can be problematic too.

The simple answer to the question about why managing risk matters is that things which go 'CRACKLE!', 'POP!', or 'SQUELCH!' are, generally speaking, bad for people, bad for processes and bad for the environment. Fires, explosions and spillages are just a few examples of the many undesirable outcomes which highlight why it's so fundamental for risk to be managed effectively, a principle which, as we shall see, can be conveyed particularly well by barrier models.

Thinking about *what* the risk is and *why* it needs managing, as is covered by these first two stages, is helpful in setting up the next stage of the process, the focus of which is upon *how* to go about managing it. Understanding the intrinsic nature of a risk, as well as the gravity of potential consequences which flow if it's uncontrolled, should steer the decisions an organisation makes about which barriers – and how many of them – to put in place to address it.

STAGE #3
WORK OUT HOW TO STOP OR MANAGE THE RISK

This stage is about determining the practical arrangements that need to be in place to effectively manage a given risk.

A focus for many high-hazard organisations is the need to control the risk of hazardous releases and loss of containment of liquids and gases, associated with their operations. It logically follows that they must also be concerned with making sure that the corresponding 'risk control systems' (groups of barriers) they put in place to block such a risk, including 'safety critical equipment', actually work. Commonly referred to as 'barrier effectiveness', this is about the level of confidence organisations have in the things and people they want to stop bad things (their barriers) actually stopping the bad things (top events). This concept is important because organisations devote significant effort and allocate substantial resource to working out *how* to stop risks but, crucially, they must also be sure that the standard they expect from their risk control systems will actually be achieved. Understanding why and how a given risk needs to be stopped or managed is important but – as outlined at *stage two* – it's also vital to have an appreciation of how the things stopping the risk can fail too. Having worked out how to stop a risk, organisations need to be clear about the level of confidence they can place in people and equipment delivering their intended function(s). Put simply, this means that, in the context of a containment scenario, their interest should be in the effectiveness of gauges, alarms, valves, and shut-off systems, together with their expectations for any activities carried out by operatives to make these work. It's this that leads to consideration of the practicalities involved in managing risk, through the use of 'barrier-based thinking'. And it's the effective handling of this stage which puts organisations on the right path to developing an effective risk model, which forms the central concern of *stage four,* the final stage set out here.

In the safety and risk context, 'barrier management' is all about primary business processes and effective risk controls which *save the day*, to stop something going wrong, or limit the consequences, if it does. In essence, it means having the confidence that the selected barriers and the linkages between them are the right ones, and that they work. But more than this, it's about understanding which are the critical barriers – the ones which absolutely *must* work – together with their accompanying status, and in turn knowing how to manage them so that bad things don't happen. And if bad things do happen, the focus of organisations needs to shift swiftly to ensuring that recovery for people, plant and the wider world is as painless, efficient and mess-free as possible.

In working out how to go about stopping a given risk – and more broadly to championing efforts towards a barrier-based risk management approach – it's advisable for organisations keep in mind three simple, but important, questions, which are: *first, 'What could possibly go wrong?', second, 'How will we stop it and will it work?'* and *third,* and finally, *'How do we know that what we want to stop it will do so?'* These questions are of use not only for analysing this fable's loss of containment ending but more particularly, in a real-world context, by helping to set good general guiding principles for anyone tasked with the day-to-day control of high-risk process operations where the performance of safety critical tasks is required. The questions go to the heart of the barrier management principle and – when answered honestly – they are insightful for the design and build of any type of risk model.

We'll revisit these questions later, to help guide the development of a risk model – specifically, a bow tie model – for the scenario the tale sets out.

QUESTION #1
WHAT COULD POSSIBLY GO WRONG?

In analysing this question for the events described by the fable, we shall identify the 'hazard' and 'top event', together with potential 'threats' and 'consequences', based on the detail it contains, just as would need to be done for any equivalent real-world scenario. Regarded as *the risk question*, this is the question that senior leaders should constantly ask themselves which, when well answered for the full scope of an organisation's operations, will inform the contents of its 'risk register' – a document seen by many as an essential risk management tool. Indeed, the risk register is often the go-to place for an organisation's senior leaders, when seeking to answer the *'What could possibly go wrong?'* question. It addresses this question by identifying, quantifying and assessing the likelihood and severity of operational failures, and documenting these risks, together with the actions required to manage and respond to them. Simply expressed, such registers typically log the risks spanning the full range of an organisation's activities (and other risks to which it is subject), which in turn helps it to determine those which are of greatest concern. When used effectively, a risk register is an invaluable tool for an organisation seeking to prioritise resource towards those risks most in need of further control – which can include plant, process, people and performance 'risk reduction measures' – also enabling it to work out how to plug any gaps, where the current level of risk is deemed to be unacceptably high.

It's worth keeping in mind that it doesn't just have to be one big thing that goes wrong. In fact, the thing that goes wrong – and that which barriers seek to block – is often symptomatic of a weakness in controlling risk, rather than the cause itself. As has already been recognised, analysis of major incidents – including *Buncefield* and *Clapham Junction*, alongside numerous others – tells us that these are often the result of a number of, on their own, small failures lining up which conspire to create top events and/or allow consequences to flow unchecked.

Following the fable, the answer to this first question will be used to initiate the building of a risk picture, as the first step towards understanding what needed to be in place to manage the particular risk.

QUESTION #2
HOW WILL WE STOP IT, AND WILL IT WORK?

This question – *the operational management question* – falls to anyone with responsibilities for the management of, or involvement in, safety critical processes. It's the answering of this question that enables a decision to be reached about which barriers to put in place, and a view to be taken as to whether the chosen barriers will be effective on demand, when called upon or required, or – to put it another way – whether risk controls will work at the point and time of need. In terms of developing a successful approach to barriers, there are two distinct aspects: *first,* putting them in place, and *second,* maintaining them, including checking to confirm that they continue to function as intended, on an ongoing basis. This fable prompts an exploration of the first *'How will we stop it?'* aspect – by selecting barriers to prevent a specific threat from leading to a top event and, if this fails, selecting other barriers which prevent or minimise the consequences which flow from it. It also offers up some basic insights as to the reasons each barrier can fail – which picks up on the second *'Will it work?'* aspect of this question.

The four little pigs' fable that follows this one sees a slight shift in emphasis, looking as it does at different 'barrier types' ('passive', 'active' and 'procedural'), and outlining how each of these functions to stop threats or block consequences. This will add to the introductory context given here, by providing a brief description of how each type operates, together with an overview of how the barrier type determines the actions required to ensure it always works. The *four little pigs' fable* will also highlight the value of instituting effective incident and emergency response planning processes, which are of importance both in testing for failure, and for anticipating and limiting potential consequences.

Practically speaking, the *'How will we stop it, and will it work?'* question is best addressed by looking at what's required from those with day-to-day control over work activities, including process managers and functional managers. In large organisations, the arrangements for managing risk at the operational management level are often informed by the outputs of risk models[171] or other risk analysis techniques, which take the risks identified at the strategic level and visually show the barriers in place to prevent the causes of a top event and/or mitigate the consequences, should such an event occur. When used successfully, these risk analysis techniques help to foster an understanding amongst process and functional managers, as well as the operatives they oversee, about the barriers for which they are responsible, or in which they have a key role to play.

We'll seek to address both aspects of this 'How will we stop it, and will it work?' question in the modern meaning attached to this fable. The answer to this second question is to be used to start developing the bow tie model – as is to be introduced at stage four of the process outlined here – to illustrate the barriers which should have been in place and functional, with reference to the account of circumstances provided by the fable.

QUESTION #3
HOW CAN WE BE SURE IT WILL WORK?

In what can be regarded as *the assurance question,* this question goes to the heart of the assurance remit, as is often overseen by an organisation's internal specialists. As such, it draws in any processes organisations have in place to test whether their barriers are operating as expected, enabling them to determine whether the selected risk controls have or will perform as intended, when required. It follows that the answer to this question will often be derived from a range of processes, including audits, inspections, quality testing and other assurance methods. A brief insight into assurance is provided in *How to... Guide Six,* which accompanies this fable and gives some indicative

---

171. There are many different types of risk models available, an example of which is the bow tie model (a particular type of barrier model) outlined in the context of this fable. Some further aspects of the model's functionality are considered in relation to *the four little pigs' fable.*

assurance question sets, focusing on the types of questions that might be asked in relation to containment arrangements. A robust assurance process should methodically check that the barriers put in place to address the *'How will we stop it, and will it work?'* question are actually used by operatives at the frontline – or indeed, anyone else with a role to play in making them work – and that their effectiveness is validated. Or, to take the reactive approach – from the perspective of analysing incident causes – it should make sure that any gaps in an organisation's arrangements for managing risk are identified, resolved and closed.

The step-by-step approach to developing a bow tie model follows within the modern meaning which accompanies this fable, being steered by both the response to question one, about what could possibly go wrong, and to question two, about how to stop it and whether it will work. Delving deeper and addressing this third question will show how the integration of bow tie modelling within a broader assurance approach can be insightful, for instance by informing the structure of audits and inspections.

When used to best effect, the practical insights offered by risk models can be used to help progress and drive forward an organisation's risk management strategy. This can, in turn, lead to effective barrier-based risk management and the delivery of strong operational performance. A robust assurance methodology is key, as it supports the risk management strategy, by providing clear signals to organisational management about the level of confidence they can put in the risk controls or barriers believed to be in place.

Having dwelt upon this third question about how a given risk is to be managed, this completes the first three stages of the process. It's the addressing of these three questions which provides the basis for bow tie model development, as forms the subject of stage four.

STAGE #4
WORK OUT WHAT THE BOW TIE MODEL LOOKS LIKE

This stage is essentially about risk visualisation and exploration.

In seeking to understand more about a risk – sometimes colloquially expressed as *'what the risk looks like'* – organisations will often use risk models. There are many different types of risk model, but broadly speaking they share a common purpose of seeking to deepen organisational risk understanding. Some risk models are very complex. Some are highly numerical, or quantitative, whilst others are more visual, or qualitative, in nature. A barrier model is just one type of risk model, which depicts a series of barriers between a threat and a risk, and between a risk and potential consequences, with the barriers selected and put in place consisting variously of equipment, processes, procedures and people elements. One particular type of barrier model is the bow tie model, which is to be the focus here.

First used in the oil & gas industry, this type of model has now been applied within many other industries – including across the rail, maritime, aviation, mining, and chemical sectors – and has enjoyed a sustained rise in popularity across high-hazard organisations in recent years. As a risk tool, its principal purpose is to help support and grow an organisation's pro-active understanding of risk, by offering insights for risk identification and effective risk management, a feature which can prove particularly effective when linked to a 'health and safety management system'. This modelling method – which sees organisations developing visual risk pictures to help them understand the scope of their risks, often in the context of a 'safety case' – produces easily comprehensible outputs and can help them with risk prediction too. Whilst it can be used to support understanding of any risks, it works particularly well for modelling those which, although rare or low frequency, are particularly bad when they do occur, having potentially large consequences. It's these potentially large consequences – amongst them multiple fatalities and major process control failures – which understandably mean that organisations are expected to put in place strict arrangements to ward off any negative effects. Colloquially expressed, examples of these large consequence-low frequency risks include big things toppling over ('structural collapses') and big things plummeting to a lower level ('dropped objects'), which are looked at in the context of Zac's fable, as well as big spills (losses of containment), which form the focus of the modelling example used in the context of this fable.

The bow tie model visually shows an organisational risk – a so-called 'top event' – together with the risk controls and mitigations – or barriers – that are, or should be, in place to prevent it from occurring or limit the consequences, if it does happen. In order for organisations to harness the full practical benefits of bow tie models as organisational risk tools – over and above the theoretical insights they have to offer – defining the extent and context of their use is both important and helpful. In short, there are two key ways in which these models can be applied. First, at a 'macro level' they can be used to illustrate the relationships between multiple parties with collective responsibilities for managing given risks – for instance, across an industry – by reinforcing understanding about the scope, extent and margins of risks for which different organisations are responsible. This is of particular importance where risk ownership is distributed between multiple parties. *Second*, at a 'micro level' the models can help to communicate the internal organisational arrangements and associated responsibilities expected to be in place for managing given risks or top events, for which an organisation has sole ownership. When used to best effect at this level, bow tie models can serve as vital internal risk tools, underpinning organisational risk strategies and helping to define lines of responsibility, by assigning ownership for barriers to different roles, functions and levels. The example used in this fable aligns more closely to this second micro level approach.

Once the context and scope of any given bow tie has been decided, it's at this point that the model's practical development can begin! Having outlined the bow tie modelling concept and made reference to the role of barriers in preventing unwanted events and consequences, it's worth rewinding for a moment to reflect on the origins of the approach, before delving into the detail. To assist with this, it's helpful to recognise the bow tie model as a derivation of the oft-quoted 'Swiss cheese model', as proposed by James Reason (1997). This model will no doubt be familiar to some readers, but for those for whom it's a novel concept, here's a quick overview. The model depicts each of an organisation's risk control systems as a series of barriers, represented by slices of randomly-holed Swiss cheese arranged vertically and parallel to each other with gaps in between each of the slices. And it suggests that most incidents can be traced to one or more of four levels of failure, namely: organisational influences, unsafe supervision, preconditions for unsafe acts (which can include mental fatigue and ineffective communication), and the unsafe acts themselves. The holes in the Swiss cheese slices represent weaknesses in specific parts of the system, observable in their continual variability in size and position across all slices. The system as a whole fails when holes in all of the slices momentarily align, permitting a trajectory of failure, which allows a hazard to pass through holes in all of the defences and thus, results in an incident. This highlights one of the basic principles of effective process safety management, which is that no single fault should be capable of leading to failure, or expressed differently, that no 'single point of failure' should be allowed to exist.

The Swiss cheese model highlights that, although many barriers may lie along the path between a given threat and top event, few barriers are perfect. This means if the flaws in multiple consecutive barriers align, an incident occurs, which is shown as a top event outcome. The central thrust of the model is that, whilst few barriers are entirely free of holes, provided that the holes don't fully align, top events will be prevented. In the majority of cases, this is successful because the probability of one or more barriers being effective is such that top events will be prevented, or the consequences of them partially or fully avoided. It's rare for all barriers to fail – or at least, for them to fail entirely – just as it's unusual to find a block of Swiss cheese with a hole from one side right through to the other! But – as was true of the incidents at *Clapham, Buncefield* and *Associated Octel,* and many more besides – unlikely outcomes can still occur, meaning organisations need to adopt suitable mitigation measures against their negative effects. The bow tie model builds upon the principle of the Swiss cheese model and, as well as providing a risk picture, offers a structure by which to monitor the status of barriers, thus enabling the effectiveness of the risk controls to be tested.

In order to visually demonstrate this approach, *Appendix D* shows a simplified depiction of James Reason's Swiss cheese model. The upper half of this image indicates – in a very basic fashion – what can happen when prevention barriers are missing, incomplete or defective. Even from this crude sketch, we see that, just as the alignment of holes through a block of Swiss cheese would provide a line of sight through to the other side, so a threat can find its way through barrier holes, creating a top event – shown as an *unhappy* or undesired outcome. And, just as a weak prevention barrier allows a threat to culminate in a top event, if a top event is allowed to occur and the mitigation barriers which are intended to stop or limit the effects following it are missing, incomplete or defective, this results in an undesired consequence. This is shown as the result, or *unhappy flow*, of outcomes from the top event, in the lower half of the image in *Appendix D*.

As we'll see shortly, this basic – but powerful – Swiss cheese principle is the foundation upon which the building of bow tie models is predicated. The partial building of a bow tie model for the porridge pot scenario this fable sets out forms a key part of its accompanying *modern meaning*. But, in addition to knowing *how* these models are built, it's also important to understand the inherent properties of each barrier type (the model's building blocks) and the role played by the respective types in either preventing a top event from occurring, by blocking a threat, or in mitigating the consequences, should such a top event occur. This aspect will be addressed in more detail, when the concept of barrier type is considered in the context of *the four little pigs' fable*, which immediately follows this one.

At this point, it's worth dwelling briefly upon some of the key benefits offered by bow tie models. As has been said, simply expressed, these models depict risks through easy-to-understand visual risk pictures and the reason they are referred to as 'bow ties' should soon become clear. Such models extend Reason's Swiss cheese principle, by showing the range of threats which lead towards, and the consequences that flow away from, a top event. They also show the barriers – both prevention and mitigation types – which should be in place to manage the risk. By displaying multiple possible scenarios in one picture, these models provide a basic visual explanation of a risk, making them easier to understand than some of the more conventional and complex risk modelling techniques, as well as overcoming the difficulties associated with articulating a risk in written form. In addition to the fresh insights these models provide, their straightforward nature means they naturally double as good communication tools, therefore appealing to a broader audience than is true of some other methodologies.

Furthermore, whilst not an area this book explores in detail, a particularly useful capability offered by barrier models – including bow tie models – is their ability to delineate responsibilities for those involved in managing risks. This feature can help people to understand their individual and collective roles in controlling risk, as well as enabling potential gaps in the control of risk – or barrier shortfalls – to be readily identified and addressed. This can in turn provide the focus for an organisation's improvement programmes and add weight to the decisions it makes about resource allocation and prioritisation too. In particular, the multi-level responsibilities they are capable of depicting can stimulate increased collaboration and co-operation between all parties involved in the control of risk – as well as making clear the expectations placed upon them too – wherever they might sit within an organisation's hierarchy. As such, a key benefit seen from the approach tends to be that it aids decision-making, in turn helping to inform and shape organisational safety and risk policy. It achieves this by extending the insights offered by the models through to broader barrier-based risk management principles.

As already outlined, one example of a top event for which an organisation might choose to develop a bow tie model is loss of containment or, colloquially put, *stuff falling or flowing out of a container which was supposed to contain it.* Containers include tanks, tankers, or buildings, to name but a few examples. Based on the same broad principles, the example of the model that is to be partially developed here will show how it can depict the threats and consequences, together with the barriers in place which either prevent a threat being manifested in a *too much porridge* (loss of containment) top event, or limit its consequences, in circumstances where a top event has already occurred. This is to include looking at the role played by each barrier in preventing the top event or its consequences and specifically, whether they are effective in delivering their intended function.

This kind of background context is invaluable when building risk models, as will be highlighted in the modern meaning to this fable.

THE FOCUS OF THIS FABLE

This fable looks at an overflowing peculiar – and ultimately perilous – porridge pot, naturally raising questions as to which were the potential points of failure that led to the undesired *too much porridge* threat evolving into a loss of containment top event. In seeking to determine these failure points, the fable acts as the trigger for insights into the use of bow tie models and the barriers required to stop things going 'CRACKLE!', 'POP!', or 'SQUELCH!' or equivalent barriers which lessen consequences, when these things do happen. As such, it seeks to provide key learning points for effective process control, which can be readily applied within a real-world context.

So what can we learn from a slight twist on a childhood fable about a surfeit of breakfast oats? We're about to find out...

THE FABLE

Once upon a time, there was a poor little girl who lived with her mother. They had very little to eat. To the outsider, their claims to poverty were somewhat inexplicable. They had a big house in a nice area. They had a car of their own too. But beneath the veneer of a comfortable lifestyle, all was not well. For whilst they had a big house in a nice area, it had been the little girl's mother's desire to acquire their big house which had meant they'd been living beyond their means for some time now. And if they wanted to keep this particular roof over their heads, it was inevitably going to mean them cutting out other luxuries, of which high-end food choices were but one example.

One day, the little girl went off into the street to play. She was so hungry that she began to cry, whereupon, as if from nowhere, an old woman vaguely known to the family approached her. 'Why are you crying, little girl?' she asked. 'Because I am *so* hungry!' said the little girl.

'Then I shall see to it that you are hungry no more...' said the old woman, recognising the little girl's distress, and presented to her a peculiar porridge pot, adding: '...your luck is in, little lady! I acquired this peculiar porridge pot at a local car boot sale, just the other day – here, take it! When you are hungry, just say to it: 'Perform, peculiar porridge pot! *Perform!*' and it will cook some delicious porridge for you.' It appeared to the little girl to be a rusty old vessel, a little like the gift-bearer, but she made a thinly-veiled attempt to hide her cynicism, replying simply, 'Why thank you! I don't know quite *what* to say...' and allowed the old woman to continue on with her lesson in pot-based cookery.

Unsurprisingly perhaps, as was suggested by its name, the peculiar porridge pot had a number of quirks. It came with some associated pipework and seemingly, there were options to connect it up in the home, meaning it offered the potential for porridge to be delivered on tap, almost like water! The old woman proceeded to explain its various features – notably a gauge, an alarm and a shut-off valve – but it wasn't long before she started to sense that the little girl wasn't listening. In truth, whilst the little girl thought the vessel would be a welcome addition to their kitchen, she had no wish to be bothered by what she perceived to be excessively complex technical information, at so early a stage of peculiar porridge pot ownership. She was at that point in life where she had still to decide whether or not an engineering career was for her. Realising that the little girl's mind was wandering, the old woman decided to cut short their conversation. 'When you have had enough and want the peculiar porridge pot to stop cooking...' went on the old woman, '...you must say, 'Pause, peculiar porridge pot! *Pause!*' and it will stop for you.' She handed the little girl an accompanying set of 'quick start (and stop) instructions', rolled her eyes, let out an audible sigh of disapproval, and went on her way.

The little girl was so hungry and was naturally eager to try out her new kitchenware. No sooner was she back home, than she said to the peculiar porridge pot: 'Perform, peculiar porridge pot! *Perform!*' And sure enough, the peculiar porridge pot did as instructed and started to cook some porridge. The little girl was suddenly overwhelmed by a sense of self-importance, thinking she might have become the unwitting participant in an exciting trial for a new application of voice-recognition software – a *porridge pioneer* or a *gruel guru* of sorts. Soon enough there was sufficient porridge to satisfy her hunger. The little girl could hardly wait to try some. When the porridge was cooked, the little girl said, 'Pause peculiar porridge pot! *Pause!*' The porridge tasted good and she devoured every last bit of it. It was difficult to judge the readiness of the porridge, as the pot's level gauge was not easy to read, but the little girl was a quick learner blessed with 20/20 vision and she estimated well on this occasion, so no harm was done. Youthful good fortune was on her side and she was one of those slightly irritating people in life, who seemed to breeze through every day on a happy combination of casual ease and lucky guesswork.

Even at this early stage of peculiar porridge pot acquisition, the little girl should perhaps have realised that the difficulty in reading the porridge pot's level gauge meant it was often unclear whether the porridge level was higher than it should be. But given the combination of her youthful enthusiasm, inexperience and unfortunate lack of basic risk awareness, the little girl wasn't going to allow herself to be troubled by this kind of minor detail.

On her mother's return home from work, the little girl proudly presented the peculiar porridge pot to her, and told her what the old woman had said. They were freed from their life of poverty and hunger, and ate sweet porridge as often as they chose. 'Now our worries are behind us! Not for us a ridiculous handful of beans, in exchange for a cherished cow...' chirruped her mother happily, in a bit of a jibe at the unfortunate boy who had been the focus of a local beanstalk-based anecdote. And, in closing the conversation, her mother declared simply: '*Verily*, the peculiar porridge pot will keep us well-fed!'

It wasn't as if the little girl had magical powers, but she knew what to say, and when and how to say it. In her youthful brain, she remained undecided as to whether she wished to be referred to as *the person in charge* or an *oat aficionado*, but on one point she was certain – she wanted to be held in high regard for anything to which she applied her mind, such was her naturally competitive nature. Whenever they were hungry, the little girl would say to the peculiar porridge pot, 'Perform, peculiar porridge pot! *Perform!*' And sure enough, porridge would appear. The porridge was very tasty, and they always enjoyed it. It had the additional benefit of being a one-pot meal too, which saved on the washing up.

A few months later...

One day, when the little girl had once again eaten her fill, having topped up the pot with the usual oaty mixture and set out on her way to school, her mother felt hungry and, remembering what her daughter had said, uttered the words: 'Perform, peculiar porridge pot! *Perform!*' in the general direction of the pot. And it did cook, and she ate until she was full, and then she wanted the peculiar porridge pot to stop cooking, but was unsure as to whether she had remembered the right magic words. This, compounded with her lack of skill in interpreting the peculiar porridge pot's gauge, did not bode well. The little girl's mother uttered the words 'Pause, peculiar porridge pot! *Pause!*' but these seemingly had no effect. This did not immediately concern her, however, so absorbed was she in her enjoyment of the tasty porridge. But to the knowledgeable onlooker, there were already some ominous warning signs. For one thing, the little girl's mother was unaccustomed with the skills required for peculiar porridge pot work. For another, it was apparent that she was tiring of the modern world's fixation with passwords having more than eight characters, including a capital letter and at least one special symbol – a mindset which possibly prejudiced her against remembering small details such as peculiar porridge pot stop commands. She was also unaware of the appropriate action to be taken in the event of an alarm sounding or indeed, the finer points about the operability of the shut-off valve. In fact, now she came to think of it, the little girl's mother couldn't recall having seen these bits of kit before. Her level of understanding was somewhat questionable and she appeared frighteningly naïve to the ways of peculiar porridge pot cookery.

After several more futile attempts, during which she frantically tried out multiple word order combination guesses of peculiar porridge pot commands, she finally gave up, having a hunch that perhaps all was not well, but recognising that she lacked the wherewithal to do anything more about it.

And so, the peculiar porridge pot went on and on, cooking more and more porridge.

The little girl's mother's lack of understanding of the gauge dial meant she failed to observe it correctly or to interpret the significance of the level reached.

And still the peculiar porridge pot went on and on, cooking more and more porridge, with the gauge level ominously rising and rising, as it did so...

The alarm sounded but was meaningless to the little girl's mother. Her mind was on other things and the occasional buzz, bleep or flashing light were just further sources of irritation, as far as she was concerned. The lack of response to the high level alarm led somewhat inevitably to a failure to prevent overfill, with the porridge flowing from the peculiar porridge pot to the kitchen and then onwards throughout the house.

So it went on cooking and the porridge rose over the edge, and still it cooked on, until the kitchen and whole house was full...and then the next house, and then the whole street, just as if it wanted to satisfy the hunger of the whole world. It was terrible and they seemed to be powerless to stop it. It appeared to have taken on a life of its own! By this time even the little girl's mother, who was slow to respond at the best of times, realised something was seriously amiss, but knew not what to do...

The failure to activate the shut-off valve meant that the porridge spilled out from the house, into the surrounding environment. Though she didn't appreciate it at the time, the little girl's mother was facing a loss of containment situation. And quite a serious one, at that.

But still the peculiar porridge pot went on, cooking more and more porridge!

Soon, all the houses in the street were full of porridge.

And still the peculiar porridge pot went on, cooking more and more porridge...

Before long, nearly all the streets in the town were full of porridge.

And still the peculiar porridge pot went on cooking more and more porridge...

The people who lived in the neighbouring houses started coming out into the streets. No-one knew how to stop the peculiar porridge pot from cooking more porridge.

It just went on and on, cooking more and more porridge.

The people in the town began to think that soon the entire county would be filled with porridge. The little girl's mother didn't know what to do. She was out of her depth and, to make matters worse, feared she would soon be up to her eyeballs in porridge too.

When the little girl returned home from her day at school, she was shocked at the scene of chaos and devastation unfolding before her eyes, shrieking at her mother: 'What *have* you done?' to which the terse reply came back: 'What have I done? What have *I* done? That's rich, coming from you, dear! What have *you* done, more like? I know we needed food, but I only wanted some basic provisions. It's true to say that we didn't have the money for a *big shop*, but I never asked for a full-scale process plant to be set up in my kitchen. You'd do well to remember, young lady, that this is a domestic dwelling, not an industrial establishment! Now I come to think of it, I'm tiring of our exclusively porridge-based diet and, whilst we're on the subject, what's with all the gauge, alarm and valve paraphernalia?' The little girl said nothing, walking away purposefully, without uttering a word, her hands on her hips and her mind filled with pre-teenage angst, finding her mother's challenge to be somewhat audacious. By this stage, all of the neighbours had emerged from their properties, wondering what on earth was happening. But no-one could see where the little girl had gone, what with all the commotion. *And porridge.*

At last, when all but one house in the town had been overwhelmed by the oaty mixture, the little girl appeared as if from nowhere – although actually from the direction of the kitchen – yelling 'Pause, porridge pot! *Pause!*' And, as she did so, the pot stopped cooking in an instant, and anyone who wished to return to the neighbourhood would have little choice but to eat their way back. Either that, or someone was going to need to engage a waste contractor for the clean-up operation, no doubt at huge expense. The little girl's mother looked on perplexed, as she had uttered exactly the same words, so hadn't been mistaken about the magic words after all…but then, it wasn't the words that were wrong. It was their whole approach to what, in an industrial setting, would have been viewed as the management of a safety critical process.

The little girl, in attempting to shake her mother out of her state of shock, said: 'Mum, for some time now, I've believed you to be living in some kind of dream world! Magic words are just something to say. I know they sound good, but mark my words, they're no substitute for effective gauge inspections, high level alarm testing or shut-off valve maintenance. I suspected the magic wouldn't last forever. I know you trust your destiny to the power of four leaf clovers, black cats and lucky heather vendors, and use of words like *verily*, but I'd prefer to place my faith in effective process safety management, robust risk controls, and operational competence! *The world's moved on Mum...and if you want my advice, you'd do well to catch up!'* If truth be told, the little girl's mother didn't want her advice but – much like the torrent of porridge spewing forth before them – the little girl's words of wisdom were hard to stop.

It was fair to say that the little girl had initially been somewhat sceptical about the quick-start (and stop) instructions and all the bits of pipework, together with the importance of the gauge, alarm and valve handed to her by the old woman at the time of peculiar porridge pot acquisition. Nevertheless, privately, the little girl had been mulling over what the old woman had said and it was this which had, over recent weeks, spurred her on to attend to the gaps she'd recognised in her knowledge of the pot's various features. She had checked that the gauge was working. She had checked that the high level alarm was functional. She had looked at how the shut-off valve was performing. *She had even started to see if she could learn some basic engineering principles, which she felt sure would serve her well for the future.*

With all this in mind, before coming over to see her mother, the little girl had manually operated the shut-off valve, thereby halting the rising tide of porridge. It turned out that it had been this action of manually shutting off the valve – rather than some strange whizzy magic – which had resulted in the little girl's stemming of the porridge flow at precisely the same moment as her utterance of the words.

The little girl paused momentarily, wiping away the traces of sticky porridge from her skirt, whilst privately rueing the fact that she would need to wash her hair again (only having done so the previous night). On the upside, she felt a sense of relief that the oaty mixture had at least cooled by the time it reached her and, having regained her composure, was quick to resume her conversation with her mother, continuing: 'I'm still learning Mum, but there is one other thing we should have considered – if only we'd thought to fit a remotely operated shut off valve, I wouldn't have needed to enter the area to manually close it, which would have prevented my being exposed to unnecessary risk. You ignoring the alarm – or otherwise failing to react to it – did little to help matters and, whilst we're on the subject of equipment, that gauge is far from ideal, as I know it isn't the easiest of instruments to read or interpret. But I'm at fault too. It's all well and good that I knew what to do, but as I didn't show or instruct you on the necessary action to take, I think I should shoulder at least part of the blame for our current predicament.'

The little girl's mother looked on, wistfully reflecting that life had seemed so much simpler and their diet more varied in the pre-porridge pot days. She was also starting to find her daughter's slightly precocious tendencies a little tiresome. Now she thought about this some more, she realised she probably should have spotted the early warning signs: whilst she had no wish to discourage her daughter's keenness to learn about basic engineering principles, there was no denying it was curious for a girl of her young years to have such advanced knowledge of gauge reading, valve operations and alarm handling. But, on the upside, the little girl's mother was slightly relieved that her daughter was offering at least a partial admission to her involvement in their present breakfast-based fiasco. Maybe, just maybe, her mother hoped, this event would mark the start of her daughter growing up a little.

Once they'd both calmed down a bit, with the porridge threat having diminished, and the levels showing signs of receding, the little girl and her mother re-evaluated their options and finally concluded that the best outcome for all concerned was for the peculiar porridge pot to go! It seemed to be the right decision on all fronts, as was borne out by their own investigation into what had gone wrong. That should, of course, have been the end of the tale, but as is true for many a fable, there's often a follow-up note, worthy of the reader's attention...

Some time passed.

One day, the little girl decided to pay a visit to the car boot-sale she believed to be frequented by the peculiar porridge pot-bearing old woman. And sure enough, it didn't take the little girl long to find her, with the old woman having found for herself a prime pitch in the midst of a number of other car boot vendors. On seeing the little girl, the old woman – who suddenly appeared slightly nervous – enquired as to whether the peculiar porridge pot was delivering the level of sustenance they needed. The little girl replied that it was, or at least it had been, but that it had got out of hand, the vessel having been used by someone unaccustomed with the skills required for peculiar porridge pot pursuits.

The little girl explained to the old woman:

'Porridge was heated, porridge got hot,
Breached the container, flowed out of pot…
Porridge then simmered and started to rise
To the first floor…upstairs…and then blocking the skies.
I think I first sensed things had gone way too far,
When the oats in Mum's engine meant she couldn't start the car.
It felt very much like a hurtful vendetta,
When the porridge was blocking her car's carburettor,
And our dire straits, the subject of much tittle-tattle,
Voiced by locals, looking on at our strange oaty battle.
And all of this happened, because I wasn't looking –
As the person in charge, I deserted the cooking.
A pot not just peculiar, but *perilous* too,
Making urgent our need for process review!
On this sorry chapter, we shall soon turn the page,
But not without thought of alarm, valve and gauge…
And so, moving forward, just two wishes I've got,
To manage containment and *GET RID OF THAT POT!*'

The old woman gave a knowing, slightly shifty look, with the reddening of her face suggesting that perhaps she'd got wind of other peculiar porridge pot owners encountering similar issues to those experienced by the little girl and her mother. She was also feeling awkward, having latterly become aware of an upgrade to the peculiar porridge pot design, which included a remotely operated shut off valve, a feature which entirely averted the need for people to enter porridge-filled properties. Shortly afterwards, there was a mysterious uptick in car boot sale pitch cancellations made by the old woman. And, if rumours were to be believed, she had also been behind the recent spike seen in the number of pre-owned peculiar porridge pots put up for sale on well-known auction websites…

As for the little girl and her mother, they were swift in taking action to shelve their plans to open *The Peculiar Porridge Kitchen*, following their own investigations into what had gone wrong. The little girl worked hard at school and, now with the full backing of her mother, continued on with her research into suitable engineering courses – covering safety critical systems, equipment and instrumentation – for her future studies. And whenever they visited a breakfast buffet, they took great pains to avoid the porridge section, opting instead for toast and marmalade. In truth, it wasn't such a satisfying meal, but they were both in agreement that it made for a much less stressful start to their day.

And the old woman was never to be seen again...

MODERN MEANING

Here, we return to the three questions posed in the prologue, seeking to answer these for the scenario which played out in the fable.

You'll recall that these were: *'What could possibly have gone wrong?'* (the risk question); *'How did they try to stop it, and did it work?'* (the operational management question), and *'How could they have known that what they wanted to stop it, would do so?'* (the assurance question). When analysing any risk scenario or incident, it's important to take the time to understand the relevant practical context that sits behind it, including its nature and scale. The fable describes an unplanned fictional venture on the part of a little girl and her mother but, given an equivalent real-world event, it's clearly the right thing to do to take steps to avoid an outcome of the type that resulted here.

Had the events the fable sets out been on a real-world organisational scale, rather than a fictitious domestic one, it would of course have been necessary for the characters involved to comply with any relevant food processing plant requirements. And had the substance been fuel, rather than an inert substance like porridge, a raft of other stringent requirements would have needed to be met, as are imposed upon 'operators' who carry responsibility for process control within high-risk sectors, where the expectations for reliable containment are understandably higher. Much, of course, depends upon the nature of the substance in question – which could possess flammable, explosive, polluting, or other properties – for which specific risk controls would need to be identified and put in place on a case-by-case basis. In a real-world context, this is a complex area and application varies according to the specific circumstances, but responsible organisations within high-risk sectors will typically focus much of their effort towards the process design stage, often asking themselves questions such as: *'Can a less hazardous substance be used?'*, *'Can smaller quantities be stored or used?'*, *'Can design parameters be adjusted?'* and *'Can pressures be reduced?'* The particular responsibilities imposed upon those that operate within high-risk sectors is a subject given brief attention in relation to *the four little pigs' fable*, which immediately follows this one.

This fable provides a good platform from which to show how the management of process safety risks can be depicted through the use of risk models. Here, the focus of process control needed to be not only upon stopping a loss of containment incident from occurring in the first place, but also – with an event having occurred – on preventing or mitigating its adverse effects. Whilst the tale concerned a perilous porridge pot, the key principles on show here, and which are about to be further explored, can be readily applied to other vessels and substances. These principles are of relevance to any situation in which effective and reliable containment is a requirement and the loss of such containment, a realistic risk. Most organisations implementing effective health and safety management systems, including those which cover process safety, acknowledge the need for continuous checking to ensure their reliable functioning. As such, their arrangements will routinely incorporate checks being made that safety critical tasks are reliably performed by operatives, enabling problems to be identified and fixed, and thus staving off the possibility of a catastrophic event occurring. This principle sits at the heart of effective barrier management and is a topic revisited by the final fable of this collection, which looks at 'performance influencing factors' and the importance of having a robust strategy in place to achieve human performance reliability, both for the good of the people involved and that of the processes within which their actions form an integral part.

For now, let's revisit the three questions posed in the prologue one by one, answering them for the scenario given and developing the bow tie model in parallel, as well as citing the points of failure.

BUILDING A BOW TIE MODEL,
HELPED BY THE THREE KEY QUESTIONS

Whilst framed in the context of a fictional scenario, it's suggested that, by posing these questions and applying the answers given to their own operations, real-world organisations can build models which both enable them to achieve confidence in the measures they have in place, and allow them to readily identify any gaps in their control of risk, which need to be addressed.

QUESTION #1
WHAT COULD POSSIBLY HAVE GONE WRONG?

The focus of this question – regarded as the risk question – is upon precisely defining what might have gone wrong, which can be addressed by building a visual risk picture. In this case, for obvious reasons, this initiates the modelling of a porridge pot overflow – loss of containment scenario.

It's here that the step-by-step building of the bow tie model begins, which leads on from the overview of the Swiss cheese model, supported by *Appendix D*, given in the *prologue*. The basic constituent parts of a generic model are shown in *Appendix E*[172]. This shows a hazard at the top of the model, leading to a top event at its centre. Four 'threat legs' are shown on the left hand side leading to the top event, with two prevention barriers shown on each threat leg. Assuming any one of these prevention barriers to be in place and fully effective, this will act to prevent – or block – the threat on that given threat leg from leading to the top event. The equivalent is true for the right hand side of the bow tie model. If a top event occurs, there is the potential for this to result in one (or more) of the four consequences via the 'consequence legs' shown on the right hand side of the model. In a similar fashion to the prevention barriers shown on the left hand side of the model, the mitigation barriers on the consequence legs can act to prevent or mitigate a given consequence, by blocking the path from the top event to the relevant consequence. But there is one fundamental difference between the two sides of the model which should be noted, and it relates back to the previously described incidents and the Swiss cheese principle, for even where there are many barrier failings or weaknesses along the paths leading between threats and the top event, it will be one threat which ultimately causes an incident. This occurs at the moment when the holes in barriers – or barrier weaknesses – align along a single threat leg. Where consequences differ is that – once the top event has occurred – it's possible for one *or more* of them to flow from a single top event, in circumstances where the mitigation barriers along a given consequence leg are ineffective, or only partially effective.

---

172. The bow tie model elements, and suggested elements, are denoted in square brackets throughout this section, e.g. [hot porridge in porridge pot] refers to the hazard component within the porridge pot overflow – loss of containment bow tie model example.

From its visual appearance, it should already be starting to become apparent why this type of model is referred to as a 'bow tie', with the top event being the central knot and the threats and consequences forming its left and right hand sides, respectively. It should be noted that *Appendix E* shows four threat and four consequence legs for indicative purposes only and that the numbers of legs on each side of a bow tie will vary from model to model, according to the threats and consequences identified for any given top event. The number of barriers also varies between models, being based upon an organisation's analysis of, and its decisions about, the risk controls required to block the threats and consequences applicable to a given top event.

Now, having gained a basic understanding of the approach to the building of a bow tie model, let's apply this practically to the points raised by the fable, to help visualise what went wrong here. Looking at the threat side (left hand side) of the model (*Appendix F*), this shows the hazard in this case to have been [hot porridge in porridge pot], with the top event being [porridge pot overflow – loss of containment]. In this instance, an example threat leg of [porridge produced exceeds porridge pot capacity] has been selected, to illustrate the principles involved. Other examples of threats leading to this risk – the top event – not explored in the fable or shown here, might have included [loss of porridge pot integrity due to a crack or hole in the pot] or [over-pressurisation of porridge pot due to temperature excursion]. Were these also to be shown on the model, they would feature as other threat legs, together with the [porridge produced exceeds porridge pot capacity] threat leg shown. The bow tie model could then be progressively built up, to the level shown in *Appendix E*, with multiple threat legs being added, as appropriate.

Turning next to the consequence side (right hand side) of the model (*Appendix G*), this shows an equivalent example to that provided for the threat leg – but this time for a consequence flowing from the same top event. This side of the model depicts the possible consequences which might have resulted if, as here, the top event materialised due to threats having been inadequately addressed, through a failure to put in place robust prevention barriers. As for *Appendix F*, for clarity one leg only – in this case, a consequence leg of [injury to people from hot porridge released from pot], is shown. Given the level of detail in the fable, however, fewer insights are available for the right hand side of the model, than is true of the left hand side. In order to better understand and plug these gaps in detail for the right hand side, it would be necessary to find out the answers to various questions, including, for instance: 'Were there any injuries, and if so, how severe were they?', 'Was there any property damage and if so, how extensive was this?' and 'Was there any environmental damage caused by the escape of the oaty sludge?', and so on. The fable doesn't make mention of any injuries – only stickiness! – but there would undoubtedly have been property damage, and environmental damage would have been a plausible outcome too. Our priority focus here however, in common with the stance taken by many organisations when thinking about equivalent real-world circumstances, is principally upon the left hand side of the model and what was done to prevent the top event from occurring in the first place.

At face value, the question as to what could possibly have gone wrong here looks to be a straightforward one to answer, but it's always an important one to address thoroughly for any given set of circumstances and as has been said, can be viewed as *the risk question*. This question is answered by the description given to the top event. The accurate definition of top events is essential when seeking to build an in-depth understanding about risks and is the first step for an organisation looking to design appropriate accompanying management systems to control them. The level of information which emerges from such risk models should both align to, and build upon, the detail seen documented within the organisation's risk register. Such registers typically include wide-ranging risks, with other common examples including 'dropped object' and 'fall from height' risks, as are showcased later on in this book, in relation to *Zac's fable*.

Reflecting on the practical outcome this fable describes, the actual level of disruption that resulted here would have depended upon a range of factors, including not only the magnitude of loss of containment and the nature of the substance involved, but also the level to which incident response plans had been developed, and were capable of being mobilised. Just as would be true for any real-world top event, this could have ranged from 'on-site scenarios' with consequences limited to minor process interruption only, right through to major 'off-site scenarios', including injuries, fatalities, disrupted operations, and environmental damage. The question about what could go wrong is one that senior leaders should always be keen to see answered, addressing this for the full extent of their organisation's operational activities. Honesty about risk scenarios is fundamental, including how likely they are to occur and – if the worst does happen – what the anticipated magnitude of harm to people, operational disruption, and environmental damage is likely to be. Having clearly articulated a risk scenario, including the top event and relevant threats, this paves the way for the next questions to be addressed, which seek to check the suitability of the barriers put in place, and to verify their effectiveness.

QUESTION #2
HOW DID THEY TRY TO STOP IT, AND DID IT WORK?

This is the operational management question, which progresses the development of the visual risk picture on a stage further, such that it becomes a 'dynamic risk model'. The focus of this question is upon developing the bow tie model, including barrier (risk control) implementation, which naturally requires that processes are assessed and their effectiveness checked. In this case, the intention should have been for barriers to be instituted which were capable of blocking a loss of containment scenario or, failing that, which worked to limit the extent and severity of the spillage consequences.

It's quite clear that this question is of a more practical nature than the first one, with it typically being answered by understanding both the physical measures put in place, and the actions and deeds of those with process safety responsibilities, specifically: *'Did people choose the right risk controls and do the right things?'* It's at this point that organisations need to take a 'hierarchy of control' approach by *first,* pursuing inherently safer options. If these fail, then *second,* options for preventing loss of containment, such as planned preventative maintenance, and inspection and testing programmes, need to be implemented. And *third* and finally, should these also fail, then mitigation measures including valves and bunding are to be employed.

Identifying the *right* barriers is really important here. Barriers can be viewed as the building blocks of barrier models. As has been said, they are the physical things and/or human actions that stop bad things from happening in the first place. And, in cases where a bad thing has already happened, they should act to stop it from getting worse, or spreading further afield. Having worked out *why* something needs to be stopped, the focus at this point is on deciding *what* should be selected to stop it. It's about making sure the right barriers are chosen and checking that they work. Considered here in the context of loss of containment – but as is equally true for other risk types – barriers operate in two different ways, as combinations of physical features and/or procedures. *First*, prevention barriers act to block the path from any given threat which might materialise, so as to stop it becoming a top event. *Second*, mitigation barriers act to block the path or to diminish the effect of consequences which would otherwise flow from a given top event.

Two further features worthy of note here are the aspirations for barriers to be both 'fully functional' and 'independent'. Typically, for any given top event, there will be a number of threats and consequences, the barriers in defence of which will necessarily be varied – likely to be a range of passive, active and procedural types – as are to be explored through *the four little pigs' fable*. But putting aside barrier type, in order for it to achieve its aim of stopping a threat becoming a top event (in the case of a prevention barrier), or a top event leading to consequences (in the case of a mitigation barrier), a barrier should possess independent and fully functional properties. *So what do these terms mean?* Well, the independent aspect means it should be capable of operating by itself, not depending upon other barriers within the same threat or consequence leg for its success – it doesn't rely on other risk controls protecting against the same threat or mitigating against the same consequence. The fully functional aspect, on the other hand, requires a barrier to be fully capable of stopping a risk scenario developing further – it either stops a specific threat from leading to a top event, or a top event from leading to a consequence(s).

On top of the role played by models in informing the selection of the right barriers for any given scenario, it's important to understand the wider benefits that bow tie modelling has to offer. Bow tie models move barrier thinking on a stage, by showing all the physical things or human actions that stop bad things happening – specifically what's needed, why it's needed, and where it features. They show how all the barrier building blocks connect together, in order to – when they perform effectively – prevent failure. Looking at *Appendix F* again, as we've seen, this depicts part of the left hand side (prevention side) of a bow tie model. It's already been determined that the hazard in this case was [hot porridge in porridge pot], the top event was [porridge pot overflow – loss of containment] and one of the threat legs was [porridge produced exceeds porridge pot capacity]. Now, in looking along the [porridge produced exceeds porridge pot capacity] threat leg, we see the barriers which could have prevented this particular threat from leading to the top event. Three barriers are shown, which can simply be expressed as 'gauge', 'high level alarm' and 'shut-off valve', the intent behind each of these being to prevent the [porridge pot exceeds porridge pot capacity] threat from evolving into the [porridge pot overflow – loss of containment] top event identified. And, in reflecting back upon the Swiss cheese model, any one of these barriers being fully effective would prevent the top event from occurring. In a well-designed model, there's also a clear logic to the order in which the barriers appear. Thinking chronologically, this means if the gauge doesn't work, there's a need to look to the high level alarm, and if the high level alarm doesn't work, we have to pin our hopes (or in the case of responsible real-world organisations, confidence) on the shut-off valve being an effective barrier, to prevent the risk from being realised.

Before looking at the different barriers and delving deeper into the particular efforts made here to stop the threat leading to the top event, it's worth paying brief attention to the intended function of each barrier. In order to prevent overfill of the porridge pot and loss of its contents into the environment – in this case the house, and onwards to the street and the town – the prevention barriers that should have been in place, and which needed to be effective, were as follows. The *first* prevention barrier [gauge & fill level monitoring by operative] should have been comprised of a gauge or 'level indicator' to show the porridge level within the pot, together with operative oversight of the gauge, which would have required the monitoring of the fill level. The *second* prevention barrier [high level alarm & operative response] should have been comprised of a high level alarm, to sound and elicit appropriate operative action, which should have been taken when the porridge level became too high. And the *third* prevention barrier [shut-off valve] should have been a valve intended to quickly and positively stop porridge flow, thereby preventing or mitigating the effects of any loss of containment incident, which was, in this case, operated by manual activation.

Three prevention barriers were therefore provided to stop the threat of [porridge produced exceeds porridge pot capacity] resulting in the [porridge pot overflow – loss of containment] top event. The barriers included both 'safety critical instrumentation' and activities by operatives. During any porridge pot filling operation, the requirement should have been for an operative to check the gauge (*barrier one*), to ensure no overfill of the pot. In cases such as that seen here – this barrier having failed because of the gauge becoming defective, or due to the operative's difficulty in reading or interpreting it and taking appropriate *stop fill* action

– a high level alarm should have initiated (*barrier two*), when the pot was full, and the operative notified to take action to stop the filling operation. And, where the high level alarm barrier also failed – for instance, due to its failure to sound or, as here, failure of the operative to respond – the shut-off valve (*barrier three*) should have been closed when the pot was full, thereby preventing overfill and any subsequent loss of containment scenario. In circumstances where the shut-off valve also failed (as was partially the case here), all three barriers put in place to prevent pot overfill would have failed, meaning that an incident would result.

In the real world, where concerns about prevention barriers failing exist, organisations need to consider and evaluate two parameters, when seeking to determine whether additional or more robust mitigation barriers are required, to further control the risk and protect the integrity of their operations. One consideration is the likelihood of all – in this case three – prevention barriers failing. The other is the magnitude of anticipated consequences, in circumstances where the loss of containment or other risk scenario materialises. Depending on the likelihood of all prevention barriers failing, and the magnitude of the consequences of loss of containment – whether because of proximity to people, property, or the environment – further mitigation barriers might be deemed a requirement for additional protection. Had any one of the prevention barriers described here – the gauge, alarm or shut-off valve (safety critical instrumentation) and accompanying operative action – been fully effective, however, the top event reported in this scenario would not have resulted from a pot capacity exceedance threat, thereby averting the overwhelming of the kitchen, the house and ultimately, the locality with porridge. Or, to put it another way, the [porridge produced exceeds porridge pot capacity] threat leg would have been blocked from culminating in the top event. In making an assessment as to whether barriers are effective in preventing a top event, it's necessary to look at each of the barriers on the left hand side in turn.

CHECKING THREAT (LEFT HAND SIDE)
BARRIER EFFECTIVENESS

Taking each of this model's prevention barriers, let's consider how they appeared to perform under test or, put negatively, at the points where failure seems to have occurred here. We start by looking at the first barrier, working along the simple representation of the threat leg shown in *Appendix F.*

Did barrier #1 work?
[Gauge & Fill Level Monitoring by Operative]

NO! *The failure by the little girl's mother (operative) to correctly read the gauge meant she did not acknowledge the gauge indication that the level was excessively high and, as a result, neglected to take the appropriate action. The gauge was fitted, but the 'fill level monitoring by operative' element was not fulfilled and there was therefore incomplete execution of the barrier.*

The function of the gauge was to visually display the contents of a vessel – in this case, the pot. A gauge is an essential piece of equipment for securing effective process control and here, this should have provided the operative with a clear indication of how much porridge was in the pot, including showing when it was full. Generally speaking, a gauge provides a simple and easy to understand visual indication of when a level is running high. A gauge can be operated on a float, hydrostatic, electronic or sight basis but, irrespective of the mode of operation, the principle behind its operation is the same and when it works as intended it's an invaluable tool for achieving successful process control. A poor gauge or a poor understanding of a gauge, by contrast, can lead to a bad decision and, ultimately, to incidents and/or process downtime.

A gauge had been fitted but was unintelligible to the little girl's mother.

The barrier was ineffective due to being incomplete. In circumstances where the operative and/or gauge fails, the spill prevention system fails. The presence of the gauge alone was therefore insufficient, there being a requirement for the *fill level monitoring by operative* element to be in place, for it to have been fully effective. In this case, it was the absence of fill level monitoring which caused the barrier to fail. This is unsurprising because monitoring is a common element for those 'active barriers' which require some form of intervention by a human operative in order to be effective[173].

Here, we are led to believe that the little girl's mother struggled with, misinterpreted, or didn't try to read the gauge. Misreading or

---

173. The basic features of 'active' barriers, as well as those of the 'passive' and 'procedural' types, are considered in relation to *the four little pigs' fable* (fable seven).

misinterpreting a gauge due to an operative's observational error can pose problems for process control, but there can be many other issues with gauges. Connections and display clarity are important, but so too are environmental conditions. If a gauge is unsuited to the environment within which it is located, for instance due to temperature extremes or excessive vibration, these are all factors which can cause the equipment to malfunction. *What* is being measured matters too. Where the substance or process media is prone to clogging – as would probably have been true of the sticky porridge here – this can interfere with the operation of gauges, caused by congealment, an issue which can be addressed by the fitting of appropriate seals. In an organisational context, the importance of maintenance regimes – particularly their need to pick up damage and degradation – should not be underestimated, as these programmes support continuing gauge effectiveness. Carrying out checks to see that gauges haven't become damaged or cracked – which could impair the ease with which readings are interpreted – ensures their continued legibility and accuracy. The checking of level transmitters is important too, these being components vital to ensuring the correct functioning of these pieces of safety critical equipment.

The final point to make on gauges here is that operatives need to be given the right instruction and awareness training in their use. When properly understood, instructions and guidance on how to read instruments enable operatives to both comprehend what is presented to them and take the right action based upon the information they receive. *But in reality, it isn't always that simple.* Conflicting pressures and 'workload' are significant factors influencing human performance in terms of barrier delivery. If operatives are overwhelmed by competing workload pressures, roles and responsibilities or other outside factors, this can impair the reliability with which they take the relevant readings and/or any accompanying action they are expected to perform as a result of them[174]. It's for this reason that, in a real-world context, the ideal scenario is for the accountability for each barrier to sit with different operatives. This reduces the possibility of there being a single point of failure, as it avoids the need for operatives to divide their attention between the responsibilities associated with multiple barriers, thus reducing the likelihood of simultaneous barrier failure.

---

174. For some insights as to the factors which influence the reliability of human performance, refer to *Not-Quite's fable* (fable ten).

Despite the operative's failure to interpret the gauge, it should still have been possible to prevent the loss of containment incident, due to the sounding of a high level alarm, which would have provided an indication of the need to take positive action. It's to the failure of this second barrier that our attention turns next...

Did barrier #2 work?
[High Level Alarm & Operative Response]

NO! *The failure by the little girl's mother (operative) to respond to the high level alarm meant that no action was taken. We are told that she found it irritating. The overfill scenario was not correctly interpreted, meaning a loss of containment resulted, with the porridge flowing out of the pot, into the house and beyond.*

Present in many safety critical environments, alarms alert us to things requiring our attention. The function of alarm warnings is to allow sufficient time to take corrective action, ensuring the safe and economic operation of vessels, and preventing overflow and consequences including injuries, plant damage, and pollution of watercourses, which, in a real-world context can result in expensive fines and clean-up costs. Often used in combination with gauges, the function of a high level alarm is to let off a sounder or other appropriate cue, such as a visual warning, when a pre-set high level is hit. In order to be complete, an alarm needs to have a defined purpose, elicit a defined response from an operative, and allow adequate time for them to carry out that response. It should be presented to the operative at a point relevant to their role at the time, clearly indicating the response required from them. And, in circumstances where multiple alarms might activate, they need to be presented at a rate which can be dealt with and easily understood by operatives. Where this aspect isn't addressed, it can lead to confusion, overload and distraction, and may result in important information not being acted upon.

A high level alarm had been fitted but it was unintelligible to the little girl's mother. Let's consider the other issues with high level alarms the fable highlighted.

It is, of course, positive that a high level alarm had been installed, notwithstanding the negative points noted, which would have undermined its effective functioning. In common with gauge interpretation, it's important for operatives not to be distracted or diverted away on to other activities or competing tasks, so that they can place appropriate focus upon alarm monitoring and handling. It didn't appear that the operative was inundated with other tasks here but rather, that she lacked the requisite focus needed to perform a safety critical task. This highlights why the [high level alarm & operative response] barrier is defined in terms of two aspects, namely the alarm itself and the operative's response to it.

Alarms can fail for all sorts of reasons. A failure might arise due to a lack of 'competence' on the operative's part, or because of their not receiving suitable instruction. Alternatively, it might be the case that the operative is fatigued or that they are physically not present, meaning that they aren't able to observe the alarm, or it could simply be that they aren't concentrating or focused on the task in hand. The alarm might not be visible or not activate at all, or it might be the case that the alarm sounds or activates, but that the operative has insufficient time in which to respond. Lack of time probably wasn't an issue here (as the little girl's mother didn't appear to have a lot else to do!) but it's possible that she was, even momentarily, confused or distracted – resulting in her failing to act upon important information[175]. For an alarm to be effective, it's important that relevant information is presented to operatives at the appropriate time. This enables them to take the requisite action in response, and consequently, controls or mitigates the impact of any event that triggered its presentation. The issues of equipment design and maintenance aren't covered in any depth by the fable but, in real-world circumstances, these are aspects which require checking, together with the performance of 'sensors' and safety devices pre-start up, with functional checks and tests being conducted on a routine basis too, so as to verify their continued operation. An alarm should also be incapable of being overridden or defeated, a requirement which is best addressed at the design phase.

With the human operative's failure to respond appropriately to the gauge and the high level alarm, it should still have been possible to prevent the loss of containment incident, due to a shut-off valve having been fitted, the intended function of which was to quickly and positively stop the

---

175. The lexicon of bow tie modelling uses the terms 'degradation factors' and 'escalation factors' interchangeably, to denote the things or actions that stop barriers functioning as intended.

flow. This naturally leads us to consider the shut-off valve, as the third, and last, of the left-hand side prevention barriers…

Did barrier #3 work?
[Shut-Off Valve]

NO, *not entirely! The failure to respond to the alarm and the delay in activating the shut-off valve meant that containment was lost, leading to property damage and off-site effects, with the porridge flowing out of the pot to the house, and onwards into the surrounding environment. Nevertheless, the activation of the shut-off valve – albeit, activation which was late – did mean that the stemming of the porridge flow was eventually successful.*

Unlike the first two barriers, it's clear that the failure of this third barrier was only partial, due to activation being delayed rather than non-existent, with valve shut-off being successfully achieved by the little girl re-entering the porridge-filled environment to manually operate it. The function of a shut-off valve is to quickly and positively stop the flow of a given substance which, in this case, was activated by the manual method. A safety shut-off valve should be fail-safe – or to put it another way, not 'fail to danger' – meaning it's closed upon the failure of any element of the input control system, such as temperature controllers, steam pressure controllers, or current from other safety devices such as low liquid cut-off and high pressure cut-off.

A manual valve should never be used where, as here, the operative effecting the isolation would be placed in danger, with a situation of this kind providing the clear rationale for a 'remotely operated shut off valve' (ROSOV) to be used instead. Manual valve isolation may be acceptable in some cases, but not in circumstances which call for rapid isolation, for instance where there's a need to prevent a 'major accident'. The application of manual valves is predominantly seen in settings where routine maintenance work is undertaken, but they are unlikely to be the safest or most effective option for emergency isolation, as was required here. Reflecting back on the *Associated Octel* case, mentioned in the *prologue* to this fable, we see equivalent concerns coming into play here in respect of delayed activation and endangerment, albeit that this was a light-hearted account of a little girl's exposure to sticky porridge when called upon to activate a valve, which was operated by the use of the manual shut-off method.

The use of a manual shut-off valve does have advantages in some contexts. It allows for an intelligent assessment of the most appropriate measure for dealing with a release to be made. Also, claims are sometimes made that manual activation is necessary to avoid the spurious trips associated with automatic systems. In such cases, however, the 'root cause' is often a badly designed system, rather than any inherent weakness in the automated response. If electing to use manual activation, this must be justifiable and the location of push buttons must not endanger the operative. A manual valve should be accessible and in a safe and suitable place in relation to any hazardous event that may occur. And there should normally be at least two alternative activation points, which should be readily identifiable, both on the plant – usually through markings or signs – and in all relevant operating instructions. A manual shut-off valve wasn't a good design option here, as its method of shut-off was such that the little girl had to enter the porridge-filled location (the house) in order to activate it. The fable isn't in-depth with regard to design detail, but *valve-open* and *valve-closed* positions need to be easily distinguishable for this type of valve and it should fail to safety. It also needs to be operated within the intended design parameters. Valve components, including seals, need to be maintained too, so as to ensure they remain intact and are not suffering wear. In a real-world scenario, specific attention should also be paid to ensuring that a shut-off valve is not tampered with by operatives.

Here, we've looked at three barriers which failed, either in whole or in part, as shown in *Appendix F*. Had any one of the barriers fulfilled its purpose, the loss of containment top event would have been either wholly or partially averted. The failure to conduct the fill level monitoring part of the first prevention barrier [gauge & fill level monitoring by operative] meant that the expected and appropriate action of stopping filling was not taken. But, had the operative response part of the second prevention barrier [high level alarm & operative response] been fulfilled, it's likely that this incident would still have been prevented. As this was not the case, full reliance was placed on the third prevention barrier [shut-off valve] and, as there was a delay to this being activated, the result was loss of containment of porridge to the surrounding environment, albeit that activation which was late, rather than totally absent, would undoubtedly have served to partially mitigate the consequences here.

As has already been indicated, in seeking to control risk effectively, it's commonplace for organisations to prioritise their efforts towards barriers on the left hand side of bow tie models (*Appendix F*) and this is entirely justifiable. Targeting resource towards blocking threats on the left hand side of a model makes good sense, as it avoids the occurrence of an unwanted top event and the consequences which can potentially flow from it, including harm to people, financial costs, environmental and reputational damage. Nevertheless, it's an unwise organisational 'risk management strategy' which allocates resource exclusively to prevention measures and reserves little or none for measures which respond to and/or are capable of fully or partially mitigating the consequences of an incident, should one occur.

CHECKING CONSEQUENCE (RIGHT HAND SIDE)
BARRIER EFFECTIVENESS

Thus far, the focus here has been upon the left hand side of the model, but the right hand (mitigation) side is important too. This half of the model handles the response if, as seen in this tale, a top event does occur. Turning to *Appendix G* – this simple representation of a consequence leg shows just one example of a consequence, namely [injury to people from hot porridge released from pot]. This type of consequence is analogous to the types of concerns which need to be addressed by organisations, in the face of real-world loss of containment 'process safety incidents'. It again shows the hazard as being [hot porridge in porridge pot] and the top event as [porridge pot overflow – loss of containment]. Less is known about this side of the model because, as is typical of fables, the details can be somewhat sketchy when the characters reach *The End*.

The same can be said to be true of the reality these models seek to depict too. Organisations recognise that a top event could occur and the likelihood and severity of any such event should typically be reflected within their risk registers. But the actual magnitude ultimately varies on a case by case basis, according to the vulnerability of the organisation to consequences, with the wide-ranging possible outcomes being dependent upon factors such as: the number of people in the area, the time of day, proximity to the natural environment, the cost of plant failure, the effectiveness with which a response plan is invoked (including the ways in which people respond and react), the handling of the media by the Chief Executive Officer (CEO), organisational resilience to failure, and so on. Understanding the variability in outcomes at *The End* of any real-world scenario is derived, to a large extent, from the effectiveness and depth of the processes organisations have in place for incident investigation.

The fable doesn't fully detail the extent of the damage caused by the porridge deluge, but let's make brief mention of the types of consequences, besides injury, which could arise, were this event to be faced by a real-world organisation rather than fictional characters. There might have been property damage – perhaps to the car which wouldn't start and maybe damage to the young girl's skirt. In an organisational context, there could have been economic losses. And there might have been environmental consequences, including clean-up costs, too. That's without even considering the associated reputational damage which – particularly for large organisations involved in real-world incidents – can be significant. Put simply, if faced with an overflowing porridge pot or indeed any other vessel, as with any incident, we would need to fully understand the range of effects, in this case answering questions such as: *'Did people get burnt?'*, *'Were they left slightly sticky?'*, *'Was a shutdown of the kitchen required?'*, *'Did people face dry-cleaning bills?'*, or *'Did they simply suffer inconvenience?'* – as the first step towards comprehensively evaluating the costs involved and any remedial action required.

Looking at the consequence leg in relation to preventing the [injury to people from hot porridge released from pot] consequence, the barriers should again be taken in priority order, just as they were for the described threat leg. This would mean firstly excluding people from the spill area, so as to minimise the numbers exposed, shown as the first mitigation barrier [exclusion of people from spill area]. Next, once safe to do so, it would mean arranging an orderly evacuation of anyone within the spill area away from it, shown as the second mitigation barrier [evacuation of people from spill area]. Finally, it would involve attending to any casualties through the mobilisation of an appropriate medical response, so as to prevent or limit the numbers of people exposed and the severity of any injuries incurred – shown as the third mitigation barrier [medical response]. No mention is made of injuries having been sustained here – we are told that the porridge wasn't hot by the time it reached the little girl – but nor is there any indication in the fable of these factors even having been considered. To reflect back on the insights offered in the *prologue*, including the real-world incidents it described, just the few issues cited here indicate how missing or incomplete barriers can line up to create or permit catastrophic outcomes – such outcomes being symptomatic of failures to stop a risk, or of circumstances where efforts to stop it are not fully effective.

QUESTION #3
HOW COULD THEY HAVE BEEN SURE IT WOULD WORK?

There was, understandably, quite a lot to be explored in relation to questions one and two, given that the answers to them steered the partial development of a bow tie model and exploration of its component parts, as based upon the fable's details. This third question – the assurance question – is considered in less depth, but remains an important one, focusing as it does on the use of bow tie models to bring fresh thought to existing organisational assurance methodologies. For the scenario given in the fable, the emphasis in addressing this question should have been upon securing affirmation that porridge containment arrangements would work as intended.

The characters involved here clearly had cause to question the robustness of their containment arrangements. Parallel concerns exist for responsible real-world organisations, who should challenge the effectiveness of control arrangements across the totality of their operations. Posing this third question enables organisations to check the performance of the barriers put in place and to capitalise on these insights, using them to drive future improvements in their control of risk. In a real-world context, an effective health and safety management system, which includes process safety, needs to incorporate a feedback loop to satisfy the organisation that its barriers are continuing to operate reliably, with their intended function being consistently delivered, on an ongoing basis. As was identified in the *prologue*, the vehicle to achieving this is assurance – the purpose of which is to ensure that people do the right things and that processes and systems perform to the levels expected. Assurance processes can be used to check that barriers are operating as intended and to address circumstances where this is found not to be the case, encompassing techniques such as audits, inspections, and incident investigations. 'Performance indicators', as are considered later in this book in the context of *the cuckoo's fable*, are another form of monitoring that can be used to check barrier effectiveness.

In reality of course, it's important that the testing of barriers is conducted in advance of their needing to be used in anger, as is called for in real-world incident scenarios. Whilst post-incident data is also invaluable, organisations with a responsible and proactive approach towards controlling risk, and barrier management in particular, will seek to employ a range of further measures to positively validate the barriers they believe to be in place and remedy any gaps, in service of the *check* and *act* steps of their '*plan-do-check-act* cycle' – a key feature of effective safety risk management and 'continual improvement'. Here, the *check* step would have included checks being made on the gauge, high level alarm and shut-off valve, and associated operative activity, so as to prevent top events or mitigate their effects. These checking activities, often included as aspects and questions within audits and inspections, are invaluable for organisations seeking to understand how their practices are performing in reality, as well as providing them with opportunities to recognise where shortfalls exist[176]. The *act* step, on the other hand, is the part of the cycle which allows organisations to learn from lessons and implement improvements – which here might have included resolving issues with safety critical instrumentation, such as gauges, alarms and valves, or indeed, addressing problems with human performance reliability, for instance, weaknesses in the checking and monitoring of porridge pot levels – including deciding upon the specific actions to take to resolve them. Furthermore, where the *act* step of the cycle is effectively executed, this should work to inform the *plan* step, in readiness for the organisation's next round of the cycle.

Irrespective of the method used, the questions asked in the course of any such assurance activity will naturally vary according to the interviewees or auditees involved, and their respective roles in controlling risk. Listed in *How to...* Guide Six are examples of the types of question which could have been posed for assessing the robustness of containment arrangements adopted within this porridge pot scenario. It is clear that this was a small-scale fictional example, but there are relevant parallels to be drawn when checking real-world process plants. The lists of questions are non-exhaustive, being indicative of those that might be asked in the course of checking containment arrangements, which could, of course, be adapted to suit an evaluation of equivalent real-world circumstances. Two sample sets of assurance questions have been provided here. The first set (*How to...*

---

176. Examples of the types of questions an organisation's senior leaders can ask, to help them work out whether their barriers will be effective when needed, include: '*How do you know that a gauge will be correctly interpreted?*', '*How do you know that people will know what to do in response to an alarm?*' and '*How do you know that valve shut-off will be successful?*'

check equipment does what it needs to do) typifies the questions to be posed in relation to an inspection of the barriers – or risk control systems – put in place, which are intended to control or mitigate a loss of containment risk. The second set (*How to...*check people do what they need to do) gives examples of questions typically asked within a management system audit. Both sets have been pitched in the context of a loss of containment top event, but it would be equally possible to frame a similar approach around other risk types, such as 'dropped object' or 'fall from height' risks, for instance, as are showcased later in the beanstalk-based encounter at the centre of *Zac's fable.*

A forward-thinking assurance approach adopted by some organisations is that of 'barrier-based risk management'. Adopting this kind of approach towards bow tie models – as is equally true for other types of barrier model – moves them up a gear, to a more proactive level. Organisations serious about risk management will often use bow tie models, or other equivalent risk modelling techniques, to evaluate how confident they are that the things they put in place to stop bad things happening – together with supporting actions by people – will actually perform as intended, when needed. But whilst bow tie modelling – just like other types of barrier modelling – can show that gauges, alarms and valves are in place, together with the accompanying actions performed by people to make barriers complete, it's barrier-based risk management which enables a judgment to be made about their effectiveness. *And how does it do this?* The simple answer is that it verifies whether barriers are an effective defence against the risk or the consequences which would otherwise flow unchecked. Requirements for this type of risk management process to be effective include: *first*, adopting a systematic process for selecting and designing barriers to protect something of value, to manage a particular threat in an appropriate manner; *second,* accounting for 'emerging risk' – being mindful of the possibility that all future incidents may not have been identified or that the barriers might not function as intended in such circumstances, and *third*, accepting barrier management as being a continuous process.

An example of barrier-based risk management being applied to good effect is 'barrier-based assurance', a particular form of which is a 'barrier-based audit', where an organisation bases its audit questions around the barriers it believes to be in place for a given risk. This approach can be invaluable for monitoring barriers, through verifying the integrity of the system. Unlike the more conventional audit methods, it takes each of the barriers set out in the model in turn and evaluates their effectiveness, by examining their constituent elements. So, taking the [shut-off valve] prevention barrier shown as the third barrier on the *Appendix F* bow tie model, by way of example, the questions which might be asked could include: *first, 'Was the shut-off valve well-maintained and inspected?'*, which shows whether or not maintenance arrangements are effective; *second, 'Was the operative capable of using the shut-off valve?'* which highlights any training gaps, and *third, 'Did the operative know where to find the shut-off valve?'* which indicates whether or not procedures are effective. Adopting this approach is an example of 'barrier-based risk management' being well-applied – particularly as it provides a feedback loop, offers a clear opportunity to enhance barriers and ultimately, helps organisations to drive improvements to the ways in which their risks are controlled.

There are clear benefits to be had from using bow tie models to support organisational risk understanding about what could go wrong, as shown by the response to *question one*. There are further advantages to be gained from using the approach to provide insights about barriers and barrier effectiveness, as was the focus of *question two*. But, as has been shown here, the optimal use of bow tie models is undoubtedly achieved when organisations also address *question three*, which sees barrier thinking driving their assurance methodologies, as well as helping to shape broader risk management processes and philosophies.

CLOSING THOUGHTS

This fable's consideration of a peculiar – *and ultimately, perilous* – porridge pot has provided a range of insights for the development of bow tie models. *First,* it has outlined the process by which a top event is identified, forming the centre of a bow tie model, around which the remainder of it can be built. *Second,* the partial building of a bow tie model has shown their potential for communicating risk in a meaningful way to experts and non-experts alike. *Third,* and finally, it has shown their value in highlighting the vital roles operatives play in managing barriers and reducing risk. Essentially, this comes down to the identification of individual actions and accountabilities, which, in the context of loss of containment, can include monitoring gauge levels, responding to alarms and activating valves for prevention barriers, and supporting evacuation and medical responses, for mitigation barriers. When organisations effectively distribute these accountabilities and assign the accompanying actions, this reduces the likelihood of an accident or incident occurring and, in cases where one does occur, lessens the severity and/or extent of the consequences which would otherwise flow. When effectively applied, this approach also fosters a positive and collaborative 'safety culture', where people understand their roles and responsibilities and take pride in reducing the likelihood of an incident occurring or limiting the extent of the consequences, by doing the right things and taking appropriate action in cases where prevention is unsuccessful. This is the ultimate goal of pro-active barrier management. The fable also touched upon the insights which can be derived from barrier-based audits.

For a summary of practical points to take away,
based upon the topics and subtopics handled by this fable,
see *How to…* Guide Six.

A NOTE ON REPORTING REQUIREMENTS

The events portrayed in this fable were of a purely fictitious nature. See the *Epilogue* for indicative reporting requirements under *the Reporting of Injuries, Diseases and Dangerous Occurrences Regulations 2013*[177] *(RIDDOR)*, as could be triggered by equivalent real-world circumstances.

---

177. S.I. 2013/1471.

Four Little Pigs, an Angry Dragon,
and the Importance of
Managing Barriers Effectively

THE FOUR LITTLE PIGS' FABLE

'It turned out that, since leaving, Pig Four had taken ownership of a successful company… Like Pig Three before him, Pig Four had put in place walls (*passive barriers*), a sprinkler system (*active barrier*) and plan (*procedural barrier*). But, as compared with Pig Three, Pig Four had shown even greater attention to detail, by making sure his plan continued to work as intended.'

PROLOGUE

Essentially, this fable is about a conflict between four pigs and a dragon. It's also about how the hogs chose to defend against unwelcome attacks, and their varying levels of success in protecting themselves, their properties and the surrounding neighbourhood from the consequences, when subjected to a dragon onslaught.

At a more fundamental level, the tale looks at the intrinsic properties of the 'barriers' put in place to either prevent 'threats' from leading to 'top events' or, in cases where top events occur, stop or limit their 'consequences'. As the second of a pair of *operatives' fables* in this collection, the tale builds upon the 'barrier thinking' concept highlighted by *the porridge pot fable*. It does this by examining in more detail the role 'operatives' play in effectively controlling 'risk' through maintaining barriers, specifically the 'active barrier' and 'procedural barrier' types. Readers for whom this topic is new will find it helpful to have read that fable first, as it gives an overview of the 'bow tie modelling' approach and its key principles. But, whilst *the porridge pot fable* set out how to develop 'bow tie models', this one attempts to give some insights as to the composition of the different 'barrier types' – with a particular focus on their potential to block or mitigate consequences, in the wake of a top event. It's true to say that this fable is mostly about 'barrier selection' (*choosing barriers*), 'barrier installation' (*putting them in place*) and 'barrier testing' (*making sure they work*), but it also provides additional context on 'barrier function' (*how barriers work*) and 'barrier purpose' (*why they are needed*), these being aspects which are clearly of interest both at the point at which barriers are put in place, and beyond.

FROM PORRIDGE POT TO PIGS:
THE LINK EXPLAINED

Recalling for a moment the three questions posed in the earlier *porridge pot fable*, and used to help build a bow tie model for the 'loss of containment' scenario there, these were *first:* '*What could possibly go wrong?*'; *second,* '*How will we stop it, and will it work?*', and *third,* '*How will we know that what we want to stop it will do so?*'. Here, albeit with pigs rather than porridge, the primary aim is to provide a more comprehensive answer to the second of these questions – a question which should be tackled by any real-world organisation seeking to ensure the robustness of their arrangements for controlling risk. As such, this fable is intended to show how the choice of different barrier types and attention to their associated 'barrier maintenance' requirements ultimately determined the degree to which the four pigs were successful in guarding against the consequences which flowed from a [hostile dragon attack on pig home][178] top event. This is an approach which readily transfers to a real-world context, because responsible organisations want to have confidence in both their choice of barriers, and the ability of those selected to stop threats becoming top events and/or top events leading to unwanted consequences.

Thinking back to *the porridge pot fable*, our focus there was upon the building of a bow tie model. This type of activity is ordinarily undertaken once a top event – in that case, a [porridge pot overflow – loss of containment] top event – has been identified by an organisation, as would typically feature on its 'risk register'. Here, then, our focus shifts to looking at whether barriers are effective in delivering their intended function. Specifically, this fable looks at the value of each barrier type's contribution, in terms of preventing a top event or, in circumstances where the top event has already occurred, in blocking or mitigating the consequences which would otherwise result. When used effectively, the details from these models can encourage collaboration between all levels of an organisation – from those at the sharp end, right up to the 'senior leaders' in charge of it – opening up communication channels and stimulating discussion, often with a focus on specific barriers. Using bow tie models in this way is particularly beneficial for senior leaders,

---

178. As was adopted for *the porridge pot fable*, the bow tie model elements, and suggested elements, are denoted in square brackets throughout this section.

because it shows them how widely 'barrier ownership' responsibilities are distributed across their organisations, which in many cases includes frontline operatives. Being closest to what is actually happening on the ground, these individuals are often best placed to comment on the control of risks and, in many cases, this means they are rightly viewed as risk experts. Adopting such an approach can help operatives to see how the things they do – their 'barrier actions' – directly contribute to a reduction in incidents, not only protecting them, but also others against harm. It can also vividly demonstrate to an organisation's senior leaders how the failure of these frontline operatives to act could threaten or compromise the robustness of any 'risk control strategy' they believe to be in place.

BARRIER BASICS

Whilst *the porridge pot fable* highlighted the importance of understanding *what* was put in place – in that case, 'gauges', 'alarms' and 'valves', together with associated actions by human operatives – this fable offers up a picture of *how* barriers work. And, whilst it would be possible to publish a thesis on this subject, that isn't the focus of the effort here! We're just going to look at some basic barrier characteristics which provide additional insights as to the bow tie model's functionality. Simply put, this fable is concerned with working out *what* to put in place to stop bad things from happening, and with understanding *why* these might not have worked in the fictional circumstances described here. In exploring these key features, the hope is that the fable will highlight some of the benefits that proactively managing barriers can bring to organisations.

In order to set the scene for this fable, let's take a two stage approach, looking *first* at barrier selection and installation, and *second*, at the maintenance, testing and assurance arrangements which need to be put in place and followed, post-installation.

STAGE #1
BARRIER SELECTION AND INSTALLATION

This stage is about understanding how to choose barriers and put them in place.

As we shall see shortly, this fable depicts a scenario with

three different barrier types – 'passive', 'active' and 'procedural' – being available for selection. There are more complicated ways of distinguishing between types, but this three-way split sufficiently highlights the basic differences in barrier purpose and function, with each type being illustrated in this tale. This kind of classification is helpful, as it describes what a given barrier *does*, thus indicating what – if any – action is required or expected from operatives, to help make it work. Furthermore, as the fable seeks to show, it's advantageous to guard against any given top event and its associated consequences with a variety of barrier types. *Why should this be?* It's quite simply because the benefit of a combination approach, where a mixture of all barrier types exists, is that full reliance for 'barrier effectiveness' rests neither exclusively with operatives nor with systems. Or to put it another way, if one type fails, others are still capable of succeeding, due to the level of operative involvement, and activation and operation modes, differing by type. Taking this approach makes it more likely that one or other of the prevention barriers will succeed in blocking a threat from culminating in a top event and, in cases where a top event does occur, increases the probability that one or other of the mitigation barriers will succeed in blocking or limiting the effects of one or more consequences. Recalling for a moment Reason's 'Swiss cheese model' and the introduction to bow tie models given in the context of *the porridge pot fable*, this is of particular importance for barriers located along the same threat or consequence leg.

As has already been hinted at, whilst classifying a barrier's type is helpful, arguably of greater interest are so-called barrier purpose and barrier function – with which the type is closely linked. Barrier purpose simply describes *why* a barrier is needed, whilst barrier function concerns *how* a barrier works to provide risk reduction, through preventing, controlling or mitigating unwanted events or incidents. This fable considers *how* the different barrier types achieve this, and shows that taking good care of them is vitally important to ensuring they continue to work well. Defining barrier purpose and function was a subject that received attention in academic articles by Sklet and Haddon, considered briefly here, and we'll draw on Haddon's classifications later, when reflecting on the choice of barriers and the methods of upkeep described in this fable. Sklet (2006) looked at the definition and understanding of barrier function. He saw this as being comprised of what barriers are, why they are there, and how they should be classified, together with the important attributes for barrier performance[179]. In terms of classification, he perceived a need for a distinction to be made between 'passive'/'active' barrier systems, and physical, technical or human/operational 'procedural' barrier systems. And, in considering barrier performance, he saw the following attributes as being important: *first,* functionality/effectiveness – the *'How does it work?'* question; *second,* 'reliability'/availability – the *'Is it there when needed?'* question; *third,* response time – the *'Is it available quickly enough?'* question; *fourth,* robustness – the *'Is it strong enough to defend against the threat it seeks to block, or consequence it seeks to mitigate?'* question, and finally, *fifth,* a description of the triggering or actuating events or conditions – the *'What should cause it to work?'* question. There's a lot to be considered when addressing questions of this kind for real-world scenarios, which often calls for a level of detail greater than that provided in this fictional context, and the intention is not to seek to answer them comprehensively here. The questions do, however, provide an invaluable practical checklist for organisations seeking to determine the sufficiency of any given barrier, in terms of its capability to achieve its purpose and deliver its function.

Haddon (1995) had previously listed ten strategies for countering energy damage of any form. These are of particular assistance both when considering the circumstances of 'barrier failure', as we shall look at here, and when proactively designing barriers, so as to avoid harm or damage being sustained. As will become apparent from this fable and its associated *modern meaning*, the barrier modelling and use theories subscribed to by many organisations today have, to a large extent, been influenced by the principles put forward by both Sklet and Haddon. And, in looking at the fictional circumstances the fable describes, we shall see how applying these principles can support decision-making about the practical measures that are put in place to control risk, of relevance to any workplace setting.

Developing an appreciation of barrier type – whether passive, active or procedural – is a good place to start for anyone seeking to design 'barrier models', including bow tie models. But as well as simply describing barrier type (*what a barrier is*), it's also important for those

---

179. Sklet, S.,(2006) defined the attributes of barrier function. The questions included here, which can be used to help evaluate barrier performance, are based upon the author's practical interpretation of the attributes defined by Sklet.

seeking to develop such models to understand a barrier's purpose (*why a barrier is needed*), together with its function (*what a barrier does* and *how a barrier should work*) too. Building bow tie models in which barrier definition and type are linked to barrier purpose and function tends to be the hallmark of those organisations with a good level of risk understanding. It's through developing models in this way that organisations are often rewarded with a richer picture of the quality of their risk control and an increased capability to identify where improvements are required. An understanding of purpose and function can also be invaluable in guiding organisational choices about *which* barriers to select and put in place. When explored, these features can offer deep insights as to why a barrier is needed and hence, enable organisations to align and prioritise their risk management efforts accordingly. In the context of this fable, as we are about to see, had the first three pigs been pushed to answer a question about barrier purpose, such as: '*What do you hope to achieve with your choice of building materials, your sprinkler systems and plans?*' with honesty, it seems likely that this would have motivated them all to pursue better barrier options.

STAGE #2
BARRIER MAINTENANCE, TESTING AND ASSURANCE

The focus of this stage is upon looking after barriers and checking that they work, as intended, after they have been put in place.

At the point of selection and installation, it's important to have confidence in the chosen barriers being of an appropriate type, coupled with a belief that they are capable of delivering their intended functions. But barrier maintenance progresses this on a stage, post-installation, and is about making sure barriers continue to work as intended, by checking their ability to consistently deliver their functions, on an enduring basis. A key aspect of this, as we shall see, lies in having an understanding of how maintenance requirements differ between barrier types. As will become apparent from the fable, this is crucial to sustaining barrier effectiveness.

Whilst barrier maintenance is important, it's when this is supplemented with a formal programme of barrier testing, accompanied by 'barrier-based assurance', that organisations are able to gain an added level of comfort that any given barrier will work on demand, at the point of need, on each and every occasion it's required. Such efforts assure organisations that their barriers are still fulfilling their expected roles in controlling risk, by ensuring that they reliably deliver their function and achieve their purpose at any given point. Satisfaction about the robustness of barriers at the time of their installation is one thing; ensuring that they continue to perform further down the line, when and where they are needed, is quite another, requiring continuous 'vigilance' by any organisation seeking to use them as part of a cohesive 'risk management strategy'. This can be achieved via a range of methods, including through formal test regimes and assurance programmes. As we are about to see, had the pigs in this fable been asked to give an honest answer to the question: '*How do you know that your building materials, sprinkler systems and plans are still in good shape?*', it's likely they would have gained useful insights – and in some cases, home truths – about whether the barriers they believed to be in place were, in fact, robust and continuing to function effectively.

MAINTENANCE REQUIREMENTS BY BARRIER TYPE

Here, attention turns to the principles of operation and maintenance for each barrier type. Having a basic understanding of the different barrier types is helpful, as their functionality is instrumental in an organisation's decision as to whether or not they will be of use in defending against a given threat, or limiting the extent of a particular consequence. It should also help to guide organisational choices about the most appropriate form of barrier maintenance in each case.

A passive barrier – such as a wall, bund, fence or dyke – is the simplest type of barrier, acting only by its presence and not needing to perform a function in order to operate. It doesn't require activation on demand, being comprised of a single element, simply needing to be present to be effective, rather than depending upon the working of multiple interactive parts for its success. Even when present, this type of barrier still requires maintenance in order to remain effective – a wall, for instance, should be inspected and maintained, if found to be crumbling – but it doesn't require assistance, activation or maintenance to deliver its function. *Once in place, this type of barrier doesn't require any action from operatives in order to do what it needs to do.*

Unlike passive barriers, both active and procedural barrier types require three components to be present in order to be 'fully functional': *first*, a 'sensor' (delivered by instrumentation, mechanical means, or by a human operative) to monitor the situation; *second*, a decision-making process (carried out by a logic solver, relay, mechanical device or human operative) to determine if and/or when action is required, and finally, *third*, an action (executed by instrumentation, a mechanical device or a human operative) to deliver the required barrier function.

The function of an active barrier is delivered exclusively by equipment or systems, an example being an automatic sprinkler system. *This type of barrier doesn't require intervention by operatives in order to be effective.* The maintenance of an active barrier is achieved by the carrying out of functional checks on equipment, systems and activation methods. This includes checking equipment and verifying that sensors come into play and work at set points – for instance, when too hot, cold, high, or low and so on.

As is the case for an active barrier, a procedural barrier also requires the involvement of *sense-decide-act* elements in order to function, but one or more of its components must be delivered by the action of a human operative. A procedural barrier is a barrier which is integral to system and organisational design. When effective, this type of barrier not only supports the day-to-day running of operations in 'normal' or 'routine' circumstances, but also assists in achieving an optimal organisational response to 'operating conditions' which are 'non-routine', 'exceptional', 'abnormal' or 'emergency' in nature. Thinking back for a moment to the bow tie partially developed by way of follow-up to *the porridge pot fable*, the procedural barrier is the type which is particularly useful on the right hand side of the model, most notably when an organisation moves into recovery mode. Procedural barriers are invaluable as mitigation barriers. In circumstances where prevention barriers fail and a top event occurs, mitigation barriers of the procedural type come into their own, being vital to the elimination or limitation of the consequences which flow from it. And because these events can be rare and unpredictable, the linking of bow tie models to methods which rely on people – such as 'scenario modelling', and 'risk and reliability assessment' – helps to ensure increased organisational preparedness, observable in improved capability and resilience to respond to, and recover from, real-world incidents. In the context of this fable, as we shall see, procedural barriers could cover aspects including the monitoring of fire-fighting operations, surface water run-off modelling, or particulate matter monitoring. When organisations apply sufficient resource to these kinds of activities, and act on the insights they provide, they tend to gain an increased level of confidence in their ability to avoid an 'escalation scenario' – otherwise known as 'domino effect' – as can arise in circumstances where there is a failure to effectively control the consequences of an initial top event.

Maintaining procedural barriers calls for the taking of a more dynamic approach than that adopted for the passive and active types. This is because their functioning can only be verified through testing, in order to constantly check the quality of operative understanding and behaviour, which can flex, fade or wane over time. There are multiple reasons why this might be so, for instance due to staff turnover, fluctuating or variable levels of knowledge retention, or a change in operational circumstances, which could include adjustments to site layout or switches made to the activities taking place. Taking the operation of an [emergency plan] barrier, by way of example, questions which might be asked include: *'Does the emergency plan – internal and external – work?'*, *'Do people know what to do?'*, and *'Is there adequate equipment available to deliver the requirements of the plan, so as to be satisfied that it will work in practice?'* The human element is integral to barrier effectiveness in these cases. For this type of barrier, the need to check that human operatives will do what is expected of them, when required, poses an ever-present challenge for organisations.

Communication is vital to the success of any procedural barrier. Organisations within high risk sectors – such as oil & gas, energy, utilities, and transport – need to have the capability to mobilise a clear, consolidated and organised response to incidents of a safety critical nature, in order to ensure continued safe process operation and the protection of human wellbeing. Making sure that the messages being communicated not only contain the information people need to know, but are also presented in formats which are useful, understandable, clear and memorable to them, makes it far more likely that they will evoke the desired response from the recipients. *Need to know* information typically includes the nature of the hazard, the consequence of exposure, and avoidance instructions. In order to ensure the ongoing effectiveness of their procedural barriers, organisations should periodically check to make sure their internal communication channels are working well, which means defining who the targeted recipients are in each case. It also means setting clear expectations about what these individuals are required to do upon receipt of any critical communications, supported by methods which verify their understanding about the responses that could be expected from them, for a range of circumstances. There are multiple contexts in which targeted communications of these critical messages are important. The focus might be on operatives within a defined geographical area, to those who are carrying out a specific work type, or those who are thought likely to face particular risks requiring a dynamic response. Whatever the context, designing systems and procedures which have the flexibility to handle unexpected events – in addition to routine day-to-day management – is indicative of a far-sighted approach to risk, which reduces an organisation's vulnerability to failure. When the outward communication of incident management procedures is supported by their regular development, review and dissemination, organisations can elevate them to an integral part of their culture, changing the way in which risk is managed and extending beyond routine 'barrier management' practice. Where required, this approach should also encompass the design of information provided to the public.

DEFINING THE EXTENT OF A BOW TIE MODEL

As was considered in the context of *the porridge pot fable*, once the scope of a bow tie model has been decided upon, from the threat (left hand) side it's relatively straightforward to think about the things – the threats – which could cause or lead up to a top event[180]. There, the focus was on the [porridge produced exceeds porridge pot capacity] threat (*see Appendix F*) but other threats could have included [loss of porridge pot integrity due to a crack or hole in the pot] or [over-pressurisation of porridge pot due to temperature excursion]. The boundaries of the consequence (right hand) side of the model (*see Appendix G*) can however, be a little harder for organisations to predict in a real-world context. This is in large part due to the model's right hand side being focused on circumstances after the point at which control has

---

180. The bow tie model elements, and suggested elements, are denoted by the use of square brackets throughout this section, e.g. [porridge produced exceeds porridge pot capacity] refers to a threat component within the porridge pot overflow – loss of containment bow tie model example, previously considered in relation to *the porridge pot fable*.

been lost, with resources often, quite logically, having been prioritised towards preventing the top event from occurring in the first place. Nevertheless, it's important for organisations to consider the range of possible consequences that might flow from a top event, and this is a theme reflected and expanded upon in relation to this fable. This is of particular significance here, given that that the tale's focus is upon the aftermath following a top event, where the capability of the chosen barriers to block or limit consequences is inevitably called into question.

The rule-set for the parameters of any given model is something which lies largely within the gift of organisations and their model developers to define. The outline given here, together with the model's application to the events of this fable, is limited to the basic principles, but where a given model starts and ends tends to be a matter of art rather than science. One approach, and that adopted here, is to define consequences at a fairly high level, such as [injury to people], [damage to the environment], or [damage to reputation]. It's often the case that, to keep matters simple, organisations pitch consequences at a basic level along these lines within their models. Those taking such an approach then have the option of transplanting any given consequence from their initial (primary) model as the new central top event around which another subsequent (secondary) and linked model can be built, in order to deepen their analysis and further explore a particular aspect. This may appear to be a minor point but, as was noted in the context of *the porridge pot fable*, from a practical perspective, defining the extent of a bow tie model is both important and helpful in securing and capitalising on its value as a risk tool. It's a relevant consideration for this fable too, particularly given that it touches upon consequences both inside and outside the site boundary, with the risk extending beyond its originating location. It's for this reason that, in addition to highlighting the passive/active/procedural distinction as related to the barrier concept, this fable is also to be used to provide an overview of an 'off-site scenario', sometimes referred to as an escalation scenario. In a real-world context, this requires relevant organisations operating within Great Britain to understand the *Control of Major Accident Hazards Regulations 2015*[181] ('the *COMAH Regulations*'), a key requirement of which is the management of the consequences of any off-site incidents as might occur[182]. As we are

---

181. S.I. 2915/483.

182. Regulation 13 of *the COMAH Regulations* deals with 'preparation of external emergency plans', whilst regulation 14 handles the 'review and testing of external emergency plans'.

about to see, this is particularly pertinent here, given the nature of the activities pursued by Pig Four in this fable, which will be considered in its attached *modern meaning*. A brief overview of the requirements of *the COMAH Regulations*, together with an indication as to how these apply to real-world circumstances equivalent to the events described here, is provided in *How to... Guide Seven*.

THE FOCUS OF THIS FABLE

This fable looks at the importance of understanding the intrinsic properties of barriers, whether to prevent an incident (top event), or to offer protection from incident consequences, in cases where prevention is unsuccessful. As such, it builds upon the understanding of barriers ('risk controls') outlined in the context of *the porridge pot fable*, including the need to consider off-site scenarios and the range of different consequences which can flow from one top event. The principal focus here is upon the different barrier types, their associated forms of activation, and how they can be defeated, if not effectively selected and maintained. And, given that the risk here is one posed by the arrival of a dragon, rather than the wolf of times gone by, the fable also touches upon 'emerging risk'. *But more on this later...*

So now it is to four pigs – and their building efforts – that we look for insights on understanding barrier types, and the accompanying arrangements necessary for the selection, maintenance and testing of these vital risk controls...

THE FABLE

Once upon a time there was a big manager pig, to whom three little worker pigs reported. Historically they had worked in an office with a tied accommodation arrangement but, in the wake of a recent company restructure, the big manager pig had said:

'In future, there are going to be more workers in the office, and I'm afraid that means it's too small for you to live here any longer. Go and build houses for yourselves in the locality, taking into account travel distances and the potential for reduced mileage reimbursement, if you stray too far away from the office location. Remember that the motorway fondly referred to as *the M25* can be hellish of a morning and also look out for dragons, making sure they don't catch you! They've never much liked pigs and seem intent on demolishing their homes, with the same relish as their wolfy predecessors, but with a more ferocious approach…and, speaking of ferocity, the three of you would do well to remember, I'm always forensic in my examination of your expenses and will be calling into question any discrepancies with the company's reimbursement procedure.'

The three little worker pigs knew the bit about expenses to be true as, in all honesty, the big manager pig had never really shaken off the traits he'd acquired in the formative part of his career, as an accountant. They were, however, slightly perplexed by his reference to the London orbital motorway; they were fully aware of the notion that *pigs might fly*, but none of them had ever mentioned to the big manager pig that they were thinking of driving into work, making his concern about the potential for inflated mileage claims appear unfounded. As for the other part of the big manager pig's warning, to date the three of them had been lucky in not encountering a dragon, generating a belief amongst them that this warning of danger was likely to be baseless too.

The three little worker pigs set off, reassuring the big manager pig that they would build properties within a reasonable distance of the office and that they would be mindful of the possibility that dragons might be living amongst them. They met together and agreed upon bricks as being their construction medium of choice – a sign that, at least in respect of picking suitable house-building materials, the trio had learnt lessons from their ancestors' failings – having swiftly ruled out straw and sticks as suitable options. The early indications of a new-found unity between the three of them appeared promising and, outwardly at least, they looked to have put their historical tensions behind them. The seemingly happy band of hogs set out on their merry way to obtain bricks.

The competitive nature of the three little worker pigs was, however, soon to re-emerge, highlighting that perhaps less of their species' feud had been laid to rest than one might have hoped. Alas, it seemed that the bad feeling vented during the historical 'straw-sticks-bricks' building materials' debate of years gone by was still festering, beneath the surface.

THE BOARS BEGIN BUILDING[183]

The three little worker pigs weren't really in the mood for a long shopping trip for building materials but, as luck would have it, there was a builders merchant's yard just two doors down from their office location. It wasn't long before the three little worker pigs met a man outside the yard with a lot of bricks. 'Please could we have some bricks?' asked the three little worker pigs. 'Our employer is no longer prepared to support our tied accommodation arrangement, and we'd like to build three little houses for ourselves.'

PIGS ONE, TWO AND THREE BUILD WALLS[184]

The man was initially taken aback at their cheek, although not altogether surprised, given that the pigs of yesteryear had displayed similarly acquisitive tendencies. On reflection, however, and knowing he was shortly due to be giving up his builders merchant's yard, he relented saying 'Yes, yes, okay – go and build yourselves some houses!' He gave the three cheeky little worker pigs some bricks and sent them on their way. Then the three little worker pigs built themselves houses, with walls made of bricks.

Pig One was easy to please and the least competitive of the piggy trio. He was delighted with his house, proclaiming 'Now the dragon won't catch me and eat me!' Being, as he was, a simple pig at heart, he was content with his lot, seeing no need to further improve upon his property.

'I shall build a better house than yours!' said Pig Two, thinking to himself that he had a sounder grasp of fire safety requirements than Pig One. The structural integrity of the building was one thing, but he thought it advisable to build in fire safety measures too. He was also more fearful of the proximity of fire-breathing dragons, with word having reached him by this point that the species was in fact

---

183. The building of houses by the pigs marked the start of their attempted fulfilment of the barrier selection and installation stage.

184. The walls to the pigs' houses are examples of passive barriers. In the author's view, the principal intended function of these walls would align to the sixth strategy put forward by Haddon (1995), being to provide '...*separation by interposition of a material 'barrier'...*', achieving physical separation from the dragon's fire (or in Pig One's case, simply dragon breath).

thriving and their population growth largely unchecked, since they had successfully driven out the remaining wolves the previous year. Wolves had historically posed the greatest threat to their piggy Utopia, but this was no longer the case. It was a sad comment on modern times that, as one threat diminished or died out, it was all too quickly replaced by another, often more sinister threat. 'I shall build a better house than both of you!' said Pig Three. He knew of Pig Two's plans for managing fire safety, but also had some other ideas about what to do after a fire had taken hold of a property. Pig One shut the door to his little brick house, sat down and settled in to watch television, with a convenience meal for one.

Pig Two and Pig Three continued along the road. As luck would have it, they soon met a man with a van unloading a delivery of sprinkler systems, at a neighbouring industrial estate.

PIGS TWO AND THREE ADD SPRINKLER SYSTEMS[185]

'Please will you give us two of your sprinkler systems?' asked Pig Two and Pig Three, in unison. 'We've just built two little brick houses, and we want to protect them, in case a fire breaks out. Your sprinkler systems are just what we've been looking for!' The man replied 'Yes!', although slightly grumpily, as there had recently been sharp rises in raw material costs and he wasn't big on charity, and he grudgingly handed over a pair of sprinkler systems to Pig Two and Pig Three. Ethical sourcing meant he felt he had already done his bit as a 'corporate citizen'. He knew that those responsible for designing and manufacturing the sprinkler systems had been well-treated and thought it a bit much that he'd been press-ganged into treating these little piggy chancers favourably too.

Pig Two and Pig Three trotted hurriedly back to their little brick houses and installed their sprinkler systems and, as compared to Pig One, felt slightly smug with themselves, knowing that if a fire broke out, their sprinklers would extinguish the flames, thereby reducing the impact of any unplanned event that might occur, including consequential personal injury and structural damage. With the

---

185. A sprinkler system is an example of an active barrier. In the author's view, the principal intended function of this barrier would align to the ninth strategy put forward by Haddon (1995), being to '...move rapidly in detection and evaluation of damage that has occurred or is occurring, and to counter its continuation and extension.'

addition of sprinkler systems, they believed their little houses to have the edge on Pig One's house.

Pig Two was very pleased with his house and was content with the measures he had put in place, to cover the event of a fire breaking out. He said, 'Now if a dragon takes against me and tries to breathe fire in the direction of my house, I stand a chance of limiting the damage.' At this, he was happy to settle into his house as it was and let Pig Three get on his way. In truth, he suspected Pig Three might have more ideas up his trotters (and he wasn't wrong) but, believing him to be something of a control freak, Pig Two was content to bow out of the competition at this point.

'I shall build a stronger house than yours, with better arrangements in place if the sprinkler systems we've just obtained need to activate!' proclaimed Pig Three, bidding Pig Two an amicable farewell. Pig Two shut the door to his little brick house, with its sparkly new sprinkler system, and settled down for the evening to read the sprinkler system's instruction guide. He knew he wasn't the most interesting of pigs, but *oh, how he loved a technical manual...*

PIG THREE ADDS AN EMERGENCY PLAN[186]

Pig Three trotted along the road by himself. Soon he met a man *with a plan.* As luck would have it, the man was a consultant, well-experienced in advising commercial and domestic clients on the design and invocation of emergency plans. Pig Three had always felt he had a slight edge over his other little worker pig friends and believed that an emergency plan was just what he needed to stay one trotter ahead of them. He knew that he had a strong brick-built property in common with Pig One and Pig Two. He also knew that he had a sparkly sprinkler system in common with Pig Two. But, in what he regarded as something of a coup against Pig One and Pig Two, he had also equipped himself with a better knowledge of what were much-needed accompanying emergency arrangements, as a means of preventing escalation scenarios. 'Please will you give

---

186. An emergency plan is an example of a procedural barrier. In the author's view, the principal intended function of this barrier would align to the tenth strategy put forward by Haddon (1995), being to move towards '...*final stabilisation...after appropriate intermediate and long-term reparative and rehabilitative measures...*' to '...*return to the pre-event status...*' or achieve '...*stabilisation in structurally or functionally altered states.*'

me your best advice for emergency planning...' said Pig Three to the man, before continuing on: '...I've built a lovely little brick house and got a brilliant sprinkler system, but I've learnt a lot about how 'firewater' can do extensive damage and I'm hoping you've got a plan for me that will fit the bill!' Pig Three believed the addition of an emergency plan was just what he needed to win himself an advantage over Pig One and Pig Two. 'Why, yes of course! It's refreshing to meet a hog with a moral compass for a change!' said the man, pleased that Pig Three's approach to controlling risk seemed to have a touch more realism to it than that of other pigs he'd had the misfortune to encounter to date. He took a folder from the back seat of his car and passed it to Pig Three, together with some supporting information – accessible via an internet application and a secret code on a memory stick – which he said he was happy to provide to him on a trial basis.

Pig Three was very very pleased with his house and was content with the measures he had put in place, in the event of a fire taking hold, including his arrangements for dealing with off-site consequences. He said, 'Now if a dragon takes against me and tries to breathe fire in the direction of my house, I stand a chance of limiting fire damage. And, if the firewater generated by the deluge from the sprinkler system causes more damage to my property, or even further afield, I can confidently say I've put things in place to deal with any problems.' He returned to his little brick house, with its sparkly sprinkler system, put the memory stick given to him by the man with a plan into his computer, and read the contents of the folder, until it was time for bed.

Some time later...

A DRAGON PAYS THE PIGS A VISIT
AND THE RISK IS REALISED[187]

Just as the three little worker pigs were starting to get a little blasé, thinking that perhaps dragons really were confined to myths and

---

187. The dragon's visits and, more particularly, his actions can be regarded as examples of barrier testing albeit that, in this case, the barriers were tested in anger, rather than as part of a proactive barrier assurance activity – the preferred approach of any real-world organisation seeking to behave as a good 'corporate citizen'.

legends, an ominous rumbling was heard coming from a local cave. It was a dragon awakening and he was in the mood for devilment and demolition! It was bright and sunny as he set out along the road, fresh from his cave, his tail swishing and his spines quivering slightly in the morning breeze. *He had a feeling it was going to be a good day.*

Soon, he came to the first little brick house built by Pig One.

PIG ONE'S WALLS ARE DEFEATED[188]

When Pig One saw the dragon coming, he trotted inside his house and shut the door. The dragon knocked on the door and said 'Worker pig, worker pig, let me come in!' to which Pig One replied: 'No no! By the twist of my taily-tail-tail, I will not let you come in!' The dragon responded: '*Then I'll puff and I'll blow, destroy your house in one go!*' So he puffed and he blew and he puffed and he blew. And sure enough, the house of bricks fell down, right on top of Pig One! The dragon said: 'Look here – Pig One – I know life can be cruel…but, as you didn't inspect them, I've demolished your walls!'

Pig One suffered life-threatening crush injuries. Unfortunately, despite the efforts of medical staff to save him, his condition deteriorated and he passed away some days later. Pig One's little brick house had initially seemed to be well-constructed but with the passage of time, some lapses in his inspection regime and his keen eye for keeping costs low (his maintenance budget having been spent on some more frivolous items), it had become vulnerable to dragon attacks. It was also thought possible that Pig One might have failed to account for the walls to his house needing to be stronger to defend against dragons' *puff and blow* than had been necessary to counter the wolves' *huff and puff* of times gone by[189].

Pig One's walls were weak and easily defeated.

Some more time later…

With a bit more of a spring in his step, his tail more definite in

---

188. The defeating of Pig One's walls can be viewed as an example of passive barrier failure.

189. The accurate judging of the load that the walls of the pigs' homes were expected to withstand is an example of the concept of 'barrier performance expectations' being applied.

its swishing and his spines glittering in the morning dew, the dragon walked further along the road. *He had a feeling it was going to be a very good day.*

It wasn't long before he came to the little brick house built by Pig Two.

PIG TWO'S SPRINKLER SYSTEM IS DEFEATED[190]

When Pig Two saw the dragon coming, he trotted inside his house and shut the door. The dragon knocked on the door and said 'Worker pig, worker pig, let me come in!' to which Pig Two replied: 'No, no! By the twist of my taily-tail-tail, I will not let you come in! The dragon replied, threateningly: *'I'll breathe smoke, I'll breathe flame, your house won't be the same!'* So he breathed smoke and he breathed flame. Pig Two's little brick house did not fall down, because its walls had been maintained, unlike those of Pig One's house. But, as the dragon was of the fire-breathing type and one true to his word, a small inferno developed which quickly threatened to engulf Pig Two's dwelling. The dragon said: 'Pig Two – your approach to maintaining – it's just far too fickle! There's no deluge to quell flames, in fact barely a trickle!'

Unlike Pig One, Pig Two managed to escape. He initially thought that the damage to his little brick house would have been limited as, like Pig Three, he too had installed a sparkly sprinkler system. Unfortunately, however, the sprinkler system failed to activate, which resulted in Pig Two's house sustaining significant internal smoke damage. Subsequent investigations were inconclusive as to the reason for the failure, but lack of maintenance of, or damage to, a sprinkler system component were implicated as possibilities.

Pig Two did well in maintaining his little brick house, which meant his brick walls didn't collapse. Unlike Pig One, it appeared that Pig Two had factored in the need for the walls to his house to meet increased performance expectations, as they seemed capable of withstanding the *smoke and flame* imposed upon them by the dragon. But, when it came to the maintenance and inspection of his sprinkler system, his arrangements simply didn't pass muster. This meant that

---

190. The defeating of Pig Two's sprinkler system can be viewed as an example of active barrier failure, due to a lack of barrier maintenance. In Pig Two's case, the passive barrier worked, but the active barrier did not.

when the dragon started breathing fire, the resulting inferno couldn't be readily extinguished.

Pig Two's walls were well-maintained, but his sprinkler system wasn't effectively inspected or maintained and was, therefore, easily defeated.

Even more time later...

Buoyed by his continuing success and visibly brimming with pride as a result of his recent victories over Pig One and Pig Two, the dragon once again set out – seeming almost to bound along, in a most undragonly fashion. *He had a tingling feeling in his spines that it was going to be a very, very good day.*

And, just as he was starting to think that life couldn't get any better, the dragon reached the house built by Pig Three.

PIG THREE'S EMERGENCY PLAN IS DEFEATED[191]

When Pig Three saw the dragon coming, he trotted inside his house and shut the door. The dragon knocked on the door and said 'Worker pig, worker pig, let me come in!' to which Pig Three responded: 'No! No! By the twist of my taily-tail-tail, I will not let you come in!' The dragon said: *'See the plan you've prepared, it's a flimsy solution! You might save your house, but what of off-site pollution?'* So he breathed smoke and he breathed flame. Pig Three's little brick house did not fall down but, as the dragon was one of the fire-breathing type, a small fire again developed, which quickly threatened to engulf Pig Three's dwelling.

Luckily, just like Pig Two, Pig Three also managed to escape. Unlike Pig Two, however, Pig Three had confidence in his sparkly sprinkler system, which successfully activated, it having been maintained and recently tested. This meant that Pig Three's house did not suffer internal smoke damage. He also had faith in his emergency plan, which catered for the possibility of loss of firewater containment, as a relevant risk.

Unfortunately, Pig Three was also not entirely successful. Whilst his house was unaffected by smoke, it was not immune to the effects of

---

191. The defeating of Pig Three's emergency plan is an example of procedural barrier failure, due to a lack of barrier maintenance. In Pig Three's case, just as for Pig Two, the passive barrier worked. But unlike Pig Two, for Pig Three, the active barrier worked too. The procedural barrier, however, whilst in place, was untested and not updated and therefore, only partially effective, when called upon by Pig Three in an emergency situation.

the firewater, the dragon's threats having been realised. This resulted in significant damage being caused to his property, with the firewater also discharging from the rear of his home to the surrounding environment. Flora and fauna were affected. There was damage to watercourses too, including drainage systems and rivers. And Pig Three had given no thought to containment, including bunds and lagoons, which might have reduced the extent of any off-site impacts. Additionally, smoke plumes carried pollutants away from Pig Three's house, in the direction of some nearby newly-built properties, inhabited by the human community who were, to say the least, not best pleased. Pig Three could not understand this. He'd bargained hard with the *man with a plan* – acquiring his plan, folder and memory stick files – and yet, still appeared to fail and fall out of favour with the local community. He had just one question: *'Why didn't his emergency plan measure up?'*

But before Pig Three had the chance to pose his question, the now boastful dragon said: 'I know, Pig Three, in your plan you've invested, but it's just smoke and mirrors, if it's never been tested! Well, maybe not mirrors, as I can tell you're not vain, but a plan not reviewed is tough to explain!'

Now the walls to Pig Three's little brick house – just like those of Pig Two's house – had been well-maintained. And, in common with Pig Two, Pig Three had also addressed the need for the walls to his house to be stronger in order to successfully withstand the *smoke and flame* imposed upon them by the dragon, which they appeared to do. But unlike Pig Two's sprinkler system, Pig Three's sprinkler system also succeeded, because it had been comprehensively inspected and maintained. Unfortunately, the same could not be said for his external emergency plan and testing arrangements, which were not fully effective, due to insufficient consideration having been given to off-site scenarios such as, for instance, firewater spilling off site and particulates carried away in smoke plumes. It was thought that this was possibly due to him having failed to renew the subscription for the memory stick application, the memory stick's files having become inaccessible after the trial period extended to him by the *man with a plan* had ended and the secret code had been changed. It might have been presumed that this would have been *the end*, but there was a little more to this sorry tale…

Even more than even more time later…

The funeral for Pig One having taken place, Pig Two having been re-homed, and Pig Three having dealt with a range of insurance claims and made attempts to rebuild community relations, one day out of the blue, a fourth pig arrived suddenly on the scene, as if from nowhere! He knocked on the door of Pig Three, who was being visited by Pig Two. Upon opening the door, Pig Two and Pig Three looked aghast. 'Who on earth are *you*?' squealed Pig Three, who was completing the last of his insurance claim forms and didn't really want disturbing. 'Yes, where did *you* spring from?' honked Pig Two. But within a matter of moments and with a crushing sense of realisation, they both remembered…

There had been another pig – Pig Four – from whom the others had parted company some years back, under somewhat mysterious circumstances. The word *in the sty* was that he'd done rather well for himself and from the look on his face, Pig Two and Pig Three had an uneasy suspicion that – much as they'd doubted it at the time of his departure – perhaps there might have been some truth to this rumour after all. Pig Four reported to Pig Two and Pig Three that he too had been visited by the dragon some time ago, but had not encountered any property issues, nor any of the off-site problems mentioned by Pig Three. He looked a picture of health, his big, shiny, impressive chemical installation was still pristine and, importantly – as Pig Four was only too keen to point out – his neighbours were still talking to him! This had reputedly irritated the dragon, as he'd made a career out of *smoking, flaming and house-downing* without a single defeat to his name. But in his encounters with Pig Four, it appeared even the dragon was stymied.

Continuing on with his boastful claims, Pig Four summarised the situation thus:

'The wolves' howl has been silenced but now new foes are known,
    Rumours rife about dragons, tales of terror they've blown.
The news in the hog world, filled with gripes and with grumbles,
    Is of pig deaths and destruction, and walls easily crumbled.
Though passive barriers, to work, don't require activation,
    Pig One's neglect of his walls saw him swift' turn to bacon!
In the fantasy dragon world, I hear witches are cackling,
No respect for this hog – turned to pork scratching and crackling!

Pig Two – you survived, homeless. *Cause?* Sprinkler system untested,
    The flames licked at your home, and could not be arrested.

A high price for a dud sensor, a cheap thing to replace,
Like your house, you seem gutted, from the look on your face!
You see, a barrier that's active might work at the start,
But you must pay attention – it's just the sum of its parts!
A little time spent inspecting, and attending to repairs
Could have saved all this upset, and banished despair!

Pig Three – you seem unscathed, but locals think you a pest,
For emergency plans need review and a test.
Without such a check, there's just no way of knowing,
The passage of smoke plumes, or where firewater's flowing.
A plan still needs refreshing: it's no one-hit wonder –
To fail to update it, the most basic of blunders.
These procedural barriers, they may seem a bore,
But they can oft' limit damage, when not ignored.

And, as for me – *Pig Four* – I'm the proudest around,
Testing off-site arrangements means my barriers are sound!
My neighbours adore me, they still shake my trotter,
Not like yours, Pig Three – many think you're a rotter!
In this day and age, dear pig pals, the message couldn't be clearer,
As threats – once so distant – seem to draw ever nearer!
Don't dismiss out of hand, as some strange premonition
A dragon's desire for home demolition.
Nor, in the wake of catastrophe, be forced to say why,
You failed to take note of the word *in the sty!*
For those things you value, for all that you cherish,
You must check your barriers, or else risk that you'll perish!'

'Oh…well, *well done you!*' said Pig Two and Pig Three in unhappy unison, their sense of irritation at Pig Four's self-adulation now almost palpable.

It turned out that, since leaving, Pig Four had taken ownership of a successful company, involved in the large-scale manufacture of chemicals which went on to be used within other industries. He had a keen eye to profit, but had somehow married this with a strong social conscience. Like Pig Three before him, Pig Four had put in place walls (*passive barriers*), a sprinkler system (*active barrier*) and plan (*procedural barrier*). But, as compared with Pig Three, Pig Four had shown even greater attention to detail, by making sure his plan continued to work as intended. *How so?* Well, in addition to the walls, sprinkler system and plan put in place by Pig Three for his house, Pig Four had also paid due attention to potential incidents – including fires, explosions, and major toxic releases – and had accounted for off-site effects too. This was all the more complicated for Pig Four, because the nature of the activities conducted at his chemical facility meant that he had to manage risks associated with 'major accident hazards', in addition to the more routine day-to-day stuff with which Pig One, Pig Two, and Pig Three had to contend. But seemingly Pig Four had this covered too, having equipped himself with a sound understanding of *the Control of Major Accident Hazards Regulations 2015*[192] ('*the COMAH Regulations*'). Pig Four had been very busy indeed, with all that setting up a successful chemicals company dealing with 'dangerous substances' entailed[193].

Pig Four had completed a detailed 'risk assessment' which took account of health, safety and environmental risks and reduced risk to a level which was 'as low as reasonably practicable (ALARP)'. He'd also informed his neighbours about the types of activities and processes carried out on site, together with the substances and hazards involved. And he'd provided them with advice on emergency response arrangements. He'd even drawn up detailed emergency plans, which he regularly tested in conjunction with the emergency services, so as to be able to deal effectively with fires and other incidents.

Now, admittedly, the risks that Pig Two and Pig Three needed to control weren't as complex, nor were they subject to the regulatory requirements faced by Pig Four, with their circumstances being on a smaller domestic scale. But, with hindsight, there had still existed the very clear need for them to anticipate and address any off-site scenarios, and little doubt that, had they done so, they too would have reaped the benefits of strengthened community relations.

---

192. S.I. 2015/483.

193. Regulation 2 of *the COMAH Regulations* defines the term 'dangerous substance', which includes substances and mixtures specifically listed, present in certain quantities, and substances or mixtures in 'CLP' categories, present in certain quantities, which bring with them certain responsibilities for operators of COMAH sites, and vary according to the tier classification. See this book's *Glossary* for definitions of these terms. Also see this book's *Glossary* for a further definition of a 'dangerous substance' as it applies in the context of *DSEAR*, considered in relation to *Ian's fable*.

Pig Four's chemical facility wouldn't collapse because, in common with Pig Two and Pig Three, he did well in maintaining his walls (*passive barriers*), which meant they didn't crumble – due to the performance expectations being met. And it wouldn't burn to the ground because – just as was true for Pig Three – the maintenance and inspection arrangements he'd put in place to check his fire suppression system (*active barrier*) meant that, should a fire start, it would be readily extinguished. But furthermore – and importantly – his chemical facility and the surrounding area wouldn't be overwhelmed because, unlike Pig Three, he'd also considered and implemented measures to ensure sufficient pollution control and containment arrangements were in place, including bunding.

It was the testing of his internal and external emergency plans (procedural barriers), however, which had given Pig Four the edge over the other three little worker pigs.

There were a few reasons why Pig Four's emergency plan was so successful. *First*, it gave him the knowledge that the alarms could be heard and understood, so as to warn everyone of the need to take protective action. *Second*, it gave him a good understanding of valve design, including the need to develop solutions to make sure his seals were tight. *Third*, it listed the contact numbers and methods of contacting emergency response and business continuity teams, enabling him to notify them if he needed a response, even out-of-hours, in the middle of the night. *Fourth*, it tested out whether the various parts of the preparedness programme would work, both internally and externally, being based upon the '*source-pathway-receptor* model'. It was the application of this model which had, for instance, given him a thorough understanding of where water pollution might come from (*sources*), where it might get to (vulnerable *receptors* on and off site), and how it might get there (*pathways*), by anticipating the likely direction of firewater. The plan also included the practical elements, an example being the isolation valves in outlets to surface water drainage, to prevent the firewater escaping from site, so it could be safely removed and tankered away. Pig Four had even enlisted a friend's support in carrying out water run-off modelling for him, which enabled him to predict and establish the flow and direction of firewater on and off site, to limit the consequences of an incident, should one occur. Finally, *fifth*, it helped him to improve the overall strength of the preparedness of the programme and the ability of team members to perform their roles and carry out their responsibilities.

Now obviously, as Pig Two and Pig Three occupied domestic dwellings, they didn't fall under the regulatory regime to which Pig Four and his site were subject. But the approach taken by Pig Four was still noteworthy, with Pig Two and Pig Three left in no doubt that, had they acted similarly, by applying a little more thought to their own circumstances, they too would have enjoyed more favourable outcomes.

And they all lived happily ever after...

Well, that's partially true. Happily ever after, except for Pig One, who didn't live at all. And Pig Two, who was left with the burnt-out shell of a house. And Pig Three, who, having upset his neighbours by failing to consider off-site effects, frequently became embroiled in disputes with them. Granted, it was mostly minor stuff – like petty refusals to accept parcels from delivery drivers whilst he was out, and inconsiderate parking, which blocked his driveway – but it was still annoying, all the same...

But Pig Four really DID live happily ever after...(and never passed up an opportunity to remind Pig Two and Pig Three of this).

MODERN MEANING

An important pervasive theme to this fable is the concept of emerging risk, where risks change, evolve in nature, or newly arise over time. Pig One, Pig Two and Pig Three may have been labouring under the misapprehension that they merely needed to defend themselves, their properties, and the surrounding environment against the wolf-based risk of times gone by, rather than the new dragon-based risk. It certainly appeared that they perceived themselves to be well-prepared for the pre-existing and known wolf-based threat, but it was to be their blindness to the newly-emergent threat posed by dragons that would lead to their ultimate downfall.

Real-world organisations, too, operate in a risk landscape that shifts ever more rapidly, with some risks falling inside and some outside their control. Charting emerging risks and opportunities in a pre-emptive way – sometimes referred to as 'horizon scanning' – speaks of an organisation adopting a pro-active risk management strategy. In order to ensure their approaches to risk management remain effective and endure, organisations should equip themselves not only with knowledge about present *wolves*, but with the traits of future *dragons* too, rather than denying their existence or shying away from the top events they can potentially cause. And, depending on the outcome of such analysis, this may give them cause to rethink the balance of their resource allocation between present (*wolf-based*) risks and futuristic (*dragon-based*) ones. Efforts should be made to recognise and block threats, and to block or minimise consequences too, with barriers designed and maintained accordingly, and due attention paid to the associated 'barrier performance expectations'. In order to ensure the robustness of their approaches, the plans that organisations put in place need to address worst case scenarios.

EVALUATING BARRIER PERFORMANCE

There are some who consider discussions about worst case scenarios to be little more than exercises in self-indulgent navel-gazing. But of course, when dragons come a-knocking at pigs' doors – or indeed, when equivalent real-world doomsday events materialise within a workplace setting – the question '*How do the various barriers perform under test?*' naturally comes to mind. So let's use the events of this fable as an opportunity to look at the different barrier types, their corresponding maintenance requirements, and how actual barrier performance measured up to the hogs' expectations.

PASSIVE BARRIER PERFORMANCE

When Pig One had built his house, he'd used sturdy bricks, but failed to take account of the increased barrier performance expectations of his walls, which needed to protect against dragons, rather than the wolves of times gone by.

Looking first at passive barriers, the quality of Pig One's brick-built house was important to him, as was equally true for Pig Two and Pig Three and their homes. Over time, however, the walls to Pig One's house had started crumbling and were showing signs of failing, with him having overlooked the increased performance expectations and associated maintenance requirements, heralded by the arrival of dragons. This wasn't picked up by routine inspections or general house maintenance either, as Pig One believed this kind of proactive monitoring to be excessive. This meant that it only took the dragon's puffing and blowing of a wall for it to topple, falling to the ground on top of Pig One, and leading to his tragic demise.

As has been touched upon already, whilst passive barriers – such as walls and fences – are the simplest of barrier types, not requiring activation to operate, they do still need to be maintained in order to ensure their continued effectiveness. Passive barriers do not perform a function in order to be operational, acting only by their presence and so, in assessing their performance, a judgment simply needs to be made as to whether they are in place or absent. But in building passive barriers, consideration still needs to be given to ensuring that they are correctly designed, including testing loading requirements and determining barrier performance expectations. Within the context of the fable, this could have been addressed by proactively finding out how much dragon *smoking and flaming* the walls could withstand. As the fable suggests, it's possible that Pig One only accounted for the performance expectations needed against a wolf's *huff and puff*, rather than a dragon's *puff and blow*. This further underlines the importance of passive barriers needing to be maintained over time. They should be inspected, via routine inspections and monitoring and, wherever necessary, be subject to preventative and reactive maintenance regimes.

ACTIVE BARRIER PERFORMANCE

Pig Two also built his house with sturdy bricks, but additionally accounted for the necessary barrier performance expectations. He added a sprinkler system too, so that he could make use of a water deluge. This meant that, in the event of a fire, provided the sprinkler system activated as intended, the probability of things getting worse, through domino effect, was much reduced.

In looking at the active barrier, the purpose of a sprinkler system is to detect and suppress fire, achieved by discharging water to extinguish or control it. In putting a sprinkler system in place therefore, it's quite clear that Pig Two's intention would have been to limit the damage caused by fire. Unfortunately, however, despite Pig

Two having installed a sprinkler system, it failed to activate at the time and point of need. The sensor had stopped working – this fault being the cause of the failed activation – meaning it didn't determine the necessity for the sprinkler to activate on demand. As a result, Pig Two's house succumbed to significant consequential internal fire and smoke damage.

The function of active barriers is delivered by equipment and/or systems. In order to ensure their continued effectiveness, functional checks of active barriers need to be performed, including making sure that sensors and activation methods are working. It's important to remember that active barriers such as sprinklers contain *sense-decide-act* elements, but they do not require operative intervention to activate. In designing and building active barriers, they need to fail-safe and either be self-testing or tested regularly. The crucial point to note, however, is that the maintenance of active barriers requires the checking of components and actuation sensors, so as to ensure they continue to activate successfully, on demand.

PROCEDURAL BARRIER PERFORMANCE

Pig Three considered that he had the benefit of a sturdy brick-built property, having accounted for the necessary barrier performance expectations, and knew he had a great sprinkler system too. But, in the spirit of one-upmanship that appeared to be rife amongst this trio of hogs, he also claimed to have a 'great plan' up his trotters in the unlikely event of things going wrong – which further lowered the probability of domino effect (or an escalation scenario) occurring – and should have averted his involvement in a more serious incident.

Looking at the procedural barrier it appeared that, superficially at least, Pig Three's *great plan* addressed the procedural emergency measures needed for incident mitigation. But Pig Three's arrangements were also not fully effective. *Why was this?* It was quite simply because Pig Three's failure to manage fire-fighting operations introduced the potential for escalation scenarios, including the spillage of contaminated firewater and the creation of vapour plumes, consequently upsetting the neighbouring human population. These issues, and Pig Three's ultimate failure, could have been avoided through the proactive testing of his *great plan*.

The function of procedural barriers is verified by testing the operation of procedures. Putting an organisational (rather than domestic) spin on Pig Three's circumstances for a moment, the types of questions typically asked to gauge the effectiveness of procedural barriers of this kind include: *'Does the emergency plan work?'*, *'Do those on site know what to do?'*, and *'Is there adequate equipment – such as fire-fighting equipment – available to deliver upon the requirements of the plan and make sure it works in practice?'* As with active barriers, procedural barriers – including emergency response plans and tests – contain *sense-decide-act* elements. Unlike active barriers, however, procedural barriers *require* operative intervention to activate. In designing or building procedural barriers therefore, it needs to be recognised that they have inherently lower reliability than most purely technical systems. It's this factor which means real-world organisations need to devote due attention to aspects including operative behaviour and testing. Here, however, it appears doubtful that considerations about what needed to be done and whether his plan would actually work even crossed Pig Three's mind! This is where the smugness of Pig Four came into play...

And much as his smugness was annoying, Pig Four did indeed demonstrate the required behaviours for ensuring procedural barrier effectiveness. This was seen in the fastidious approach he took towards his emergency planning responsibilities, including off-site arrangements; specifically, he paid due attention to the requirements he needed to meet under the COMAH Regulations – obligations which had to be satisfied for a facility of the kind he operated. As such, Pig Four's plan considered fire-fighting strategies and possible methods of reducing the amount of firewater run-off generated, for instance, by the use of sprays rather than jets, controlled burn and the possible recycling of firewater, where safe and practicable to do so. He'd also taken heed of advice from the Fire Service, based on fire-fighting best practice.

Pig Four took his responsibilities seriously. *First*, he prepared a 'Major Accident Prevention Policy' ('MAPP'), setting out his major accident policy, on the prevention of 'major accidents'[194]. *Second*, he prepared a 'safety report'[195], which included his MAPP. Within his safety report he gave a comprehensive description of the site and its

---

194. Regulation 7 of *the COMAH Regulations* deals with the preparation of major accident prevention policies, a requirement of all operators.
195. Regulations 8 to 10 of *the COMAH Regulations* cover the purpose, requirements for preparing, and review of safety reports by operators of upper tier COMAH sites (establishments), with schedule 3 detailing the minimum data and information required to be included within them.

surroundings, together with the associated hazards and risks and 'control measures' in place. He also sent the necessary information to the 'competent authority', to demonstrate he'd done all he needed to do to prevent major accidents. And he methodically considered major accident hazards, as well as setting out his approach to risk control and mitigation. *Third*, he prepared and tested an 'internal emergency plan'[196], to ensure the consequences of a major accident on his site were minimised. *Fourth*, he supplied information to the local authority for incorporation within the 'external emergency plan'[197] – enabling them to specify the measures taken outside his site, when needed. *Fifth*, and finally, he provided information to the public, likely to be affected by a major accident at his site[198] – detailing the dangerous substances, possible major accidents and their potential consequences – and explaining what they needed to do in the event of such a scenario unfolding, written in easy-to-understand terms, and avoiding complex technical jargon.

CLOSING THOUGHTS

Following on from *the porridge pot fable* and the introduction to barrier principles given there – specifically prevention barriers preventing top events, and mitigation barriers stopping, or limiting the extent of, consequences – this fable progressed the consideration of these concepts on a stage further, by looking at the intrinsic properties of different barrier types. It also prompted thought as to the maintenance requirements associated with each type, these being measures essential to ensuring that barriers continue to perform as intended on an enduring basis, and for securing their success in preventing harm, property damage and other undesirable consequences.

---

196. Regulation 12 of *the COMAH Regulations* handles the preparation, review and testing of internal emergency plans for upper tier COMAH sites, with schedule 4 detailing the information to be included within them.
197. Regulation 13 of *the COMAH Regulations* deals with the preparation of external emergency plans by local authorities, with schedule 4 detailing the information to be included within them.
198. Regulation 17 of *the COMAH Regulations* deals with the provision of information to the public, with regulation 18 handling the provision of information to those likely to be affected by a major accident at an upper tier COMAH site.

Finally, in reflecting back on the comments made in this book's introduction, this tale provides a salutary reminder about just how important horizon scanning can be. And, in drawing an analogy between the fiction of this fable and parallel real-world events, we see that withstanding the challenge of a *wolf* such as seasonal influenza was no guarantee that our level of individual, organisational, or even societal preparedness would be sufficient to defend against the aggression of a (then future) *dragon,* Coronavirus disease (COVID-19) being the go-to example of modern times.

For a summary of practical points to take away,
based upon the topics and subtopics handled by this fable,
see *How to…* Guide Seven.

A NOTE ON REPORTING REQUIREMENTS

We know, of course, that the events of this fable were of a purely fictional nature. We are also given to understand that no incident took place at Pig Four's site, with his management of it – as a successful chemicals magnate – said to have been exemplary! For completeness, however, it's appropriate to make brief mention of *the COMAH Regulations* which set out the reporting regime that would apply to a facility of the kind Pig Four was said to operate, in the event of a real-world scenario unfolding. These reporting requirements are outlined in this book's *Epilogue,* together with a brief overview of the environmental obligations applicable to real-world organisations, given a firewater run-off event of the kind which followed Pig Three's mishandling of fire-fighting operations.

Zac and the Beanstalk:
The Gravity of Falls from Height, Dropped Objects and Legal Consequences

ZAC'S FABLE

'So angry was the Giant Man that, not knowing what he was doing, he stumbled and, in the kerfuffle, the magic harp fell from his clutches. It fell right to the foot of the beanstalk in fact, with an almighty thud, hitting the ground just a few yards behind Zac, where he'd been running only a matter of seconds before.'

PROLOGUE

I don't suppose it will spoil the fable that follows here for many readers when I say that this fictional account centres on an enthusiastic but bored youth who, in an ill-judged moment of madness, makes a poor decision, exchanging a cherished cow for a handful of beans. Nor is it likely to come as much of a shock that, as the story unfolds, a big plant emerges from *terra firma*, giving rise to all sorts of trouble – in an escalation of events rarely witnessed outside fairy tales and full-scale Armageddon. This twist on a well-known classic affords us a look at *one* massive beanstalk, *two* big risks and *three* upset magic chickens, of average size. It also naturally leads readers to consider such legal consequences as might flow from the events described and, more importantly, from equivalent real-world scenarios.

BEANSTALKS AND BONDS

This is the first of the two *support fables* in this collection, the common intention of which is to show how organisations can both defend against, and provide support in response to, failings or shortfalls in the control of 'risk'. In this fable, it's not only the roles played by people that are important, but also the bonds *between* them. *Why might this be?* It's because these are the relationships that shape the types of legal action which might follow, given events of the kind depicted here, or indeed other risk scenarios as regularly play out in any real-world workplace and beyond, examples of which are parodied throughout this book. Set against the backdrop of 'fall from height' and 'dropped object' risks, this fable is principally concerned with the possible legal solutions which might be sought, whilst also suggesting some positive practical methods by which adverse outcomes can be prevented. As such, it explores a multiplicity of relationships and bonds between the characters involved – most notably those of occupier to trespasser, and employer to employee – as well as the connections that those who carry responsibility for controlling risk have with others in the outside world, including members of the public and visitors. A particularly important feature to note about this fable's central character, Zac, is that he's a child – a factor suggesting his 'risk perception' skills are likely to be poorer than those of a typical adult. If we take a moment to think about this, it isn't all that surprising. Generally speaking, children are poor estimators of scale and it's likely that the inclination of many of them, when confronted by a big plant of the kind that sprung up before Zac, would be to view it as an exciting challenge, rather than a source of risk. There's a beauty in seeing the world through a child's eyes – *let's face it, we've all done it* – but there are, of course, dangers too. This makes it worthwhile for us all occasionally to take a little time to put ourselves back in a child's shoes, remembering what it was like to be one and helping us to better comprehend the challenges and risks they face. And this duty isn't just a moral one; the British legal system also rightly affords children a higher level of protection, recognising that the development of their ability to fully understand risk and danger still has some way to go.

LOOKING TO REAL-WORLD DATA FOR SCALE:
One Massive Beanstalk

Here, we'll be accompanying the central character, Zac, on his beanstalk-based forays, paying particular attention to a dropped or thrown harp, a harp-dropping or throwing giant, anyone falling from the plant, and those hastily making for a place of safety on the ground below too. But, whilst fables are works of fiction, there are times when a sense of scale – *and even realism* – adds weight to the lessons and messages they seek to convey. And it's through applying some feasible data to Zac's activities that there arises here a clear opportunity for this updated modern version to bring added value to the original tale – which saw a central character, Jack, involved in antics of a similarly foolhardy nature.

So, let's start by asking: *'What's the worst thing that could have happened here?'* Much overused in the safety management arena, this question is shamelessly churned out across the land, in the course of 'audits' and 'inspections', spoken from the mouths of many a qualified professional or as the opening gambit to some worthy 'safety culture' crusade. I'll admit I've asked the question myself, and heard others ask it too, with awkward silences, witty repostes and occasionally snide comments returned, by way of response. The truthful answer to this question – although fortunately not the case here – could have been a harp embedding itself in a boy's skull. Answering speculative questions about *worst things* is helpful and important. Indeed, gauging the potential for equivalent real-world events to occur – or *'What if...?'* scenarios, a fictional example of which plays out here – in line with the outputs of theoretical models, is something in which all manner of people have an interest, amongst them lawyers, actuaries, safety and risk managers, to name but a few.

But when gauging how bad this worst thing is, just where exactly should we begin? Making an attempt to get beyond the fiction of a flung or otherwise plummeting harp, and towards an understanding of the real-world problem of a dropped object outcome, seems like a worthwhile, if not entirely straightforward, endeavour. It certainly calls for facts and data, in order for any kind of calculation to be attempted! *So how should we proceed?* For one thing, there's a clear need to plug the gaping hole in numeric data left by the tale, offering as it does only the basics of a heavy harp and a tall beanstalk. *We need to know the weight of the harp and the height of the beanstalk.* For another, we need to gauge how hard the harp might have hit the ground. *This calls for a calculation of 'fall energy'.* More specifically, it requires the application of physics to explore the non-linear relationship between 'mass' – *how much stuff or matter is in an object,* 'drop height' – *the height from which it's dropped,* and 'impact force' – *the force with which it hits the ground.*

So how exactly is this gaping data hole to be filled? In order to help evaluate the potential harm that might have flowed from the circumstances the fable outlines, let's first nominally calculate fall energy, with the help of an impact force calculator. There are many tools that can assist with performing this calculation, but all operate on the principle of plotting the mass of a dropped object against the distance it falls, allowing the possible consequences to be gauged[199].

---

199. www.dropsonline.org provides an impact force calculator tool, which has been used here, to give an indication of possible outcomes. [Viewed 1 May 2021].

The calculation for fall energy is thus:

IMPACT FORCE CALCULATOR:

DROPPED OBJECT

Mass (*kilograms*) * Height (*metres dropped*) * Gravity (*9.8 metres/second*)

= Fall Energy (*joules*)

In attempting to predict the magnitude of the outcome for the scenario the tale describes, some basic assumptions are to be made, using the following real-world data as inputs to the calculation:

A standard harp weighs *36 kilograms*[200] and...

...the tallest beanstalk ever recorded was a speckled butterbean vine, which was *14.1 metres tall*, and was grown by Staton Rorie of Rienzi, Mississippi, USA[201]...

...which means that, assuming a standard harp were to drop from the top of just such a beanstalk, the calculation becomes...

IMPACT FORCE CALCULATOR:

HARP DROPPED FROM TOP OF BEANSTALK

Mass (*36 kilograms*) * Height (*14.1 metres*) * Gravity (*9.8 metres/second*)

= Fall Energy (*4,974 joules or 4.97 kilojoules*)

Now, given that any object achieving an impact energy of over 40 joules is likely to result in a recordable (minor) injury or worse on impact with a human body, it's clear from this calculation that the probable – indeed, almost certain – outcome of a standard harp dropping directly on to a person from the top of a 14.1 metre high beanstalk would be a fatality. *But it's not only big objects which should concern us!* Whilst here we are dealing with a big harp, it's worth remembering that even the dropping of small objects can give rise to significant injuries. Taking a small screwdriver

---

200. The harp weight given in the prologue to this fable, used to calculate impact force here, is that of a typical pedal harp. There is some variability in weight as between different harp models.

201. Guinness Book of World Records., (2020) [online]. Guinness World Records. [Viewed 1 May 2021]. Available from: http://www.guinnessworldrecords.com This was recorded on 7 November 2003.

- which is sharp and pointy – we see that this too is capable of causing severe penetrating wounds. And, presuming such a screwdriver were to fall from the same height as the harp, this gives rise to the following calculation, which again produces a fall energy result of over 40 joules, the likely incident outcome being a recordable injury of some kind. The calculation for a screwdriver weighing 0.5 kilograms is thus:

IMPACT FORCE CALCULATOR:

SCREWDRIVER DROPPED FROM TOP OF BEANSTALK

Mass (0.5 kilograms) * Height (14.1 metres) * Gravity (9.8 metres/second)

= Fall Energy (69.1 joules)

This calculation leads to the conclusion that, on impact, even a small screwdriver has the potential to cause a small penetrating injury of varying severity, with the actual outcome in any given case being dependent upon the part of a human body it strikes. *But so what?* Well, the screwdriver calculation confirms that even small objects can present big injury risks. And the harp calculation indicates that the risk of a giant falling lyre is much bigger, with the likely outcome quite clearly towards the catastrophic end of the injury spectrum. This makes it seem fair to deduce that a harp falling on to a human from a beanstalk would culminate in a fatal ending. It also makes reasonable the presumption that a person falling an equivalent distance would suffer consequences of a similarly gruesome nature.

So, keeping these scenarios in mind, let's take a look at the two big risks which sit at the heart of this fable, both of which can result in events of a significant magnitude when transposed from the fictional context described here to a real-world one...

FALLS FROM HEIGHT AND DROPPED OBJECTS:
Two Big Risks

'Work at height' means work in any place including places at, above or below ground level – including getting into and out of workplaces – where a person could fall a distance liable to cause themselves personal injury, as defined within *the Work at Height Regulations 2005*[202] (*'the*

---

202. S.I. 2005/735.; the term 'work at height' is defined in regulation 2, together with other terms used within the regulations.

Work at Height Regulations'). The main focus here will be upon two big risks, a distinction reflected in the regulations – efforts to stop a person falling from height (*big risk one: fall from height*) and efforts to stop a thing – in this case, a harp – falling from height and hitting people on the ground below (*big risk two: dropped object*). In our exploration of this fable, we'll be considering these two big risks – or, to draw upon the risk terminology outlined in *the porridge pot fable*, 'top events' – both of which carry with them the potential for an incident to occur, with sometimes fatal consequences. A further foreseeable consequence of the dropped object risk is a major process incident or upset. *But more on this later...*

The scenario that plays out here requires us to answer two big risk questions for work at height activities, linked to the risks just mentioned, these being *first*, *'What would happen if someone were to fall from height, in this case, from a beanstalk?'* and *second*, *'What would happen if an object – say a harp – were to drop on to a person?'* Clearly defining and differentiating between risk types is important and helpful, making it right to afford them some separate attention here. To revert back to the use of the 'bow tie model' concept and terminology – as previously applied to the events of *the porridge pot fable* and *the four little pigs' fable* – they are generated by separate 'threats', each of which has the potential to lead to different 'consequences' and requires associated 'barriers' to be put in place for prevention or mitigation purposes. The distinction between incident types is one made in the statistics produced by Great Britain's Health and Safety Executive, and they are separately handled by *the Work at Height Regulations* too. So, keeping in mind the calculations just performed, let's take a moment to consider briefly some background context for each risk, before turning to the fable and the associated meanings which might be drawn from the events it sketches out. Whilst the numbers, harp and beanstalk referred to so far have been linked to this fable's fictional details, the data about real-world events shows that these risk types are always to be taken seriously.

BIG RISK #1
THE FALL FROM HEIGHT RISK

Over the five year period from 2016/17 to 2020/21, falls from height accounted for 25% of all fatal injuries to the workforce in Great Britain with an average of 34 per year being attributed to this risk type[203]. These figures alone confirm that this remains a serious and widely felt workplace issue. The personal consequences which attach to the fall from height risk cannot be overstated, and this is rightly reflected in the levels of penalties imposed where organisations are found to have fallen short of the expected standards. A notable example was the case of *Health and Safety Executive v. Sir Robert McAlpine Ltd.* [2019][204], in which the injured party suffered serious injuries including psychological damage, when he fell through an opening at Stone Gappe Hall, Keighley. This resulted in a fine of £260,000 being imposed upon the defendant organisation, for failing to ensure the safety of a non-employee; this was an incident which could easily have been prevented, had a thorough risk assessment been undertaken and adequate edge protection installed.

In terms of how the fall from height risk is handled by *the Work at Height Regulations,* this follows a 'hierarchy of control', an approach common to much health and safety legislation, and one already highlighted in the context of *the piper's fable* and *Ian's fable.* Industries where *persons falling from height* is a recognised risk include construction, forestry and arboriculture. 'Immediate causes' (or threats) which lead to this type of event can include: a lack of, or poor quality, scaffolding; gaps in 'working platforms'; defective ladders, and missing or deficient 'edge protection', to cite just a few examples. 'Underlying causes' are varied but, as far as 'workers' are concerned, they tend to be rooted in poor standards of 'competence', failures to adopt 'safe systems of work', inadequate 'risk perception', including 'risk assessment', and low levels of compliance or equipment maintenance. At an organisational level, on the other hand, underlying causes are often to be found in poor training, weak standards of management and/or supervision, sub-optimal safety culture, and flaws in process design.

The events of this fable are to be used as the basis upon which to explore several of these possible causes of falls from height.

---

203. *RIDDOR* data up to March 2021 – reported in HSE's Annual Statistics – *Kinds of Accident Statistics in Great Britain, 2021* (published 16/12/2021), *provisional as at the time of going to press.* Note that this is also the source from which data has been drawn for *big risk two* – the dropped object risk – an outline of which immediately follows this one. 204. See the Health and Safety Executive's website www.hse.gov.uk for further details of this case (*case reference no: 4553238*) date of hearing: 18/12/2019. Leeds Magistrates' Court.

With the context having been set for the risk of people falling from above, there remains a need to consider those on the ground below. Their safety matters too, of course, and the scene is set for this risk next…

BIG RISK #2
THE DROPPED OBJECT RISK

Over the five year period from 2016/17 to 2020/21, dropped objects (included within the figures for 'struck by moving object, including falling or flying…') accounted for 14% of all fatal injuries to the workforce in Great Britain, and 10% of non-fatal injuries in the same period.

Much like the effects upon individuals involved in fall from height incidents, those felt by the victims of dropped object incidents can be profound, even fatal. It's therefore unsurprising that these outcomes are similarly reflected in the penalties imposed upon organisations found to have failed to control this type of risk. This was apparent, for example, in the level of fine handed out in the case of *Health and Safety Executive v. Fresco Environmental Limited and Lee Heaps* [2017][205]. There, a waste processing firm was fined over £70,000 and the company's managing director received a six-month suspended prison sentence after an employee was crushed to death when the carpet bales that he was processing fell on to him, from a stack. It was found that the company had failed to ensure that proper controls were put in place, to reduce the risk of bales falling or causing injury to workers, and that it had omitted to set up any exclusion zones around the stack of bales, as well as the managing director of the company having failed to ensure that a safe system of work was in place for the processing of carpet bales. These factors pointed to a clear failure on the organisation's part to control the avoidable risk of dropped objects, with a tragically fatal outcome.

A 'dropped object' is any item which falls down or over from its previous position, with the potential to cause injury or death to a person, or damage to equipment or the environment within which it is situated; it can be further classified as static or dynamic. The 'static' type covers objects which fall from their previous static position, under their own weight, such as a light fitting which drops, due to

---

205. See the Health and Safety Executive's website www.hse.gov.uk for further details of this case (*case reference no: 4491389*) date of hearing: 21/08/2017. Liverpool Magistrates' Court.

its fasteners coming loose over time. But, as will become clear, the principal focus here is upon the other type – so-called 'dynamic' dropped objects – which fall from their previous static position due to force being applied by a person, equipment, machinery or moving object, an example being an object which is knocked off a platform and falls to a level below. In this fable, the object in question is a falling harp – a dynamic dropped object – with the force here being the push or drop action applied by a big Giant Man.

Setting aside harp-dropping and pushing for a moment, in a real-world context the ramifications of falling or dropped objects can be multiple and serious, largely due to their quickly building up a significant impact force – a principle outlined earlier in this *prologue*. On striking a person they are unlikely to simply bounce off and, even if they don't result in a fatality, they have the potential to penetrate soft tissue with often severe consequences. Just as is true of falls from height, dropped object risks have many causes too. The risk is seen where tools and equipment are inadequately stored or secured, and in circumstances where they become redundant or neglected. It's also seen where fixtures and fittings fail. Collisions and snagging can be problematic too, and of course environmental factors, including weather – which can be changeable – should never be overlooked. The underlying causes of these issues are varied. It might be that the standard of risk assessments, procedures or inspections is inadequate. Maybe levels of housekeeping or repair are poor. Or it's possible that maintenance schedules – whether planned or otherwise – are not being met. All of these causes need to be addressed, both at a management level, through measures including the proper resourcing of maintenance and inspection plans, and at the sharp end, by seeking reliable performance from the 'operatives' who perform activities which carry a recognised dropped object risk.

The events of this fable are to be used as the basis from which to explore several of these possible causes of dropped objects.

In thinking more broadly about the types of industrial setting in which dropped object top events can occur, it's worth noting that these are a particular concern for the oil & gas sector. *Why might this be?* It's simply because the nature of their operations tends to be such that if dropped objects land in the wrong place, the potential consequences are big – as, for instance, where critical pipelines and facilities, including sub-sea facilities, have the potential to be damaged – in some cases leading to 'loss of containment' scenarios. Such events can be viewed as 'escalation scenarios', arising from initial dropped object top events and it's through such scenarios – examples of so-called 'domino effect' – that major process incidents or process disruptions are most acutely felt. But oil & gas settings are by no means the only locations where dropped objects are of concern. Across multiple industries there are plenty of other locations where work at height and associated dropped object risks pose challenges, including on wind turbines, pylons and – in a location not dissimilar to that depicted in this tale – trees, which are of understandable interest in the arboricultural world! The risk of dropped objects is widely recognised, but some industry sectors have a more keenly felt interest in managing it; this is no act of altruism – on the contrary, they need to, because of the high consequences and large-scale publicity that failures attract, when they occur within complex operational settings. For certain activities, the planned movement of such objects is designated a 'safety critical task', requiring specific 'control measures' to be applied. By way of example, let's consider a container which needs to be moved by a crane to a new location, where the only available route for transporting it is above a production area. Should such a load drop during transit, it could rupture vessels and pipework, leading to the potential release of a highly flammable gas, or whatever else might be contained within them. Circumstances such as these – often seen within the oil & gas sector – underline the acute need for detailed mathematical calculations and other measures to be applied. This is achievable through any number of hazard and risk analysis techniques, which differ in complexity, but share a common purpose of ensuring that movements of objects, or indeed, any other high-risk activities, are correctly planned and executed, whenever they are undertaken.

But what happens in cases where the movement of objects goes wrong and an unplanned event occurs? A basic reading of *the Work at Height Regulations* tells us that organisations need to consider just such scenarios – requiring them to set up 'danger areas' – so that should objects fall, they do so in areas which are *no go* for individuals who are not directly involved in the tasks. As a control measure, exclusion from a danger area is naturally paired with the dropped object risk, which – as we shall see – is reflected in the legislation. Simply put, this means if an object can't be stopped from dropping in the first place, the next best option is for people to be kept out of the area in which it lands or is likely to land.

TYPES OF LAW

The introduction to these tales made reference to the benefits to be gained by avoiding the use of *impenetrable jargon* within the safety discipline, wherever possible. Hopefully this is something that this book's fables and their attached *modern meanings* largely achieve, but there are times when a basic understanding of a few key legal terms is helpful and one of those times is now! This is because, in contemplating the events of this fable, as is equally true when thinking about any real-world scenario, it's invaluable to keep in mind the key differences that exist between civil and criminal law. For any given set of circumstances, it's only by looking at *who* was wronged or harmed, *how* wrong or harm resulted (which requires an understanding of the relationship dynamics between those involved) and *what* the solution is that they want to achieve, that injured parties are able to determine the best legal route(s) to pursue, from the range of possible options open to them.

Under 'civil law' we'll look at the *Occupiers' Liability Act 1984*[206] ('*OLA 1984*') and the responsibilities it imposes upon 'occupiers', with a particular focus on 'trespassers'. These responsibilities should strike a chord for real-world organisations because, whilst the scenario to be considered here is a fantastical beanstalk-based one, the lessons from the fable can be readily applied to equivalent situations including, for instance, where children stray on to railway tracks or into electricity sub-stations, with their actions often being sparked simply by an innocent curiosity.

'Criminal law', on the other hand, handles circumstances in which legal duties – for instance, those under the *Health and Safety at Work etc. Act 1974*[207] ('*HSWA 1974*') or accompanying regulations, including *the Work at Height Regulations* – have potentially been breached by organisations or individuals, with those found guilty being convicted of an offence(s). We'll take a look at the general responsibilities *HSWA 1974* sets out, with a focus on the 'general duties' that employers have towards employees[208] and non-employees[209]. Also within the bounds

---

206. 1984 c. 3

207. 1974 c. 37

208. Section 2 of *HSWA 1974* sets out employers' general duties to ensure the health and safety of their employees, whilst at work.

209. Section 3 of *HSWA 1974* sets out employers' general duties to ensure the health and safety of persons other than their employees.

of the criminal law, we'll explore the specific regulatory regime that applies to those managing and/or working at height set out by *the Work at Height Regulations,* as well as the responsibilities they have for ensuring that the safety of those on the ground below isn't compromised by any work taking place. And we'll look at some other possible offences too, based upon the events described in the fable.

As we are about to see, it's fortunate that in this work of fiction no-one was injured or killed but, in the real world, it's important to remember that the risk focus of health and safety legislation means that the actual outcome doesn't always matter, when it comes to judging the level of penalty to be imposed in any given circumstances; if a risk is so badly controlled that something *could* happen, this will be dimly viewed by those seeking to enforce *HSWA 1974* and its accompanying regulations. In short, there isn't a requirement for actual harm to have occurred, with the fact of no adverse consequences flowing from an incident being no bar to prosecution, where it's deemed that the offender fell short of the legal requirements[210]. This means that in considering the events this fable describes, just as is true when looking at real-world scenarios, it's worth keeping in mind the full spectrum of the consequences of failure – not just the obvious personal injury and fatality outcomes – both in terms of civil claims and criminal prosecutions.

THE FOCUS OF THIS FABLE

Having outlined two types of risk associated with work at height and considered briefly the mathematics of impact force, let's dwell for a moment on this fable's focus. We'll be using this beanstalk-based scenario to examine the physical risks – amongst them dropped object and fall from height ones – in more detail, which naturally leads to thoughts about what can be done to control them. And we'll also look at some of the potential legal consequences which can flow when something bad happens, *or could have happened*, due to shortcomings or gaps in managing these risks. This inevitably requires thought

---

210. *The Sentencing Guidelines,* introduced in 2016, specify that it is only necessary to show that an offence created the *risk of harm,* with no requirement for actual harm to have been sustained. This is consistent with the approach taken by *HSWA 1974* and its accompanying regulations, which focus on the risk, rather than simply the outcome.

to be applied to the nature of the relationships between the parties involved, as depicted in the fable, and as is also a necessary step when contemplating the potential legal ramifications of equivalent real-world events.

The central theme we'll see emerge from this fable concerns the multitude of legal options which can be pursued by or on behalf of injured or aggrieved parties – which is to be handled here by looking at just some of the many potential 'civil claims' and/or 'criminal prosecutions' – against both individuals and organisations. These options – or legal routes of recourse – are to be highlighted within the *modern meaning* attached to the fable. As such, this fable naturally leads us to consider: *first*, pursuing civil claims for damages under *OLA 1984*, which protects trespassers, in circumstances where occupiers are deemed to have fallen short of the expectations for controlling their activities; *second*, pursuing criminal prosecutions, where an employer is believed to have breached general duties towards employees and others under *HSWA 1974*, including obligations to ensure their health, safety and welfare; *third*, pursuing criminal prosecutions under *the Work at Height Regulations*, which created a distinct regulatory regime for the control of work at height activities and protects workers, and *fourth*, and finally, pursuing prosecutions for other offences, including corporate manslaughter and gross negligence manslaughter, where organisations and individuals variously fail to take their responsibilities seriously, or otherwise fall short of what is expected of them.

We'll use this fable to look at how the risks of falls from height and dropped objects – together with other work at height-related risks – can be controlled, so as to avoid civil claims being made and/or criminal prosecutions being brought. With this in mind, let's first take a look at Zac's activities, before considering some of the results and consequences that might have flowed here, which, as it just so happens, also have relevance for equivalent real-world scenarios…

THE FABLE

Zachariah – or 'Zac', as he was known for short – and his mother were very poor. *They only had one cow.*

One day, Zac's mother said: 'Son! We need money *and fast!* Go and sell our cow for a good price, and bring the money back to me!' Zac led the cow away to sell her. On the way, he met a man who wanted to buy the cow. 'I have no money...' said the man, '...but I will give you three magic beans in exchange for your cow.' Zac replied: 'Alright, my man! You have yourself a deal!' and he gave the man his cow. Zac wasn't good with money – financial prudence being one of many life lessons he had yet to learn – and he was therefore unable to discern that this was, in fact, *not* a good deal. In his mind, he was just happy that the selling of the cow had been so easily accomplished. *His happiness was, however, to be short-lived.*

Zac took the three beans back to his mother. *She was furious.* 'These beans are no good to us!' she said, and she threw them out of the window. She was capable of a surprisingly good overarm throw, meaning that the beans were propelled quite some distance. She threw them so hard, in fact, that they came to rest on the grassy field of an adjacent landowner.

The next day when Zac awoke, hoping to see a beanstalk, he was bitterly disappointed. From his window, he could see only trees, sky and the occasional bird. *Zac had never known boredom like it.* And the next day when Zac woke up, there was still no beanstalk...nor the day after that...nor even the day after the day after that...*nor indeed, for some weeks after the day after the day after that...*In fact, most of the summer holidays passed, and still nothing could be seen. This irritated Zac, because his mother had recently declared to him that they were *staying local* this year, rather than touring American theme parks and, whilst their home was set amidst rolling hills, there was little of interest to a boy nearing teenage years. He was also annoyed, because it was starting to look like his mother was right. *As usual.* Zac was deeply upset. He knew he could be gullible – stupid even – but he also felt he'd been badly let down by what were less than ideal conditions for bean germination and growth. It was by turns, too hot, too wet, too shady, until some weeks later, when the climatic conditions seemed suddenly favourable...

On one particular morning, just days before Zac was due to return to school following his summer break, he awoke in his usual bleary-eyed fashion. But today already felt different. He had a feeling in his bones that maybe, just maybe, things were on the up. *And for once, this slightly wayward boy was right!* Upon drawing his curtains and peering out of the window, he was sure that a giant beanstalk was just perceptible down the lane leading from their house. And the more he looked, and the more he rubbed his eyes, the more this confirmed his belief. '*Woooooohoooooo!* I want to climb to the top!' shrieked Zac excitedly, his eyes now able to focus on what was – unmistakably – a beanstalk. Zac's '*Woooooohoooooo!*' went unheard by his mother, however, because unbeknown to him, she had popped out to the local shop, as they were running low on bread and milk. She had left a note for him on the table saying that this was so, signed off simply with the words 'Back soon! Mum x'. Having hastily dressed himself and with, as he saw it, no time for note-reading, nor even to contemplate the risks that might be involved in his intended activity, Zac bounded down the stairs, tripping over the dog (who wasn't best pleased) as he went, his trainers leaving a muddy trail on the hall carpet in his wake. He burst out through the door, sprinted down the lane (ignoring a little wooden sign he passed along the way, which read simply 'DANGER AREA') and started to climb the beanstalk.

True to her note, Zac's mother returned in short order. And no sooner had she pulled her car on to the drive than she detected that all was not quite as it should be, the front door being wide open. The first possibility that crossed her mind was of a break-in, but this was swiftly replaced by thoughts of beanstalk-ascent-related issues, as her eyes panned around, only for them to be strangely drawn to the sight of her errant son scaling the mighty plant in the distance. Leaving her groceries scattered on the drive, she yelled out 'No, Zac! NO!' as she ran hurriedly after him, heading as fast as she could towards the beanstalk, but it was too late. He was already halfway up it. Alas, she could only look on, open-mouthed, in troubled wonderment as to what might happen next. *She was right to be concerned.*

Zac climbed up...and up...AND UP...right to the very top of the beanstalk! Now, to the casual onlooker, it would have been acutely obvious that he'd made no plans as to how he would get up or down it, nor given the slightest thought as to what might happen were he to fall. But Zac had little time for the cynicism that seemed to dominate many an adult mind. He preferred instead to rely on youthful exuberance and a generally happy-go-lucky philosophy to see him through life, rather than troubling himself with what he regarded as unnecessary detail. And, having had it drilled into him by his mother since he'd been knee-high to a grasshopper that he was to make for their local hospital's accident and emergency department if things went really wrong for him, Zac felt he had most bases covered.

Having reached the top of the beanstalk, Zac could see a giant house with a giant door. On opening the giant door, he saw a big Giant Woman. He knew not how this beanstalk kingdom nor the pursuits carried on way up in the clouds had arrived, seemingly without warning (and certainly not in keeping with typical germination periods), but even before the big Giant Woman had opened her mouth, there was a look in her eyes which spoke of peril ahead. 'LOOK OUT!' yelled the big Giant Woman to Zac. 'The big Giant Man I work for is coming! He's generally decent to the Big Beanstalk Business' employees, but those who cross him quickly rue their actions...he has quite a temper on him, let me tell you!'

Zac would soon come to realise he'd made an error of judgment. In truth, he hadn't thought things through and shouldn't have started his ascent of the large plant unaided. And, whilst he was blessed with a vivid imagination, the presence of the giant folk wasn't something even he could have anticipated. At this stage someone of a more reflective temperament, and better placed to understand the circumstances before them, might have added to their risk list 'meeting of hostile giant stranger' and 'unwise ill-thought out ascent of big plant'. But not Zac. For the time being, at least, he was just content to follow his dreams and see where life might take him. 'Hee-Hi-Hum-Ho! WATCH OUT THOSE WHO STAND BELOW!' roared the big Giant Man, unaware that Zac had already sneakily clambered up to his level.

'You must hide!' whispered the Giant Woman to Zac. And, being of a kindly nature, she helped him to hide under a giant table which, as luck would have it, was covered by a giant tablecloth. The Giant Man came in and sat down at the giant table with some giant bags of money. He started to count up his money. Zac watched him from beneath the table, scarcely daring to breathe. From his crouched-down hiding position, Zac's imagination was – as usual – running wild. His wonderment as to how this whole other world had arisen, all from three measly beans hastily cast aside by his mother, simply refused to go away. There was no denying it, the Giant Man had certainly been industrious and done well for himself in super-quick time, but Zac was curious as to how he had plucked success from a business model based ostensibly upon a big plant, a harp and a few chickens. Still, having realised he wasn't going to get to the bottom of this any time soon, he put it to the back of his mind, choosing instead to focus on the more pressing matters, closer at hand...

Soon, the Giant Man fell asleep. Seizing his moment and with, as Zac saw it, there being no time to waste, he dashed out from under the table and took all the money. Then he climbed down from the beanstalk, and handed the money to his mother. But whilst there was no question that Zac's mother needed the money, she didn't hold back in giving him a piece of her mind about the ill-advised nature of his actions, nor in insisting that he should get the vacuum cleaner out to remove the muddy trail he'd left on the hall carpet, earlier that day.

Some days later...

All too quickly it seemed, Zac forgot his earlier brush with danger and, with the beanstalk never far from his thoughts, one morning over his cornflakes he casually mentioned to his mother his urge to climb it once more. 'No, Zac! NO! Your behaviour is *really* trying my patience...' she said, '...and if I find out you've gone behind my back again, young man, you're going to be in *so* much trouble!' And, considering her words to have closed the matter, Zac's mother turned on her heels and went to their utility room to unload some clothes from the washing machine.

Alas, it was to transpire that her warning about going behind her back would be a strangely prophetic one, because just as she was pegging out the laundry on the washing line in the back garden, she heard the front door slam. This time she knew instinctively what was wrong. Dropping her laundry basket to the ground, Zac's mother ran back through the house. She ran through the utility room. She ran back past the kitchen table, strewn with traces of cornflakes and a slight milk spillage. She opened the front door and ran towards the beanstalk. And sure enough, as she looked into the distance, she could just pick out her son running down the lane once again, beanstalk-bound for a second time. But before Zac's mother could reach him, he'd vanished from view, and she just caught sight of the soles of his shoes, before they disappeared with the rest of him, up into the leaves at the top of the beanstalk.

Zac was greeted once more by the Giant Woman. 'LOOK OUT!...' she said, '...the Giant Man is angry because his money has been stolen!' And right on cue, and seeming to corroborate her warning to Zac, the Giant Man roared: *'Hee-Hi-Hum-Ho!* WATCH OUT THOSE WHO STAND BELOW!', the tone of his voice noticeably lower than the first time he'd had cause to roar, what with all the pent-up anger rattling his ribs and booming around inside his gigantic frame. 'You must hide under the giant table again...' said the Giant Woman '...*and don't move a muscle!'* The Giant Man came in and sat down at the giant table. He carried with him a magic chicken. The magic chicken laid golden eggs. It was one of a few magic chickens he reared. Before long, the Giant Man fell asleep. Seizing his moment, Zac emerged from beneath the giant table and took the magic chicken. Then he climbed back down the beanstalk.

The tension was palpable that evening with Zac having, once again, ignored parental advice. Zac's mother was also at pains to point out that a magic chicken had no place in their family home.

The next day...

Zac's mother awoke in a good mood, which was perhaps a little surprising given the events of the previous day. For one thing, she'd reassured herself that bad luck was unlikely to visit her for a third time, so soon after the previous two instances of Zac's beanstalk-based bad behaviour. For another, she had a day off, and was just enjoying a few extra minutes in bed, before getting on with her daily chores. But no sooner had she got up than the realisation dawned on her that this was to be no relaxing day's holiday. For a start, Zac was not in his bedroom, in itself unusual given that he was never the first one up out of bed. For another, on entering the kitchen, it quickly became apparent that he hadn't eaten breakfast, with the boxes of cereal still standing tidily in the cupboard and her son nowhere to be seen. His badly scrawled note on the kitchen table, stating simply 'back soon!' sent shivers down Zac's mother's spine and gave her cause to swiftly rethink the theory that bad luck wouldn't visit her for a third time. And she knew it to be overly-optimistic on her part to think that Zac might have popped out for bread and milk, given that he had never knowingly done anything useful. As she reached the front door with a growing sense of foreboding, Zac's mother recognised that, whilst lightning was unlikely to strike twice, there seemed to be no limit to the number of times her son would veer away from sensible parental guidance.

With Zac's mother now regretting her decision to have a lie in – and her son having got a head start on her, brought about by his earlier than usual start – this time he really was nowhere to be seen. He was already at the top of the beanstalk, being greeted once again by the Giant Woman. 'Oh, now this is getting to be beyond a joke young man! LOOK OUT!' said the Giant Woman, continuing '...The Giant Man is angry because one of his magic chickens and his money have been stolen.' The Giant Man roared: 'Hee-Hi-Hum-Ho! WATCH OUT THOSE WHO STAND BELOW!' Suddenly, Zac felt, things were not looking so good for him. In what was a rare moment of self-doubt, he was forced to admit that he hadn't really thought things through and that, in retrospect, it had perhaps been an unwise move to have climbed the beanstalk – for a third time – on a whim. 'You kids – you're all the same! *Will you never learn?* You must hide under the giant table again,' said the Giant Woman, her exasperation at Zac's impulsive actions all too plain to see.

The Giant Man came in with a magic harp. He sat down at the table and started to play the harp. For all his big Giant Manliness, even with his chubby sausage-like Giant Man fingers, he was capable of a surprisingly melodic tune when he put his mind to it. Soon, the Giant Man fell asleep, apparently lulled into a relaxed state by his own beautiful music. The Giant Woman having signalled to Zac that the coast was clear, he crawled out from under the giant table and tried to pick up the harp but, being as he was only of slight build and not having thought the manoeuvre through, before he could get very far, it slipped from his grasp. This caused the Giant Man to wake up with a start and made him very angry. He grabbed the harp and ran towards Zac who was, by now, beating a hasty retreat down the beanstalk. 'RUN AWAY!' yelled the Giant Woman. 'The Giant Man is right behind you!'

Zac descended the beanstalk, with the now angry Giant Man hot on his heels.

So angry was the Giant Man that, not knowing what he was doing, he stumbled and, in the kerfuffle, the magic harp fell from his clutches. It fell right to the foot of the beanstalk in fact, with an almighty thud, hitting the ground just a few yards behind Zac, where he'd been running only a matter of seconds before. Whether the harp was thrown in frustration, or had simply been carelessly dropped, was the subject of a debate which would undoubtedly find its place at the heart of local folklore for many years to come. Three chickens also plummeted to the ground from above, looking startled and bewildered what with all the commotion and their sudden loss of altitude. *They might have been magic chickens, but that didn't mean they liked chaos!* When Zac reached the safety of his home, having narrowly escaped a nasty harp-through-skull type injury and the wrath of the three slightly irritated chickens, his mother dashed out and cut down the beanstalk. Not being one to do anything quietly – and harbouring, as she did, a feeling that she might have missed her calling in life as a professional singer – she had no qualms about voicing her disapproval, with a little ditty that had come into her mind some minutes before, the inspiration for which she claimed to have drawn from recent events, as well as other life experience.

> 'A dreamer will speak about fairies on trees,
> Oblivious to the risk that rational folk see;
> The thought never enters this wistful one's brain,
> About ogres up beanstalks, *so let me explain...*
> These past few days, son, it's been abundantly clear,
> That of hazards and risk, you have not a fear.
> Your actions, your errors, no end of mistakes,
> That seem swiftly to follow your morning cornflakes.
> You gave not a thought to a sign marking danger,
> And from that point on, your actions got stranger.
> You said 'Look at me Mum, young Zachariah!'
> With the urge in your bones, thought you had to get higher!
> And the height of the plant – and your speed of descending
> Makes me surprised there's a happy-ish ending.
> More than once, I feel sure that my heart's skipped a beat,
> From your failure to learn and your urge to repeat,
> The climb up to the clouds and the mystery above,
> So please hear me out, *please listen, love...*

> Rumours abound, I once heard a rumble,
> Of the big Giant Woman, who took quite a tumble.
> She wasn't one to *harp on*, didn't like to complain,
> The dropped instrument aspect, I shall shortly explain.
> And being embarrassed, she thought not to call,
> Nor to speak to the Giant Man, or report on her fall.
> This wasn't the first time, and it won't be the last,
> Accidents – just failings to learn from the past.

> The repeat of your actions says you've no thought of stopping,
> No regard for the chickens, nor the harps that are dropping.
> When I think of the risk of harps bumping to earth,
> Though it seemed fun to you, I've no time for your mirth!

The Giant Woman tells of once, when, from this vine's summit
A harp missed her by an inch and to ground it did plummet.
The last thing *you* need is a harp in your head –
You could have been hurt, you might have been dead...
It remains a conundrum: *was this lyre thrown or dropped?*
But I tell you, my boy, that my ageing heart stopped,
As you ran for the hills, as you ran for your life,
A harp landing from height cuts as sharp as a knife!
Just like life, this floor's fragile, or so it would seem,
You have to wake up from this dangerous dream.

You know that I love you, my little buffoon,
But it seems your brain's wired, like a wolf, to the moon.
The Giant Man played music, way up high, on his harp,
But you toyed with risk – it wasn't even ALARP![211]
You've caused me no end of worry and fright,
With your lack of regard for the troubles at height.
It's true that – in life – people strive for the top,
But, in terms of this beanstalk, YOUR ANTICS MUST STOP!
And as for the Giant Man, he must understand,
If he can't stop a harp drop – he must fence off his land!'

CRASH! Moments later, the Giant Man fell to earth with an almighty thud! Although unhurt he was, understandably, a little shaken by this, but quickly managed to recover his composure. The Giant Man's natural instinct was to become angry at Zac's mother's butchering of his beanstalk, but the Giant Woman was quick to placate him, pointing out the many shortcomings that might be levelled against his harp and chicken-based enterprise. She suggested to the big Giant Man that his shoddy approach to safety matters was such that he might have fallen for all manner of reasons, eventually managing to persuade him that his energies would be better channelled into other, more worthy, initiatives. She thought one such project should involve a reappraisal of his control of work at height and dropped object risks, stressing to the big Giant

---

211. ALARP (as low as reasonably practicable) is the level to which workplace risks are expected to be controlled and is the standard against which the control measures of the kind put in place by the big Giant Man would be judged, given an equivalent real-world scenario. This can also be expressed as SFAIRP (so far as is reasonably practicable), being the amount by which risks are expected to be reduced.

Man the need to apply more thought to the threats the Big Beanstalk Business's activities posed to child trespassers, members of the public and those it employed to carry out work for it too. She also kept on badgering him about the need to attend to the fencing of the property boundary, as a priority. Zac, meanwhile, was full of sorrow, wondering just how long it would take him to do something in life of which his mother approved. And, much as he hated to admit it, he hadn't the slightest idea what ALARP meant – which was, curiously, starting to bother him.

But that's not quite the end of the story...

For Zac and his mother, of course, there were the many unanswered questions. One such question was how the beanstalk had sprung up so suddenly from a humble handful of beans, seemingly bringing with it a whole *other world*. Another was how it had come to pass that the big Giant Man had been occupying it, working alongside the big Giant Woman from the plant's summit.

And of course, with the passing of time, there came other questions. Like how Zac and his mother had previously been poverty-stricken and were now seemingly destined for the predictable *happily ever after* conclusion common to many a fairy tale. The reasonable observer might fairly assume that the royalties from Zac's mother's low-brow song wouldn't be enough to sustain them forever. It wasn't even that well-written, sparking local rumours that matters might have been privately settled. There seemed to be no other logical reason for the rapid turnaround in the family's fortunes, and there was also no denying that the avoidance of legal wrangling and negative publicity was uppermost in the Giant Man's mind. A further notable factor was that charges were never pursued in relation to Zac's petty thieving. Speculation of this kind is perhaps only natural, given the gaps in detail left out by this tale, a flaw it shares in common with many others.

As for the Giant Man, these events had given him cause to have a major rethink. Much as he'd been angry, Zac's mother's hastily-penned soliloquy had brought with it the crushing realisation that things could have been a whole lot worse for all concerned. Whilst his inclination was to be over-protective of his little empire in the clouds, in his heart, the Giant Man knew he'd meant Zac no real harm. Of particular worry for him were the anecdotes circulating locally about the Giant Woman's involvement in a couple of earlier incidents – one of which centred around an unintentionally dropped harp nearly causing her to come to harm on the ground below, and another which apparently involved her tripping on the floor at the top of the beanstalk – in brushes with danger bearing an uncanny resemblance to those encountered by Zac. Admittedly, these had gone unreported but, had they been recorded and investigated appropriately, they would have served as clear warnings to the Giant Man and indeed, to the wider Big Beanstalk Business, that a more serious event was likely to occur at some point, if they didn't take heed and learn from them. Conflicting rumours abounded too, about whether the harp had been deliberately dropped or perhaps fallen through some less than perfect flooring. But whatever the reasons, the fact of these failings having come to light, together with his own firsthand experience of tumbling to earth with a bump (seemingly brought about by Zac's mother's impulsive arboriculture) looked, at least, to have served a useful purpose in knocking some sense into the Giant Man. It also appeared to have been these events which had prompted him to reflect on his working practices and the robustness of his reporting processes. And whilst, to outsiders, the nature of the business remained something of a mystery, shortly after these events had taken place the big Giant Man started searching for single-storey work accommodation, fuelling speculation that there really had been no need for his activities to be carried out from the top of a tall beanstalk, after all.

As for Zac's mother, she yielded to pressure and agreed that, for the sake of a quiet life and to stop her son from complaining all summer and generally being out looking for trouble, next year they should just *do Florida...*

...and the Giant Man and the Big Beanstalk Business resolved to conduct their operations from lower level premises, ever after...

A POST SCRIPT:
The Fate of Three Chickens*
(*of average size)

This tale has centred around one massive beanstalk and two big risks, but for completeness it seems only right and proper to make mention of the three upset (but averagely-sized) chickens, the magical properties of which the story leaves undisclosed. For those readers concerned about matters of animal welfare, word has it that no poultry suffered permanent harm as a result of the events described here, albeit that a couple of chickens were left dazed and confused, one had a slightly bruised beak from sudden impact with the ground, and egg production was temporarily down, most likely brought on by the stress of it all...

MODERN MEANING

Before getting into the detail of this fable – of which there is quite a bit – it's worth noting that Zac's mother would naturally have held parental responsibility for her son and the hair-brained antics the tale describes. The suggestion that Zac was *'nearing teenage years'* should, ordinarily, have meant he was capable of being left alone for short periods of time – with those supervising him able to pop out for some basic provisions, hang out laundry, or perhaps, even have a well-deserved lie-in – but this would have required his mother to make a judgment call, before reaching a decision about whether to leave him at all. The law does not prescribe an age when a child can be left, but if this would place them at risk, those leaving them can be prosecuted if they are unsupervised *'...in a manner likely to cause unnecessary suffering or injury to health.'*[212] In Zac's case however, his immaturity – and clear tendency towards misadventure – perhaps calls into question whether his mother's decisions to leave him unsupervised, even for a few minutes, were wise ones.

The key emphasis of this *modern meaning* is not, however, upon judging the parenting capabilities of Zac's mother, but rather upon exploring the types of obligations and expectations to which occupiers and employers are routinely subject, within organisational settings. Parents can only do so much to make sure their children are safe, meaning organisations have a very clear part to play in taking responsibility for the risks they generate or allow to exist. As such, here the focus shifts to exploring the possible legal options which might be pursued, given an equivalent real-world scenario to that which played out in the fable, involving the potential for falls from height and dropped objects. Fortuitously, in this case, all that occurred was a 'near-miss' incident – referred to by some as a 'near-hit' – between harp and boy, with Zac making it to a place of safety, just in the nick of time, a Giant Man suffering no more than a dented ego, and a trio of chickens, slightly

---

212. Section 1 of the *Child and Young Persons Act 1933*, c. 12.

ruffled feathers. But of course, things could have been very different, such are the fine margins that exist between lucky avoidance and catastrophic outcome in many an incident scenario. Had the harp hit and injured Zac or the big Giant Woman or, even worse, hit and killed either of them – or if they'd come to harm as a result of falling from the beanstalk's top – the consequences would have been significant, with these alternative climaxes to the fable falling some way short of the utopian *happily ever afters* we were lulled into expecting as infants. We'll consider just such scenarios here, paying due attention to the relationships involved, and looking at the range of possible legal consequences that might play out, in the wake of these kinds of incidents.

In circumstances where occupiers or employers are involved, a fundamental principle is that they are to take due care of all visitors, including those who are uninvited. Whilst a reasonable occupier is expected to take more care of lawful visitors than unlawful ones (trespassers), a 'duty of care' is owed to them all albeit that, in the case of trespassers, this is limited to protecting them from personal injury. And where organisations fail to take such responsibilities seriously, they expose themselves to liability for civil claims for 'damages'. It's often the case that visitors face a greater level of risk when confronted by the same hazards as employees, simply due to their unfamiliarity with the workplace, activities or people with whom they might have cause to interact. This would have been true for Zac and the allure the beanstalk held for him. In addition to the route for civil claims, we'll also consider the options for criminal prosecution, of the kind pursued in response to potential real-world legislative breaches, using the scenario involving Zac, the beanstalk and the relationships between the characters seen in this fable as a comparable fictional example.

Whilst this fable is set against the backdrop of a fantastical beanstalk, the general control principles for work at height and dropped object risks explored here hold true whether work is carried out on a wind turbine, a meteorological mast, or a pylon. So before allowing a sense of grown-up cynicism to creep in – which would undoubtedly give rise to questions about the relevance of the bizarre precipitation of the magical lyre and confused poultry at the centre of this tale – it's worth reflecting on the kinds of real-life risk scenarios that organisations are frequently forced to consider, and which carry similar potential for harm to those that unfolded in the fictional scene which played out here...

In the real world, the concern might be with a 'dynamic dropped object'. It could be a tree branch dropped by an arborist (tree surgeon). It might be a spanner dropped from a wind turbine by an engineer. Or alternatively, it could be with a 'static dropped object', of which a dome falling from a meteorological mast would be an example, where harsh weather conditions can cause nuts and bolts to fail, due to corrosion. And of course, in any such locations, thought always needs to be given to the risk of a person falling too.

By considering the activities described by this fable from a risk perspective for a moment – and through applying the same principles used in the context of *the porridge pot fable* and its loss of containment top event – we see that it would be perfectly possible to develop bow tie models for these work at height and dropped object risks along similar lines. The shenanigans of the characters in *Zac's fable* could just as easily be analysed in the context of potential top events, threats, and consequences[213]. And even taking the first steps of that same approach here shows us that from one [work at height] hazard there arise at least two key risks or top events, namely [person falls from height] and [person is struck by dropped object]. Moving on and applying 'barrier modelling' principles to the details of the tale enables some typical threats that might lead to these top events to be quite quickly identified. For the fall of a person, this could range from [unsuitable working platforms], to [fragile floors] and [lack of edge protection]. For a strike by a falling object on the other hand, it might include [poor storage] or [inadequate securing arrangements]. But the development of risk models isn't going to be pursued any further for these scenarios, as to do so would be to duplicate the principles highlighted by the earlier *porridge pot fable*. Instead, here our focus shifts to the potential civil law obligations and criminal law duties which might have been breached, had Zac or others involved in the events described – or a slight variation of them – been injured or killed by a dropped harp, or suffered a similar fate by plummeting to the ground themselves.

Keeping the real-world examples of branches, spanners, and masts in mind, let's look at four different options for redress – or civil claims and criminal prosecutions – which might have flowed from the two big risks

---

213. In the same way as was adopted for the analysis of *the porridge pot fable*, the bow tie model elements and suggested elements are denoted in square brackets throughout this section.

outlined in this fable, in response to failures to stop people falling from height, and failures to stop objects striking people on the ground below.

It's worth remembering that every situation is different and that other options might be available to aggrieved or injured parties, in addition to those considered here, for real-world scenarios equivalent to the fictional one described. Examples of other routes of redress that could be pursued in contexts akin to that which played out here might include seeking prosecution for a failure to carry out risk assessment under the general provisions of regulation 3 of *the Management of Health and Safety at Work Regulations 1999*[214] (*'the Management Regulations'*) and for a failure to provide suitable work equipment under regulation 4 of *the Provision and Use of Work Equipment Regulations 1998*[215]. Given any real-world scenario however, those seeking redress always need to keep in mind which claims or prosecutions offer them the greatest prospect of success, for the particular circumstances.

OPTION #1
PURSUE A CIVIL CLAIM FOR DAMAGES AGAINST THE BIG BEANSTALK BUSINESS

This option concerns a hypothetical claim that could have been made against the Big Beanstalk Business, in its capacity as an occupier, under the *Occupiers' Liability Act 1984*.

In this version of events, Zac, a child trespasser – an uninvited visitor – might have been hit and injured by a falling harp, or alternatively, fallen from the beanstalk, giving rise to a civil claim for damages under *OLA 1984*. When things go wrong, an individual can be awarded damages, in cases where it is demonstrated that they suffered injury from an accident on premises under the control of an occupier, as a result of their 'negligence' (a failure to fulfil their duty of care obligations). There are limited details supplied here about the parties involved, but let's assume that the Big Beanstalk Business was the occupier of the beanstalk. This would have meant that the organisation had imposed upon it responsibilities for managing the risks on the beanstalk and in its environs, relating to: climbing up and down it; ensuring it was free of

---

214. S.I. 1999/3242.
215. S.I. 1998/2306.

trip hazards; making sure that arrangements were in place to maintain any flooring, and establishing and maintaining safe methods for the lifting and lowering of harps (or indeed, other objects).

From the description of events the fable offers, there would have been a clear rationale for pursuing a civil claim for damages here, had Zac been struck by the harp or fallen from the beanstalk and sustained injury. Taking this perspective on the scenario means such an outcome would potentially have been caught within the scope of *OLA 1984*. This is because – continuing on with the presumption that the Big Beanstalk Business was the occupier – Zac would have been considered a trespasser, having got on to the beanstalk without having first been invited. In order to determine the likelihood of any such civil claim succeeding, there's a need to answer five questions, which, when applied to this particular scenario, would be: *first, 'Did a duty of care exist towards Zac?', second, 'What factors should have influenced the level of protection given to Zac?', third, 'Was a higher duty of care owed to Zac than others?', fourth, 'Did Zac voluntarily accept the risk?', and fifth, and finally, 'Did the Big Beanstalk Business do enough to discharge the duty it owed to Zac?'*

So let's take each of these questions in turn...

QUESTION #1
Did a duty of care exist towards Zac?

YES! *The scope of OLA 1984 establishes a duty of care to 'persons other than visitors', so this predominantly applies to trespassers – in this scenario, Zac – as illegitimate visitors*[216].

This duty is equivalent to that set out in the earlier *Occupiers' Liability Act 1957*[217] (*OLA 1957*), which protected invited visitors. The occupier's duty under *OLA 1984* is to '*take such care as is reasonable in all the circumstances of the case to see that (he) does not suffer injury on the premises by reason of the danger concerned.*'[218] The duty applies when, as

---

216. It's worth noting that, just as was the case for Zac, it's likely his mother would have been similarly viewed as a trespasser, albeit that her actions have not been considered in detail here. It is, however, unlikely that anything she did would have been viewed as sympathetically as would be true for Zac, with adults generally being held to higher account for their actions than minors.

217. 1957 c. 31.

218. Section 1(4) of *OLA 1984* sets out an occupier's duty of care towards trespassers.

set out in *OLA 1984*, the occupier – which, in this case, would have been the Big Beanstalk Business – satisfies several requirements. *And what are the requirements for a duty of care to exist?*[219] Simply put, they are, *first*, the occupier needs to be aware of the danger or have reasonable grounds to believe it exists; *second*, if either of the first criteria are met, the occupier needs to know or have reasonable grounds to believe that the trespasser is near, or may come to be near, the danger, and *third*, the risk needs to be one from which the occupier may reasonably be expected to protect visitors. Now, for the events as they appeared in the fable, it would have been clear to the Big Beanstalk Business that there were others in the vicinity of the property it occupied, and that the beanstalk and the activities carried out on or around it posed a risk to them. And the risks associated with a tall beanstalk would make reasonable the expectation that the Big Beanstalk Business would have offered Zac some protection.

QUESTION #2
What factors should have influenced
the level of protection given to Zac?

Whilst any occupier can be expected to offer some protection to a trespasser, the level at which this is offered depends upon various factors. These relate to: *first*, the premises; *second*, the risk itself, and finally, *third*, the trespasser involved. These factors are considered briefly here, insofar as they would have applied to Zac.

In thinking of the premises factors, it's important to look at the nature of the premises, the activities carried on there – or the type of activity the trespasser might envisage being carried on – and the nature of the danger. To take a comparable real-world example, for the premises, a location such as an electrified railway line would naturally be perceived as more dangerous than, say, a private dwelling, bringing with it the expectation of an accompanying higher level of protection. And, in seeking to protect against the danger itself, the position is that hidden dangers should attract a better level of protection than those that are more obvious, with the degree of danger present also being relevant. The sudden arrival of a tall beanstalk would have been a danger against which some form of protection should have been

---

219. Section 1(3) of *OLA 1984* sets out the requirements to be met, in order for the occupier's duty of care towards a trespasser to exist.

provided. And the risk of falling harps might reasonably be viewed as a hidden danger, thus raising the level of protection expected!

Turning to look at the level of risk here, just as is true when considering or assessing any risk, there are two key parameters of interest. The *first* is the likelihood – whether there is a high or low risk of injury – and the *second* is the severity of any injury which could occur. In terms of the details the fable offers, there were two key risks with a *high* likelihood in this case. *First,* there was the dropping or throwing of a harp to the ground below, within an area which was unprotected, as evidenced by Zac climbing up and down the beanstalk, and having cause to run away from it as the harp was dropped – a risk seemingly already realised, given the anecdote of a previous occurrence which saw the big Giant Woman encountering a 'near miss' of this ilk. *Second,* was the clear potential for Zac to fall from height, a risk which the fable suggests had been the subject of another near miss involving the big Giant Woman. A *high* rating would also seem to apply to the severity of any injury that might have resulted from either of these events, not least because, as the *prologue* to this tale highlights, the seriousness of injury that attaches to fall from height and dropped objects risks is universally accepted to be severe, often fatal. And whilst the intricacies of risk management fall outside the scope of this book, suffice it to say that where – as here – an activity is scored as *high* for both likelihood and severity, this results in an overall risk rating of *high* or *severe,* giving rise to a level of risk requiring more stringent control measures to be in place than would be the case for lower level risk types. It's incumbent on real-world organisations to make sure they understand the level of risk generated by all of their activities and to prioritise their risk management activity accordingly[220].

The particular characteristics of the trespasser involved also have a bearing on the level of protection required. A young trespasser – as typified by Zac, here – can expect to be afforded greater protection by the law, given that their risk perception skills are likely to be less

---

220. Note that the terms applied to different risk levels vary according to the nomenclature of the chosen methodology. Some are quantitative, whilst others are qualitative, but whichever approach is taken, when properly applied they allow those organisations using them to evaluate the robustness of their current controls and determine the need for any additional ones. See this book's *Glossary* for a definition of a 'risk matrix' which tends to be central to such methodologies.

developed than those of an average adult. Foreseeability of trespass is also a pertinent factor for consideration. It would perhaps have been natural for a newly-arrived beanstalk to be viewed as an exciting prospect by Zac, just as might be true of a railway line or an electricity substation for any child based in the real world. Such environments can seem alluring, making it more likely that trespass will be attempted, but the obvious dangers associated with these locations are of such gravity that additional control measures need to be put in place by those who carry responsibility for them. This highlights the point that the *accidental child* who ends up in difficulty, as well as the *inadvertent adult trespasser* who strays out of the area in which they are permitted to be, in error, are likely to be treated more kindly by the law than would a burglar. This is because the nature and character of their entry is well-intended, rather than being to cause harm to the property or its contents. It's quite easy to empathise with a recreational climber's desire to climb trees – which would presumably extend to tall beanstalks too – but most of us would also recognise that it's rare for this to be accompanied by an urge to destroy them!

QUESTION #3
Was a higher duty of care owed to Zac than others?

YES! *A higher duty of care would have existed towards Zac.*

OLA 1984 sets the basis for occupiers' liability towards trespassers and other uninvited visitors, whether they are adults or children. A particular problem in relation to uninvited visitors who are children is that they often don't appreciate the risk related to their own actions, when they venture out looking for fun. If something attractive, but potentially dangerous, is left accessible to them, the occupier of land will be liable for creating such a danger. The sudden arrival of a beanstalk, as here, would almost certainly have been regarded as an attraction, hence making it likely that the corresponding duty of care would have been higher towards Zac, than would be the case for most adults. The temptation for Zac to climb the beanstalk, and the likelihood of his needing to run from a hastily dropped and rapidly plummeting harp, are both factors which should have been within the contemplation of the Big Beanstalk Business, introducing the need for it to take action, so as to meet the expectations of the higher duty of care it would have faced in this case.

QUESTION #4
Did Zac voluntarily accept the risk?

NO! *Zac did not voluntarily accept the risk.*

OLA 1984 includes the so-called *'volenti'* defence[221], which provides that no harm is done to a willing person. Or, put more simply, it's the legal principle that if someone willingly and knowingly places themselves in a position where they might come to harm, they will be unable to bring a claim against another party if they suffer injury as a result. The question here is whether the defence of *'volenti· non fit injuria'* (no harm is done to a willing person) would have been available to the Big Beanstalk Business, given Zac's actions. In answering this, it has to be said that, whilst Zac's behaviour appears to have been impulsive, the chances of this defence succeeding for the Big Beanstalk Business would have been low in this case, given that children cannot voluntarily accept risks that they don't fully understand. This supports the point made in the *prologue* that the law seeks to protect children from dangers that might be amplified by their innocent curiosity.

QUESTION #5
Did the Big Beanstalk Business do enough
to discharge the duty it owed to Zac?

NO! *From the detail provided in the fable, it seems unlikely that enough was done here to discharge the duty owed.*

Other than the beanstalk itself, the only physical feature of which the tale makes mention is a little wooden sign at the edge of the danger area. Seemingly there was an absence of demarcation here, with no fencing installed around the beanstalk to prevent climbing, nor any clear warning given about the risk that existed within the 'danger area'. And the big Giant Man's refrain of *'Hee-Hi-Hum-Ho!* WATCH OUT THOSE WHO STAND BELOW!' smacks of threatening behaviour, rather than a genuine intent to caution Zac against succumbing to possible harm. The climbing of a beanstalk would have been of natural curiosity to a child. And the presence of a sign might have been

---

221. Section 1(6) of *OLA 1984* sets out the *volenti* defence, which an occupier can use against a trespasser, if the criteria for it are met.

sufficient to warn adults, but this would not have been the case for a minor, as here. Additionally, the fable reports that this was a repeated occurrence – and one known about by the Giant Man – a further factor which would have counted against the Big Beanstalk Business had Zac been harmed, particularly as there's no suggestion made here of any action having been taken to address the identified risks during the period that elapsed between Zac's visits.

Under this civil law route, hypothetically speaking, it's apparent that there was a duty which was breached here and, had an injury or worse occurred, it's clear that damage would have been sustained. Had this been set in a real-world context, rather than a fictional one, it's thought likely that this would have resulted in a successful claim being brought against the Big Beanstalk Business, with Zac's immaturity meaning there would be little, if any, reduction for 'contributory negligence'. As has been explained, the involvement of a child is a factor which attracts a higher duty of care[222].

CASE LAW COMMENTARY

With what little is known of Zac's visits, it's difficult to speak with complete confidence about the civil law consequences that might have flowed from the events – albeit fictional ones – of the fable. There is, however, some useful case law in this area which gives an indication as to how the factors described might be viewed and the chances of any such claim succeeding, when transposed to a real-world context, some examples of which are considered here.

In the case of *Tomlinson v Congleton Council and Cheshire County Council* [2003][223] ('the *Tomlinson* case'), it was held that a claimant's recklessness is to be taken into account when determining the level of award made for any claim. That case indicated to

---

222. In cases where contributory negligence does apply, damages may be reduced by virtue of the *Law Reform (Contributory Negligence) Act 1945*, c. 28., where it can be demonstrated that a visitor has failed to take reasonable care for their own safety. As was referred to in relation to question two, had the focus here been upon Zac's mother, she would have been viewed less sympathetically than him. As such, were any claim to follow as a result of her activities, it's more likely that an element of contributory negligence would be found on her part than would be true for any equivalent claim pursued on Zac's behalf.

223. *Tomlinson v. Congleton Borough Council* [2003] 3 WLR 705 – House of Lords.

occupiers that they were not obligated to spend excessive sums of money in fencing or landscaping large parts of open land under their ownership or control, the point of difference there being that the claimant was an adult (Tomlinson was aged 18 at the time), rather than a child, like Zac. Tomlinson broke his neck, as a result of jumping into a shallow lake at a country park, despite there being a warning sign which stated: 'Dangerous water. No swimming.' The House of Lords upheld the earlier Court of Appeal decision in that case, finding the council not liable, because the risk arose from the claimant's own action, rather than the state of the premises. He was a person of full capacity who voluntarily, and without pressure or inducement, engaged in an activity which carried with it an inherent risk. The danger was obvious and he exercised his free will in acting as he did.

A similar approach was taken in the case of *Buckett v. Staffordshire County Council* [2015][224] ('the *Buckett* case'), where the duty of care requirement under *OLA 1984* was not satisfied. A duty of care was not owed by a Local Authority to a youth who, in the course of trespassing on school grounds, climbed on to the school roof, put his weight on to a skylight and fell through it. The skylight's structure, together with the make-up and location of the roof did not constitute a danger within the meaning of *OLA 1984*[225]. The claimant's injuries arose directly from his own action of jumping on to the skylight and, even though his presence near it ought to have been foreseen, the local authority did not owe him any duty to control his activity as a trespasser. Taken together, the *Tomlinson* case and the *Buckett* case show that trespassers are expected to be shown a humanitarian attitude, albeit that there is only a requirement for reasonable steps to be taken to allow them to avoid risks.

A contrasting case, and one seeming to bear a closer resemblance to Zac's circumstances is that of *Jolley v. Sutton London Borough Council* [2000][226] ('the *Jolley* case'). That case involved a child, with the

---

224. *Buckett v. Staffordshire County Council* [2015] QBD (13.4.2015) – High Court; *case no: 3SO90263.*

225. The rules set out by *OLA 1984* determine '...*whether any duty is owed by a person as occupier of premises to persons other than his visitors in respect of any risk of their suffering injury on the premises by reason of any danger due to the state of the premises or to things done or omitted to be done on them, and if so, what that duty is.*' (section 1(1) of *OLA 1984*)

226. *Jolley v. Sutton London Borough Council* [2000] 1 WLR 1082 – House of Lords.

presence of a risk on easily accessible land pointing to a defendant's negligence. There, a 14 year old boy sustained serious injuries inflicted by a small boat which had been abandoned in the grounds of a block of local authority owned and occupied flats. The council knew about the boat, but failed to remove it. Of particular interest in the case were Lord Hoffman's comments, where he spoke of the '...*ingenuity of children in their play...*'[227] making it more likely that they would be attracted to the boat and consequently at risk of serious injury. The House of Lords ruled against the local authority in the *Jolley* case, deciding that, having identified a risk, they should have made arrangements for the boat's removal.

Along similar lines, an earlier case with particular relevance here is that of *BRB v. Herrington* [1972][228] ('the *BRB* case'). There, a six year old trespasser was electrocuted on the defendant's railway line, having gained entry to the property through a fence which had previously been pushed down, as a short cut to a park. The defendant knew of the defect and it was held that the trespasser could sue, having been injured on property over which the defendant had control. Whilst the *BRB* case pre-dates *OLA 1984* there are clear parallels to be drawn for Zac and the Big Beanstalk Business here. It doesn't seem too far-fetched to suggest that a tall beanstalk might hold the same level of excitement for a child as a railway line, nor does it seem unreasonable to speculate that the Big Beanstalk Business, much like the defendant in that case, would have been all too aware of the risk and therefore expected to do more to address it. Indeed, with the passing of *OLA 1984*, had Zac been injured it's difficult to see any other outcome being reached. It follows that, had Zac's fate assumed the same trajectory as that of the child in the *BRB* case, and the events been of a real-world order, rather than a fictional one, the Big Beanstalk Business would have been similarly ruled against. And reflecting again upon Lord Hoffman's '*ingenuity of children*' comments from the *Jolley* case, it's clear that the courts are willing to recognise childish imagination as a relevant factor. It's the same kind of imagination which appears to have drawn Zac to the beanstalk and it's this, coupled with the clear danger posed by the big plant and its environs, which should have motivated the Big Beanstalk Business to take appropriate action.

---

227. ibid. Lord Hoffman, in the *Jolley* case, at 1093 C
228. *BRB v. Herrington* [1972] AC 877 – House of Lords.

If the Big Beanstalk Business needed any further persuasion to act to put things right, it could do no better than to heed the words of Lord Reid in the *BRB* case, where he stated:

> *'...It would have been very easy for them to have and enforce a reasonable system of inspection and repair of their boundary fence. They knew that children were entitled and accustomed to play on the other side of the fence and must have known...that a young child might easily cross a defective fence and run into grave danger. Yet they did nothing.'*[229]

These words still resonate today and appear to readily apply to the kind of obligations the Big Beanstalk Business would have had towards Zac. Whilst the action of the fable takes place within just a few short scenes – with the time elapsing between Zac's visits perhaps giving the Big Beanstalk Business little, if any, opportunity to make alterations – in a real-world context, rather than a fairy tale one, the *BRB* case could not have made any clearer the consequences for those that fail to suitably secure premises which contain a known danger.

So whilst on the basis of the information the fable provides, it would appear that Zac was trespassing, it's probable that the Big Beanstalk Business, as occupier, would have been legally blameworthy for any reasonably foreseeable injuries suffered by him and therefore, feasible that a claim would succeed against it, under *OLA 1984*. Here, the probability of trespass occurring on the Big Beanstalk Business's land would have been deemed to be *high* and if it could be proven that, as the occupier, it failed to take adequate security measures to prevent access or ensure that the land was safe, the chance of an *OLA 1984* trespass claim being successful, in the event of a child like Zac sustaining an injury, would have been high. It is, of course, important to remember that liability under *OLA 1984* is civil, rather than criminal, meaning that an occupier cannot be prosecuted, but can be sued through the civil courts by an injured party in certain circumstances.

Having recognised the point that children often don't understand danger in the way adults do, it's important that occupiers should address this through the practical control measures they apply to any given risk. Warnings such as *'danger area'* as described here, or *'no entry'*, can easily

---

229. *ibid.* Lord Reid, in the *BRB* case, at 899 G

be ignored, or may not be able to be read or understood by them. Even the erection of a fence demarcating the beanstalk 'drop zone' might not have been deemed sufficient here, if the gaps between fence posts still allowed small bodies to wriggle through, or if the temptations contained within were perceived to offer alluring challenges. It's important for occupiers to ensure their land is safe if a child should trespass, but the preferred option is, of course, to ensure that security measures make it hard for them to enter in the first place. *Why should this be?* It's simply because it lowers the likelihood of a trespass being committed, as well as isolating the hazards and risks inside.

Taking all of this into account, the position here can be summarised as follows. It's been established that a duty of care would have existed towards Zac. It's thought likely that this would have been higher for him than for others. And it's been said that a defence of *volenti* would have been unlikely to succeed for the Big Beanstalk Business. It therefore appears that, on the basis of what the fable tells us, the actions taken by the Big Beanstalk Business here would have been insufficient to discharge the duty it owed to Zac. Taking all these factors into consideration, a civil claim made by Zac under *OLA 1984* would have stood a good chance of success, had personal injury – *or worse* – befallen him, with little, if any, reduction being made for contributory negligence.

Having looked at the options for civil claims, let's now turn to look at some of the possibilities for the bringing of criminal prosecutions. Unsurprisingly, there is a plethora of case law in this area, but the intention here is primarily to look at the range of available options, rather than becoming distracted by the minutiae of particular cases, the detail of which is to be found in any number of academic texts.

OPTION #2
PURSUE A CRIMINAL PROSECUTION AGAINST THE BIG BEANSTALK BUSINESS FOR BREACHING GENERAL DUTIES

This option concerns a hypothetical prosecution that could have been brought against the Big Beanstalk Business for a breach of its general duties under the *Health and Safety at Work etc. Act 1974*.

Had this been a real-world harp-strike or beanstalk top fall, rather than a fictional one, there would have been every chance that the injury, or even death, of the big Giant Woman employee[230] or Zac might have resulted. And had the consequences of these events been of a severe nature, the most likely route for prosecution to have been pursued by them, or on their behalf, would have been for a criminal 'conviction' under *HSWA 1974*. But the law's quite clear that a death or injury doesn't have to occur for a successful prosecution to be made, merely that the potential for one existed. Indeed, significant real-world sentences have been handed out for both fatal and non-fatal incidents, following prosecutions of this kind. Both section 2, which protects employees, and section 3, which protects non-employees, have presented organisations with difficulties, as their wide scope makes prosecution for breaches difficult to defend. It's this wide scope which often makes prosecution under *HSWA 1974* the preferred route, over and above that offered by *the Work at Height Regulations*, covered next, as the third option for legal redress considered here.

A key point to note is that this would have been a case to which the 'reverse burden of proof' applied. What this means is that had the Big Beanstalk Business been prosecuted for a breach, or indeed breaches, of its general duties – under sections 2 or 3 of *HSWA 1974* – it having being alleged that, on the face of it, a breach of health and safety law had taken place, then the burden of proof would have fallen upon it, as defendant, to provide evidence of the control measures it had in place, and that the effect of these was to reduce the risk to a level that was 'as low as reasonably practicable'. So it would have been for the Big Beanstalk Business to prove that it met the expected standard, not for those prosecuting on behalf of Zac or the big Giant Woman to prove that it fell short of it. The upshot of this here would have been that the threshold for proving the guilt of the Big Beanstalk Business would have been low. Keeping this context in mind, let's take a look at the potential failures to comply with these duties and the corresponding options for prosecution under sections 2 and 3, in a little more detail.

---

230. It's important to note that in the context of this fable, the big Giant Woman is the only character known to have been an employee. Had the big Giant Man also been acting in this capacity, the Big Beanstalk Business would have been subject to the same obligations towards him, as have been set out here in relation to the big Giant Woman.

FOR FAILING TO ...
ENSURE THE BIG GIANT WOMAN'S
HEALTH, SAFETY & WELFARE

Had this tale featured the serious injury, or even death of the big Giant Woman employee, a range of prosecution options would likely have been pursued by her, or those acting on her behalf. But, as has been said, there's no actual requirement for a death or serious injury to occur, merely the possibility of one occurring, due to shortfalls in the health and safety arrangements put in place, which in this instance were alleged to have been due to the shortcomings of the Big Beanstalk Business. As such, one possibility here would have been to prosecute the Big Beanstalk Business for failing in its duty under the general provision of section 2, '...to ensure so far as is reasonably practicable the health, safety and welfare at work of...employees...' More particularly, prosecution could have been sought for any one of a number of failings on the part of the Big Beanstalk Business under this section. There was the apparent failure to implement a safe system of work for the lifting and lowering of the harp, with it being dropped to the foot of the beanstalk in an uncontrolled manner[231]. Arguably, there was also the failure to institute safe arrangements for its storage or transportation[232], given that it appears the harp was capable of dropping, simply by being knocked or carelessly handled. And additionally, there was the basic failure to provide a safe place of work – with the big Giant Woman seemingly unable to climb up and down the beanstalk safely, and Zac's mother apparently being able to walk right up to the beanstalk unchallenged, to chop it down![233] Another likely oversight here was the Big Beanstalk Business's failure to provide the big Giant Woman with information, instruction, training and supervision[234].

Taken collectively, both the description of the big Giant Man's fall, and the anecdotal previous near miss in which the big Giant Woman

---

231. Section 2(2)(a) of *HSWA 1974* sets out the requirement for safe systems of work.
232. Section 2(2)(b) of *HSWA 1974* sets out the requirement for articles and substances to be safely used, handled, stored and transported.
233. Section 2(2)(d) of *HSWA 1974* sets out the requirement for places of work to be maintained, so as to be safe and free of risks to health, including safe access and egress.
234. Section 2(2)(c) of *HSWA 1974* sets out the requirement for employees to be provided with information, instruction, training and supervision, so as to ensure their health and safety at work.

had similarly taken a tumble, would tend to back up assertions of this workplace having been an unsafe one for employees! And the suggestion of other previous near misses having gone unreported – involving dropped objects and trips on fragile floors – would have done little to avert the unfortunate scenes that played out in the fable, these being events which carried with them a clear potential for serious, even fatal, consequences.

FOR FAILING TO ...
ENSURE ZAC'S HEALTH, SAFETY & WELFARE

Had Zac been injured or killed, it's likely that prosecution of the Big Beanstalk Business would have been sought for its failure to protect him from harm, as a non-employee, under *HSWA 1974*. Section 3 places upon all employers a duty *'...to conduct his undertakings in such a way as to ensure so far as is reasonably practicable, that persons not in his employment who may be affected thereby are not thereby exposed to risks to their health and safety.'* Notable elements to the tale which seem to support assertions about the Big Beanstalk Business's shortcomings under this provision of *HSWA 1974* would include its failure to demarcate the site, fence off dangers, and warn of them. And given Zac's urgent need to run from the beanstalk, on the face of it at least, it seems the Big Beanstalk Business fell short of the requirement for it to protect non-employees from harm. It's worth reiterating that the option of seeking prosecution would have remained here, even though no-one was actually harmed; for an offence to be committed, it would be enough simply to show that there was a risk of harm to Zac, and that the Big Beanstalk Business failed to do enough to manage and control that risk. And whilst, as has already been noted, the intention here is to consider the range of options, rather than getting lost in the weeds of legal 'precedent' in this area, the clear message to take from this is that where organisations fall short of the expectations placed upon them, the penalties involved can be significant.

The fictional circumstances involving Zac do bear some similarities to those of the case of *Health and Safety Executive v. National Grid Gas plc.* [2015][235], which saw the defendant fined £2 million, for breaching

---

235. See the Health and Safety Executive's website www.hse.gov.uk for further details of this case *(case reference no: 4411011)* date of hearing: 08/12/2015. Preston Crown Court.

section 3(1) of *HSWA 1974*. In that instance, Robbie Williamson, an 11 year old school boy climbed on to a ledge on Dugdale Bridge, Burnley and then on to a pipe owned by the defendant, running beside and next to the bridge, before unfortunately falling on to the canal path (canal-side) and then into the water, resulting in his tragic death. It was found that the defendant organisation's failure to assess the risks to members of the public associated with the pipe meant it omitted to put in place measures to prevent or deter access on to it, which had been a significant cause in the school boy's death. It takes little imagination to see the clear parallels that can be drawn between the real-world circumstances of *the National Grid case* and the fictional account of Zac's antics and the big Giant Man's omissions given here, which could so easily have ended in an equally catastrophic fashion.

Just to recap, we've looked at the potential for civil claims for Zac as a trespasser, as are dealt with under *OLA 1984*. And we've just considered the potential for a prosecution to be brought directly under the general provisions of *HSWA 1974*, as tends to be the preferred route for employees and non-employees seeking redress in more serious cases, with the general nature of the duties it sets out making it harder to defend against and meaning it continues to be a popular choice for the bringing of prosecutions. But, given an equivalent real-world scenario to the fictional events considered here, it's still relevant to think about the specific requirements of *the Work at Height Regulations*, because the distinct regulatory regime they created for work at height activities would have applied to those working up in the clouds, just as they would also have covered the risk that the dropped object harp presented to those on the ground below, looking up.

OPTION #3
PURSUE A CRIMINAL PROSECUTION AGAINST THE BIG BEANSTALK BUSINESS FOR BREACHING SPECIFIC (WORK AT HEIGHT) DUTIES

This option concerns a hypothetical prosecution that could have been brought against the Big Beanstalk Business for a breach of its specific duties under *the Work at Height Regulations 2005*.

You'll recall that the general duties placed upon employers to ensure the health, safety and welfare of employees and non-employees under

HSWA 1974 were set out in the introduction to this book, and we've just seen how these duties might have applied here. Together with their supporting Approved Code of Practice, *the Work at Height Regulations* expand upon these general duties, fleshing out the requirements insofar as they particularly apply to work at height activities. As such, they are a good example of regulations covering a specific risk area. Practically speaking, *the Work at Height Regulations* supplement the fundamental basics of *HSWA 1974* for risk to be reduced to a level which is ALARP, for employers to put safe systems of work in place, and for accompanying information, instruction, training and supervision to be provided to the employees who are carrying out that work. They are also additional to the requirements to be met under *the Management Regulations*, which set out *how* reduction of risks to ALARP is to be achieved – by specifically calling for a 'suitable and sufficient'[236] risk assessment to be carried out and setting out the need to ensure the implementation of the control measures identified by it. This includes making sure control measures stay current and effective on a continuous basis throughout the 'risk management cycle', and applying the principles of prevention which, in the context of work at heights, means: *first*, that it is better to design a system of work which avoids the risk of working at height; *second*, where avoidance isn't possible, that the risk is to be reduced by putting in place appropriate control measures to mitigate it – preferably by adopting 'engineering controls', and *third*, and finally, where the risk can't be fully controlled, that instructions are to be provided – for instance signs warning of the danger of dropped objects, or of people working above.

So, if it's not possible to avoid working at a height liable to cause injury, what are the particular requirements to be met when carrying it out? Well, just as *the Management Regulations* flesh out the duties contained in *HSWA 1974*, so too do *the Work at Height Regulations*, but in the specific context of the risk of work at height, namely, *first*,

---

236. Regulation 3 of *the Management Regulations* sets out the requirement for a 'suitable and sufficient' risk assessment to be carried out, covering the risks to the health and safety of employees and non-employees. Whilst not directly considered here, it would also be possible to pursue a prosecution for failing to meet this requirement. The risk assessment needs to consider, amongst other things: the inexperience, lack of awareness of risks and immaturity of young persons; the fitting out and layout of the workplace; the form, range and use of work equipment and the way in which it is handled, and the organisation of processes and activities. In these kinds of circumstances, the risk of unauthorised access would need to be assessed and addressed.

that it is to be properly planned, organised and supervised, *second*, that those involved are to be competent, *third*, that the risks of the work, including falls from height and dropped objects, are to be assessed and controlled to a level that is ALARP, and *fourth* and finally, that workers are not to be exposed to risks from fragile surfaces. A further requirement is for equipment to be properly selected and inspected, although this is only considered in general terms here, within the context of assessing and controlling risks, given that the fable neglects to mention what – if any – equipment was provided to those involved.

Having considered a general overview of the requirements of *the Work at Height Regulations*, let's now look at some particular criminal prosecutions that might have been pursued under them, for the offences likely to have arisen from this fable's beanstalk-based shenanigans.

FOR FAILING TO...
PROPERLY ORGANISE AND PLAN THE WORK[237]

The scenario depicted in the fable offers up some fairly clear indications of the Big Beanstalk Business having failed to organise and plan its work at height activities, with notable shortfalls in its standards of management and supervision. We see this in the account of the big Giant Woman's previous involvement in two near misses – one of which was a close-shave fall from the beanstalk, and another which saw her almost being struck by a falling harp. These events not only point to potential breaches of *the Work at Height Regulations*, but also to the broader failure of the Big Beanstalk Business to implement an effective risk management cycle, an omission which suggests the Big Giant Man probably lacked the required understanding of the importance of assessing and mitigating risk, on an ongoing basis. In terms of the particular circumstances the fable describes, the planning and organising of the work here should have accounted for factors including: the planning and supervision of the activities carried out by the big Giant Woman, weather conditions, and the checking of the safety of the beanstalk and the area below it, both before work began and on each occasion it was used. It should also have catered for the arrangements for both stopping the harp

---

237. Regulation 4 of *the Work at Height Regulations* sets out the requirement for work at height to be properly planned and organised and appropriately supervised.

from falling in the first place and, in cases where this wasn't possible, the use of appropriate control measures to reduce the risk. Sensible control measures to consider here might have included, for instance, physical measures such as mesh to catch falling harps, together with procedural measures, including the instituting of exclusion zones (secure, fenced off zones, which keep people out of danger areas) in circumstances where the harp dropping risk couldn't be fully avoided, as well as ensuring the harp's safe storage, so as to prevent it from causing injury in the event of its disturbance, or even, following the collapse of the beanstalk workplace!

In properly planning and organising the work, an additional expectation placed upon the Big Beanstalk Business would have been for it to institute suitable emergency planning and rescue arrangements of its own, rather than placing exclusive reliance upon the emergency services. Such arrangements would have needed to consider scenarios including those in which the big Giant Woman came to fall and the harp came to drop, together with other foreseeable situations as might have arisen, with this also being reflected in agreed procedures, including for getting down and away from the beanstalk, and for the safe lifting and lowering of the harp. For such arrangements to have been effective it would, of course, have been important for the big Giant Woman employee to have known about them, which the Big Beanstalk Business would have achieved by giving her instructions and checking her understanding of these.

FOR FAILING TO...
ENSURE WORKFORCE COMPETENCE[238]

The reports of a close shave fall from height and near striking by a falling harp naturally trigger some concerns about the big Giant Woman lacking the necessary competence for work at height, or at the very least suggest she was an individual who would have benefitted from being closely supervised by someone with the appropriate knowledge, understanding and experience of this type of work. It's unclear from the fable whether the Big Beanstalk Business carried out checks as to her

---

238. Regulation 5 of the Work at Height Regulations sets out the requirement for anyone who is involved in work at height to be competent or, if being trained, that they are supervised by someone who is competent.

level of competence. Given the litany of errors that came to pass in this fable, however, it's perhaps questionable whether the big Giant Man even possessed the required level of competence himself. There's no reference made to his having been aware of the key hazards and risks of people falling, harps dropping and fragile floors giving way, nor of his having set any standards or taken accountability for safety and, right from the get-go, it's unclear how the Big Beanstalk Business chose to assign roles and responsibilities for work performed at the top of the beanstalk.

FOR FAILING TO...
ASSESS AND CONTROL FALL FROM HEIGHT
& DROPPED OBJECT RISKS[239]
AND MEET EQUIPMENT REQUIREMENTS[240]

There were many risks apparent here, but the two of particular note were the Big Beanstalk Business's failure to control the risk of people falling from the top of the beanstalk (fall from height) and that of a harp dropping (a falling object). It certainly appears from the tale that these were neither assessed, nor controlled. And it seems likely that it's the absence of risk assessment which would have led to poor decisions being made about work equipment, or even perhaps to none having been selected at all, the lack of detail in the tale being such that this aspect can only be considered in outline here. The general approach to risk assessing and controlling work at height activities is no different to that taken towards any other type of work activity – it's for this reason that *the Work at Height Regulations* refer back to *the Management Regulations*, as the first step in seeking to avoid work at height risks. It's *the Work at Height Regulations* and their accompanying guidance, however, which

---

239. Regulation 6 of *the Work at Height Regulations* deals with the avoidance of risks from work at height, a key aspect of which is risk assessment. It specifically requires account to be taken of the general risk assessment carried out under regulation 3 of the *Management Regulations*. Regulation 10 of *the Work at Height Regulations* handles falling object risks, with the priority being to prevent them falling SFAIRP, so as to prevent injury to any person. Regulation 11 of *the Work at Height Regulations* requires the setting up of 'danger areas', where there is a risk of a person at work being injured due to falling a distance or being struck by a falling object, including requiring the prevention of access and making sure that such areas are clearly indicated.

240. Regulation 7 of *the Work at Height Regulations* deals with work equipment selection, regulation 8 with requirements for certain types of work equipment, and regulation 12 with the inspection of work equipment.

speak to how the particular fall from height and dropped object risks are to be controlled, and it's these that are considered here.

In terms of falls from height – of particular concern here, given the anecdotal account of the big Giant Woman having '...tripped on the floor at the top of the beanstalk...' – there are no indications of efforts having been made by the Big Beanstalk Business to manage such a risk. The approach that should have been taken, however, would have been for it to follow the so-called 'hierarchy of control' [241] from *the Work at Height Regulations*, which has three levels of priority, namely: *first* – avoidance – whether the activity as a whole could have been avoided, this being a key principle of the regulations; *second* – 'fall prevention' – whether efforts, if any were made to prevent falls, were sufficient, prevention of falls being achievable through collective or, if not, personal means, and *third*, and finally – 'fall protection' – minimising the distance and/or consequence of falls, which covers the selection and types of work equipment (both 'collective protection' and 'personal protection'), including collective mitigation and safeguards, personal protection measures, and personal mitigation or restraint. It's worth taking a quick look at how the three levels of the hierarchy of control would have applied in this scenario.

The *first* step that the Big Beanstalk Business needed to take was to avoid unnecessary work at height, by planning for as much of its work as possible to be done from ground level. It's questionable whether this was a business which *had* to be carried on way up in the clouds, rather than from somewhere else, and there's no doubt it would have been preferable, at the very least, for the heavier harp-based elements of its operation to have been carried out at ground level, even if not the lighter chicken-based ones! Indeed, this is a point the big Giant Man appears to have latterly taken on board, with the end of the fable reporting on his search for lower level premises (perhaps suggesting the big Giant Man had experienced an epiphany moment), the events described possibly

---

241. Regulation 6 of *the Work at Height Regulations* deals with the hierarchy of control for work at heights. Specifically: regulation 6(3) requires employers to take measures to prevent 'so far as reasonably practicable' anyone falling a distance liable to cause them personal injury; regulation 6(4)(a) requires that where work is to be carried out at height, this is to be carried out from an existing place of work, or for access or egress, for this to be carried out using an existing means, where possible; regulation 6(4)(b) requires that sufficient work equipment is provided, where the requirements of regulation 6(4)(a) cannot be met so as to prevent, so far as is reasonably practicable, a fall occurring, and finally, regulation 6(5) requires employers to minimise the distance and consequences of a fall, where it is not possible to prevent one.

having prompted the Big Beanstalk Business to rethink its whole approach to the control of work at height risks.

Second, assuming the Big Beanstalk Business wasn't able to avoid work at height, it being impossible to do otherwise, it would have needed to focus its efforts upon preventing falls, the nub of the issue here being whether it did enough by way of putting in place measures to stop people falling a distance liable to cause them injury. Let's be clear, it's questionable whether it did anything – and even if it did, it's unlikely that it did enough – by way of implementing fall prevention measures. This is an argument that seems to be backed up by an anecdotal account of the big Giant Woman's involvement in an incident which saw her taking a tumble, one which '…apparently involved her tripping on the floor at the top of the beanstalk…' Alternative options don't appear to have been discussed here – or at least there are none described – but it would be key to know whether the big Giant Woman worker might have been able to use an existing safe place of work, or if not, to use an existing means to gain access (way on, or in) and egress (way off, or out).

There's also no mention given to the types of work equipment she might have used, but factors needing to be considered by the Big Beanstalk Business would have included: making a selection which accounted for the nature, frequency and duration of tasks being undertaken, as well as the risks to safety; making sure equipment was in good condition and assembled in line with any manufacturers' instructions, and making sure it was inspected by someone competent to do so, at suitable intervals, appropriate to the environment and its use, with this also being carried out every time something happened which might have affected its safety and stability, including factors such as adverse weather and accidental damage. The fable doesn't enlighten us as to the precise geography of the workplace's physical layout, nor does it say whether it was in close proximity to an existing workplace, meaning that the considerations here have been confined to the generic work options which might have been feasible in the circumstances described.

The fable only ever makes mention of one employee – the big Giant Woman – and nothing is said of any equipment having been put in place to prevent her, as an individual, from falling. In its consideration of fall prevention methods, however – and assuming that more than one worker might have been involved – the Big Beanstalk Business would have been expected to prioritise the so-called 'collective control measures' which stop a group from falling, above any 'personal control measures', which only prevent an individual from falling[242]. 'Fall prevention – collective protection' to prevent a fall might have included the use of appropriately configured work equipment such as mobile elevated work platforms (MEWPs), tower scaffolds or scaffolds, positioned alongside the beanstalk. 'Fall prevention – personal protection' on the other hand, could have included the use of work equipment such as a work restraint (travel restriction) system, which would have acted to prevent the big Giant Woman – as well as any other employee by whom they were used – from getting into a fall position. We would need to know more about the physical structure that was in place at the top of the beanstalk, over and above the limited description offered by the fable, however, in order to be able to say which of these personal measures might have been workable options here.

Third, if the Big Beanstalk Business was unable to prevent falls, there would have been an expectation for it to take action to minimise the distance and/or consequence of such falls to the big Giant Woman, or indeed anyone else. Additionally, it would have needed to provide its workers with any additional training and information[243]. There's no suggestion, however, of any thought having been applied to this aspect, nor of the big Giant Woman or any other worker even having been supplied with suitable equipment which might have helped to reduce their risk of sustaining an injury. Given equivalent real-world scenarios, these types of control measures can be effective where other types of work equipment have been considered, but are not deemed reasonably practicable to achieve. Examples of 'fall mitigation – collective protection'[244] work equipment types include safety nets and

---

242. Regulation 7(1)(a) of *the Work at Height Regulations* specifically requires collective protection measures to be given priority over personal protection measures, when making a selection of equipment for work at height.

243. Regulation 6(5) of *the Work at Height Regulations* states that where falls cannot be prevented, employers are to provide sufficient equipment to minimise the distances and consequences of falls, as well as training, information and other measures to prevent any person falling a distance liable to cause them personal injury. The regulations adopt the same type of hierarchical approach towards catching people who have fallen as they do for stopping people falling in the first place, namely that collective protection measures are to be prioritised above personal protection measures.

244. Regulation 8(c) and schedule 4 of *the Work at Height Regulations* refer to a method which catches a group as a 'collective safeguard for arresting falls', with the regulations requiring collective fall protection – collective safeguards for arresting falls which do not form part of a personal fall protection system – to be in place to catch a fallen group.

soft landing systems, such as airbags, installed close to the level of work. Alternatively, types of 'fall mitigation – personal protection'[245] range from fall arrest systems using high anchor points, to rescue systems and harnesses. Using these fall mitigation – personal protection control measures is, however, to be viewed as a last resort, with other methods needing to be considered first. Fall arrest equipment acts to prevent the user of a fall arrest system from colliding with the ground or structure in a free fall and, whilst not preventing a fall, should minimise the injury in the event of a fall occurring. Had this form of protection been selected here, the big Giant Woman would have required training in its fitting and use, to ensure its effectiveness. Also, as was true for the fall prevention measures and is applicable to any real-world workplace at height, it would be necessary to understand the physical structure in place – in this case, at the top of the beanstalk – so as to be able to determine which, if any, of these options might have worked here.

Turning to the falling object risk, it's clear from the fable that this was uncontrolled. We see this manifested all too clearly in Zac's urgent need to run from a harp rapidly plummeting from the beanstalk's top. It's quite apparent that, had the choreography between the dropping of the harp and Zac's running been only marginally different – with the harp having been dropped just a second or two earlier – the outcome would have been catastrophic. From an employee perspective too, it's clear that the exact same scenario might have befallen the big Giant Woman and, given what we learn from the fable about a harp-based near miss having occurred, it's perhaps fortuitous that such an incident hadn't already happened here. In any event, it's vital to question whether there's a need for an object to be held at height at all – a consideration which extends to objects made up of separable components. Taking a real-world example of a nacelle[246] for a wind turbine, if the components inside it can be put together at ground level, with it subsequently being raised and put into place, this is deemed to lower the risk, as it stops the components themselves – including hubs, rotors and bearings – falling from height.

---

245. Regulation 8(d) and schedule 5 of *the Work at Height Regulations* refer to a method which catches an individual as a 'personal fall protection system', with the regulations requiring personal fall protection to be in place to catch an individual who has fallen.
246. A nacelle is the part of a wind turbine which houses the components that transform the wind's kinetic energy into mechanical energy to turn a generator that produces electricity.

In circumstances where it is decided that the only option is for an object to be stored or otherwise handled at height – as the big Giant Man claimed to be true for the harp – *the Work at Height Regulations* are quite clear that the risk of it falling must be controlled. Furthermore, where this is not possible, sufficient steps must be taken to prevent people from being struck. This brings to the fore two linked aspects, namely dropped objects and danger areas. The regulations are clear that objects are not to be thrown or tipped in such a way as to cause injury, and that they are to be stored so as to prevent risks to people arising from their collapse, overturn or unintended movement. It's clear that here, if asked: *'Did you do enough to prevent the risk of falling objects?'* and *'If the risk of falling objects could not be fully controlled, did you do enough to exclude people from danger areas?'* the Big Beanstalk Business would have struggled to come up with a robust answer to either question.

Looking at the measures which can prevent objects from falling – in this case harps dropping – these bear similarities to those that prevent people from falling. The measures include a range of 'engineering controls', of which covering openings in floors to prevent people from being struck is but one example. Toe boards or kick boards and handrails plus additional closed mesh solutions can often provide coverage of all the gaps through which objects – *including harps in this case!* – might fall. And failing that where, as here, it's accepted that the risk of falling objects is not an entirely preventable one, safety mesh or netting can be put in place so as to catch them, thus stopping them from dropping to a lower, or indeed ground, level. Another measure that might have worked here would have been to employ the use of tethering systems, which work by securing tools and other items used during work at height activities, helping to avoid their unintended movement. Whilst this method is generally viewed as being more effective for tooling, it's equally possible that the tethering of the harp might have prevented it from falling – an important consideration here, given the clear risk it posed.

In cases where the falling object risk cannot be fully controlled, there's an expectation that people are to be excluded from 'danger areas' – with them being barred from entering, supported by appropriate procedures, instructions and supervisory arrangements. In seeking to ensure that enough is done to exclude people, there are two key components the regulations set out which need to be met, namely *first*, the prevention of access, and *second*, the marking of danger areas. Whilst

Zac was not an employee, his ability to enter the area unchallenged and, indeed, his need to beat a hasty exit from it, highlights these as having been circumstances which would have called for additional measures such as the secure fencing of the area, accompanied by more robust signage. In this fictional account, the report of the big Giant Woman having previously been exposed to an equivalent risk, which '…centred around an unintentionally dropped harp nearly causing her to come to harm on the ground below…' underlines the need for such measures.

Let's look *first* at the need to prevent the unauthorised access of danger areas, supported by their policing, so as to ensure people are not exposed to a dropped object risk. As the risk of falling harps remained here, the Big Beanstalk Business (as a duty holder) needed to set up an area around the beanstalk, to which the access of those not participating in the work was prevented, with it also being clearly marked as such. This was clearly a situation which called for the fitting of access prevention measures – these being devices, accompanying barriers or secure fencing – something which appears to have been neither attempted nor achieved here. Given that Zac was able to run unimpeded, right through the danger area and up and down the beanstalk, it seems reasonable to conclude that this was the case! The setting up of an 'exclusion zone' in such circumstances – *or 'danger area', to use the terminology applied by the regulations* – is an acknowledgment of the point that the full control of a falling object risk might be unachievable, and is a so-called 'administrative control', which excludes people and needs to be supported by appropriate procedures, instructions and supervisory arrangements, so as to ensure its effectiveness.

The *second* aspect to consider when setting up a danger area is that where risks of persons at work falling a distance or being struck by falling objects remain, there is a need for its clear identification with 'warning signs'. Admittedly the 'danger area' sign described in the tale purported to do this but, being as it was a tricky-to-read wooden sign, this would have fallen some way short of the expectations of the regulations for the marking out of an exclusion zone. The specific requirements for safety signage are to be found in *The Health and Safety (Safety Signs and Signals) Regulations 1996*[247] *('the Safety Signs and Signals Regulations').*

---

247. S.I. 1996/341; regulation 4 requires appropriate safety signs to be provided if the risks to employees and others cannot be avoided or adequately reduced by other means, and regulation 5 requires employers to provide information, instruction and training to them on the meanings of the signs used.

In terms of real-world application, control measures of this kind are commonly adopted within arboriculture, where it's difficult to fully prevent the falling of cut branches, but it *is* possible to prevent risks to persons not engaged in the work, by excluding them from entering the area directly below it, into which the branches might fall. The designation of danger areas in this way is a recognition of the point that it's not always reasonably practicable to prevent 'falling objects'. Furthermore, it's worth remembering that, as well as posing a significant personal injury risk, dropped objects present a further concern from a process interruption and asset damage perspective.

Finally, on the point of controlling dropped objects, a fair and relevant question to ask would have been: '*What if the dropping of harps wasn't an 'accident', but was incidental to a routine activity which was a normal part of the way the Big Beanstalk Business operated?*' It's difficult for those of us inhabiting the real world to comprehend exactly how the dropping of a harp from height would form a necessary part of a business activity but, to continue with the example of a scenario that might play out in a real-world arboricultural context, workers should not enter a danger area during tree-felling operations, just as here they should not have worked or walked within the danger area, where a harp was liable to fall without warning. In circumstances of the kind this fable describes, safe methods of operation should be agreed to ensure that safe working distances can be maintained at all times and that no-one – other than those directly involved in the work – is within the proximity of the activity being undertaken.

FOR FAILING TO...
PROPERLY CONTROL THE RISKS
FROM FRAGILE SURFACES[248]

Given the lack of detail the tale provides, it's difficult to say for certain why the harp or the big Giant Man came to fall but one reason could have been due to work taking place on fragile surfaces at the top of the beanstalk, where platforms may have been insufficient. Aside from the big Giant Man's fall, there is a reference made to his having

---

248. Regulation 9 of *the Work at Height Regulations* sets out the requirement for employers to manage the risks to employees associated with work on or near fragile surfaces. This includes preventing employees from having to pass across or near, or work on, from or near a fragile surface, where it is reasonably practicable to do otherwise.

previously stumbled at the top of the beanstalk, with no concrete reason given as to why this happened. As well as platforms needing to bear the weight of any loads, there's also a need for them to support the weight of workers, so as prevent the risk of their falling. The fable is notably sparse on details of how the big Giant Woman – and indeed anyone else – nearly came to fall. Nonetheless, there would have existed a clear need for the Big Beanstalk Business to ensure that the big Giant Woman didn't pass across or near, or work on, from or near a fragile surface, if it was possible for her to do otherwise. And if the Big Beanstalk Business couldn't achieve the full removal of this risk, it would have needed to provide suitable and sufficient platforms to take loads, and to minimise the distance and consequence of any falls, where the possibility of these occurring remained. Finally, on this point, if the big Giant Woman's work still required her to work near fragile surfaces, the Big Beanstalk Business would have needed to display suitable warning notices, or to make her aware of the danger that existed by other means. It's unclear from the fable whether these anecdotal, though unreported, falls had fragile surfaces as an underlying cause, but this was certainly an aspect that should have been investigated further by the Big Beanstalk Business, with remedial action being taken by it, if required.

OPTION #4
PURSUE CRIMINAL PROSECUTIONS
FOR OTHER OFFENCES

It's here that the bringing of other hypothetical prosecutions falls to be considered, for offences potentially committed by the Big Beanstalk Business, the big Giant Man, and other characters featured in the tale.

The fable highlighted the clear potential for the activities of the Big Beanstalk Business to cause physical harm to Zac, the big Giant Woman and anyone else with the misfortune to be in the vicinity of the beanstalk. This has already prompted consideration of the claims that might have been pursued under the civil law, in relation to *OLA 1984*. It has also flagged up some possible corporate offences which might have arisen from these events, including for breaches of general duties under *HSWA 1974* and other duties under *the Work at Height Regulations*. But there are some additional offences for which organisations and individuals might be pursued, in relation to failings at the more serious end of the spectrum, and it seems appropriate to conclude the *modern meaning* to this fable with a round-up of how these could have applied to the circumstances described, as well giving broader consideration to their application in a real-world context.

CORPORATE OFFENCES

The introduction of the offence of corporate manslaughter by the *Corporate Manslaughter and Corporate Homicide Act 2007*[249] ('*the Corporate Manslaughter Act*') did not create new duties, but rather, sought to address the shortcomings of criminal prosecutions of corporate bodies. As such, its concern is with corporate liability, rather than the liability of directors or other individuals who perform senior roles within organisations. This extremely serious offence was introduced to ensure that effective laws are in place to prosecute organisations – irrespective of their size – where a disregard for the proper management of health and safety has been shown, with fatal consequences.

The corporate manslaughter offence has serious implications for organisations, where it's found that corporate mismanagement led to the death of a person. As such, it compels those who occupy senior management positions within organisations to take health and safety matters seriously and, where they fail to do so, it ensures they face significant consequences[250]. The introduction of this offence means that companies and organisations can now be found guilty of an offence if it's shown 'beyond reasonable doubt' that the management failures involved were negligent ones – being *so* serious as to amount to a 'gross breach' of a relevant duty of care. Unlike cases brought under *HSWA 1974*, which have a low threshold for the guilt of the defendant to be shown, the bar for liability in corporate manslaughter cases is set high, applying only to the gravest of corporate failings.

So, how might this have applied here? Well, in the event of Zac's death, and assuming the big Giant Man to have been a 'senior manager' within

---

249. 2007 c. 19.

250. In the majority of cases in this book, the author has used the term 'senior leader' to refer to those who occupy the most senior level positions within organisations. For the purposes of considering this fable only – and as referred to within its accompanying *modern meaning* – the term 'senior management' has been used, due to this being a defined term within *the Corporate Manslaughter Act*.

the Big Beanstalk Business, the following requirements would have needed to be met for a jury to have found the Big Beanstalk Business guilty of an offence under *the Corporate Manslaughter Act. First,* a duty of care would have had to be owed by the Big Beanstalk Business to Zac. *Second,* there would have had to be a gross breach of that duty of care causing Zac's death, with an offence only deemed to have been committed where a death was shown to have been *caused by* a gross breach of duty. And *third,* and finally, the way in which the Big Beanstalk Business's activities were managed or organised by 'senior management' – of which, here, the big Giant Man has been assumed to have been part – would have needed to have been a substantial element in the breach. *The Corporate Manslaughter Act* makes clear that the seriousness of the breach of legislation and the level of risk of death posed by the breach are key factors for a jury, when seeking to reach a decision about whether an offence has been committed, and in considering evidence, wide-ranging sources of information can be drawn upon[251].

In reaching its decision as to whether there has been a gross breach of duty, this offence requires a jury to focus upon how the overall organisational management of activities is carried out, rather than the actions of a particular individual – as was the case under the previous law – with it now being possible for it to be found that a gross breach occurred by adding up the actions of a group. And, whilst the failings of senior management must have formed a substantial element of the breach, it's not the case that failings have to be confined to senior management level for a gross breach of duty to be found. It's enough to find that there was some fault at a senior management level and that, when looking at the organisation in totality a gross breach is found to have occurred. Furthermore, in determining whether there has been a gross breach, consideration can also be given to the overall management of health and safety within an organisation, including its health and safety leadership.

There's merit to be had from pausing at this point to think about *who* might be classed as senior management. This is a term defined

---

251. Section 8 of *the Corporate Manslaughter Act* sets out the factors for consideration by a jury, in order to prove a gross breach and determine whether an offence of corporate manslaughter has been committed, the approach being a wide-ranging one. In considering whether an offence has taken place, the emphasis is upon factors including organisational culture, other relevant matters such as codes, relevant health and safety guidance, and manuals issued by enforcing authorities (together with similar publications) and so on, rather than on the decision-making of individuals.

within *the Corporate Manslaughter Act,* but it's worth paying brief attention to what it actually means to be a senior manager. Essentially, it requires a qualitative judgment to be made, very much depending upon the role played by an individual rather than the title they hold, which is of interest in considering this fictional scenario, as well as when looking more broadly at equivalent real-world events. Thus far, the presumption has been made that the only person to have been operating in this capacity was the big Giant Man. *But what of the big Giant Woman?* We are only afforded a limited glimpse of her involvement in these activities, but if it was deemed that she too had played a significant role in making decisions, or in actually managing a substantial part of the organisation's activities – here, beanstalk-based work at height – then, in the event of a death, her actions could also have been relevant to determining whether the offence of corporate manslaughter under *the Corporate Manslaughter Act* had indeed been committed by the Big Beanstalk Business.

  Having looked at the corporate offences, let's now look at some of the individual offences that might have been committed here.

INDIVIDUAL OFFENCES

The most likely offences the fable calls to mind have already been considered, but it's important to remember the other options that exist under *HSWA 1974,* in cases where it's felt to be in the public interest for these to be pursued too. This includes an offence by the 'body corporate' – which means that, as well as their organisation being found guilty, senior managers can also be found criminally liable as individuals, if it's shown that the breach by the organisation took place with their consent, connivance or neglect[252]. Here, this would have meant that the big Giant Man could have been pursued as an individual – in addition to the Big Beanstalk Business being prosecuted for corporate offences – with his conduct judged against what he should have known in his position, rather than simply what he actually knew. In practical terms, this would have meant that his turning of a blind eye to any health and safety breaches that took place – including, for instance, his lack of knowledge or failure to follow up workforce anecdotes of unintentionally dropped harp near misses, or

---

252. Section 37 of *HSWA 1974* covers these offences, being offences by a 'body corporate'.

reports of fall from height close encounters of the kind experienced by the big Giant Woman, who '...tripped on the floor at the top of the beanstalk...' - would not have been an acceptable excuse for his failure to control the risks associated with the Big Beanstalk Business's activities.

Additionally, reserved for the most serious of situations and regarded as the sister offence of corporate manslaughter, there exists an option for the offence of 'gross negligence manslaughter' to be pursued - an offence which can be committed by anyone connected in some way to a workplace, of any nature - where there's sufficient evidence and it's in the public interest to do so. Indeed, this is an approach often taken in addition to pursuing an organisation for corporate manslaughter, with *the Corporate Manslaughter Act* specifically offering two possible routes of redress, arising from the same set of circumstances: *first,* the making of a charge for either corporate manslaughter or corporate homicide, and *second,* for charges to be made for health and safety offences, under any health and safety legislation[253].

In cases of gross negligence manslaughter, liability attaches to the individual. What this would have meant here is that, had Zac's death resulted, the test for the jury would have been whether having regard to the risk of death involved, the conduct of the big Giant Man had been *so* bad in the circumstances, as to amount to a criminal act or omission. In the event of Zac's death, therefore, for it to have been found that the offence of gross negligence manslaughter had been committed by the big Giant Man, there would have needed to be proof of: *first,* a duty of care having been owed by the big Giant Man to Zac; *second,* a breach of that duty having occurred through the big Giant Man's negligent act or omission; *third,* the breach of the duty having caused Zac's death, and *fourth,* and finally, the negligent cause having amounted to gross negligence.

Having so far looked only at the expectations placed upon organisations and employers, and senior managers, it's important to remember that employees have responsibilities too. As such, it's also possible for them to be found in breach of their obligations, as individuals - for failing to take care of their own or someone else's

---

253. Section 19 of *the Corporate Manslaughter Act* makes clear that a conviction of corporate manslaughter or corporate homicide, and the charging of an organisation with a health and safety offence, can both be pursued for the same set of circumstances.

safety[254], for failing to co-operate with their employer[255], or even for falling foul of the duty not to interfere with or misuse things provided for health, safety and welfare[256]. So in this case, if the big Giant Man had put in place things to ensure the big Giant Woman's safety and she had, for instance: ignored or failed to follow instructions about how to work safely at height or to lower objects safely to ground level; failed to use fall restraint equipment, such as body holding devices connected to reliable anchor points, or had neglected to don a safety harness, despite having been provided with one and instructed on its use, then she too could have been found guilty of an offence.

DAMAGES, SENTENCING AND OTHER PENALTIES

From a civil law perspective, when something goes wrong, individuals can claim for 'damages', if it can be shown they suffered harm as a result of negligence on the part of a 'duty holder'. In circumstances where an individual suffers loss – whether injury, ill health or death – the victim or their dependents are entitled to sue for damages, in the form of compensation through the civil courts.

From the criminal law perspective, on the other hand, the failure to comply with the requirements of legislation often gives rise to the bringing of criminal prosecutions and enforcement action, which can be taken by Great Britain's Health and Safety Executive (or other appropriate regulator) and/or Local Authorities. Where organisations fall short of the minimum legal standards, the 'enforcing authority' can elect to pursue offenders in the criminal courts. The powers of enforcing authorities are wide-ranging and can include the issuing of warnings, enforcement and prohibition notices. In cases where organisations or individuals are prosecuted and convicted, this can ultimately lead to fines and custodial sentences, with the penalties

---

254. Section 7(a) of *HSWA 1974* requires employees to take reasonable care for their own health and safety – including acts and omissions – whilst at work.

255. Section 7(b) of *HSWA 1974* requires employees to co-operate with their employers in respect of any measures put in place by them to comply with health and safety duties and requirements.

256. Section 8 of *HSWA 1974* sets out this duty, applying to any person and requiring them not to '*intentionally or recklessly interfere with or misuse anything provided in the interests of health, safety or welfare*'.

imposed being decided by reference to a pre-determined set of criteria, as well as a range of orders being made, including 'remedial orders', 'community orders', 'compensation orders' and 'publicity orders'.

The potential damages and penalties which might flow from successful claims and prosecutions, arising from events of the kind seen in this fable, are summarised here.

CIVIL CLAIMS FOR DAMAGES

It's difficult to talk in precise terms about the outcomes, in terms of damages, that might have arisen from any civil claims for negligence being successfully brought against the Big Beanstalk Business, under *OLA 1984*. This is because each case turns on its facts and no two cases are the same. If, however, it was found to have breached its duty of care, Zac, as claimant would have been entitled to 'damages', with it being more likely that a breach would have been found, by virtue of his being a child. Furthermore, as a child, his involvement would also have made less likely the possibility that such damages would be reduced for any element of contributory negligence.

The story here would have been quite different, had the focus instead been upon Zac's mother suffering injury in the course of trespassing on the Big Beanstalk Business' land. Having already established that it would have been more likely that an element of contributory negligence would have been found on the part of Zac's mother, it follows that any damages awarded to her would have been lower than those arising from any equivalent successful civil claim on her son's behalf. This is because, as an adult, it would be expected that she would have been better able to understand the risks involved.

PENALTIES FOR CRIMINAL CONVICTIONS

In terms of the penalties arising from criminal prosecutions, if the Big Beanstalk Business had been found wanting in respect of its general duties towards the big Giant Woman employee under section 2 of *HSWA 1974* and the case was heard in a Magistrates Court, this could have resulted in the organisation facing an unlimited fine, a term of imprisonment for the big Giant Man of up to six months, or both. In the Crown Court, the penalties could have been anything up to an unlimited fine or imprisonment of up to two years, or both. Both courts also have the discretionary power to make compensation orders for any personal injury, loss or damage, as well as the ability to impose remedial orders or community orders. If the Big Beanstalk Business were to have been found wanting in respect of its duties towards Zac, a non-employee, under section 3 of *HSWA 1974*, equivalent penalties would also have applied in that case as for the duties it had, under section 2, towards the big Giant Woman.

If the big Giant Man were to have been found guilty of an offence under section 37 of *HSWA 1974* – the so-called offence by a body corporate – as a director of the Big Beanstalk Business, he could have found himself liable for a fine and, in certain circumstances, imprisonment. This also might have included him being disqualified as a director in connection with the management of a company.

If the Big Beanstalk Business were to have been found guilty of corporate manslaughter, a court could have imposed penalties including unlimited fines, remedial orders (requiring it to remedy any management failure that led to the death of Zac or the big Giant Woman) and publicity orders requiring the Big Beanstalk Business to publish details of its conviction, which would clearly also have reputational repercussions. In their consideration of the level of liability, juries must consider breaches of health and safety legislation, and can make reference to other health and safety guidance too.

Finally, on the point of particular criminal convictions, if the big Giant Man were to have been found guilty of gross negligence manslaughter, his conduct having found to be *so* bad as to amount to a criminal act or omission, he could have faced a maximum prison sentence of life imprisonment.

In passing sentences, following conviction for corporate manslaughter or gross negligence manslaughter, courts work out the appropriate penalty to impose by reference to the Sentencing Guidelines published by the 'Sentencing Council'[257]. The level of sentencing depends upon the

---

257. For further detail on the Sentencing Guidelines, see www.sentencingcouncil.org.uk [viewed 1 May 2021].

type of offence, the seriousness of the outcome and the circumstances of the case, with factors including the scale of turnover and degree of culpability also needing to be taken into account. Furthermore, in addition to fines and custodial sentences, there is a range of other sanctions available for prosecutors to impose where individuals and organisations are found to have committed an offence: examples include compensation orders, community orders, publicity orders and remedial orders.

The guidelines take the approach that health and safety offences are concerned with failings in the management of health and safety risks, therefore meaning there is now only a need to show that the offence created a *risk* of harm, rather than having to prove that actual harm resulted. These guidelines have significantly increased the levels of fine imposed upon those found to be in breach of health and safety legislation, not only to larger organisations but also, to a lesser degree, smaller firms too.

CLOSING THOUGHTS

In concluding the review of this fable, it's apparent that the events described here were small-scale and fictional. Nevertheless, it has stimulated broader consideration of the range of possible consequences that could occur in an equivalent real-world workplace. We've looked at some significant risk types – notably work at height and dropped object risks – and used these as a basis from which to consider different routes of legal recourse, touching upon possible civil claims and criminal prosecutions that might be brought by those involved or, indeed, those acting on their behalf. And we've considered the possibility of damages being awarded to individuals in the event of their making a successful claim, as well as the penalties that can be imposed upon those convicted of criminal offences. This has extended to the serious penalties faced by organisations under *the Corporate Manslaughter Act,* as well as those which can be imposed upon individuals found guilty of the sister offence of gross negligence manslaughter.

So, whilst it's true that the events of the fable were small-scale and fictional, it's clear that there are many *modern meanings* which flow from it, worthy of serious consideration in a real-world context.

Quite simply, the stakes for organisations have never been higher and those taking a shambolic approach to the control of safety risks walk a dangerous path. Furthermore, fatalities and serious injuries arising from work at height activities continue to be the most frequently reported health and safety prosecutions. The reality is that organisations and those leading them must take their health and safety responsibilities seriously, by complying with laws and guidance, clearly defining roles, learning from mistakes including 'near misses', and seeking to improve their working practices wherever shortfalls are identified.

For a summary of practical points to take away,
based upon the topics and subtopics handled by this fable,
see *How to…* Guide Eight.

A NOTE ON REPORTING REQUIREMENTS

The events portrayed in this fable were of a purely fictitious nature. See the *Epilogue* for indicative reporting requirements under *the Reporting of Injuries, Diseases and Dangerous Occurrences Regulations 2013*[258] *(RIDDOR)*, as could be triggered by equivalent real-world circumstances.

A NOTE ON REGULATORY REGIMES

As the events of this fable take place on land, the legal requirements considered here have been limited to those affecting businesses operating inside Great Britain. It is however, worth noting that workplace health and safety risks arising from work activities in the offshore oil & gas sector – some examples of which were referred to within the *prologue* to this fable – are covered by additional legislation and regulation, the details of which fall outside the scope of this book.

---

258. S.I. 2013/1471.

The Cuckoo, some Less Than Golden Eggs,
and Avoiding
Performance Indicator Problems

THE CUCKOO'S FABLE

' The safety advisor said: '...leading and lagging indicators need to be selected such that they dovetail together, enabling a comparison to be made between efforts put into managing safety upfront, and the resultant safety performance...*cuckoo data* doesn't do this – the data and relationships between it, and the desired safety outcomes and process controls to which it should relate, are skewed and dysfunctional.' '

PROLOGUE

...and now, for something a little more abstract...

A long way back in history, Aesop spoke of a *beautiful hen* and *golden eggs*. For those readers unfamiliar with the original tale, here's a quick summary. A man had a hen that laid golden eggs. He believed the hen to have gold inside her belly but, on killing her, the man discovered that she was just the same as all the others. There was no gold, and the death of the hen destroyed in an instant the man's hope that he might have all his wealth at once. The killing of the hen meant the man lost his steady stream of income from egg production too. The lesson from the original fable was that we should be content with our lot, rather than being greedy and losing everything[259].

As the second of the two *support fables* in this collection, this fable's primary focus is upon the potential benefits to be gained from using proactive and reactive 'performance indicators'. Much like *Zac's fable*, the intention behind this tale is to show how organisations can both defend against, and address failings or shortfalls in controlling 'risk'. As we're about to find out, *the cuckoo's fable* identifies some key parties with an interest in performance indicators and the quality of data they yield. It also touches upon the different relationships involved between those who develop, gather, analyse and respond to data, with the role played by each of these parties seen as integral to the effective functioning of organisational 'assurance' processes. Both the processes involved and those who contribute towards them are vital to ensuring that the 'risk control systems' an organisation believes to be in place are actually effective, whether for 'work at height', containment arrangements, 'confined spaces', 'manual handling', or some other risk type. And whilst,

---

259. The original fable is to be found in Aesop, *The Complete Fables*, translated by Olivia Temple. Penguin. 1998.

in relation to this fable and its accompanying *modern meaning*, there are no specific references to Acts or regulations, the need for performance indicators and those ultimately selected should be driven by a range of legislative, regulatory and in-house requirements relevant to the operating circumstances of those organisations seeking to use them.

From previous fables, we've already seen highlighted the need for risk to be effectively controlled, with *the porridge pot fable* providing one such notable example. This is a collective endeavour, often involving multiple parties and, whilst there is some variability in the terms organisations apply to the roles assigned to individuals with an interest in controlling risk, these broadly speaking include: 'risk owners' – responsible for managing particular risks; 'risk leads' and 'risk champions' – responsible for running programmes and championing other aspects which promote risk management, and 'senior leaders' – being managers or directors who hold overall accountability or carry responsibility for the oversight of risk within their organisations (of whom the board members in this fable would be examples). But there is another set of characters with vital roles to play too, and upon whom the risk owners, risk leaders, and senior leaders rely heavily to keep their risk knowledge up to date. Included amongst these other characters are the 'data analysts', 'data architects', 'data harvesters' and 'data miners' – who collectively develop and maintain performance indicators, in service of sustaining and improving organisational risk understanding. These characters – and what they do – are key to the effective management of performance indicator data and, together with others, they can be viewed as the keepers of an organisation's assurance armoury.

Here then, in an ornithological variation on Aesop's original fable, the focus is upon a cuckoo, rather than a beautiful hen. *And why should this be of interest?* Well, the traits of the cuckoo are such that it urges us to look upon the subject in hand with fresh eyes. And, unlike the hen, this is a species which is parasitic on its host bird – a contrary creature that seeks to disrupt natural relationships – with the eggs produced as a result being anything but golden in appearance. *But exactly how is the dysfunctional relationship displayed by this alternative bird and its host relevant to the data challenges faced by many an organisation? Is it just possible that this relationship could provide a different perspective on how to develop and maintain a meaningful set of performance indicators?*

Well now, let's see…

PERFORMANCE INDICATORS:
VITAL INSIGHTS FOR CONTROLLING RISK

In our journey through these fables thus far, we've encountered some specific things that could cause harm. One 'example was the surfeit of porridge for the container intended to contain it, as described by *the porridge pot fable*. You'll recall that there, we looked at some 'barrier failures' – problems with 'gauges', 'alarms' and shut-off 'valves' and/or the accompanying actions performed by 'operatives' – which meant the halting of the 'top event' was unsuccessful and mitigation of 'consequences', only partially achieved. It's a logical next step to say that the 'barriers' put in place, whether for 'loss of containment' or any other significant risk type, should be checked by proactive and reactive means, from which a robust set of data can be derived and serve as a management system health check. The effective measurement of safety performance is a key component of good safety management, being of invaluable support to an organisation's broader 'risk agenda'. Alongside other sources – including amongst them, annual safety reports and reports of accidents and incidents – performance indicators are recognised as being central to measuring performance within the *check* step of the '*plan-do-check-act* cycle'. Checking is a crucial component of any effective health and safety leadership agenda, a point acknowledged within numerous guidance documents, of which the Health and Safety Executive's '*Leading Health and Safety at Work*'[260] publication is a notable example.

Performance indicators are considered to be a vital tool for understanding risk, essential to verifying that operations are being safely and efficiently performed. They are just one of many valuable sources of information, which reveal the operational effectiveness of arrangements for controlling risk, as defined within 'health and safety management systems'. And, if we agree that understanding risk is essential to safe and efficient operations, it's only natural that we should want to acquire data which validates, informs and shapes our perspective on the health of such management systems. To help set this fable in context, there's a benefit to be had in reading *the porridge*

---

260. See Health and Safety Executive (2013). *Managing for Health and Safety.* HSG65, cited in Health and Safety Executive Guidance document (2013). *Leading Health and Safety at Work.* INDG417 (rev.1).

pot fable first, as it's for a loss of containment risk that the indicators are to be selected here. It was there, if you recall, that we saw the lessons that could be learnt from loss of containment incidents. And, who knows, had appropriate data been made available and acted upon by the characters within that fable – or indeed, provided to those at the heart of the other tales – perhaps some or all of the events described might have been averted, or at least curtailed before control was lost!

With this in mind, and in order to demonstrate this point more clearly, it seems timely to pose a few theoretical questions about the characters and goings-on featured within these earlier fables, so as to give an inkling as to the types of insights that an effective set of performance indicators can bring...

FICTIONAL QUESTIONS

In *the piper's fable*, had the Pest Control Piper been aware of the number of reports of 'Weil's disease' or other cases of occupational exposure to 'biological agents', might he have chosen to adopt safe working methods, as well as making more conventional personal protective clothing choices?

If the organisation in *the goats' fable* had known of the numbers of physical assaults, or even verbal threats, made against its 'workers', might this have prompted it to review and, if necessary, adjust its 'lone working' arrangements?

Had the agricultural workers in *the swede fable* been informed of previous 'manual handling' injury reports, might this have motivated them to change tack towards their pulling and pushing of the super-sized swede, or even paved the way for the organisation to take an entirely different approach to such activities, perhaps introducing the use of some form of powered assistance?

Would the 'ergonomic' endeavours of the three bears at the heart of *Pixie-Locks' fable* have been supported to a greater degree, if accompanied by occupational health data reports, recording instances of 'work-related musculoskeletal disorders', or data implicating poor design as a root cause of incidents?

Given circumstances equivalent to the kind *Zac's fable* describes, might prior knowledge of reports on the number and severity of 'dropped object' and 'fall from height' incidents have delivered insights about beanstalk-based forays that the Big Beanstalk Business and big Giant Man simply couldn't ignore?

Had the little girl and her mother at the centre of *the porridge pot fable* been armed with knowledge of other previous 'loss of containment' incidents, might this have furthered their understanding of the importance of gauges, alarms and shut-off valves – and meant they better appreciated the need to take appropriate action in response to them?

Reflecting on this set of questions for a moment – just a sample of the many raised by the actions of the characters in these tales – they share a common thread, by highlighting how knowledge and incident data can be harnessed and actively used to help drive, support and influence both organisational and behavioural change, in support of the goal of risk reduction. Despite these being works of fiction, equivalent questions are readily applicable in a real-world context too, and when calls come to investigate real-world incidents, there's an inevitable uptick in the volume of data requests which flow in. In the face of real-world circumstances, the questions put to the human counterparts to these characters differ little from those just posed and, when answered with honesty, they can often leave organisations facing uncomfortable truths. And data about things which go *'CRACKLE!'*, *'POP!'*, and *'SQUELCH!'* is very much in demand, in the real world...

REAL-WORLD CHALLENGES

There's no denying that the data topic which inspired this penultimate fable isn't instantly exciting, but it was inevitable we would arrive at this point eventually. *Why might this be?* It's because, unlike many of the traditional occupations which have all but died out in Great Britain, the *data industry* and the roles which support it appear to be thriving. Indeed, the data discipline has even borrowed its lexicon from that of other industries in a bid to earn its place in the contemporary corporate landscape. The modern 'data miners' replace the miners of yesteryear, who worked tirelessly underground. The 'data harvesters' who show no interest in fields seem to yield bountiful data crops all year long, with apparent ease and no suggestion of fallow periods, whilst 'data architects' build data villages, towns and 'data lakes', with scant regard for underpinning construction or hydrological principles. And yet, it's to the expertise of these present-day miners, harvesters and architects we must defer, if we are to establish and maintain our understanding of these newly-defined operating environments.

Data. It's inescapable. It's the thing an organisation reaches for when called upon to answer the – often uncomfortable – questions of '*Why?*' and '*How?*' an incident could have happened and, more particularly, what else might have been done to stop it. On the other hand, when used proactively, it's a crucial defence weapon in an organisation's assurance armoury, providing confidence that something won't happen, by confirming that what's believed to be in place is actually there, to protect people, systems and the environment from harm.

Data. The world's full of it, and it's to be found strewn in bountiful quantities across the offices, websites, on-line 'portals' and 'apps' of many an organisation. Pie-charts adorn screens, like corporate Catherine wheels, with a myriad of hues which send the report recipients' eyes spinning. 'Dashboards' – once the preserve of the pilots in cockpits and drivers in vehicle cabs – now act as the control panel for many a senior leader, confirming to them at a glance whether everything is *okay* or *not okay*. And, at times, it can seem as if the lines of rolling trend graphs weave some kind of hypnotic spell over those who commission their production – it often being the case that the data's beauty outweighs the actual value to the viewer – such is the beguiling nature of the information that appears before them. The simple truth is that, in order for these data reports to prove their worth as anything more than interesting works of art, performance indicators need to be *selected* on a logical basis, *connected* to the risk processes they monitor and periodically *checked* to ensure they remain valid and effective; it's in so doing that they justify their worth as invaluable management system assurance tools. *And where this isn't the case, we should of course be concerned, making it timely, at this point, to heed two warnings...*

WARNING #1
RESIST ADDICTION TO FRUIT-MACHINE OUTCOMES

It's worth saying this upfront. It's important that performance reporting isn't approached with the mindset of a fruit machine gamer. Nor should it be permitted to create expectations of optimal outcomes. For, much like the scrolling wheels of a fruit machine display combinations of, say, green apples, red tomatoes and yellow bananas, many a performance report has the capacity to yield an array of green, red and amber ratings. But that isn't to say we should allow performance reporting to become about *nudging* and *holding* possible winning combinations. Or let it lead to feelings of disappointment when we end up – as we sometimes will – with red tomatoes, when we want green apples. Sometimes in the workplace, just as in life, we win green apples. Sometimes we end up with red tomatoes. But ratings should be validated and describe outcomes or predict the strength of 'risk controls' (barriers), not the result of a game of chance or good fortune. We mustn't allow ourselves to be driven by the pursuit of *jackpot data* – which, on the face of it, appears to show optimal combinations – at the expense of accepting sometimes inconvenient truths. *Or else, just like an unhealthy obsession with fruit machine combinations, we might lose the lot!*

WARNING #2
DON'T BECOME COLOUR-BLIND BY CONVENIENCE

It might just be coincidence, but sufferers of colour-blindness can struggle to detect red, yellow and green hues. This is of interest because, as chance would have it, these are similar to the colours frequently chosen for the grading of performance indicators – sometimes referred to as *traffic light* or *RAG (Red, Amber, Green) ratings*. It's often the case that the recipients of such reports are highly sensitised to red-rated measures and, to some extent, amber-rated measures too, whilst others are intolerant to a view which is anything other than green (always seeing green apples, rather than red tomatoes). When left unchecked, expectations of favourable performance indicator outcomes can create a culture in which the upward reporting of bad news is suppressed. And, when such views become entrenched within an organisation, this should trigger concerns about a reluctance to address 'process safety' failures. *Why should this be?* It's because when performance indicator data becomes skewed, it can paradoxically undermine the very health and safety management system it's intended to defend. And just as, at a sight test, an optician will pose the question as to whether black circles appear clearer against a red or green background, if our response is always 'green', irrespective of what we actually see, it's probably timely for us to question the wisdom of our approach.

But that's enough about fruit machines and opticians – let's get back to more serious real-world matters...

KEY DRIVERS FOR DEVELOPING STRONG PERFORMANCE INDICATORS: TEXAS CITY AND THE BAKER REPORT

In order to give this fable some real-world context, it's worth dwelling briefly on the details of the *Texas City incident (United States, March 2005)* and the accompanying 'Texas City report', together with the 'Baker report' which followed it. The incident itself, together with these reports, provided the driving force to set out 'good practice' for the derivation and use of effective performance indicators and, to this day, they provide helpful insights as to why their development – particularly in a process safety context – is so important. Additionally, the Health and Safety Executive's publication '*Developing Process Safety Indicators – A Step by Step Guide*'[261] drew upon learning points from 'major accident' investigations at chemical and major hazard installations and still offers invaluable guidance to those seeking to establish and maintain effective and appropriate sets of performance indicators. For those unfamiliar with this field, or others who perhaps simply want further detail on the principles for developing performance indicators as are considered here, it's a great place to start.

In March 2005, a series of explosions occurred at the Texas City refinery in the course of a hydrocarbon isomerisation unit restart operation. *The consequences were devastating.* Fifteen workers lost their lives and 180 others were injured. Many of the victims were situated in or around work trailers located near an atmospheric vent stack. The explosions occurred when hydrocarbons flooded a distillation tower, causing over-pressurisation, which led to a release from the vent stack. The Baker report which followed documented a number of key findings, including requirements for clear process safety leadership, a comprehensive management system and a more effective two way

---

261. Health and Safety Executive Guidance (2006), *Developing Process Safety Indicators – A step-by-step guide for chemical and major hazard industries* (HSG254).

'process-safety culture'. Another of the findings called upon the organisation to develop and implement a reasonable set of integrated performance indicators, covering both 'leading' and 'lagging' performance measures for process safety. This recommendation was made, in part, due to the report identifying an issue with underlying culture, in which early-warning indicators were lacking, with an over-reliance having been placed on failure data. A sign that a reactive culture of this kind exists is seen where people only respond to things going 'CRACKLE!', 'POP!', or 'SQUELCH!', rather than seeking out precursor signs, and proactively addressing these. To return to the earlier example from *the porridge pot fable*, this means there is a tendency to report loss of containment incidents (*porridge spills*), rather than gauge, alarm or valve performance malfunctions (*failures of porridge control equipment or by operatives*). Such an approach is flawed because it creates bias towards improvements being made only when things go wrong. The Baker report motivated many in high-risk process industries to act. It urged those concerned by matters of process safety to seek out appropriate sets of performance indicators, befitting their operations, and it's upon this quest that *the cuckoo's fable* – and the *modern meaning* that accompanies it – is primarily focused.

Approaches taken in Great Britain and the United States since Texas City and the reports which followed have focused upon what performance indicators reveal, from either an early warning '*What could happen?*' or a hindsight '*What went wrong?*' perspective. The reports into the events which took place collectively contain a wealth of insights and principles upon which organisations can draw, helping to steer them towards the development of good data, aligned to both pre– and post-event viewpoints. And, whilst Texas City was a product of activity within high-risk industry, the findings and corresponding recommendations it raised offer a useful checklist for any organisation seeking to verify the robustness of its approach to process safety. An underlying theme to the findings was a tendency common to many organisations to prioritise their attention towards 'occupational (personal) safety', sometimes distracting them from the more troubling – and often more pressing – process safety risks.

There's no denying that much positive work has taken place since the time of *Texas City* and the Baker report, but challenges with data are ever-present for many organisations. There remains an unhealthy appetite in some quarters for *any* data or, arguably worse, data which is externally beautiful, but internally rotten. Such data does nothing to assure organisations – or, more worryingly, provides them with false assurance – that their risks have been robustly identified, controlled and effectively addressed by the putting in place of appropriate mitigation measures. It always pays to keep in mind that the main reason for measuring process safety performance is to provide ongoing assurance that risks are being adequately controlled. Organisations need to monitor the effectiveness of their process controls against the risks to which they relate. The key point to remember is that, when used to best effect within the process safety arena, performance indicators can provide early warnings in advance of catastrophic failures that critical process controls have deteriorated to unacceptable levels. It's in this way that they can collectively serve as a crucial defence mechanism to ward off process safety failures.

Let's revisit the context of this fable for a moment. It will come as little surprise to many readers to learn that it takes no more than a brief walk through the reception of an organisation's head office, a wander through its website pages, or a tap of its corporate app, to yield a bountiful array of management information, in all its forms – of which the contribution of safety performance indicators is a significant one. On an initial viewing, this *art form* can give a sense of security to the observer – indeed, all manner of *pie-chartery, scorecard sorcery* and *webpage wizardry* may be found. *But are they the right indicators?* This fable is all about the need for indicators to be founded upon good relationships, rather than dysfunctional ones. It seeks to explain how, if badly chosen, performance indicators can have more in common with the *cuckoo/host* relationship – where the data has no discernable link to the risk it purports to monitor – rather than the *golden egg/golden hen* relationship which is, of course, the desirable one.

LEADING AND LAGGING INDICATORS: CHEESE-BASED INSIGHTS

Thinking back for a moment to Reason's 'Swiss cheese model'[262] – which this book first considered in the context of *the porridge pot fable* – 'leading indicators' reveal holes in risk control systems or groups of 'barriers' during routine checks (*flaws in individual cheese slices or barriers*), whilst 'lagging indicators' show barrier holes, which allow a

---

262. See *Appendix D* of this book, for a basic depiction of the Swiss cheese model.

'threat' to flow through, resulting in an incident or top event (*slipping or flowing through the holes in multiple cheese slices, or alignment of the gaps in each barrier*). There will inevitably be some instances where opinions differ as to whether an indicator is leading or lagging. In reality, making this distinction is not the top priority. What is more important – and as is borne out by the Health and Safety Executive's guidance document – is that organisations should choose measures which truthfully describe how well process controls are working, irrespective of whether indicators are of a leading or lagging type. Just to be clear, both leading and lagging indicators can support organisational understanding of 'barrier effectiveness' on either the threat (left hand) or consequence (right hand) side of a 'bow tie model', albeit that there will typically be more leading indicators on the left hand side and more lagging on the right hand side of a given top event[263].

Widely regarded as predictive precursors of harm, leading indicators are viewed as 'before the fact' (*pre-event*) proactive measures, generated by 'active monitoring'. When used effectively – and supported by well-defined tolerances for the resulting performance ratings – they give organisations sufficient warning of performance deviations and opportunities for risk control weaknesses to be corrected before harm occurs. They do this by connecting to the 'process controls' of each risk control system – these being the actions or processes which must function correctly to deliver the outcomes – providing the basis for checks to be made on system functioning, clearly highlighting where deviations from set tolerances have occurred, and giving the impetus for these to be resolved. Lagging indicators, on the other hand, are seen as 'after the fact' (*post-event*) direct outcome measures of harm, being generated by 'reactive monitoring' and connected to 'desired safety outcomes'. Also being linked to the risk control systems that are deemed to be in place to prevent major accidents, they provide evidence of key outcomes having failed or fallen short of objectives, for example through 'near miss' or incident data, thereby enabling deviations from tolerances to be followed up.

---

263. See *the porridge pot fable*, for an overview of the approach towards developing barrier (bow tie) models. Note that an example of an alarm handling leading indicator (*hole in a cheese slice*) would be 'number of times alarm sounds to correctly warn and prevent a potential loss of containment top event', whilst an example of an alarm handling lagging indicator (*alignment of holes between different cheese slices*) would be 'number of cases of loss of containment where alarm failed to sound'.

This fable seeks to provide insights as to how performance indicators – both leading and lagging – can be set so as to support and drive organisation-wide process safety performance improvements, on an ongoing basis.

THE FOCUS OF THIS FABLE

This fable is all about data. As has already been said, data is rarely in short supply but, setting aside considerations about quantity, it's important for organisations to question its intrinsic worth, by constantly asking themselves: *'Does it tell us what we need to know about the risk?'* and *'Does it give us confidence in our systems, processes and people?'* Answering *'No!'* to either question should motivate organisations to follow up on any apparent shortfalls and prompt them to arrange for action to be taken by the right people, either to correct shortcomings in the data itself or, if the data is valid, to address any gaps it reveals in their control of risk. In order to suggest how to tackle such concerns, this fable considers how performance indicators should be chosen, and who should be involved in the process. It also looks at the link back to the risks on which performance indicators report. And it offers insights as to how performance indicators can remain relevant and appropriate to organisational activities, on an enduring basis. Finally, it shows the relevance of the parasitic bird to the subject under discussion. *So, what are you waiting for? Grab your binoculars and get ready for a spot of ornithology...*

...we're off to find the cuckoo!

THE FABLE

Once upon a time, there was a safety director who worked for a large chemicals company, at a facility from which bulk tanks and tankers were operated. The safety director had a beautiful safety performance indicator report, filled with measures he regarded as *golden eggs*. He cherished his Golden Egg Performance Report, parading it in front of many a Board meeting and sharing it with his safety advisors, for them to discuss with the operational managers they supported. This helped the safety advisors to identify any concerns and pinpoint potential areas for improvement, as well as enabling them to talk knowledgeably, when engaging with their frontline operational colleagues.

Every month, the safety director would collect up the data for the Golden Egg Performance Report. He took it the Board, who read it and formed a view on the current performance level. For quite some time, everything had been *golden* with the Golden Egg Performance Report or, at least, all of the performance indicators it contained had been green-rated for as far back as the Board members could recall. But despite this, some had voiced concerns that there were no visible signs of improvement to the levels or types of incidents being recorded, a trend which might reasonably have been expected to accompany such a glowing report.

One day, one of the safety advisors who reported to the safety director decided to carry out a full-scale review of the Golden Egg Performance Report. His role was to provide guidance and support on *all things safety* to a group of operational managers within a defined geographical area. The safety advisor was brimming with enthusiasm – not yet disillusioned by the realities of organisational politics – and was keen to gain a better understanding of the safety risks which were of greatest concern. He went into raptures about the benefit of performance indicators, as a means of providing data for near real-time monitoring of the performance and efficiency of the health and safety management system, to a level of detail which left the safety director frankly bewildered. Seemingly unfazed by the safety director's muted response, however, and in a bid to kick-start his project, the safety advisor called together the operational managers who managed teams with key roles to play in controlling the risks associated with the organisation's main processes, including FAILURE TO MANAGE PLANT CHANGE, FAILURE TO PROPERLY CO-ORDINATE ACTIVITIES, and PLANT OR PROCESS OUTSIDE SAFE OPERATING CONDITIONS[264].

---

264. The use of upper case text for terms used within this fable denotes those taken from Guidance document HSG254, with the methodology it sets out being applied to the fable's fictional circumstances. The focus here is upon the PLANT OR PROCESS OUTSIDE OPERATING CONDITIONS risk, analysed at pages 45-46 of the Guidance document, with the accompanying desired safety outcome, process controls, leading indicators and lagging indicators selected for the events the tale describes also being emphasised in the same way, being other features of the methodology. Whilst there are some differences between the lexicon of this approach and that of the bow tie methodology showcased in relation to *the porridge pot fable*, they are broadly similar and the example of a [porridge pot overflow – loss of containment] top event described in that fable – and applied later in this one – can be regarded as an instance of a 'plant or process outside operating conditions' risk having been realised, containment having been lost.

In truth, much as the safety director didn't like to admit it, the safety advisor's project was causing a bit of worry for him; he was perplexed as to why anyone would want to call into question his highly-prized Golden Egg Performance Report, the contents of which had admittedly been allowed to evolve piecemeal, rather than on a planned basis, over the years. Recognising that he had little option however, he reluctantly granted his approval to the review taking place. In no time at all, the safety advisor had scoped out the project and duly advised the safety director of its remit. He confirmed he was to take a PLANT OR PROCESS OUTSIDE SAFE OPERATING CONDITIONS risk example, through which he intended to highlight some potential performance indicator issues, an approach which he believed would emphasise the importance of providing good data. The safety director said he didn't find the project remit particularly exciting, but reassured the safety advisor that he would consider its findings. Retirement was an ever closer prospect for the safety director and, unbeknown to the safety advisor, he had been hoping to coast smoothly towards it, rather than enduring a bumpy ride in, over his last few months with the organisation. Alas, it appeared that coasting wasn't to be an option for him, with this project and a number of others starting to grow arms and legs at precisely the wrong moment. Seemingly undaunted, and with his enthusiasm undimmed, the safety advisor continued on, explaining that he saw the project as being made up of two key parts: *first*, the linking of desired safety outcomes to 'lagging (outcome) indicators', and *second*, the linking of process controls to 'leading (activity) indicators'. Hoping this information offered enough of a carrot to whet the safety director's appetite and that it might just have sparked interest in his project, the safety advisor thought it best to allow him time to mull things over and so, without further ado, wished him a good day and went on his way...

The next day would see the safety advisor providing operational managers with an overview of the phases involved the project...

PROJECT PHASE #1
LINK DESIRED SAFETY OUTCOMES
TO LAGGING INDICATORS

The enthusiastic safety advisor first set to work on linking desired safety outcomes to lagging indicators, calling three of the operational managers he advised to an important meeting and asking them what lagging indicators they could provide to show that the organisation's plant and processes were operating as intended.

He explained to them that the information he was requesting was vital, stressing that it would help to ensure that they had their safety risks under control. He was looking for a lagging indicator which reflected the desired safety outcome. The desired safety outcome in this case was: SAFETY CRITICAL INSTRUMENTATION AND ALARMS CORRECTLY INDICATE WHEN PROCESS CONDITIONS ARE ABOVE SAFE OPERATING LIMITS.

The first operational manager said: 'How about the number of times the bulk tanks or road tankers are overfilled due to level indicator or alarm failures?' He was keen to provide this data, because it was information he already had to hand. 'I like that...' said the safety advisor, '...but I don't think it will give us the full picture!'

The first operational manager looked slightly miffed at this response.

The second operational manager said: 'What if I could tell you the number of times that the bulk tanks or road tankers are over or under-pressurised, due to level indicator or alarm failures?' The safety advisor replied: 'I like that too, but it still isn't quite what I'm after!'

The second operational manager looked slightly perplexed by this reply.

The third operational manager said: 'How about if I could tell you the number of times product is transferred at the wrong flow rate or pressure, due to pressure gauge or alarm failures?' The safety advisor replied: 'I like that very much, but I still think it needs a bit more work!'

The third operational manager looked annoyed, as 'a bit more work' was the last thing he wanted.

Some time later...

Having consolidated the suggestions offered by the three operational managers, the safety advisor called them back together again, thanking them for their input and providing his feedback. Noting that the safety advisor seemed less than impressed by their proposals, the third operational manager, looking suddenly quizzical, asked: 'Why don't you like the indicators we've suggested?'

The safety advisor replied that he wanted a lagging indicator which looked at THE NUMBER OF SAFETY CRITICAL INSTRUMENTS OR ALARMS THAT FAIL TO OPERATE AS DESIGNED, EITHER WHEN IN LIVE USE OR DURING TESTING, because this indicator would detect all failures in instruments and alarm systems, irrespective of whether or not these resulted in containment being lost. This was preferable to the indicators they had suggested, which would only have provided him with part of the picture. *It was the best lagging indicator because it linked to the desired safety outcome.* It showed whether or not the desired safety outcome had actually been achieved.

A bit more time later...

PROJECT PHASE #2
LINK PROCESS CONTROLS
TO LEADING INDICATORS

The enthusiastic safety advisor next set to work on linking process controls to leading indicators, calling together two of the other operational managers he advised to an important meeting and asking them what leading indicators they could provide to show that the organisation's plant and processes were operating as intended.

Then, just as he had done with the three operational managers who had looked at lagging indicators before them, the enthusiastic safety advisor explained to the two other operational managers that the information he was requesting was vital, pointing out that it would help to ensure they had their process safety risks under control. He was looking for leading indicators which linked to the process controls. In this case, the process controls were: OPERATIONAL PROCEDURES: INSTRUMENTATION AND ALARM SYSTEMS.

The fourth operational manager piped up: 'I can tell you the percentage of safety critical instruments and alarms that correctly indicate the process conditions', to which the safety advisor replied: 'That isn't too bad, but I still think there's a bit more to this!'

The fourth operational manager looked askance, harbouring a feeling that perhaps the safety advisor was generating unnecessary work for her, and the others.

Finally, and knowing that his meetings about performance indicators were fortunately nearing a conclusion, the safety advisor asked the fifth operational manager if she had anything she wanted to add to the discussion. The fifth operational manager said: 'Wouldn't you like to know the percentage of safety critical instruments and alarms that activate at the desired set point?' to which the safety advisor responded: 'Sounds terrific...but let me give it some thought and I'll get back to you!'

The fifth operational manager looked a bit cross. In truth, she was livid, as she was just about to head off on holiday and had wanted this project tidied up before her departure that evening.

Some more time later...

Shortly after the fifth operational manager had returned from holiday, the safety advisor called her and the fourth operational manager back together, thanked them for their contributions and gave them his feedback. Just like the first three operational managers who had gone before them, the fourth and fifth operational managers were keen to understand why the safety advisor wasn't willing to adopt their performance indicator suggestions wholesale. He explained that he'd decided to pick two leading indicators, one of which looked at THE PERCENTAGE OF FUNCTIONAL TESTS OF SAFETY CRITICAL INSTRUMENTS AND ALARMS COMPLETED TO SCHEDULE and another at THE PERCENTAGE OF MAINTENANCE ACTIONS TO RECTIFY FAULTS TO SAFETY CRITICAL INSTRUMENTS AND ALARMS COMPLETED TO SCHEDULE, in preference to those that they had suggested, because these were the main inputs which ensured that instruments and alarms were continuing to function as designed. The ones they had put forward were covered instead within the functional testing and maintenance system. *The chosen indicators were the best leading indicators because they linked to the process controls.* They showed whether the INSTRUMENTATION AND ALARMS risk control system was in place to deliver the outcome. They also confirmed whether it was operating as designed, with the safety critical elements to achieve process control including: INSTRUMENTS CORRECTLY INDICATE PROCESS CONDITIONS; ALARMS ACTIVATE AT THE DESIRED SET POINTS; INSTRUMENTS AND ALARMS ARE TESTED AND CALIBRATED TO THE APPROPRIATE DESIGN STANDARD, and REPAIRS TO FAULTY INSTRUMENTS AND ALARMS ARE CARRIED OUT WITHIN THE SPECIFIED TIME PERIOD.

The safety advisor sensed that an awkward conversation with the safety director was in prospect. Knowing, as he did, that the Golden Egg Performance Report was much cherished by the safety director, the safety advisor realised he needed to be tactful in submitting new proposals to him. He called the safety director to a meeting, enthusiastically opening up the current Golden Egg Performance Report file on his laptop, on his arrival. The safety advisor had marked up several sections of the report where he'd identified concerns and reassured the safety director that, as well as sharing his findings, he also wanted to give him some suggestions as to how these might be addressed. The safety advisor went on to explain that, in a bid to clearly highlight his points, he had taken the PLANT OR PROCESS OUTSIDE SAFE OPERATING CONDITIONS risk to show, in practical terms, how to pick the best types of indicators.

And, not being one for the more mainstream styles of presentation, the safety advisor put his own poetic twist on the introduction to the topic:

'In case you're unclear, or if you've forgotten,
I'm here to talk indicators (and of eggs that are rotten)!
Like Aesop's hen's eggs, our data should be gold
And set out a story that needs to be told.
Not just some fictional work, but factually true,
A snapshot of performance, that's easy to view!

To date, we've picked eggs we can gather with ease,
Without gauging their value, we've been eager to please.
These eggs lacked all beauty, were of doubtable worth,
They were rogue from the start, they were troubled from birth.
Or else, stolen from others, who had used them before
And, together with good sense, our purpose, left at the door.
Whether *leading* or *lagging*, we should look for a picture,
That doesn't just dazzle, but makes our risk vision richer...

And much like offspring to their mothers connect,
Our risks need to link up with those things we inspect.
And not just for one clutch, this must be true for all weathers –
Check the baby birds still to their mothers' hearts tether.
This applies too, to data, which tells of things that must stop
And which if unchecked might 'SQUELCH!', 'CRACKLE!' or 'POP!'

We need to take time to get a risk-data match,
Thus staving off trouble which would otherwise hatch.

But to stay ever golden, those that hatch still need care,
Or they could become cuckoos, so look out, beware!
They must link to the host bird, they should still relate,
Or else be flung from the nest, for being out of date.
You see, without these reports of buzzers and bells,
We get no advance warning of tank overswells
Nor achieve confidence in how plants operate,
Or figure out areas we might need to update!

The life of some processes may be winding and long
But even good indicators aren't forever strong.
Just because popular or simply in vogue,
We still need to question, checking data's not rogue.
Our eggs haven't been golden – they were cuckoos instead,
Rogue indicators, that lacked golden thread.
We need good eggs instead, of a logical sort,
Which paint a fair picture and our risks truly report.
By constantly checking on this family's bonds,
We can confidently say to our risks we respond.
It might be data that lags, which says we need to invest
Or that which leads us, to perform at our best.
Whether the health of our plant, or an operating condition,
Data should cling to our purpose, and map to our vision.
We need to report on risks, such as containment losses,
Not hide awkward truths from leaders and bosses.
Beware of reports rose-tinted or showing flashes of gold,
Or those that boast 'all's well' in a tale not fully told.
Instead, data needs to inform those who read the reviews
Of the health of performance – it should never confuse!

And no matter the data, always question its worth,
Has it just turned out rotten, or was it cuckoo from birth?
Check it's not just a squatter, taking more than it gives,
For a parasite steals much from the place where it lives.
For gold eggs to be dominant, to evolve and to last,
They need to assist, or from the nest swiftly be cast.

To keep these eggs golden requires nurture and care,
With cuckoos discarded, when our truths they impair.'

'I'm not quite sure I follow all this – where did the cuckoo spring from?' asked the safety director, never ceasing to be surprised by this particular safety advisor's eccentricity.

'Ah well now, *I'm glad you asked...*' said the safety advisor, '...because, for performance indicators to work, they need to connect with the process controls and desired safety outcomes to which they relate!', and he proceeded to give the safety director an outline of some draft training materials, featuring a case study about a perilous porridge pot, overflowing with porridge. Some who had reviewed these training materials thought the tale it contained to be far-fetched, but legend had it that this pot had been breached by an excessive amount of porridge being produced, the containment arrangements in that case having been woeful. If organisational rumours were to be believed, the training department considered this example to be a little complex for their needs, and so had put it on the back-burner for some other time.

There was a stunned silence which lasted for some moments – a silence which the safety advisor sensed might become strained. Being eager to keep the safety director's attention, and in a bid to win over the other Board members too, he continued on seemingly undaunted, to summarise the detail of the tale he'd used in a workshop-based scenario some time back. It was true to say that this particular case study was set in a small-scale domestic kitchen environment, but the safety advisor was of the firm belief that the principles it highlighted could be readily applied to large-scale operational plants too.

He started: '*Once upon a time...*there was a poor little girl, who lived alone with her mother. They no longer had anything to eat...' The safety advisor paused for a moment before continuing on: '...she started making porridge...until she had eaten enough...and then she wanted the pot to stop, but the pot kept on cooking more and more porridge. The failure of the pot's high level alarm and shut-off valve – what we might regard here as the INSTRUMENTATION AND ALARMS risk control system or group of barriers – meant a failure to prevent overfill, the result being that porridge flowed from the pot to the kitchen and then throughout the house and beyond! To use organisational terminology, this could be described as a PLANT

OR PROCESS OUTSIDE SAFE OPERATING CONDITIONS risk, which here materialised due to a failure to block the [porridge produced exceeds porridge pot capacity] threat[265]. And if we were seeking to address such a risk from an organisational perspective, we'd say that the safety critical elements should have included: *first*, INSTRUMENTS CORRECTLY INDICATE PROCESS CONDITIONS; *second*, ALARMS ACTIVATE AT DESIRED SET POINTS; *third*, INSTRUMENTS AND ALARMS ARE TESTED AND CALIBRATED TO AN AGREED DESIGN STANDARD, and *fourth*, and finally: REPAIRS TO FAULTY INSTRUMENTS AND ALARMS ARE CARRIED OUT WITHIN A SPECIFIED TIME PERIOD – but these hadn't been in place – or at least, there had been no evidence of testing, calibration, or documented history of repairs presented in the workshop-based scenario within which this case study had featured.'

The safety advisor hesitated momentarily, before continuing on: 'Exploring this still further, had the little girl had a bit more risk understanding, she might have appreciated that what she needed to know was that the SAFETY CRITICAL INSTRUMENTATION AND ALARMS CORRECTLY INDICATE WHEN PROCESS CONDITIONS EXCEED SAFE OPERATING LIMITS. We call this a desired safety outcome but, in reality, there was no such early warning of excursion from these limits. Had she recognised the importance of this kind of outcome, she would also have understood the need to look for a suitable lagging indicator, which might be expressed here as THE NUMBER OF SAFETY CRITICAL INSTRUMENTS AND ALARMS THAT FAILED TO OPERATE AS DESIGNED, EITHER IN LIVE USE OR DURING TESTING. These were clearly circumstances in which the desired outcome wasn't achieved, which is why an indicator which allowed all failures in instrumentation and alarm systems to be detected, irrespective of whether or not containment was lost, would have worked best in this instance...'

The safety advisor suddenly became aware that he was surrounded by a sea of blank faces. Undaunted, he continued on: '...but that's not quite how this story ends...you see, the little girl would have had opportunities to detect these problems before a single spoonful of porridge had been produced but, using our own terminology

---

265. This was the description given to the threat in *the porridge pot fable*.

again for an event of a similar ilk, we'd say that the OPERATIONAL PROCEDURES, INSTRUMENTATION AND ALARM SYSTEMS were ineffective – they were inadequate process controls. And continuing to look at the scenario from an organisational perspective, rather than a domestic kitchen-based one, we'd also say that had a little trouble been taken to check gauges, high level alarms and shut-off valves, there would have been a clear opportunity to report on the PERCENTAGE OF FUNCTIONAL TESTS ON SAFETY CRITICAL INSTRUMENTS AND ALARMS COMPLETED TO SCHEDULE and THE PERCENTAGE OF MAINTENANCE ACTIONS, TO RECTIFY FAULTS TO SAFETY CRITICAL INSTRUMENTS AND ALARMS, COMPLETED TO SCHEDULE, these being the main inputs to ensure that the instruments and alarms continued to function as designed, as potential leading indicators...'

In wrapping up his findings, the safety advisor said: '...now, I'm not saying it's a classic anecdote, but the suggested workshop example does at least show how leading and lagging indicators can provide 'dual assurance' of any top event requiring control which, if successful, helps to ensure the plant or process consistently operates within 'operating conditions' and that any excursions from these are readily identifiable and resolvable in a timely manner. In order for them to deliver effective dual assurance, leading and lagging indicators need to be selected such that they dovetail together, enabling a comparison to be made between efforts put into managing safety upfront, and the resultant safety performance.

...so the short answer to your question about what this has to do with parasitic birds is that *cuckoo data* doesn't do this – the data and relationships between it, and the desired safety outcomes and process controls to which it should relate, are skewed and dysfunctional. But panic not, because I feel sure these issues can be avoided by applying the measurement principles that flow from the fictional example I've just described to any of our top events!'

The safety director relented, yielding to pressure, in the face of the safety advisor's irrepressible enthusiasm. He authorised the safety advisor to set up a working group to devise a set of performance indicators that was more reflective of the organisation's process safety 'risk profile'. The working group had a clear remit, reporting into a steering group, and being led by the safety director. The safety advisor became a risk champion. An implementation team was formed. And employees and the organisation's senior leaders worked harmoniously together, in a collaborative effort to integrate the organisation's performance indicators within a robust assurance framework.

And they all lived happily – *and their process plant operated predictably* – ever after.

MODERN MEANING

Reflecting back upon the cuckoo references scattered throughout this fable, there are some key lessons to be drawn from the tale – not least the very clear need that exists for organisations to prevent the kinds of traits displayed by this errant bird emerging within their performance indicator sets! Putting it in a nutshell, the fable highlights that organisations shouldn't allow themselves to be deceived by the outward appearance of *golden* performance reports. To this end, they should ensure that the performance indicator data they gather is sound, checking that it delivers critical insights across the full spectrum of their risk profile. The fable shows that, when performance indicators are well-developed – with the right people being involved in their development – organisations can place confidence in them and their capacity to report on the health of process controls and desired safety outcomes. But it also highlights that they should not let complacency creep in, by allowing the belief to develop that initially healthy performance indicators will always remain so, without being nurtured – instead, they should be mindful of the need to constantly refresh them, for instance, in response to a newly 'emerging risk', or the findings of an incident investigation.

The fable also shows that organisations should not be blinded by performance data *per se*, with further gains to be had by their understanding the context and limitations of its use. This means they need to make sure performance reports link back to, and are reflective of, their risks – performing an effective dual assurance function – with both leading and lagging indicators adopted for each risk control system. Getting into the practical detail, a key message to take from this fable about performance indicators is that leading or 'proactive indicators' need to focus on the effectiveness of process controls, whilst lagging or 'reactive indicators' should be used to highlight when a desired safety outcome hasn't been achieved. There are many lessons organisations can draw from this fable, to help steer their development of effective safety performance indicators. A robust set of leading and lagging indicators is imperative for any organisation seeking to drive and secure 'continual improvement' in its performance levels. And following logical principles for the setting of performance indicators is fundamental too. It's taking this kind of approach that allows organisations to secure data which warns of 'major accident scenarios' (leading indicators), through focusing on a few critical risk control systems, thus ensuring that risks continue to be controlled effectively, on an ongoing basis. It also provides causal insight (lagging indicators) when incidents do occur, by adding to organisations' understanding of the systemic failures of risk control systems which, in turn, means they can readily identify the actions they need to take to prevent recurrence.

In order for organisations to achieve effective process safety management it's important that they, *first:* understand what could go wrong, by identifying risks and major accident scenarios; *second,* know what's in place to prevent things going wrong, by recognising the importance of barriers, and *third,* make sure there's enough information available to check on the effectiveness of control actually delivered by barriers – through developing the right leading and lagging indicators. The first two of these points were covered by *the porridge pot fable* and its associated *modern meaning,* and it's primarily the third point on information sufficiency which is examined here. Forward-thinking organisations appreciate the value of building up sets of performance indicators by analysing each risk in this way, which provides them with meaningful data and gives advanced warning of deterioration (leading indicators), as well as helping them to react appropriately when deviations from expected performance are predicted or observed (lagging indicators). This approach helps to prevent the emergence of bias towards improvements only being made when something has gone wrong, which can prove to be particularly problematic in relation to events which are low in frequency, but still of high consequence.

As outlined in this fable's *prologue,* it's important to keep in mind that performance indicators are just one of many types of 'assurance tool'. Being in receipt of leading and lagging indicator reports enables senior leaders to *check* what's actually happening within their organisations, and in turn to *act* to address any areas of identified weakness. As such, when used in the right way, performance indicators form an integral part of any effective 'risk management cycle' (or *plan-do-check-act* cycle). Furthermore, when used in conjunction with other tools, such as 'audits', 'safety tours', 'inspections' and the like, this elevates them to another level, providing critical insights into the effectiveness of safety management system standards and risk control systems, and helping organisations to target and prioritise areas for improvement. Making decisions about what information to communicate about risks and how they are managed – of which performance indicator reporting is a key component – is really important for organisations. Ensuring this information reaches all those who need to know it, is particularly crucial. *And why is this?* It's simply because it creates transparency about areas of organisational vulnerability, encourages an open culture – due to workers feeling that management have nothing to hide – and makes it much more likely that all organisational levels will buy into the accompanying performance improvement programmes, which should naturally follow on, to address any weak areas identified by performance indicator reports.

Three key principles have been derived from this fable and it's suggested that, when used to best effect, these can help to steer the development of a set of leading and lagging performance indicators, fit for any real-world organisation. In summary, these are to: *first,* create a great set of performance indicators; *second,* make sure the links from performance indicators to both process controls and desired safety outcomes are effective, and finally, *third,* make sure these links are defended and maintained over time.

So, taking each of these principles in turn, let's see what they entail…

PRINCIPLE #1
CREATE GREAT PERFORMANCE INDICATORS
'A Clutch of Golden Eggs'

Creating a great set of performance indicators, as is the subject of this first principle, is about making sure they are intrinsically good, by developing a 'clutch of golden eggs' right from the start. It's important that these have not been stolen, borrowed or adopted from elsewhere, without thought being applied to the risks and/or risk control systems they purport to monitor.

The responsibility for creating a great set of performance indicators ultimately sits with an organisation's senior leaders, who need to be directly involved in the process right from the start. This is logical, because it's with them that the buck stops, if there are shortfalls in the control of risks generated by the organisation's activities. It follows that they must be satisfied that the selected performance indicators provide a good barometer for judging the effectiveness of risk control, which requires the instituting of the right organisational arrangements. By first identifying their key risks and the accompanying risk control systems, senior leaders put themselves in a good position to choose and devise appropriate indicators, determine the scope of the accompanying measurement systems, and assign lead responsibilities for each data flow. It should also fall to senior leaders to stipulate the organisational level at which data is to be recorded – whether at site, function or whole business level – as well as the accompanying tolerances and thresholds assigned to any given indicator. It's entirely apt that accountability should sit at senior leadership level, given that it's the senior leaders who need to ensure that resources are aligned towards monitoring the risks – in particular the high scoring ones – as identified on its 'risk register'. It's also they who are best placed to understand how the chosen indicators contribute towards successful health and safety management, based upon the intrinsic qualities of the indicators themselves, and to detect areas where increased assurance activity efforts might need to be focused. When senior leaders take their responsibilities for setting performance indicators seriously, an effective two-way relationship should be seen, with the measures not only reflecting the organisation's risk profile but also helping to inform it.

But senior leaders don't ordinarily develop performance indicators in isolation. Typically, they will enlist the support of risk champions (often safety advisors) to co-ordinate efforts on their behalf, these being individuals who are well-placed to bring stakeholders together, gather information on best practice, and form an impartial view as to the intrinsic worth of the indicators selected. Also, in seeking to develop a good suite of performance indicators, senior leaders will often reap benefits from taking a wider team-based approach, by drawing more broadly on the insights available from risk owners inside their organisations, these being individuals with a deeper knowledge of the idiosyncrasies of different operational areas and activities. They can be approached both on an *ad hoc* basis and as the participants on 'working groups'. Such groups are usually convened at the behest of senior leaders who chair 'steering groups' (or implementation teams), being set up to oversee the whole process of performance indicator development, with the remit of such development projects typically including: establishing the organisational architecture to implement the indicators; determining the scope of the measurement system; identifying the expected risk control systems to prevent major accidents, and setting lagging indicators; working out which are the critical elements of each risk control system, and setting leading indicators; establishing data collection and reporting systems, and instituting a review process. Setting up such an approach from the start should lend a clear direction and purpose to the organisation's performance indicators – with responsibilities being delegated out for specific development work to be undertaken by risk owners and risk leads, and with a shared understanding and ownership of risks and controls being fostered amongst the workforce – ultimately leading to a high quality output.

The creation of a great set of performance indicators requires a clear, logical development path to be followed. For a 'high-hazard organisation' this will typically start with the identification of major accident scenarios, of which 'loss of containment' is a prime example, these being events with the potential to affect the organisation or the outside world – relating to people, business assets, the wider community or the environment. The next step in this process is to develop lagging indicators which directly link to desired safety outcomes, thereby ensuring it's possible to measure the degree of success or failure in meeting them. It's also at this point that leading indicators should be developed and matched to 'safety critical elements' – based upon a direct link to process controls, to show whether these are working as intended. If selected appropriately, the chosen indicators – both leading and lagging – should map to the risks documented within the organisation's risk register, this being a tool which captures the range of major accident scenarios envisaged by an organisation, as based upon its activities. Applying this kind of logical approach ensures that the full extent of an organisation's risk profile has been suitably considered. Each performance indicator – together with the accompanying measurement and calculation methods, data sources and tools, reporting frequency and business priority weighting – needs to be clearly defined within an appropriate performance indicator methodology. *It's both natural and logical to want to know most about that which gives greatest cause for concern, and this should be reflected within an organisation's approach to performance indicator development.*

In order to test the intrinsic properties of the performance indicator set, rather than linkages within or outside it (as is addressed by the second principle here) several aspects should be taken into account. It's important for the right blend of performance indicators to be developed, so as to enable the organisation to accurately gauge its achievement against the goals of its 'risk control strategy'. It also needs to be determined whether there are any gaps within risk registers, where data is unavailable. Knowledge gaps of this kind tend to arise in organisations with a low state of risk maturity, where a '*We don't know what we don't know*' mindset is prevalent. Equally, consideration should be given as to whether there is any superfluous data being provided, which neither links to desired safety outcomes, nor to process controls. In these cases, it's both logical and legitimate to question *why* such data is being produced. It might be that a situation of this kind arises due to performance indicators evolving informally – a flaw referred to by the fable – rather than as a result of the regular and systematic assessment and review of what is required or appropriate. As well as such data being irrelevant or failing to add value, a further unintended impact can be the diversion of organisational focus and resource away from what's really important, when the overriding purpose of performance indicators being gathered and used should be to shine a light on those risks in need of priority attention. Alternatively, it might be that a legacy report is inherited, with the incoming managers unclear as to the reason for data being produced, but equally aware that if data submission is discontinued, they are likely to be asked testing questions about why it is no longer available.

One sign of a failed data set can be that data providers knowingly provide unsuitable data – albeit that it might be similar to the requested data – simply because it's preferred or easier for them to produce. A common reason for this is that data providers can often find it more straightforward to provide data which is already produced for an existing – possibly commercially driven – purpose, so avoiding the need for them to plough additional effort into the activity. *This is not a good option!* If it cannot be shown that the provided data relates to desired safety outcomes, process controls or major accident scenarios, or if the pathway between each element is unclear or skewed, then little or no value will be derived from its inclusion. To return to this fable's premise, this is *cuckoo data* which bears no relation to the *parent* process control or desired safety outcome it seeks to serve. Data collation should not be unduly burdensome for data providers, and the reason behind any data request should be made clear to them. This is because understanding the rationale as to *why* particular data is needed – as related to the overall goals of data provision – makes it far more likely that data providers will engage with the process and comply with information requests, by submitting data which is appropriate, accurate and filed in a timely fashion, so as to meet reporting requirements and timescales.

Selecting an appropriate number of performance indicators is important too. Whilst it's true to say there's no *magic number,* it's worth checking the quantity of data in the data set before release, as too much data can potentially overwhelm an organisation, much like cuckoos often place an additional burden on host birds to the detriment of their natural offspring. Selecting too few indicators, on the other hand, runs the risk of insufficient real-time monitoring being conducted, so as to be able to inform an organisation about how well its risks are being controlled.

Finally, on the point of creating a great data set, it's important to ensure that the logging mechanisms which feed reports are established and ready to use or populate with data, enabling report compilation needs to be satisfied, before they *go live.* Using the example outlined in this fable, as applied in a real-world context, it's likely that this would require the setting up of a system which facilitated the recording of: *first,* the number of safety critical instruments and alarms which failed to operate as designed, either in live use or during testing (lagging indicator); *second,* the percentage of functional tests of safety critical instruments and alarms completed to schedule (leading indicator), and *third,* the percentage of maintenance actions to rectify faults to safety critical instruments and alarms completed to schedule (leading indicator). It's vitally important to make sure that those recording data – including, for instance, maintenance or testing teams – are sufficiently resourced and have the necessary level of understanding so as to be able to fulfil the report requirements, which are often set by a central or head office function. This is not to say that the method has to be dictated – paper-based records might be entirely appropriate in some cases – but whatever the format, it must be a reliable record that meets the expectations set by legislation, organisational standards and procedures, together with those of 'regulators' and other interested parties. This underlines why it's so important for senior leaders – including, amongst them, safety directors – to commit to the development and maintenance of the right performance indicators, supported by additional resources as required, particularly where shortfalls are identified by the data contained within performance reports.

Having considered the intrinsic properties of the set of performance indicators, next it's important to check the linkages between them, and the process controls or desired safety outcomes to which they relate, so as to verify their provenance.

PRINCIPLE #2
BUILD STRONG PERFORMANCE INDICATOR BONDS
'Golden Eggs need Golden Threads'

The focus of this principle is upon making sure that performance indicators truly reflect the health of process controls and desired safety outcomes, on which they report. Fulfilment of this principle is fundamentally about linking the 'great set of performance indicators' – explained under the first principle – back to the organisation's risks, or colloquially, the idea that 'golden eggs need golden threads'.

As was true for the first principle, the responsibility for making sure that the performance indicators link to process controls and desired safety outcomes also lies with the organisation's senior leaders, who need to ensure that they reflect the risks of the organisation and thus perform a valuable assurance function. Given the crucial role they play in establishing these connections, it's also these individuals who need to understand exactly *why* the linkages matter – with performance indicators showing the level to which safety objectives are being met. If this ownership is passed to risk owners, there's a real danger that their vested interests might skew the very relationships the data is intended to protect. Furthermore, given that senior leaders should have sight of the overall organisational risk profile, this places them in a superior position to evaluate the integrity of the performance indicator set in its entirety, rather than just one part of it. It's particularly important that choices about setting tolerances are not passed to risk owners. This is because the decisions made about whether performance has deviated from acceptable levels – and whether performance indicators continue to give confidence in process controls and desired safety outcomes –

must remain with senior leaders. But, whilst the primary ownership for creating these connections should be vested in senior leaders, this in no way diminishes the value of the critical inputs required from risk owners and risk champions. After all, it's the risk owners who need to have confidence that these linkages enable the performance of the parts of the operation for which they are responsible to be fairly and accurately reported, and to speak up where they feel there are risks which are not being appropriately reflected within the data too. And it's the risk champions supporting the activity who need to be satisfied that the linkages identified mirror the logic of the organisation's risk register.

An organisation's risk register typically documents the information about risk, with which performance indicators need to connect; this is crucial, because being able to demonstrate clear lineage between indicators and risks in each case is important. Specifically, leading indicators need to be linked to the activity's process controls, in order to highlight whether these are operating as designed and will hence deliver the intended outcome. Lagging indicators, on the other hand, should attach to desired safety outcomes, showing whether these have actually been achieved. Where these connections are successfully made, two *parent-child* relationships should be observable: one between process controls and leading indicators, and another between desired safety outcomes and lagging indicators.

Let's look at the types of questions to ask, which help to make sure the creation and validation of the *golden threads* is successful, by applying the principle to *the porridge pot fable's* loss of containment example. *The first question* to be asked in that case would have been, '*What were the risks and what could have caused harm?*' The answer to this was straightforward, namely, the spillage of porridge, which carried with it consequences for people, property and the environment. *The second question* would have been, '*Which were the risk control systems, or the things that could have stopped or controlled the risk?*' Here then, the answer would have been a combination of gauges, alarms and valves, with accompanying operative involvement and/or action, where relevant. *The third question* posed would have been, '*When and how would the risk owner have wanted to be warned of the potential for overflow?*' (the leading indicator). The desire here would have been to be warned of the potential for overflow, in advance of porridge overflow, so-called 'before the fact' data. This would then have translated into a leading indicator which looked at the presence of alarms, the threshold at which the alarms were set, and the number of alarms activated. *The fourth and final question* in the set would have been *'When and how would the risk owner have wanted to be notified of overflow having occurred?'* (the lagging indicator). The desire here would have been to be notified of porridge overflow after the event, so-called 'after the fact' data, the before the fact data having failed in whole or in part.

In seeking to answer questions of this kind, organisations need to decide on their thresholds for degrees of failure, and it's worth thinking for a moment about what this might have meant in the context of the porridge pot scenario. *Would they have wanted to be notified when it breached the pot? Breached the kitchen door? Breached the walls of the house?* The answer to each of these questions – as would also be true in an equivalent real-world context – would have been *'yes'*, because those responsible for such processes (including real-world organisations) should want to know of *all* such breaches, no matter how small they might seem, as they highlight failures in controlling risk, at different points and to varying degrees, with the level of the breach being relevant too. In the context of the porridge pot scenario, this might have meant dividing any loss of containment events into 'minor' (*pot to kitchen*), 'major' (*kitchen to house*), or 'catastrophic' (*house to town*) level breaches – in much the same way as, for real-world scenarios, it's often appropriate for organisations to link levels of failure to organisational, legislative, or regulatory requirements, including those set by regulators[266].

Answering questions of the kinds just listed helps to inform the building and shaping of real-world performance recording and reporting mechanisms which, when designed and constructed appropriately, should satisfy the needs of internal and external stakeholders alike. And once this has all been worked out – the complicated bits about the risk and the tough questions about what should be in place to control or mitigate it – it's only right that the

---

266. Data reporting requirements will vary from case to case. What is measured, how an organisation measures it, and the party/parties to whom a submission is to be made, often needs to align with various parameters, thresholds and other industry-led, legal or regulatory requirements. This includes those set by external regulatory bodies, for instance those instituted by Great Britain's Health and Safety Executive, and the Environment Agency.

linkages or *golden threads* should be tested. This requires organisations to be confident that the connections between all the different elements of the performance indicator set are valid, meaning that they need to check the relationships between the indicators and the risks on which they report. This is about always being unafraid to ask: '*Are the relationships functional ones?*' Performance indicators which are set and correctly adopted really should be *golden eggs* and not the randomly scattered offspring of *cuckoos,* with no discernable connection to *host birds* (or, indeed, process controls or desired safety outcomes!). The failure to take a logical approach when developing a set of performance indicators as an effective assurance mechanism – being appropriate to organisational risk profile and demonstrating the health or otherwise of its activities and systems – is, quite simply, an opportunity missed. It's only when correctly applied that 'process safety indicators' provide *golden eggs*, these giving valuable insights into management system performance[267]. Whether such indicators are truly golden should always be questioned, in addition to checks being made that they have been attributed to the right *parent* process controls for leading indicators, or desired safety outcomes for lagging indicators.

In reflecting more broadly upon this second principle, it's worth noting that it's not only the bonds between the performance indicators and process controls/desired safety outcomes themselves which are important, but also the connections between all those involved in controlling the risks on which they report. The instituting of a clear reporting structure is just one way in which an organisation can drive the right accountabilities and behaviours for controlling risk across all levels. Together with the management and organisational structures it has in place, this ensures that the activities carried out to manage and monitor risks – and upon which its performance indicators report – are consistent with its broader vision for health and safety management, as is set out and communicated by its senior leaders. Much like the audit and inspection activities described in the *modern meaning* attached to *the porridge pot fable,* the use of performance indicators forms a key part of the *check* step of an organisation's

---

267. Note that, whilst not considered in the context of this fable, the approach explained here can also be readily applied to the development of equivalent 'occupational safety indicators'.

plan-do-check-act cycle. As such, performance indicators perform a vital role in the delivery of effective safety risk management and 'continual improvement', particularly when coupled with the next *act* step of the cycle, this being the point at which any identified shortfalls can be resolved and opportunities taken to spread good practice.

When used to best effect, performance indicators relay important messages in both upward and downward directions through organisational hierarchies. Effective 'upward communication' is really valuable, because it means frontline workers are able to directly influence management decisions – from operative level at the sharp end, channelled through line and process managers – with the right and accurate information finding its way up to the appropriate level, including to senior leaders, where required, to enable it to be evaluated and presented at board meetings, or elsewhere. For upward communication to be effective, it needs to be backed up by the alignment of attitudes and decision making at all levels. Thinking about the example discussed here, from a real-world perspective, upward communication signals could include, for instance – *upgrade safety critical instrumentation,* or *invest in better containment solutions.*

Effective 'downward communication' is also key, in relation to the outputs of performance indicator reports, because it's about senior leaders sending the right messages down to anyone in the organisation needing to know them. As such, this is about aligning the attitudes and decisions made, from senior leaders, down to 'line manager' and process manager level, and right through to frontline operatives, so that the right outputs are disseminated from the top level and steps are taken to ensure that they percolate organisational culture, being driven and instilled into the working practices of those at the sharp end. This can include new messages, but can equally involve the reinforcement of previously communicated messages, in circumstances where weaknesses are discovered. Thinking again about the example discussed here, from a real-world perspective, this could include downward signals to operatives, for instance – *make sure you carry out the required checks on gauges, alarms and valves (safety critical instrumentation),* or *make sure you take actions A, B and C, in response to hearing an alarm.*

The final principle addresses how best to maintain performance indicators, over time.

PRINCIPLE #3
MAINTAIN PERFORMANCE INDICATORS
'Defending Nests of Golden Eggs'

This third and final principle is about ensuring the relationships between leading indicator data and process controls, and lagging indicator data and desired safety outcomes, remain sound – becoming stronger, rather than weakening over time. This requires the protection of the indicators (or 'defending the nest of golden eggs'), and is concerned with maintaining the parent-child relationship in all cases, ensuring they don't mutate or get overwhelmed by invasive 'cuckoo data'.

As has already been recognised, such relationships can become skewed in circumstances where it appears to be easier to provide pre-existing data in preference to that which serves as an apt and valid assurance measure, based upon current risk profile. In practical terms, this can be avoided by having a strict rule-set which is understood and followed by all those involved in collecting, reviewing or taking action in response to data, these all being steps which collectively help to defend the *nest* of measures.

The focus here is upon making sure that the performance indicators continue to be intrinsically good on an enduring basis, as well as the bonds with process controls and desired safety outcomes remaining intact. In judging whether their indicators remain of sufficient quality over time, organisations need to be mindful of both internal and external factors, also taking opportunities to horizon scan and benchmark with similar organisations wherever appropriate to do so. And whilst the primary ownership for checking the strength of the links between performance indicators and process controls/desired safety outcomes on an enduring basis remains with senior leaders, critical inputs are required from risk owners here too. Furthermore, for their parts, risk champions should be confident that what is being reported continues to reflect the risks known to them, being in alignment with the indicators' intent, as well as their being content that the logic of the organisation's risk register is still being served. This often requires organisations to conduct periodic reviews which look at process safety performance in totality, taking into account the scope of the indicators and the tolerances of failure assigned, whilst being mindful that these aren't always right first time and are unlikely to weather all storms. For their part, risk owners need to be satisfied that the reports they submit continue to reflect the full extent of risks within their remit, as well as putting forward proposals for new aspects to be brought into scope, where their knowledge of current operations indicates that this is required. On the flip side, they also need to highlight indicators which are no longer adding value.

The underpinning activity set at this level should be driven by an organisation's internal assurance function – their primary role being to lead periodic reviews on an independent basis – with checks being made on the linkages with process controls and desired safety outcomes, as well as on the overall performance of the health and safety management system. It's appropriate for adjustments to be made – both to the performance indicators themselves and the thresholds for ratings applied to them – in response to formal review processes; indeed, it's healthy to see organisations fine-tuning their performance monitoring mechanisms to reflect current risk understanding.

This third principle centres around how to defend the data set (*or nest*) over time or – to follow on from the question posed for *principle two* – it addresses the question *'Are the relationships still working?'* This requires that constant attention is paid not only to the indicators themselves, but also to the process controls/leading indicator and desired safety outcome/lagging indicator relationships. And for these relationships to remain effective, senior leaders and other key players must always be willing to challenge a data set which no longer appears to be fit for purpose, or which has otherwise become outdated. It's particularly important to make sure that the right data is collected, rather than information being provided simply because it has historically been gathered, or is more straightforward for the data providers to supply.

The effective long term defence of performance indicators can only be accomplished by building up a strong knowledge and understanding of organisational risks which, as has been said, starts with the development of a robust risk register, supported by a sound process to identify gaps within it. This needs to be underpinned by the right organisational culture, structure and accountabilities being in place: *first*, a network of risk owners – designated people within the organisation, with whom the risk accountability sits; *second*, a support network of risk champions out in the field drawn from operatives with frontline responsibilities, who manage the risks on a day-to-day basis, and *third*, data analysts who collate data from risk leads and provide it to risk owners. The function performed by this third group is just as vital as that delivered by the others and, in order to perform it well, they need to understand the role that they, and the performance indicator data they supply, play in the delivery of effective assurance. They should be empowered to highlight data which points to risk being ineffectively controlled and, where appropriate, brought into dialogue with risk owners (to understand strategic purpose) and risk champions (to understand how well risk is actually being controlled at the sharp end), so as to support collaborative resolution efforts.

Irrespective of their level of involvement, however, it's vital to make sure that the right behaviours are promoted amongst all those involved in the process, so that the integrity of the data is protected. This is why the instituting of an effective 'risk governance' structure driven from the top of the organisation, secured by the firm commitment of those at Board or senior leader level, is so fundamental. It's in taking such an approach that an organisation arms itself with the ability to formulate consistent and coherent responses to performance indicator outcomes, which not only address sub-standard reports, but also transfer learning from good reports. Any responsible organisation should want to verify that its risks are being effectively addressed on an ongoing basis, which requires periodic checks to be made that the governance structure put in place remains robust and that the right responses are continuing to be delivered on receipt of any negative performance indicator outcomes.

All those in the data-chain, whether data analysts, reporters, managers or owners – *or indeed, harvesters, miners or architects* – need to appreciate the value of their roles and the importance of speaking out in circumstances where they believe data to be incorrect or skewed, particularly where there seems to be a misalignment with the purpose underlying its provision. It also needs to be understood that performance indicator sets are dynamic things, with risk champions being proactive and feeling empowered to challenge indicators which are no longer fit for purpose, and risk owners being held to account if they fail to speak up about indicator sets which no longer reflect the full risk profile of the operations and activities they oversee. Performance indicators inherited or transplanted from a previous time period or from a different department – as can sometimes occur following an organisational restructure – may not fit to current requirements and be of negligible value in terms of assurance delivered. The adoption of a vigilant corporate mindset, driven right from the top of an organisation, is arguably the most effective weapon in warding off many of these problems.

In terms of the actual data supplied to populate reports, risk owners should be encouraged to *relish the red* and *challenge the green*, constantly scrutinising data sets to check that the value they add is truly golden. This means that data should not simply be taken at face value. Indeed, there is a groundswell of opinion that individuals reporting their performance indicators as *green* on a frequent basis should, in fact, be more closely scrutinised than those who report performance indicators to be *red* rated, but with the support of robust action plans to address areas of known weakness. A term sometimes applied to a data item reported as green, but which is in fact red, is a *watermelon indicator*, which clearly shows as green on the surface and yet, upon digging deeper reveals a mass of red beneath. Such indicators do not provide a realistic or useful measure of safety success! Whilst these reports might give an outwardly favourable impression, senior leaders need to be ever-vigilant to contrary signals at the frontline – such as negative feedback from 'users' or operatives – which can paint quite a different picture of performance. Often in these circumstances, organisations can be found to be relying on outmoded performance indicators, which simply no longer work or add value.

Data owners should never be allowed to define their own performance indicator sets in a vacuum. This is because there can be a tendency for them to suggest those which are either easy to produce or already produced for another – perhaps commercial – purpose, rather than selecting indicators which provide the opportunity to fully reflect the risk picture. They may present an overly favourable version of events, but add little value. A further cautionary note worthy of mention here is against the introduction of performance indicators which carry the potential to drive the wrong behaviours, whether or not this is intentional. Even a well-chosen indicator should be defended, because if those reporting performance have fears about failing to meet workplace targets, this could have unintended consequences. An example of this is seen where data providers or data analysts feel pressurised into prematurely closing down test reports on company systems before testing has actually been completed, in order to meet or exceed standards, thereby unwittingly compromising data quality. The work of those who provide and input data needs to be valued and supported – it's acceptable to challenge errors in the data entered, but not to seek to blame those who input accurate data. Following confirmation of data accuracy, therefore, cases of sub-standard performance should be resolved through the development of recovery plans by risk owners, with these being ratified by senior leaders and appropriately resourced wherever needed, so as to restore performance to acceptable levels.

Performance indicator data really can be golden – even that which leads to red-rated performance indicators! When accurately produced, such measures describe how well risk is being controlled. They can help organisations to work out how best to allocate and prioritise resources too. The relationship between leading and lagging performance indicator *broods*, and their respective process control and desired safety outcome *parents* really should be a beautiful thing. Far better for data to have been well-conceived and nurtured, than that it should find for itself a place in a report (*or room in a nest!*) where it simply doesn't belong. It's important to remember that performance reporting is just one piece of the assurance jigsaw. If there's uncertainty surrounding the data, it often pays to go to the source and observe directly where the pain is most sharply felt. It might be concern about red-rated performance indicators. It could be cynicism about some green-rated performance indicators. It may even be anecdotal words on the ground from those at the sharp end, which suggest a disparity between reported data and reality – possibly from workers who don't realise that their comments provide valuable insights about how well risk is actually being controlled.

The motivations behind making adjustments to performance indicators, to ensure their continued linkage to process controls and desired safety outcomes, can be manifold. In addressing the need to constantly revitalise and refresh their performance indicator sets, senior leaders need to ask themselves questions including: *'Have new high-risk processes been introduced, which require monitoring?', 'Have improvement programmes been pursued, which call for increased detail to be captured by performance indicators, to determine their effectiveness?', 'Have alterations to plant design triggered a need for performance indicator and threshold adjustment?', 'Have reduced staff numbers or a loss of competence given rise to a need to acquire increased levels of detail, so as to ensure a well-managed risk doesn't become a poorly controlled one?', and 'Are there new and emerging risks (sometimes seen as the result of horizon scanning), meaning there's a need to start monitoring or measuring areas not previously recognised as being of concern?'* If the answer to any of these questions is *'yes'*, it's likely that the performance indicator set will require some kind of adjustment.

Performance indicators are just one method of monitoring, but they shouldn't be considered in isolation. If the business is an operational business and the data is operational data, it makes sense to speak to those engaged in day-to-day operations, to see if they can shed light on differences between actual performance and performance as reported. This type of discrepancy could be highlighted by a formal audit, but equally might be caught by *ad-hoc* conversations between senior leaders and the workforce, for instance through the less formal dialogue which can arise in the course of safety walkabouts or tours, or as the outputs of effective safety culture surveys.

STRONG INDICATORS MATTER...
BUT SO DO WEAK SIGNALS

Strong indicators matter. This has been the focus of much of this fable and the meaning attached to it, and it's absolutely true. In the process safety arena, in particular, there's clear logic that sits behind why this is so. As highlighted in the *prologue* to this tale, this is an approach supported by the Texas City incident findings and the Baker report, as well as by authoritative guidance, including that published by the Health and Safety Executive. There's much to be gained from performance indicators being developed in a structured way, as has been described here – including their linkages with process controls and desired safety outcomes – and by their being maintained on an ongoing basis. Particularly for high-hazard organisations, this is a pragmatic approach to take. But alongside these structured methods, there's a growing recognition of the need to pick up on more subtle signs of trouble too.

'*Weak signals*' *also matter.* Analysing data in a structured fashion – of which performance indicators form a key part – is important, but the signals that an incident is looming aren't always readily detectable, even for those that surround themselves with swathes of management information. It's often the case that high-hazard organisations are awash with data, but, if we reflect on activities of the types highlighted by *the porridge pot fable*, if they fail to notice and respond to deviations from filling procedures, unusual valve maintenance requests or unexpected sounds from storage vessels, then their efforts at keeping containment may be in vain. Some organisations – and more particularly, their senior leaders – are satisfied by the sense of security gained from performance indicators, accepting the limitations of their efforts and drawing comfort from their current methodologies and data. *But they shouldn't be.* High-reliability performance comes not only from organisations having a robust set of performance indicators, but also by their demonstrating so-called 'chronic unease', being receptive to the more subtle and less obvious signs of sub-optimal safety performance.

It follows that, when senior leaders take the time to complement their structured approaches for gathering performance data with apparently *ad hoc* questions including *'What could go wrong here?'* and *'What do you not want to tell me?'* they can pick up on early warnings – based on intuition, change which would otherwise go undetected, and situations which simply *don't feel right* – these being responses which the more formal methods might fail to pick up. They also avoid the pitfalls of expecting data to say certain things – for instance that sensors, alarms and valves are performing well – by being receptive to a broader range of responses than those which are believed to be true, or are desired or expected. Those senior leaders who maintain a healthy scepticism about how effectively their risks are actually being managed – and, more particularly, those who are able to identify, interpret, integrate and act upon early warnings – are ultimately the ones who steer their organisations away from failure. After all, most incidents arise not from one big thing, but from organisations falling prey to an unhealthy combination of incorrect assumptions, inadequate communications, neglected warning signs, and a misguided belief that everything *seemed to be okay...*

CLOSING THOUGHTS

This fable has underlined the clear need for organisations to think carefully about the links between their performance indicators and the process controls or desired safety outcomes to which they purport to relate. Furthermore, it has highlighted that the links between them – even those which are initially strong – should not be presumed to be unbreakable. These connections need to be constantly verified and periodically reviewed, with performance indicator sets updated and the contents of reports revised, as appropriate. In revisiting the premise of this fable for a moment, it's entirely fair to question how a cuckoo came to be involved, rather than a hen, as in Aesop's original fable! The answer to this is simply that the behaviour of the cuckoo skews the normal *parent-child* relationship – an important parallel with a broken set of performance indicators – where there is no discernable link, or perhaps a creeping misalignment, between performance indicators and the process controls or desired safety outcomes to which they should relate or map.

So then, how might this alternative fable read?

> *'An organisation's senior leaders had a performance indicator report which they believed to be 'golden'. In fact, they thought the report to be gold through and through. But closer examination showed it to be flawed. Some of the indicators had no inherent worth. Others bore no resemblance to the process controls or desired safety outcomes they purported to describe. And a further group had initially been strong, but allowed to tarnish, over time. The meaning of this contemporary fable, then, is that performance indicators need to be constantly nurtured. It's only when organisations understand their provenance, ensure they link effectively to process controls and desired safety outcomes, and have confidence in their power to endure, that they are likely to see their performance indicators taking flight, as valuable assurance tools.'*

Whilst this fable appears as one of the simplest in this collection, the *modern meaning* which attaches to it is a bit more complex. Organisations promote themselves via all manner of different performance indicators and yet, for them to truly add value, they need to join to organisational processes, just as a baby bird should enjoy a natural bond with its mother, rather than a foreign host. If the importance of data accuracy, validity and appropriateness is positively promoted to all relevant parts of an organisation – backed up by budgetary commitments to support resolution of any identified problems – the workforce is much more likely to engage and work collaboratively to address areas of weakness, by looking honestly at all points of failure. As well as being *the right thing to do*, it makes clear business sense to get performance indicators right. In combination with other monitoring methods, performance indicators help organisations to increase the robustness of their safety risk management, protect reputation and demonstrate the appropriateness and sufficiency of risk control systems.

In addition to showing the importance of performance indicators being properly selected, effectively connected and well maintained, and the vital functions they perform as part of an organisation's assurance armoury, this fable has also highlighted the crucial roles they play in offering insights to senior leaders, and more broadly, in driving wider safety cultural improvements. Effective upward communication of performance indicators allows for their proper review and consideration by senior leaders, whilst also providing them with assurance that legal compliance is being delivered and maintained, and in turn plays a key role in shaping future direction and policy. Effective downward communication, on the other hand, which can follow on from the outcomes of signals sent via upward communication, allows senior leaders to drive wider cultural messages across all organisational levels. This downward dissemination of performance indicator report outcomes means that anyone in the workforce who needs to know about or act upon them – wherever they sit in an organisation – is informed of these and empowered to act to address any areas of weakness highlighted. And it's through soliciting workforce involvement and gaining their commitment to take action – with increased cultural engagement (or buy-in) – that an organisation is most likely to be rewarded with improved operational performance. It's by taking such an approach that performance indicators are elevated from being merely data instruments, to weapons of wider management and cultural change.

For a summary of practical points to take away,
based upon the topics and subtopics handled by this fable,
see *How to...* Guide Nine.

Not-Quite and the Seven Imps:
The Value of Reliable Human Performance

NOT-QUITE'S FABLE

' 'But first things first...' continued Not-Quite, clearly unfazed by Sly's cynicism, '...something's been bothering me. I just need to ask you little folk the obvious question that's been weighing on my mind. Think of it as an ice-breaker, if you will... *What exactly is 'imp' short for?* ' '

PROLOGUE

This fable sees us being introduced to the atypically named *Not-Quite*, a central character who unwittingly acquires an unusual band of seven followers. Starting with his birth, the tale swiftly skips twenty or so years, with the focus shifting to his working life and his progression to the role of oil storage depot manager, and a well-respected one, at that. And, whilst he doesn't realise it at first, it's the understanding and management of the seven *imps* under his stewardship which are to prove key to his success. That's not to say that his rise through the ranks of the organisation is without its challenges along the way, the most notable of which comes from a beautiful but vain depot manager with a somewhat unhealthy interest in performance scorecards. With the passing of time, this is an obstacle Not-Quite manages to overcome, as he reaches for safety excellence with his team, but is a flaw which ultimately leads to the undoing of the beautiful but vain depot manager. But, as we are about to learn, there's an added meaning the tale brings, because the interactions the imps have with Not-Quite highlight the importance of understanding the influence of various factors upon the quality of human performance.

'ACCIDENTS HAPPEN' AND 'WE ALL MAKE MISTAKES': FROM TRITE PLATITUDES TO HELP FOR HUMANS

Throughout the course of our own childhoods, many of us will have been on the receiving end of phrases including *'accidents happen'* and *'we all make mistakes'*, these often having been meted out by adults to whom we looked up, with adoration. Provided that the actions which provoked these well-worn phrases were well meant, such words were usually sufficient to fully resolve any awkward situations, to the happy acceptance of parent and child alike. Of course, having grown up and entered the adult world of work, for most of us the realisation has long since dawned that accidents don't just happen, coupled with a recognition of the need to limit the mistakes that are made – by staving them off in the first place and if not, by seeking to understand why they occurred and figuring out the steps needed to prevent future recurrences. The reasons for such mistakes are to be found across any number of investigation reports, and also form the basis of many an organisation's 'safety culture' improvement programme. *The causes of people failing are, of course, complex and manifold.* There are some who totally fail to see risk. There are others who see risk, but believe it to be under control and so carry on regardless. There are some too who, more worryingly, are indifferent to it, or simply don't care and are prepared to run the risk anyway. And there are those who, even with apparently good levels of 'competence', miss steps out of well-defined procedures or cheat well-designed systems, for any number of different reasons, ranging between boredom, distraction, fatigue, poor memory and buckling under the weight of peer pressure. It's these various reasons – and the accompanying strategies for dealing with the problems they create – which are to be explored through this fable and its accompanying *modern meaning*.

At the *first*, superficial, level this last fable is about the kind of contrived workshop approach adopted by many an organisation for training purposes – where a group of individuals with a perhaps questionable level of interest in a given safety topic meet to discuss it – the high point for the majority being the lunch provided mid-way through, strategically inserted to break up the day's agenda. On a *second*, more important, level, it's about what can be done to protect the 'personal safety', health and welfare of individuals, by understanding the complexities of their varied mental and physical characteristics and behaviours. On the *third*, and arguably most significant, level it's about 'reliable human performance' and how the degree to which this is achieved is shaped, influenced and ultimately determined by the various traits and fitness of individuals – the people, or human 'operatives' – called upon to carry out tasks. This is of particular importance in relation to the conduct of tasks which are safety critical, these being vital to the control of 'process safety' risks and the prevention of 'top events', such as 'loss of containment'. We've already seen one fictional example of this in *the porridge pot fable*, where the 'reliability' with which a human operative acted to manually shut off a valve was key. Analysing and optimising individual factors relevant to the carrying out of 'safety critical tasks' – when taken in combination with job and organisational factors – reduces the likelihood of people failing, leading to increased performance reliability. But as well as bringing direct benefits for process integrity, this also carries with it advantages for the personal safety, health and 'wellbeing' of the operatives responsible for performing tasks, together with that of others with whom they interact.

As the ultimate tale in this collection, this can be regarded as *the human performance fable,* the intention of which is to highlight the vital contribution that people – as operatives – make to securing high standards of process safety. Reflecting back upon *the porridge pot fable,* this clearly showed the reliability of human performance in respect of safety critical tasks to be a key factor in controlling 'major accident hazards'. This includes the systems operated by people, as well as the processes within which they have a crucial role to play. It was also *the porridge pot fable* that drew attention to the role played by 'barriers' in preventing a 'top event'. This theme was broadened out further in *the four little pigs' fable,* touching as it did upon the distinction between 'passive barrier', 'active barrier', and 'procedural barrier' types. Here, we move on to consider the vital role played by reliable human performance – which an operative is called upon to deliver – of particular value for organisations seeking to strengthen the active and procedural barriers they have in place. Just to recap a key point, it's important to remember that actions by operatives *might* be required for active barriers, but are *always* a requirement for procedural barriers. The fable also prompts consideration of how to go about protecting the personal safety and welfare of the operatives involved, taking due account of the challenges and demands placed upon them by their various work activities and tasks, alongside other factors.

As one of the longest in this collection, this tale draws on many of the aspects touched upon by previous fables and offers up some additional insights in relation to the desirable skills and behaviours of operatives. *Humans are brilliant, but they can also fail.* They may have a great track record of knowing what to do, proving they can do it and showing that they care about getting it right but, as highlighted by some of the real-world incidents referred to in this book and many more besides, they can still get things wrong. Reliable human performance is central to the understanding and management of key processes across the board, but nowhere is it more important than in circumstances where major accident hazard control is required. Before turning to the fable itself – and to put the tale in some context – this *prologue* outlines a four step process for securing reliable human performance and achieving process control. The steps involved in this process are to: *first,* identify the major accident hazards that need to be controlled; *second,* work out which of the major accident hazard tasks involve people; *third,* work out which tasks performed by people are the most important – safety critical – ones, and finally, *fourth,* make sure that people – the human operatives – always do the most important tasks brilliantly. The first three steps are, in some respects, a recap of the points highlighted by *the porridge pot fable* and it's the fourth step on *how* to go about securing the reliability of human performance – and its linkage with 'safety critical task analysis', referred to in the context of that earlier tale – which is to be considered in greater depth here, as the focus of this final fable.

Purists from the process industries tend to take the view that safety critical task analysis and the delivery of reliable human performance, as explored here, should remain the preserve of 'high hazard organisations', where the carrying out of safety critical tasks associated with major accident hazards is required. This specifically includes organisations operating 'COMAH sites', where 'dangerous substances' are present in certain quantities – which, as we shall see, applies to the fictional organisation within which this fable is set – where catastrophic consequences such as explosions, fires, or releases of toxic substances could occur, if the risks are not properly controlled. There are others, however, who promote the benefits of such approaches being applied across wider settings.[268] Arguably organisations *do* have more to gain by reserving use of the safety critical task analysis technique for circumstances where process safety and safety critical tasks are involved, rather than those that simply concern matters of personal safety, where individuals carrying out a task might be hurt. This means that the fact that tasks involve risks to health and safety, for instance work at height, confined spaces, or manual handling – as considered in relation to *Zac's fable, Ian's fable* and *the swede fable* – is rarely sufficient justification for carrying out a full-scale safety

---

268. Within healthcare settings, for instance, describing and analysing human actions can be valuable for user tasks which, if performed incorrectly or not performed at all, would or could cause harm to a patient or user, including compromising their medical care.

critical task analysis. But whilst the focus of this fable and its *modern meaning* are geared more towards the high-hazard organisation, the accompanying *How to...* Guide Ten – which pays specific attention to the factors affecting reliable human performance and, more specifically, the management and mitigation measures organisations might apply in seeking to address them – is likely to find broader interest across both personal and process safety disciplines.

SIMPLE STEPS TO SECURING RELIABLE HUMAN PERFORMANCE

Set out here are four simple steps which, when followed, should help to secure reliable human performance and thus, prevent human failure.

STEP #1
IDENTIFY THE MAJOR ACCIDENT HAZARDS REQUIRING CONTROL

Organisations often have active involvement in a diverse range of activities, but this first step is about working out which of these require the most stringent level of control – whether by systems and/or people – due to the major accident hazards involved.

Typically this information is to be found within a site's 'safety report' and/or from 'risk assessments'. But documentation aside, an organisation's senior leaders can often perform a simple sense-check for identifying their major accident hazards, by asking themselves: *'Which are the things that keep us awake at night, if the right level of risk control isn't applied here?'* Answering this question with honesty provides a good basis from which to start judging the quality of major accident hazard control. It can also sometimes help to identify guilty knowledge – the kind of knowledge which no senior leader worth their salt would want to possess![269]

Let's return to some basics for a moment. *Accidents are a bad thing. Major accidents are a really bad thing.* They're bad for the people and

---

269. When an organisation proactively seeks out answers to awkward questions of this kind, this shows positive application of the concept of 'chronic unease', as was briefly explored in the context of *the cuckoo's fable*.

plant directly involved. They're bad for those who might be caught up in the background. They're bad for the wider community too. But they often come about as the unintended and unwanted consequences of vital processes. We want organisations to provide essential products and services which are good for society, keeping lights on, utilities flowing, engines running, and people moving. *But we don't want this done at unlimited cost.* Society rightly expects high-hazard organisations to have systems and processes in place to control their 'risks', particularly the really big ones, keeping them safely contained so as to avoid harm, disruption and inconvenience to people and the environment. This is reflected by the legal requirements which govern their activities including, for example, those which regulate major accident hazards, set out in *the Control of Major Accident Hazard Regulations 2015*[270] ('*the COMAH Regulations*'). The meeting of such expectations is obviously of paramount importance to any organisation seeking to prove its worth as a good 'corporate citizen'.

Thinking back to *the porridge pot fable* for a moment, producing porridge was an ostensibly good thing. It kept people fed. And keeping the porridge contained – as is true of other substances – was a good thing too. Losing containment, on the other hand – or spilling porridge, as *the porridge pot fable* also demonstrated – was a bad thing. It filled the kitchen, overwhelmed the house, damaged the car and caused the little girl's skirt to need dry-cleaning. Not to mention the upset it caused to neighbours in the locality. Losing containment is bad – not just in a fairy tale context, but in the larger scale of reality too – and it's for this very reason that loss of containment is a risk commonly recognised by high-hazard organisations. Now, let's be clear, *the porridge pot fable* only focused on the physical failure to retain containment and in the real world there's every need to be concerned by the nature of any substances involved too – the '*What is released?*' question. It's also worth noting that this loss of containment risk sits alongside a multiplicity of risks on the 'risk registers' produced by real-world high-hazard organisations, with others typically documented including *loss of structural integrity (things falling apart or over)* and *product quality failure (things not lasting as long, or performing as well, as they should)*. The point to note here is that organisations want to avoid all such incidents, and more besides, which they achieve by keeping control of their major accident hazards, whatever they may be. Essentially, these are the things which, if badly

---

270. S.I. 2015/483.

controlled, lead to compromised safety, human health or environmental standards, both inside and outside organisations. The fictional characters want porridge to stay in the pot, just as their real-life counterparts – the human operatives – want fuel to remain contained within pipes. And in order to achieve these equivalent objectives, responsible real-world organisations rightly want to understand the points at which they simply cannot afford for things to go wrong – within all of their processes and for everything they do – just as the fictional porridge pot characters want to avoid being overwhelmed by porridge. *This is where the second step of this process comes in...*

STEP #2
WORK OUT WHICH MAJOR ACCIDENT HAZARDS REQUIRE CONTROL BY PEOPLE

Having recognised the bad things – the major hazards – they need to control, the next important step for organisations is to understand the tasks involved within their processes, which enable people to keep these bad things contained. This is something they often achieve through the use of a technique called 'job task analysis'.

Historically, it was often the case that more importance, accompanied by a deeper level of analysis, was attached to technical failures than was true for human failures. But there's a growing recognition of what people do, too – with the benefits of their involvement often being observable in improved operational control, the maintenance of standards, and reduced losses. It's true that systems can achieve lots of things, but there remain many points within processes – always in procedural barriers and often in active barriers too – where the involvement of human operatives is crucial to the control of risk. When used to full effect, a job task analysis approach should inform the design and type of barriers selected; it also strengthens organisational understanding of how the things that people do can determine the success or failure of risk controls. We've already seen highlighted – albeit obliquely by *the porridge pot fable* and *the four little pigs' fable* – that taking the trouble to understand specific types of failure can add to the robustness of 'barrier management'. Building upon the same theme, this fable seeks to provide an overview of the various human failure types and what can be done to keep them in check.

For major hazards, it's crucially important to understand all aspects of an activity, paying particular attention to those tasks requiring human involvement. Taking the filling of a storage tank by way of example, the tasks required of the operatives involved, as seen through a basic job task analysis, might be:

Task A: when a request is received, start to transfer fuel into tank;

Task B: monitor increase in tank level, and,

Task C: when tank level reaches a certain point, stop transfer of fuel into tank.

Breaking activities down into lists of tasks and identifying what people do at each stage in this way, through job task analysis, is important. *It sets the scene for recognising which tasks are the safety critical ones in the process, which is handled by step three.*

STEP #3
WORK OUT WHICH PEOPLE TASKS ARE MOST IMPORTANT

Actions by people are important in two key respects. *First*, prior to any top event, there are so called 'prevention barrier actions' which are intended to prevent it from occurring in the first place. *Second*, after a top event, there are so called 'mitigation barrier actions', which work to mitigate consequences and are of particular importance in avoiding, or limiting the extent of, 'escalation scenarios'.

But wherever within a process human actions are required – and whether pre– or post-top event – the focus of this step is upon identifying the most important (or safety critical) tasks, from all of those that people perform.

It's clear that people do lots of things to make processes work, but this step is about organisations identifying the precise points at which they simply cannot afford for their risk control processes, including operatives' involvement in them, to fail. In the example just given for *step two*, it's about deciding whether this is at the point of starting transfer (*task A*), monitoring (*task B*) or stopping transfer (*task C*). It's possible to pick out this point – or in some cases, points – by working out where the interaction people have with systems cause a source of risk, if errors occur.

It's this third step of the process that elevates a job task analysis to a more advanced level, specifically that of a safety critical task analysis (SCTA). Having used job task analysis to recognise all the things that people do at *step two*, the focus of SCTA methodology is upon narrowing the analysis down to the key points of the process where the reliability of human performance matters most. Reliable performance is central to the performance of safety critical tasks. All the tasks matter, but it's in relation to their safety critical tasks that organisations must ensure they secure performance reliability from their operatives. *Applying this to the fictional porridge pot example, this would have been about stopping pot overflow.* These, then, are the points at which it's most crucial for individuals not to fail – which, as seen from the basic loss of containment job task analysis example described at *step two*, would be *task C* – the point at which filling must be stopped. This is because it's *task C* which is the safety critical one, albeit that there may be elements of *task A* and *task B* which could contribute to an overflow (loss of containment) scenario. *Why should this be?* It's simply because it's at the point of *task C* being executed that there is the potential for control to be lost, resulting in an incident; failing to stop filling the tank directly leads to an overflow scenario. Poor performance of starting fuel transfer (*task A*) and tank level monitoring (*task B*) are still problematic, but it's the poor performance of stopping fuel transfer at the right point (*task C*) which is potentially catastrophic.

Gaining an understanding of the linkage between human performance and safety critical task analysis in any given case is helpful, because it starts to show the point(s) – here, *task C* – where the actions or inactions of operatives are vital to safe and effective process control. SCTA highlights the potential for error within safety critical tasks and – when used proactively – helps with the pinpointing and development of appropriate 'risk controls' to reduce the hazardous event risk to a level which is 'as low as reasonably practicable (ALARP)'. And it gives the necessary insights as to what an operative or teams of operatives need to do in order to play their part(s) in reducing the level of risk. But even when failure does occur, SCTA remains a powerful tool, because it also retrospectively shows *where* and *why* failure occurred, thus allowing control to be improved in the future, by proactively informing barrier design and choice too. This is important because, on top of the obvious moral reasons, organisations face constant societal and, in many cases, regulatory pressure to adopt a proactive approach towards reducing the risks associated with, and generated by, their activities.

Reflecting back on *the porridge pot fable* for a moment, in that case our analysis of the events essentially stopped at *step three* – simply highlighting where, from a process perspective, the little girl and her mother went wrong, by showing the importance of the tasks they were expected to perform. What the *modern meaning* to that tale didn't do, however, was to analyse in any depth *why* this failure might have occurred. *And it's these various reasons for human failure – or human reliability shortfalls – that are picked up at step four here, and explored further through the lens of this final fable.*

STEP #4
ENSURE PEOPLE ALWAYS PERFORM
THE MOST IMPORTANT TASKS BRILLIANTLY

The focus of this step is upon ensuring that tasks – in particular, the safety critical ones – are always performed well. But what does this mean exactly, and how can it be successfully achieved?

Put simply, this step is about understanding and addressing the factors which determine whether people do things brilliantly or badly. This is not, however, a binary toss-of-the-coin kind of choice. Taking the time to analyse these – often complex – factors is widely seen as the most effective way of securing reliable human performance, which is key to the conduct of safety critical tasks. In essence, this step's about how to make sure that people always do the really important things in the right way.

Coined by the Health and Safety Executive, the term 'performance influencing factors' covers 'the characteristics of the *job*, the *individual* and the *organisation* that influence human performance'. The job and organisational factors obviously differ as between roles and companies, but when it comes to human traits and actions, it's possible to talk in more general terms. These individual factors encompass the reasons for people doing things brilliantly or badly – or somewhere in between these two extremes – and it's upon each of these that the imps who feature in this fable have been loosely modelled. The intention is that these characters should help foster a basic understanding of the types of human actions or inactions which might make a failure more likely or more serious or, phrased positively, how they can be harnessed to secure reliable human performance. Taking the time to understand these factors helps organisations to determine the steps needed to control the risk of human failure or – to put it another way – improve the reliability with which operatives perform tasks, particularly the safety critical ones. It's already been said that the conduct of a safety critical task is a crucial point in any process, as it's here that there is the highest potential for control to be lost and an incident – whether loss of porridge, loss of fuel containment, or some other incident – to occur. Those organisations that recognise the complexities of the safety critical tasks associated with their operations, as well as the need to address human performance reliability challenges, will seek to defend against such failures by adopting appropriate 'prevention barriers', and to manage error recovery, through their use of robust 'mitigation barriers'.

This fourth step is, arguably, the most important of the steps set out here, and success at this point is achieved when intelligence about performance influencing factors is used to help drive improvements in the ways in which people – as operatives – carry out tasks. Once organisations have identified the main hazards associated with their operations, the next important step for them is to determine the safety critical tasks involved and to understand who does what, when and in which order. The ways in which organisations analyse safety critical tasks vary, some of them being highly complex. But whichever analytical tools are chosen, those organisations serious about risk will seek to harness the insights and outputs they provide to help them understand exactly *how* specific human failure types can undermine the performance of safety critical tasks. When taken in conjunction with knowledge about the consequences of failure, this can inform the judgments they make about the sufficiency of their current risk controls. This, in turn, rewards them with an understanding as to the value of managing the array of performance influencing factors, which directly feed 'barrier effectiveness'. It's only on reaching this point that organisations are able to determine the need for additional risk control, manage human failures, and progress towards their ultimate goal of reducing risk to ALARP levels. *But this is not a one-off exercise!* The entire process needs to be reviewed on an ongoing basis, with improvements made whenever necessary. This is crucial when dealing with the control of major accident hazards, as we'll see highlighted by the imps in this fable. *The porridge pot fable* was principally concerned with identifying the points at which the little girl and her mother failed but, in a real-world organisational context, it's important to use these insights to develop an approach which positively accounts for performance influencing factors. This is achievable through understanding the roots of any such failures and addressing the factors that degrade the reliability of human performance through a proactive strategy, which lessens the likelihood and/or severity of an incident, due to the quality of human behaviour being consistently high.

The steps looked at so far here have: shown the value organisations can derive through recognising the things they need to control – their major accident hazards (*step one*); given an understanding of the tasks involving people within that process (*step two*), and indicated the kinds of tasks which must be performed reliably well by people every time they carry them out (*step three*). For its focus however, this fable looks in more depth at the particular aspects which, if left unchecked, inhibit people from doing things well (*step four*) – perhaps badly, slowly, with poor attention to detail, or even recklessly, or due to a combination of these and other factors. Working out *why* people might fail and practically addressing these reasons is vital when seeking to control major accident hazards. A key part of this is the need for organisations to be clear about what makes people *mess up*, or degrades the reliability with which they perform safety critical tasks. *And why is this helpful to them?* It's simply because organisations want to be sure that the activities carried out by people – including details about the tasks involved which may, on the surface, appear trivial – are performed by operatives who aren't tired, bored, or disenfranchised, or less effective than desired for any other reason. And it's in being armed with this knowledge – and by using it to inform the design of their work processes, procedures and equipment – that senior leaders of high-hazard organisations are able to rest easy, by gaining the confidence that their major accident hazards are being effectively and reliably controlled.

Thinking back to the fictional porridge pot example, we see that a partial insight into the role of performance influencing factors has already been provided. It's helpful to recap the key points from that fable, given that it's to be used again here[271]. You'll recall that there a hazard of [hot porridge in porridge pot] was identified, which gave rise to a top event of [porridge pot overflow – loss of containment]. In looking at the control of that risk, several barriers were identified,

---

271. As was the case for *the porridge pot fable*, the bow tie model elements, and suggested elements, are denoted in square brackets throughout this section.

comprised of equipment and – where relevant – accompanying operative activity, which made these barriers complete. These activities were *first:* checking the 'gauge' level and stopping the flow of material; *second,* detecting and responding appropriately to the sounding of a high level 'alarm', and *third,* shutting off a 'valve' at a critical point. It was through looking at these barriers that the crucial task was identified – in that case, the shutting of the valve – where operative action (or inaction) was most likely to affect the risk. Some potential failures associated with the operative's performance at this most important stage of the process – what, in the real world, would be regarded as the carrying out of the safety critical task – were identified too.

This fable moves the understanding gained from *the porridge pot fable* on a stage further, through its quest to work out *what* might impair the reliability of human performance. Where these factors are satisfactorily addressed, failures ('threats') can be better managed and/or recovery (the limitation and addressing of 'consequences') assisted. In a real-world organisational context, of course, just as this fable sets out to show in a fictional setting, this helps to secure the safety and welfare of the operatives who carry out such tasks, as well as protecting the integrity of their processes, as a whole.

THE FOCUS OF THIS FABLE

This fable looks at the actions of human operatives as related to 'barrier effectiveness'. As such, it devotes some attention to the different types of human failure in their own right, but additionally considers them insofar as they impede reliable performance, and therefore have the potential to disrupt or compromise process safety. In order to give some structure to the exploration of its central theme, the fable runs through various operative characteristics – both physical and mental – which organisations need to understand, both to ensure the integrity of their processes and to protect their operatives and others from harm. For those readers who choose to pick out individual fables from this collection, a look back at *the porridge pot fable* is advised prior to reading this one, because it provides some useful context, through which the importance of reliable performance is to be demonstrated. It's also – *as chance would have it* – the example drawn upon by the imps within this fable's workshop scenario!

In common with *the porridge pot fable* and *the four little pigs' fable* which preceded this one, in this tale the term 'operative' tends to be most prevalent, when describing the capacity in which people operate, given that the focus here is upon the roles they play in diligently following processes and procedures, and their reliable interaction with systems. Nowhere is the performance of operatives more crucial than in the carrying out of safety critical tasks in a process safety context, and it's hoped that the imps in this fable will fulfil a key purpose in highlighting this function[272]. The imp characters featured here have been assumed to be shift workers, these being operatives involved in work activities typically scheduled outside standard daytime hours, where there may be a handover of duty from one individual or team to another, and a pattern of work where one operative replaces another on the same job, within a 24-hour period[273].

So, without further delay, let's join this band of little folk...

THE FABLE

Once upon a time, there was a lovely depot manager, who worked at an oil storage depot. The lovely depot manager gave birth to a baby boy. The baby's skin was sallow and he had scruffy red hair. The lovely depot manager called her baby *Not-Quite* as, in all honesty, she could tell from birth he was to be a slightly quirky successor, but still she loved him dearly, in a way that only a mother could. There was no getting away from the fact that it was a surprising name choice, but then, he was an unusual boy and historically there had been plenty of other names, like

---

272. It has been assumed that the characters in this fable were workers for an organisation operating sites which, in the real world, would have fallen subject to *the COMAH regulations*. These regulations were outlined earlier in this book, in the context of *the four little pigs' fable*. The extent to which these might have applied is not explored here however, with the principal focus of this fable and its *modern meaning* being more generally upon how reliable human performance by those carrying out safety critical tasks within a major accident hazard setting might be secured.

273. As outlined in this book's introduction, employers are required to have 'consultation' arrangements in place with those who carry out work, or their representatives. Where employees are to become subject to shift-work arrangements – or changes to existing arrangements – with the potential to substantially impact their health and safety, it would be expected that they would be consulted in advance of their introduction.

Snow for a girl, which had never really caught on in popularity terms, so why not Not-Quite, the lovely depot manager thought?

Some twenty or so years passed.

Not-Quite got a job working for his mother. He worked hard, quickly becoming a team manager at the depot she managed. They enjoyed working as a mother/son combination, making their packed lunches together every night before work, sharing the driving to and from the depot, and helping each other out with any tricky queries which arose during the course of the working day. For a time, life was nigh on perfect but, as tends to be the way in many of the darker fairy tales and fables, this perfection was to be prematurely curtailed.

More time passed.

Unexpectedly and tragically, following a short illness, the lovely depot manager died. Not-Quite was naturally devastated by the loss of his mother. His father felt bereft too but, after grieving for a time, he picked himself up, dusted himself off, and was married for a second time – to a depot manager from a rival depot. His new wife was also beautiful but, unlike Not-Quite's mother who had always been a kindly lady, she had a dark side, with a reputation for being manipulative, competitive and vain. And, whilst the lovely depot manager had doted on her son, finding his funny ways endearing, the beautiful but vain rival depot manager found him a little odd and perceived him to be something of a threat. It was that typical stepmother/stepson friction. *And then some.*

Not-Quite's father, knowing of the burgeoning friction between his son and his new beautiful but vain depot manager wife, was always careful to avoid making mention of one in front of the other. He loved them in very different ways, but in equal measure, and had no wish to become caught up in their conflict, going to great pains to make clear that he never wanted to hear either of them speaking ill of the other. And so, whilst mutually harbouring deep-seated feelings of resentment, both Not-Quite and the beautiful but vain depot manager respected his views, with each of them being careful to avoid making disparaging remarks about the other in the presence of Not-Quite's father ever again.

It was no secret that the beautiful but vain depot manager had some deep-rooted insecurities, which pervaded many of her business and pleasure-related activities. In her depot, she displayed an obsessive desire to check her performance data, such was her unwavering resolve to be the best. She had a magical scorecard and could often be heard cooing over its rows of numbers and coloured ratings. Every day, on her arrival at work, she would open up the scorecard on her computer, whilst chanting the mantra: 'Scorecard, scorecard of the yard, In terms of safety, who works hard?' And every day the magical scorecard pixie would respond with the line: 'From depot near, to depot far, m'lady – you're the safety superstar!' or some other such platitude.

Now, the *magical scorecard pixie* was not, of course, a real pixie, but a 'macro' operating from deep within the scorecard, calculating depot safety performance scores. All of the organisation's depots had scorecards and most managers saw them simply as providing snapshots of their safety performance but, as with all things, the beautiful but vain depot manager was hard to satisfy, always craving more. It had been with this in mind that, some time back, she had instructed her performance manager to link her scorecard to a voice-recognition software widget – a project he had dutifully completed – and it did indeed seem to spring into life on hearing the beautiful but vain depot manager's dulcet tones. The beautiful but vain depot manager found the responses of her magical scorecard pixie reassuring, especially given the apparent tendency of this ego-stroking elf to speak in her favour. But, whilst confident in its injury calculations and other statistical analysis, her deep-seated feelings of inadequacy meant her obsession was never far beneath the surface and she continued to practise her ritual on arrival at work each day. *Just to be sure.*

Not-Quite, meanwhile, was justifiably building for himself a good reputation and, in no time at all, got promoted to the depot manager post at the depot formerly overseen by his mother. This made him happy, as he felt he was continuing on her sterling work and honouring the family name. He worked hard, gaining for himself a good knowledge of operational procedures, the *Health and Safety at Work etc. Act 1974*[274] (*HSWA 1974*), and associated regulations, but also balanced this with an appreciation of the practical challenges faced by frontline staff, always keeping his feet firmly on the ground. He had a sound control of the risks within his remit too, earning a reasonable salary and being widely revered by his work colleagues, across all other oil storage depots...with one notable exception – the one run by the beautiful but vain depot manager! There was no denying that she perceived Not-Quite as a threat and an inconvenient one, at that.

---

274. 1974 c. 37.

One day, on arriving at the depot, the beautiful but vain depot manager logged on to her computer and went straight to her scorecard. Now of course, there was nothing unusual in this but, on that particular day, events were about to take an unpleasant turn for the beautiful but vain depot manager. She did some fancy work with the scorecard and saw – to her horror – that she was no longer top of the table. She knew this because, upon uttering her usual refrain of: 'Scorecard, scorecard of the yard, in terms of safety, who works hard?', on this occasion, the magical scorecard pixie responded with: 'I'm afraid now it seems that the tables have turned, it would appear that Not-Quite now is in first place – well-earned!', in a tone that seemed almost sarcastic.

The beautiful but vain depot manager was angered by the magical scorecard pixie's latest retort. And lacking, as she was, in Not-Quite's scruples and integrity, she attached more importance to status than to hard work, with no wish to co-exist in a depot structure with anyone more competent than she was, step-son or otherwise. Added to this, she had a personal performance review due imminently, upon which her chance of a bonus depended. She did everything that the IT helpdesk asked – including repeatedly turning her computer off and back on again and getting a slightly geeky chap she knew to check which formulae had been used – but it was no good, the answer was always the same: she was heading down the performance league! It was an uncomfortable truth, but the scorecard never lied and it seemed no amount of formulaic fiddling or spreadsheet shenanigans was going to change that. The realisation having dawned on her that adjusting the figures was going to be no small task, the beautiful but vain depot manager telephoned her performance manager, saying: 'Please take Not-Quite to some of our more remote high-risk operational sites and lose him and his risk-based inspection documents, on a permanent basis. Failing that, see if you can pull some strings and redeploy him to one of our worst performing depots, so that he no longer poses a competitive threat to me!' And before her performance manager even had the chance to reply, let alone express his concerns about the ethics of her suggestion, the beautiful but vain depot manager had ended the call, being conveniently unavailable when he tried to call back to resume their conversation.

Some time passed and the performance manager dutifully took Not-Quite out on some site visits.

Whilst he was a loyal member of her team and only ever wished to act in accordance with the instructions of the beautiful but vain depot manager, the performance manager had unshakable scruples and had latterly been struggling to handle some of her unethical tendencies. In his heart, he knew he shared far more in common with Not-Quite's way of thinking, finding his approach more relatable and his commitment to high safety standards honourable. The pair of them went on and on all day, but he could not 'lose' Not-Quite. He had too much respect for his safety prowess. On realising that he couldn't, in all conscience, comply with the beautiful but vain depot manager's demands, the usually calm performance manager suddenly yelled out to Not-Quite: 'RUN AWAY! The beautiful but vain depot manager wants to ruin your credibility. You must never come back for, if you do, I foresee that you'll succumb to an *unexplained workplace injury*. And, I'd venture to suggest, that's the best case scenario...'

Not–Quite could tell from the look of panic etched on the performance manager's face that his motives were genuine. Looking the performance manager in the eye and giving him a reassuring smile in gratitude for his advice, he turned on his heels and ran away from him, down a path he hadn't noticed before.

In no time at all Not-Quite came to a little house, situated next to an outbuilding.

Ironically – quite by chance and unbeknown even to the performance manager, from whom he had parted company a few hundred metres back – Not-Quite had indeed happened upon the organisation's poorest performing depot! He was breathless and couldn't run any more and, on seeing the little house as a place of refuge, he burst through the door and went on inside. Luckily for him, the occupants of the little house were a generally trusting bunch, who worked from the depot in the adjacent outbuilding, and habitually left the front door to their living quarters unlocked. Once inside the little house, Not-Quite saw a table with seven little stools. Then he saw seven little beds. 'These beds are so little...' said Not-Quite to himself, continuing: '...whoever could sleep in them, *I wonder?*' Not-Quite was so tired that, before he had chance to ponder this question some more and with his heart-rate still struggling to regain its normal rhythm, following his impromptu run, he went to sleep on one of the little beds.

A short while later, the little folk who lived in the little house returned.

They were seven imps whose days were fairly evenly split between carrying out operational tasks across the district and working from the outbuilding adjacent to the little house, for the organisation's poorest performing oil storage depot. The roles they performed included some safety critical tasks, one of which was to stop fuel transfer, when the contents of tanks and tankers reached pre-determined levels.

IMPISH INTRODUCTIONS

It wasn't long before the imps happened upon Not-Quite, soundly asleep on one of their little beds. 'Who is this pale fellow and what is he doing in our little house?' they murmured to each other. Suddenly Not-Quite woke up, rubbed his eyes, and jumped to his feet with a start. *'Who on earth are you?'* said Not-Quite to the impish occupants, not realising he'd just unwittingly written off an evening of his life he was unlikely ever to get back…

'Ah, well there's a question!' said Sly, in a tone which suggested he was slightly riled. 'Although, whilst we're on the subject, I think it's *us* who should be asking *you*! I'm not sure if you've noticed, but this is *our* little house and I don't recall us having invited *you* in! Anyway, in a way, I'm glad you asked, but you might want to sit down first…this could take a little time! *We* are the seven imps and *I* am *Sly*!' said the first of the little folk holding out his hand, as if to shake Not Quite's, before hastily withdrawing it, letting out an involuntary snigger and gathering his six little co-workers together to introduce themselves. Sly relished the opportunity to ingratiate himself to anyone who he felt might be able to help him gain an advantage over the other imps. Some of the imps had good reason to doubt his integrity and, from the looks on their faces, Not-Quite discerned that Sly's abrupt tone had left them less than impressed.

'I am Weedy…' said the second imp, meekly, a slight tremor clearly detectable in his voice, '…and I have to move heavy plant and equipment – tankers, hoses, pipes, you name it – including carrying out coupling and uncoupling procedures and operating large manual valves, sometimes in cramped conditions, which causes me significant physical strain. I'm convinced I'm pushing myself beyond my limits – I'm not strong enough and I just don't have the endurance needed! I don't think anyone's considered the strenuous nature of the activity I

have to carry out, from start to finish – but let me tell you, sometimes I've climbed several flights of steps and walked quite a distance around the depot, before my work's even begun! I feel weak all the time and under relentless pressure, with managers often telling me I need to quicken my pace and lift and move more plant and equipment, with little or no chance of taking a break. And it surely must be within their gift to provide some kind of assistance, to ease the burden on me!'

Weedy suffered from a physical weakness, which placed him at increased risk of personal injury. He wasn't alone in this. Nationally, many other imps were known to suffer from similar complaints, including young imps whose limbs were still developing and those experiencing temporary conditions, such as pregnancy, which could reduce their capability or strength for a time. Leaving such issues unchecked, or without further control measures being put in place, had the potential to lead to personal injury, long term health problems, or to exacerbate existing conditions for any imp so affected. Knowing, as Not-Quite did, that industrial tasks of the kind performed by some of the imps placed high physical demands upon them or required the carrying out of a large number of repeat physical tasks within a given timeframe, he already felt some sympathy for the concerns voiced by Weedy. But no sooner had he started to reflect on this, than the next imp had started to introduce himself!

'I am Stressy...' pronounced the third imp, pacing backwards and forwards, before continuing on '...and one of our colleagues from a team at a neighbouring depot has been off on long-term sick leave, so now I have *twice* the amount of work to cover, over a much wider geographic area. And our team leaders are *so* unsympathetic! I've told them I'm suffering from stress and low self-esteem and feel unable to cope, but they couldn't be less interested if they tried. I am, by turns, anxious, tense and worried, and sad, blue and lacking in energy, which means I sometimes find it difficult to concentrate. *Now, what was I saying...?* Ah, yes, I'm sure some of the other imps find my irritability and defensive behaviour challenging at times, but let me tell you, it's tough feeling constantly tired and exhausted and struggling to sleep – I'm quite sure my blood pressure's higher than it should be! And I put my migraines down to stress factors too! With all this going on, it's hardly surprising I sometimes make mistakes, now is it?' He held the back of his hand to his brow – with a slight hint of melodrama – and took a step back from the group for a moment.

It struck Not-Quite that Stressy was a sensitive fellow, with the potential sources of his stress being multiple and varied. Not-Quite knew from experience that there could be benefits to having a challenging job role – opportunities to meet others, use skills, and increase technical understanding, which might support an imp's progression through the organisation – all of which could be generally positive for psychological and emotional health. But he also knew that excessive or unreasonable demands – such as instructions by managers to work faster, or even others hinting that urgency was needed – weren't a good thing, when they pushed an individual towards feelings of inability to cope, or perhaps caused their judgment to be impaired, with them possibly succumbing to pressure to complete tasks more quickly, or to a lower standard than expected. Furthermore, where this impacted upon performance, there was clear potential for far-reaching or devastating consequences, not just for the imp concerned, but also for their co-workers, together with the systems and processes for which they carried responsibility. Often the stressors faced by Stressy related to the nature of his work activities, with too many demands being placed upon him – due to multiple factors including shift patterns, workload variability (sometimes too little, sometimes too much, but never just the right amount!), time pressures, excess complexity, monotony, a lack of clear objectives or control over his own work. But on other occasions, the causes were of an environmental nature – variously including excessive noise and vibration, inadequate light and ventilation, bad weather and extreme temperatures – *the list went on and on...*

Whilst not wishing to jump to any premature conclusions, Not-Quite thought it likely that there were adverse working culture factors at play too, contributing to the situation Stressy described. If rumours were to be believed, there were pockets of bad practice, as well as other organisation-wide challenges, with numerous examples of poor team working and of imps becoming unhelpful or unwilling to assist each other. Issues of job insecurity, bullying and harassment weren't unknown either, and deteriorating relationships with colleagues, a common complaint. Conflicts between safety and commercial priorities were increasing in frequency too, with jobs being rushed and mistakes inevitably made as a result. Worryingly, these cultural cracks were starting to emerge throughout the organisation – right from the top to the very bottom. Stressy made no secret of the fact that his feelings were deep-seated. Adding to his earlier claims about unsympathetic team leaders, he cited further issues of unsupportive supervisors, and senior managers who failed to engage in effective discussions with the workforce about the potential impact of business change. Not-Quite pondered to himself that non-work related aspects might be playing a part in Stressy's circumstances too – with possible stressors including poor work-life balance, life changes (perhaps marriage or child-related), illness, bereavement, relationship difficulties or financial concerns. But, whilst keen to explore these issues further with him, Not-Quite felt this probably wasn't the right moment to do so. He didn't doubt the complexities of the situation and thought it best that any matters of a personal nature should be handled sensitively and privately, so as to start fostering a relationship of trust and confidence with Stressy, as well as with the wider imp community.

The mood of the group had turned a bit subdued all of a sudden, with a reluctance to speak up painfully apparent amongst the remaining imps. Sensing that the focus of the other imps might soon shift to him, and in a bid to deflect attention, Sly jabbed Idle in the ribs, causing him jump with a start…

'Oh! I…I am Idle…' said the fourth imp, seemingly flustered, but quickly managing to recover his composure, before continuing '…I have to monitor system variables on multiple screens, to detect abnormal plant operating conditions, with little change ever taking place. It's really tedious work and I'm sure I sometimes miss things over the course of a shift, by simply *switching off*. In fact, on some occasions a whole shift can pass, with nothing much of interest to report, so it's not unknown for me to take my eye off the ball for a time.'

It was a view widely held by the imps that Idle's problems stemmed from the demands of the tasks he was required to undertake being so low as to negatively affect his performance, with his failing to notice new events and having slower response times than those of the average imp. This might have been due to overstaffing. Or the job's routine, repetitive or under-stimulating nature. Or possibly even induced boredom, brought on by it being so mundane which could, in turn, have led to him lacking in motivation, causing his skills to get rusty (so-called 'skill fade'), with consequential errors, notably impaired alertness and more distraction observable in his behaviour. Left uncontrolled, this boredom and reduced attentiveness posed a major threat to the carrying out of safety critical tasks, with low arousal levels, decreased vigilance, increased reaction times, and dips in performance levels, all undesirable traits in an individual performing activities where reliability was crucial. Idle's errors typically saw him missing things due to failing to take in information from his surroundings, essential to the maintenance of safety and the optimal operation of the work environment. He wasn't as bad as some, admittedly – like Sly, for instance – who seemed to be prone to seeking out trouble, for trouble's sake. But it still concerned Not-Quite that boredom and low job satisfaction might have led to Idle becoming so demotivated that he had started to make errors or, worse still, was resorting to thrill-seeking activity, including finding other inappropriate tasks to do, simply with a view to making his job more interesting.

'That's lucky for you that you have so little to do…it must be nice to have time on your hands, Idle! *I am Spent…*' said the fifth '…I have lots to check on a minute by minute basis, with so many variables changing on the screens in front of me and endless monitoring to do, right across the depot. I know I need to concentrate really hard on what are very demanding tasks, but it's impossible, when there's so much work and I'm told it's all *so* important. My role includes monitoring tanks and pipework, including systems which warn of abnormal plant operating conditions. I have too much to do, no time in which to accomplish it, and there's no-one willing to help, nor any tools to assist in reducing my workload. *But be in no doubt!* If I get something wrong, I'm sure to be hauled over the coals for my oversight! The slightest error in my calculations, judgments, decisions or plans – some of which have to be undertaken simultaneously or in quick succession – could have catastrophic consequences. *Let me tell you – that's a source of stress in itself!* And it's anyone's guess what might happen if I were to be confronted by an emergency, or even abnormal operating conditions. I simply don't have any spare capacity, so as to be able to respond efficiently! To be honest, I'm not entirely sure any of us is fully trained or competent to handle all of the tasks we've been assigned.'

There was a belief that the difficulties suffered by Spent were potentially due to understaffing, which had increased the level of workload demanded of him. It was also possible that the difficulty of tasks was partly to blame, with the amount of information the imp needed to perceive to make a decision being beyond his attention span. Another theory was that too many responses were required of him within the time available. Or it might even have been that the pressure

Spent felt was due to his own approach towards the tasks he needed to complete – perhaps he was an imp who was unprepared, badly organised, or one who simply failed to prioritise the work ahead. On occasions, he appeared to show symptoms of high stress, degrading his performance still further and leading to poor decision-making and slower reaction times, all of which had major implications for the carrying out of safety critical tasks. Whatever the reasons, it occurred to Not-Quite that the sheer size of Spent's workload was highly likely to swamp any such tasks he was required to perform, with the possible consequences – albeit unintended – of him skipping, postponing or missing out vital steps, or simply carrying them out too fast. It was well-known that increasing workload beyond a certain optimum point could lead to degraded performance. And, whilst it was hard to say for certain exactly how or why an excessive workload had arisen at the seven imps' depot, there was no doubting the range of problems it caused, including: too many tasks requiring completion in the time available, tasks being too similar and easily confused, or conflicts between the types of tasks required. A further possibility was that important information would be missed when the workload was high, due to any imp so affected narrowing or focusing their attention on only one aspect of a task, or even simply because they possessed insufficient skill or experience for the tasks they were required to perform.

Reflecting on their discussions so far, Not-Quite was starting to feel a degree of empathy towards Spent – in truth, even listening to some of the imps had left him exhausted! But, setting aside his own feelings for a moment, he was keen to ensure that where the imps fulfilled roles involving tasks which demanded mental or physical effort, accurate problem solving, decision-making, analysis, or activities requiring sustained attention or vigilance, these should be tightly monitored. And even where this wasn't the case, it was still in the imps' interests for activities to be well controlled, for the sake of their health and welfare.

Not-Quite had started to detect a trend for undesirable workload levels common to three of the imps. This was a feeling backed up by the rest of them colloquially referring to this little group as *the workload imps* – a clique who seemed keen to bemoan all manner of work aspects, whether relating to the need for too much physical effort in Weedy's case, too much mental effort being demanded from Spent, or even too little mental effort being called for from Idle. And, whatever the reasons for these apparent workload imbalances, Not-Quite felt sure that much needed to be done to turn this sorry situation around. He perceived that an issue common to this trio lay in management failures to look at both the number and types of operative required for the various tasks that needed to be undertaken – having the right imps in the right place at the right time. Alternatively, he reasoned to himself, the problem might have started some time ago, with the organisation having failed to recruit operatives in sufficient numbers, or with suitable competencies, knowledge, skills and experience, so as to be able to work safely. Whilst Not-Quite recognised that imbalances in the distribution of work tasks could be tricky problems to fix, there were some basic flaws to *the workload imps'* working arrangements he was keen to put right without delay including, amongst other things, increasing the level of support they were given, and addressing instances of imps failing to take their rest breaks. Realising, however, that like Spent he was also short of time, and that two of the other imps had yet to speak up, Not-Quite was keen to keep the conversation moving along, so as to be able to start collectively addressing some of the group's shared concerns.

'And you are...?', said Not-Quite, in the direction of an imp who had so far remained silent. *'I am Bumbler...'* said the sixth '...and before you ask, let me be candid with you, I'm not altogether sure *what* I should be doing, but my eagerness to please has probably meant I've inadvertently exceeded authority levels from time to time, and, between us, it's got to the point now where I feel unable to raise my concerns. I haven't completed all my essential training, so I'm mostly just feeling my way through the situation. I know I'm supposed to monitor the arrival of various grades of fuel, including checking for control room error, but I don't feel confident in my skills, which leads me to feeling I need to bluff for any gaps in my knowledge. I don't doubt that there have been times where I simply haven't seen risks. And others where I've seen them, but have assumed they were under control and so carried on regardless. I'm sure I've made some wrong decisions in the past and it's a particular worry to me that I can't easily recognise key hazards and risks, or see when a safe situation is deteriorating into an unsafe one. It's just my view but, for what it's worth, I think an imp in my role should be able to fulfil their responsibilities, by undertaking tasks and performing activities to a recognised standard, on a repeated and consistent basis. And I don't think it's too much to ask that that the processes and documents we're expected to follow should be clearly defined, comprehensive, in easily understandable formats and accessible to us, whenever and wherever we might want to refer to them. As for any support we might need, well I, for one, wouldn't know where to start, my friend! I don't recall any of our managers ever having asked for our point of view, let alone them looking to help solve any problems we might have raised...'

Not-Quite believed that the possible causes of the weaknesses identified by Bumbler might have included poor training, low standards of monitoring and supervision, or his managers being oblivious to what was taking place. Left unchecked, he felt sure that these issues had the potential to inadvertently encourage bad decision-making, with this imp's behaviours and those of others like him contributing to a poor safety culture. It was Not-Quite's belief that the causes of the competence concerns voiced by Bumbler needed to be addressed from the very first day an imp started work – with training needs assessed right from the beginning and considered throughout the course of their employment with the organisation – at times of depot transfer or imp redeployment, for instance, or even simply to refresh their knowledge on a regular basis. Such training also needed to encompass rare, unusual or emergency events, an aspect which Not-Quite thought was likely to have been overlooked in Bumbler's case.

'And finally, *you are*...?' said Not-Quite in the direction of the last imp. It was getting late and the sense of relief that the introductions were nearing an end was now all too apparent in his face.

'I am Drifty...' said the seventh imp, just about finding his voice, in between yawns. The others said they were unsurprised at him showing signs of fatigue, given the number of extra shifts he'd taken on in the recent past, also reporting that it was commonplace for him to doze off without warning during a shift, and to appear drowsy, lethargic or generally slow to move around, for much of the time. Anecdotally, Idle said he'd regularly heard Drifty admitting: '...I've been working hard all week and I'm absolutely done in...' And, whilst Idle failed to see the benefit in taking on extra work, it struck him that Drifty was an imp who had his eye fixed firmly on overtime payments, apparently being willing to compromise his personal wellbeing for the sake of this extra income. It appeared that Drifty wasn't unique in his insatiable desire for overtime either, with the group speculating that there were others in the organisation who displayed a worrying sense of bravado – imps who had no hesitation in boasting of clocking up a huge number of weekly working hours, with alarming regularity – seeming to confirm that he wasn't alone in placing greater value on his financial, rather than physical and mental, wellbeing. Another possibility was that he was preoccupied by some other issues outside work, which – if team talk was to be believed – were making him tired. Perhaps, Not-Quite reasoned, aspects of his home life were causing him problems, preventing him from getting the undisturbed sleep he so badly needed, albeit that it seemed to be well understood by the rest of the group that going to bed late, having a broken night, poor quality or insufficient sleep invariably meant any imp so affected was unlikely to give of their best. It occurred to Not-Quite that Drifty's tiredness could have arisen from other issues too, such as the use of medication (whether prescribed or over-the-counter) or even, that it might have stemmed from problems with alcohol, or recreational drug use. But whatever the particular underlying reasons in Drifty's case, there was a groundswell of opinion that management had turned a blind eye to the possible causes, which Not-Quite suspected might have been at the heart of the problem.

Whilst it was impossible to pinpoint with any degree of certainty the primary cause of Drifty's state of lethargy, on top of the personal factors, there were other potential work-related reasons likely to have played a part. These could have included his working at low points in the day (early morning, mid to late afternoon, or just after a meal), lengthy working hours, poorly designed shift work and inadequate opportunities for rest breaks during the working day. Drifty knew that the adoption of such practices wasn't always consequence-free, with possible outcomes including reduced alertness, memory failure, irritability, increased reaction times and poor decision making all particularly concerning traits in an imp performing safety critical tasks. But he mostly addressed this through indulging in a diet of convenience food on long shifts and drinking copious amounts of coffee, a routine that went some way to masking his tiredness but which, perhaps unsurprisingly, sometimes gave him cause to complain of gastric discomfort. He was an affable imp though, and apparently well-liked by the others, who seemed accepting of his occasional absent-mindedness and lack of concentration, taking such traits to be part of his charm.

Privately, Not-Quite was relieved, the realisation having just dawned on him that the imps' introductions were drawing to a close. If truth be told, he just thanked his lucky stars that they were fewer in number than the Dalmations that had featured in the bygone tale! He was, however, keen to stay focused on the task ahead of him and so – remembering his manners and not wishing to be rude – Not Quite expressed his gratitude to the little imps, before realising he'd missed an imp out…

'Hang on a moment, Sly…' said Not-Quite, continuing on '…I know your name, but that's about all! I don't believe you spoke about yourself or what exactly it is that you do?' Sly looked troubled for a moment, feeling his coyness might have sparked concern, before saying evasively, 'Oh, nothing much – you know, *just this and that*…'

There was a widely-held view amongst the team that perhaps Sly had set his sights upon getting to the top of the organisation, by whatever means that might take, even if he had to occasionally jettison his integrity to get there. It was clear he had other priorities and – unlike the other imps – he seemed unwilling to lay all his cards on the table. Sly's six co-working imps appeared to feel that his behaviours were motivated by a negative intent which, if true, pointed to the outcomes being non-compliances rather than errors in his case. Taking Not-Quite to one side for a moment, Bumbler speculated that, whilst personally he felt out of his depth, he believed Sly's failings to be deliberate violations. At this stage, however, Not-Quite could not be sure as to whether Bumbler's claims held water and he thought it an unwise move to be drawn into impish politics so soon after meeting them. But if these claims were true – and Sly was behaving as he did in a bid to make personal gain, simply because he was a reckless individual, or even based on a misguided belief that it might benefit the organisation – these underlying issues needed addressing as a priority. He knew he would need to take a firm stance against any imp displaying such behaviours, and made a mental note to revisit these with Sly in the future, but thought it wise to bide his time before pressing him further on the more questionable aspects to his approach.

Not-Quite thanked Bumbler for sharing his thoughts and was already starting to ponder what might be motivating Sly's apparently subversive behaviour. It could have been that Sly was an individual who recognised risk, but simply didn't care, or even that he gained some kind of thrill from being a renegade thinker. Maybe Sly and others like him found it difficult to obey all the organisation's rules and requirements and still get the job done. Perhaps his actions had grown from a perception – wrongly or rightly – that it was more convenient, less trouble or quicker to break rules, regulations or procedures, than to follow them.

Alternatively, it might have been that Sly found himself ill-equipped to deal with unusual or non-routine situations. It was also possible, Not-Quite reasoned to himself, that the answer sat deeper within the organisation, with failures to find out the cause of what had gone wrong in the wake of any incidents and to reprimand those breaking safety rules or regulations just some of the issues which had allowed poor practice to become entrenched. Another possibility, he thought, was that there might have been a message from management – albeit a subtle one – that productivity targets were to be prioritised over safety ones. And it could have been that this had, in turn, led to some of the imps taking short cuts, with them feeling secure in the knowledge that lack of reprimanding, discipline, monitoring or supervision meant their actions were, usually at least, consequence free. Not-Quite suspected that the question about supervision levels might be a particularly pertinent one in Sly's case, given that he appeared to be a young, inexperienced operative, who was potentially more easily influenced than the other imps. But, irrespective of the reasons, Not-Quite was clear that allowing such behaviours to go unchecked was a high risk strategy. It put the imp and others in danger. It exposed the organisation to liability. And it was likely to encourage a rise in violations – with the imp breaking the rules in spite of the risks involved – whether for personal benefit or reward, or out of plain recklessness. Even just starting to think about the behaviours of this particular imp had sown the seed of an idea in Not-Quite's mind that a programme of significant cultural change was likely to be needed, in order to turn this tricky situation around.

'Well, perhaps we can pick up on Sly's story another time…as for the rest of you, thanks for being so candid with me…some of those were more like life stories than introductions!' said Not-Quite to the imps – a wry smile spreading across his face – partly rueing his judgment in having asked such an open question of them in the first place. In truth, he'd almost forgotten the purpose of his enquiry, and so resolved to pay a bit more attention to his own time management skills when they had cause to reconvene as a group! But, on the upside at least, he sensed that from this chance encounter he was likely to be able to reap benefits too. He recognised that the imps might be able to assist him, but he also knew that he would only be able to reduce the likelihood of any type of operative failure by getting the best out of each and every one of them. And for that to happen, he knew he was going to need to encourage the imps to be open and honest with him about any issues that might be troubling them.

NOT-QUITE ASKS FOR HELP

Having humoured the imps up to this point – by listening to their back stories at quite some length – Not-Quite felt it timely that he should share with them some insights into his own predicament. Gathering them in a huddle around him and speaking in a hushed voice, he told them that the beautiful but vain depot manager was trying to force his exit from the organisation, and that he had run away and needed their help. The little imps looked at one another, enthusiastically nodding their heads in agreement, before Bumbler spoke for all of them saying: *'You must stay here!* You'll be safe in our little house and you can work here with us, at our depot.'

It was late, they all agreed that Not-Quite's staying over was the best option by far – an offer that he gratefully accepted – and so, with Spent having made up the spare room for him, the eight of them retired to bed.

The next day...

As soon as they had awoken, Not-Quite hurriedly made a couple of telephone calls, explaining his situation to one of the organisation's top managers, and to Derek from the internal recruitment team. These conversations caused Derek to become flustered to say the least, as the last thing he needed was a sudden increase in workload, but the eventual outcome was a happy one for Not-Quite, with Derek's negotiations securing for him a temporary move to the role of depot manager at the seven imps' depot. The beautiful but vain depot manager, meanwhile, had been moved on to another depot, where she could be more strictly supervised and her activities more closely scrutinised, whilst investigations into her conduct continued, with Derek having referred this aspect to Human Resources.

Not-Quite's transfer was swiftly made, in large part due to there being no shortage of work to be done, and it being universally known that a litany of performance improvements was needed at the seven imps' depot. Derek, meanwhile, was curious as to why anyone would want to move to the poorest performing of the organisation's depots! But having no wish to rock the boat, and being happy to do anything for an easy life, he filled in a few forms – as had been his primary function for the last thirty or so years – and the deal was sealed, to everyone's satisfaction. The little imps were elated at this outcome, as was Not-Quite, and he started working with them right away.

The imps who were, in the main, an ordinarily trusting bunch told Not-Quite that he must never talk to anyone who came to their door, explaining to him that this was for his own good. It seemed that news had reached them that not everyone within the vicinity of their depot and little house was of a goodly nature, which had prompted their words of warning to him. Not-Quite thanked them for their advice, although he was slightly surprised that this was seemingly the only aspect to their site induction, with not so much as a cursory mention given to first-aid arrangements or the location of muster points, at which they would be required to gather in an emergency situation. But, whilst sensing they were a team functioning below par, he found their well-meaning, easy charm curiously endearing and was already beginning to feel at home. Not-Quite got settled in and wasted no time at all in learning the ropes, seeing what he might be able to do to help them, and getting a little better acquainted with each of the imps and their various foibles.

Some weeks passed...

Things appeared to be going rather well for Not-Quite and the seven imps. Alas, the same could not be said for the beautiful but vain depot manager! Her obsessive desire for performance data was seemingly insatiable and her nervousness about the continuing investigations into her conduct was doing nothing to quell her ritualistic habit. One day, back in her new depot, the beautiful but vain depot manager sat down at her computer and asked: 'Scorecard, scorecard of the yard, in terms of safety, who works hard?' And the reply came back: 'Oh, that's quite a shock, still the scales are tipped, Not-Quite remains top, your performance outstripped!' *And sure enough, the scorecard did indeed show Not-Quite to be the hardest working and highest performing of all the depot managers.*

The beautiful but vain depot manager was very angry, as she had done much in the recent past to ensure her scorecard-leading performance went unchallenged. The message coming back from her computer was at odds with her belief that Not-Quite had been removed or redeployed, despite the clear edict she'd issued to her performance manager. *It certainly seemed to fly in the face of the notion that he'd been placed at the poorest performing depot!* A rumour had been circulating in recent weeks that Not-Quite remained a highly regarded depot manager, and a call to Derek confirmed the beautiful but vain depot manager's worst fears to be true: Not-Quite was still very much around and, if truth be told, doing rather well for himself and the seven imps.

The beautiful but vain depot manager knew she had to do something, but equally saw the need to keep up a serene facade. Barely able to contain the angry rage building up inside her, she left her depot and went out into the streets. Soon she found the little house and outbuilding, along the path where her performance manager had reportedly left Not-Quite, some time back. Little did she know that most of the imps were out on the patch, with the exception of Sly who was waiting in for a depot delivery. The beautiful but vain depot manager knocked on the door to the depot, which was soon answered by Sly. As the sneakiest of the imps, he had no fear of answering the door, being confident that no-one would outwit him. '*Hello, dear fellow*…I'm sure you'll be able to help me, you're *bound* to know…Where is Not-Quite?' the beautiful but vain depot manager asked, trying desperately to endear herself to him. 'I have *no* idea…' replied Sly, evasively, '…he's not been seen for days!' But Sly knew exactly where he was. He was out and about delivering materials, whilst also shadowing some of the imps in a bid to start gaining an understanding of some of the more deep-seated problems with the depot and his impish operatives. The beautiful but vain depot manager was livid but, knowing that she must conceal her anger, thanked Sly for his help, and pulled back. It was all she could do to stifle momentary sincerity. Privately, however, she was seething, as she'd hoped to dupe Not Quite's happy band of imps into disclosing the secret behind the recent turnaround in their depot's performance. Alas, it wasn't to be. It was painfully obvious that her charm wasn't washing with Sly and, as there wasn't so much as a tainted apple on offer to tempt him, he was giving nothing away. Realising that this conversation was getting her no further forward in locating Not-Quite, and with her less than elaborate plan seemingly in tatters, the beautiful but vain depot manager turned and headed off back down the path, away from the depot.

Some more time passed…

Back at her own depot, the beautiful but vain depot manager continued on with her computer-based ritual, saying: 'Scorecard, scorecard of the yard, in terms of safety, who works hard?' And, as was all too often the case, her question was met with the response that Not-Quite was the hardest working and top at safety.

Now, despite the magical scorecard pixie not being a real pixie, some of those based at the beautiful but vain depot manager's depot had started to notice that even the voice behind the scorecard had taken on a somewhat flippant tone, most likely a reaction to her persistent badgering. Still, such was the scale of her vanity that the magical scorecard pixie's irony was lost on the beautiful but vain depot manager and, with the passing of time, she was once again pleased to receive a positive response to her question, with the answer coming back: 'M'lady, don't fret, for there's no-one gets near – in scorecard reports, you're the one they revere!' Not-Quite had got wind of this development too and, whilst he lacked the beautiful but vain depot manager's narcissistic tendencies, he was becoming concerned. He believed a sense of apathy might be starting to creep in amongst the imps, meaning he had no time to waste! He also knew he needed to start mapping out a way forward, by developing a plan of action, to deal with the issues he'd uncovered. And fast.

A few months later...

The beautiful but vain depot manager was continuing to revel in the sense of glory she felt at her performance achievements going unrivalled; in fact, she'd even allowed herself to start believing that Not-Quite really might have had left the organisation. She reasoned that if this wasn't the case he must, by now, be so far down the scorecard as to pose no threat to her at all. This was borne out by the fact that, nowadays, when she posed her time-worn question of 'Scorecard, scorecard of the yard, in terms of safety, who works hard?' he was no longer mentioned, a point that appeared to be confirmed one day, when the answer came back: 'Don't worry, don't panic! Your performance is sound...and as for Not-Quite, there are no records found!'

In secret, however, having recognised the weaknesses in his new team, but with a strongly held desire to play to their strengths and get the best out of them too, Not-Quite had been arranging a number of collaborative workshops for them. The focus of these was upon improving any weak areas and clarifying the parts they each needed to play in securing reliable performance. Not-Quite knew he had to do something. He wasn't the most dynamic of line managers, but he did care deeply about his team and wanted them to flourish. With this in mind, he had been busily putting together a change management strategy and setting in motion arrangements for the first of the workshops, to gauge their strengths and weaknesses and start developing individual action plans for them, for the year ahead. Not-Quite's approach was already gaining traction in the organisation and there was a simple reason why he was nowhere to be found on the scorecard: the in-house performance information team had temporarily removed his name from it and were busily working away recalculating his performance scores, following his recent move to the seven imps' depot.

A few weeks later...

NOT-QUITE RUNS A WORKSHOP SESSION

Not-Quite arranged for a series of workshop sessions to be held at the seven imps' depot, in the outbuilding next to the seven imps' little house. The purpose of the first workshop was to provide some insights for the imps as to what they could all do to improve the strength of their barriers – *or risk controls* – helping to contribute towards more reliable performance from their depot[275]. He got some nice little tables and moved the seven stools across from the seven imps' little house to the outbuilding. He also arranged for a really big plasma screen to be put on the wall to show some historical performance data, and acquired a smart flipchart stand. He'd even put a little presentation together and taken advice from a close friend as to how best to structure the schedule for the day, including sending out the agenda in advance and asking the imps to prepare for the session by identifying weaknesses in their personal performance and one area in which they each felt they could improve, in order to help drive the team forward. In fairness, although he had thought it unlikely at the time, Not-Quite reflected that they had been open and candid on that first day he had barged in unannounced, giving him some cause for optimism that perhaps things were on the up, and hopefully paving the way for a constructive session.

The day of the first workshop dawned and Not-Quite greeted each of the imps as they trooped in to the outbuilding.

By this time, the beautiful but vain depot manager had received confirmation back from her (now ex-) performance manager that Not-

---

275. Whilst the scope of Not-Quite's workshop sessions is not fully defined, real-world employers are expected to consult with employees or their representatives about the planning and organisation of health and safety training.

Quite was indeed still around, and operating from the little house and outbuilding alongside the seven imps. She had also been the unhappy recipient of troubling tales of a new-fangled safety cultural initiative he was setting up at his depot. Now unbeknown to Not-Quite, earlier that morning, being keen to find out what was going on and eager to learn more about his safety success secrets, the beautiful but vain depot manager had awoken at dawn, skipped breakfast and headed out towards his depot. She waited behind a tree when she got near – a ploy she'd seen adopted by many a comic-book villain – until the seven imps had gathered together for their workshop session, before creeping out on tiptoes and trying to sneak a peek in through the window to the outbuilding. Alas, she was unable to see what was taking place! *How could this be?* she wondered. Well, seemingly without her knowledge, the seven imps had recently installed one-way security glass in response to recent reports of a local intruder having gained unauthorised entry to a dwelling inhabited by three local bears. Most thought it likely that this tale of porridge theft and chair breaking – sparked by an uninvited visitor in the form of a locksmith's daughter – had been somewhat exaggerated but, whether or not it was true, the seven imps quite liked the sense of mystery and privacy that the one-way glass had brought to their workplace, believing it to have been money well spent for them. This was not a feeling shared by the beautiful but vain depot manager, however, and with the concealment of Not-Quite's workshop only serving to further fuel her anger, she grumpily made her way back to her own depot.

Being unaware of the beautiful but vain depot manager's previous visit to Sly, as well as her failed attempt to spy on that morning's safety proceedings by looking the wrong way through the one-way glass, Not-Quite continued on undaunted, preparing himself for the workshop ahead. With the imps having settled in, Not-Quite highlighted the key points he planned to cover in the workshop. Addressing the group, he said:

'*Welcome!* Welcome all of you! Today, we're going to be looking at two aspects. *First,* what happens when barriers – or risk controls – don't work, are ineffective, or are defeated. *Or, to put it another way, how each of you might limit the capability of active or procedural barriers to deliver their functions.* And *second,* the role each of you has to play in ensuring effective barrier management and maintenance. To help us to address these points, I'll be introducing the *'Perilous Porridge*

Pot, Oaty Overflow and Preventing Loss of Containment' case study, to give you an understanding of performance influencing factors, the importance of reliable human performance and the part we can all play in getting this right.' This suggestion was met by a sea of blank faces, the group of imps being, as yet, unaware of the detail of this story. 'Sounds *thrilling...'* muttered Sly, not quite quietly enough.

'But first things first...' continued Not-Quite, clearly unfazed by Sly's cynicism, '...something's been bothering me. I just need to ask you little folk the obvious question that's been weighing on my mind. Think of it as an ice-breaker, if you will...*What exactly is 'imp' short for?'* This question was met with sniggering amongst the assembled crowd, with Bumbler and Sly leading the challenge back to Not-Quite: 'What is 'imp' short for? *What is 'imp' short for?* Surely you must realise – a tall imp would be as ridiculous as a diddy giant! It just wouldn't work on any level! *It would be positively oxymoronic!'* said Bumbler. Sly chuckled ominously. The momentary hilarity was interrupted by Stressy, who protested 'NO! NO! Not-Quite didn't mean that. He meant what's the full version of 'imp'? To which question, *I'm not really sure we have an answer...!'*

In a bid to keep up the pace of the session, engender a sense of calm and restore order amongst the imps, Not-Quite replied, in answer to his own rhetoric: 'Oh well, I wasn't sure when I first met you all. I did, however, look the word up, by way of research for this session, and found it to mean *'a small mischievous devil'.* Now, I'm quite sure the seven of you aren't devilish in the slightest...' he said, his gaze flicking momentarily towards Sly, '...but the more I've seen all of you in action, the more you've convinced me it's short for *'IMP*-EDIMENTS TO RELIABLE PERFORMANCE!',* letting out an audible chuckle, as he uttered these words. Not-Quite's laughter echoed around the walls of the outbuilding and he sensed that, just maybe, he'd overstepped the mark and failed to read the mood of the room, the feeling of relaxed openness having vanished in an instant. This gave Not-Quite cause to question whether it had been such a wise move to be so free with his thoughts. In that moment, he felt, he'd lost the buy-in of his audience, being as he was now surrounded by a circle of frowning faces and furrowed brows. There seemed to be a perception developing amongst the group that their idiosyncrasies – and even inadequacies – might have been rumbled. Being keen to get the imps to refocus, however, Not-Quite emphasised that it was going to take all of them to make sure they achieved reliably high performance in the future. He set the scene for the afternoon's activities, which was to include the development of action plans. *He knew that this was to be no walk in the park!* He wasn't under any illusion that this was going to be an audience easily won over to his way of thinking, nor that there were likely to be any quick wins for turning their sorry performance around. And, just like any line manager, he knew only too well how hard it could be to make an action plan seem like an attractive proposition, even at the best of times. The session had barely begun and already Not-Quite feared that this was to be a long day. Nevertheless, he wanted the imps to make the most of their time together as a group, away from the pressures of their day jobs and, having mulled over their earlier introductions, he'd already started to form an impression about their relative strengths, weaknesses and aspirations. This had provided him with some useful insights as to how each of them perceived their current circumstances and, more importantly, had given him some ideas about how they might be able to help him to turn things around.

The morale of the group steadily waned with the progression of the morning session and so it came as something of a relief to Not-Quite when, out of the corner of his eye, he caught sight of their lunch having arrived. Fortuitously, the beautiful but vain depot manager hadn't successfully extended her expertise into catering. It was suspected that she might have been barred from so doing following the introduction of more stringent procurement requirements, in the wake of the apple-based incident caused by a cold-calling displaced depot manager (an old woman protagonist) way back in the organisation's history. Not-Quite had located a reputable caterer and had high hopes that lunch boxes containing sandwiches, sausage rolls, samosas, fruit and fairy cakes would help to endear him to them. *He wasn't wrong...*

The imps having devoured their lunches, with only a few pieces of fruit remaining, which had proved inexplicably unpopular, Not-Quite called the group back together. With the morning's tensions fortunately behind them, the imps sat back down happily with renewed focus, to run through the case study Not-Quite had prepared.

Not-Quite opened up the afternoon session by saying to the group: 'What I'm about to tell you isn't a true story, but it does provide us with some valuable lessons and highlight the possibility of a similar thing happening here, if each and every one of us isn't vigilant in our day-to-day activities. And if you can't quite comprehend how big an effect you can all have upon the performance of safety critical tasks, just bear with me and we'll run through the ways in which your behaviours, decisions, actions and even inactions might help to determine the outcome of a loss of containment scenario, by way of example. Just supposing for a moment that this *was* a true story, I'd like each of you to try to think about how you might have affected or influenced the path of events. Consider, if you will, how things might pan out if something similar were to happen here, by discussing it with the imps at your tables, and we'll come back together as a group in half an hour's time. And Drifty! *DRIFTY!* If you could get up off the floor and join Sly, Stressy and Weedy at their table, that would be just splendid!' He was greeted by silence from the group, and so – after a pause – continued on: 'Now, listen up all of you! I know that *'The Gauge, the Alarm and the Shut-Off Valve'* case study we're going to run through today doesn't have quite the same literary ring to it as, say *'The Lion, the Witch and the Wardrobe'*[276], but trust me…in the sphere of reliable human performance workshops, it's the best I could come up with at short notice. And, whilst we're on the subject, it's questionable whether witches, wardrobes, lions, or any combination thereof would ever achieve the same level of success in preventing loss of containment events anyway, as compared with the joint efforts of gauge, alarm and valve. When it comes to story-telling with real-world value, by my reckoning, the porridge pot tale wins hands down, every time!'

NOT-QUITE PRESENTS THE WORKSHOP CASE STUDY
'The Perilous Porridge Pot, Oaty Overflow and an Unfortunate Case of Loss of Containment'
(or 'The Gauge, the Alarm and the Shut-Off Valve')

Not-Quite summarised a case study for the group, which he'd based upon a time-honoured tale. He recounted a story told to him many moons back about a little girl who had a peculiar – *and ultimately perilous* – porridge pot, which she'd somehow installed in her mother's house. But, when her mother had taken on an operative role in that

---

276. This appears to be an attempt by Not-Quite to make an oblique reference to the well-renowned work of C.S.Lewis, albeit that his anecdote of overflowing oats is undoubtedly inferior to Lewis's fantasy, in which an imagined world is accessed via a wardrobe door. See: Lewis, C.S., *'The Lion, the Witch, and the Wardrobe – The Chronicles of Narnia, Book 2'* (Harper Collins, 2009).

scenario, she hadn't understood the design, the gauge had been faulty, unreliable or misread due to her being preoccupied, the alarm didn't work or had been ignored and – when things went really wrong – there had been no obvious means of stemming the seemingly endless flow of porridge! From the fable, as Not-Quite told it, the group had to agree that there was a certain inevitability to the catastrophic porridge spill outcome that had resulted there.

Looking at the key aspects of the porridge pot scenario, Not-Quite got the imps to recognise some areas of just such an operation – associated with the gauge, alarm and valve – where their behaviours might have a detrimental impact on process control, in a real-world context. They did this by considering each of the stages involved in the porridge pot loss of containment scenario – which had become something of a legendary tale and the subject of many a safety newsletter over recent months – as well as relating the equivalent challenges from their own work setting to it, where appropriate. Taking each stage of the process in turn, Not-Quite asked the imps to think about how what they did or didn't do might affect this kind of outcome, with the exception of the design, which he acknowledged couldn't be readily influenced by them, as operatives. He added that, in future, he would also be advising his fellow managers as to how they might work more collaboratively to influence their senior leaders. He believed the support of his fellow managers would be invaluable, if he was to get the approval of senior managers to change plant design, the ultimate purpose of this being to remove some of the issues the imps faced at their own location on a daily basis. Not-Quite knew that, wherever possible, designing out risk was the best option all round.

Half an hour passed and, having reviewed the case study presented to them by Not-Quite in their sub-groups, the imps returned to discuss their thoughts with the others.

For the gauge, Bumbler acknowledged that his somewhat hapless approach might mean he wouldn't know how to read it, due to him lacking in the necessary competence or knowledge, understanding or experience of what to do. And together with Stressy and Spent, Bumbler also recognised that they might misread it, or that too many other control room responsibilities could distract their attention – in Stressy's case because he had other things on his mind, or in Spent's case, perhaps because he was looking at too many screens or had too much equipment to monitor. The opposite could be said to be true for Idle, who had so little to do that his levels of vigilance were known to be poor, due to his failing to stay alert. And as for Drifty, he had to concede that, given how he often lacked fitness, restfulness or alertness, he was probably a weak choice for the gauge monitoring role. When it came to the gauge itself, there were concerns raised about poor records, due to Spent being so exhausted from other activities as to be unable to devote sufficient time to, and focus his attention on, maintenance tasks. And Bumbler had to concede that another possibility was that the gauge was poorly calibrated, because he was often unsure as to what needed to be done, when a request went out for him to maintain the equipment.

For the high level alarm, the imps recognised the possibility that it might not sound at all. Another issue could have been that it wasn't functioning due to lapses in the preventative or reactive maintenance schedules. Or, if it did sound, there might have been an element of confusion in the minds of the imp operatives – maybe a case of alarm flooding with too many alarms overwhelming Spent, a lack of competence or confidence on Bumbler's part to make the right decisions, or Stressy's inability to make the right decision at the critical moment. And, much as it was unlikely he'd admit to it himself, the other imps also recognised that the alarm might have been wilfully interfered with by Sly, because of an inappropriate desire he harboured to prioritise production levels above safe process operation, or to get work done faster, possibly due to him being motivated by money or some other factor.

Finally, they came to the shut-off valve, the last line of defence in preventing the loss of containment event from occurring. Many of the imps' observations about their involvement with the gauge and high level alarm were recognised as being equally valid here. But additionally, the group acknowledged that there might have been confusion in the minds of Spent, Drifty, Idle, or Bumbler, when seeking to distinguish between valve-open and valve-closed positions; the possible subverting or sabotaging of the valve by Sly (motivated by malice or just thinking he could get the job done more quickly) or, if the valve required manual effort to operate it, a weakness or lack of sufficient physical strength on Weedy's part to close it.

Not-Quite thanked the imps for their contributions, all of which he'd found useful. Some of them appeared slightly troubled, however, maybe thinking they'd been too honest or upfront with their responses.

In the case of the more shifty imps, it was possible this reaction had been brought on by an awkward sense that they'd been caught out and might be about to get their comeuppance. In realising this and seeking to reassure them, Not-Quite said: 'I hope you can see now why I thought of you as '*imp*-ediments to reliable performance' before... but it doesn't have to stay that way. Between you, I'd say you have all the qualities needed to turn this around – I've every confidence that each of you has it in you to deliver reliable performance – and making sure you play your part in this will really help to increase the effectiveness of our risk controls.'

The imps readily agreed, without a hint of the resentment that had surfaced in some of them during their previous conversation, when Not-Quite had speculated about the origins of the imp name. But being an imp unable to let sleeping dogs lie, Bumbler – in his typically inept way – piped up all of a sudden, Not-Quite's recollection of their earlier meeting having triggered a memory which had obviously been playing on his mind. Bumbler asked: 'Remember when you first came to us, you posed the question as to why we were called 'imps'...well, if you don't mind me saying, in the same vein, I've always found the name 'Not-Quite' to be a little...you know...*odd*? And it got me to thinking, do you have any idea why your Mum would have picked that name, rather than say, Peter, Darren...*or Colin, perhaps?*'

'Well...' replied Not-Quite, wiping a tear away from his eye, as he reminisced on the mother he'd lost to the angels a long time ago, '...I'm really glad you asked that, because until I met the seven of you, it had been something of a mystery to me too. But I think I know now... I believe I've been 'Not-Quite' because of one or more of my *inner imps* holding me back and stopping me from achieving my full potential, at any point in time. And I like to think that maybe, just maybe, my mother was ahead of her time, that perhaps she was something of a visionary in the human factors field, and that she would have wanted me to do anything I could to be the best I could be in life. Of course, I'll never know for certain now, but I reckon she'd have been proud of me for carrying on the good work she started...'

The imps broke out into a spontaneous round of applause, before Not-Quite continued on: '...I hope that now you can all see how important it is for us to recognise weaknesses in our capacity to perform brilliantly, whenever required, and to act to correct these flaws as necessary. And wherever I can, you have my word that I'll help you – it's my job to bring about this change with you all!' said Not-Quite, sincerely.

The topic of the workshop having begun as an awkward sell to the audience, there was a sudden change of mood. Each of the imps was starting to see how they could help to improve the management of their safety critical processes or indeed, how they might compromise them, if they didn't address their respective flaws as a priority. Not-Quite added: 'Okay, now I know this might seem a bit blunt, but if we are going to turn this poor performing depot around, I'm going to need you all to help me out with this. So, are you with me? *Do you want to be a part of a bright and exciting future?*'

There were nods and murmurs of approval, which Not-Quite took as a positive sign – and even Drifty seemed to stir from his nap! The only dissenting voice in the room appeared to be that of Sly, who muttered cynically: '...it seems *someone's* been on a motivational course!' In truth, Not-Quite had prepared himself for this kind of response; he was a realist and knew that it wouldn't only be plain sailing from this point on. Having sensed that the mood of the group was generally on an upward trajectory, however, Not-Quite tasked the imps to come up with a list of personal actions to tackle their particular weaknesses and the challenges they each faced. They wasted no time at all in starting to compile their own plans, before presenting these to the rest of the group and receiving feedback from Not-Quite[277]. As the workshop drew to a close, Not-Quite thanked the impish delegates for their help and said he'd be looking to identify some common focus areas for them going forward, as a team, supported by a monitoring programme. He was also keen to get some suggestions from them as to how to maintain their efforts – to help achieve continual improvement – including spreading the word about what they'd learnt to the wider organisation. And, in directing a final comment to Sly in particular, he reminded the group that all of their contributions were equally valuable to him, with no single imp mattering more than any of the others. As the session drew to a close, even the most cynical of the imps had to admit that, whilst the workshop case study had been all about porridge and a fictional kitchen-based fiasco, the points they'd discussed were clearly pertinent to their own oil storage depot. Their feedback forms showed the imps to be overwhelmingly supportive of Not-Quite's approach.

---

277. For the imps' action plans, refer to *How to...* Guide Ten, which accompanies this fable.

Some time passed...

With Not-Quite at the helm, under the banner of his reinvigorated management initiative, the impish team underwent quite a transformation, rebranding themselves *'Just-So and the Get It Right Sprites'* and further developing the action points required for them to achieve reliable performance in the control of their key risks. As time went by, their approach to risk management was lauded organisation-wide and beyond, and they went on tour with their workshop, winning plaudits, accolades and all manner of industry awards. The action plans they'd put together received buy-in from their senior leaders too. It was quite a turnaround for a group of imps with humble beginnings as operatives at the organisation's poorest performing depot. And, in what was seen as a spin-off from their initial success, they recorded a team-building song too, written by Not-Quite, but with input from each of the imps. They'd composed it at the end of a follow-up workshop, recognising their respective roles in securing reliable human performance, and their need to work together in reaching for their safety goals.

The song went like this...

> 'Our time's drawing near, our workshop's just ending,
> So let's pause to reflect on what it is we're defending.
> There's no point protecting 'gainst a wolf once worth fearing
> If scanning horizons shows other threats nearing.
> There are times, I'm afraid, when *Not-Quite's* not enough
> With barriers defeated, when dragons get tough...
> A need now to defend, 'gainst new troubles we face,
> And in that...my dear friends...you each have a place!
> A time's fast approaching and that time is now,
> For a raising of standards, and I'll show you how...
>
> There's *Stressy* – who's bothered by troubles at home,
> And *Drifty,* who dreams of being some other gnome.
> *Weedy*, meanwhile, can't move the valve that needs shifting,
> A fact not picked up during interview sifting.
> As for *Idle*, work's dull, but he doesn't mean harm,
> Though he's likely to miss the most crucial alarm.
> And *Spent*, overwhelmed by all manner of screens,
> Who can't – every time – understand what they mean.

> *Bumbler's* good natured, but doesn't see all it takes,
> For catastrophe – one or two of his casual mistakes.
> And lastly, there's *Sly*, an imp with agenda that's hidden,
> Gauges, valves, alarms – all he's overridden.
> Well, not on my watch, not any more,
> Not now these issues have been brought to the fore!
> You've given me cause for internal reflection,
> And much sharper focus on barrier selection…
> …But not just selection, maintenance too –
> Which I just can't entrust to unreliable crew!
> Taken one by one, you will likely impede,
> But working together, we're sure to succeed!
> And now I'm *'Just-So'* – control has to be tight…
> With reliable performance from you *'Get It Right Sprites'!'*

Just-So, as he was now known, quickly became a highly-regarded depot manager, gaining widespread recognition for his ability to secure reliable performance from his team, all of whom were coming to understand that what they did – *or didn't do* – directly influenced how well barriers worked. But most importantly…they all lived *reliably* ever after.

I say 'all', but you may be wondering what became of the beautiful but vain depot manager…

Some months later…

After quite some time of noticing Not-Quite's name had vanished from the scorecard results – a gap which led her to believe his workshop approach was having little impact – the beautiful but vain depot manager was perplexed to see a new name, *Just-So*, listed at the very top. Thinking that there must have been some kind of mistake, she contacted the in-house performance information team, who were responsible for validating the data. She logged a call with the helpdesk, who gave her a fault reference number and promised her faithfully that they would investigate the issue. Unsurprisingly, she was livid and vented her anger at anyone who would listen – including the helpdesk operator and her ex-performance manager. *But it was no good!* The helpdesk call was swiftly closed, it having been confirmed that the data was indeed accurate. And it wasn't long before it became painfully apparent to the beautiful but vain depot manager that the scope of Not-Quite's new-fangled safety cultural initiative on which she'd previously tried to gain insight – by peering the wrong way through the one-way glass – was more far-reaching than she could have dared to imagine! The harsh realisation soon hit home for the beautiful but vain depot manager that it was too late to turn her performance around: Not-Quite had changed his name to Just-So and, with the support of the imps who'd been rebranded as the Get It Right Sprites, was now achieving a level of safety excellence which was simply unsurpassable.

Within a matter of days, Just-So's permanent move to the role of depot manager at the seven sprites' depot was confirmed and the deal for his promotion, sealed. Happily, things also worked out well for the beautiful but vain depot manager's ex-performance manager, who, having rescued Just-So (formerly Not-Quite) was appointed to the role of performance manager at the Get It Right Sprites' depot, reporting directly to him. These moves became part of a wider depot restructure – a new world order, within which there was to be no place for depot managers of the beautiful but vain kind. This was thought to have been linked to the findings of the investigation to which the beautiful but vain depot manager had been subject, the outcome of which was for her to leave shortly afterwards by mutual agreement, her departure being widely seen as the best result for all concerned. But even with workplace tensions seemingly resolved for the best, Just-So's father still faced a testing time ahead. The now angry and beautiful, but vain ex-depot manager could no longer suppress her feelings, and went on to serve up to him awkward meal time silences and barbed insults about misplaced loyalties, in almost equal measure.

Even more time passed…

Whilst some familial discord remained, it came as some small consolation to the beautiful, but vain ex-depot manager when she eventually secured a new employment opportunity, gaining work at a nearby peculiar porridge pot facility. This was widely rumoured to be a downward step for her career-wise but, on the upside, at least it improved her understanding of safety critical equipment and processes, and the value of securing reliable performance from the human operatives tasked with carrying them out, a skillset that had been found much wanting in her previous approach! *Maybe she would see the error of her ways, but only time would tell…*

MODERN MEANING

In many respects, this tale can be viewed the last piece of the jigsaw, which is perhaps fortunate, given that it's the final fable in this book!

Earlier fables prompted us to look at the identification and control of some big risks. *Zac's fable* naturally led us to think about 'fall from height' and 'dropped object' top events. *The porridge pot fable* gave us cause to consider 'loss of containment', by using the fictional problem of a surfeit of porridge to show how to identify threats and put in place barriers (or risk controls) which prevent or limit the extent of a top event. And *the four little pigs' fable* steered our attention towards features including barrier type, barrier function and barrier maintenance requirements. In the real world, the identification and recording of major accident hazards is the stuff of an organisation's risk register, which should be endorsed by its 'senior leaders'. In a systems context, this type of information can be recorded and further developed within 'bow tie models' or through the use of other 'risk modelling' techniques. And finally, at the frontline – as we've seen in this fable – individuals need to play their part, by doing the right things to control risk, through applying their skill, judgment and expertise to make sure barriers work, not just where the 'operating conditions' are 'routine', but also in 'non-routine', 'exceptional', 'abnormal' and 'emergency' circumstances.

This fable brings into sharp focus the vital role performed by operatives in ensuring the effectiveness of barriers, by showing how what they personally do – or don't do – can strengthen or undermine them.

More importantly, the fable suggests how organisations can act where barrier weaknesses are identified, by understanding *why* and *how* people fail, and using this knowledge to address the specific characteristics and other factors that drive operative behaviour, thereby improving performance reliability. *But why should this matter?* It's simply because by appreciating the different traits and motivations that drive operatives – not only in terms of their conduct of safety critical tasks, but also in relation to ensuring their wellbeing whilst performing them – that organisations can be propelled into achieving higher performance levels. Furthermore, when used proactively, such insights can help to inform and shape the types of characteristics and requirements organisations choose to define within the roles and responsibilities, 'competencies' and job descriptions of those who work for them. Other positive indications, which tend to be observable where this approach is effectively applied by organisations, include fewer and less severe incidents being reported, together with a more visible and felt safety culture.

The use of the imps in this fable has allowed us to look in turn at each of the performance influencing factors relevant to individuals, and how these might impact upon barrier effectiveness. Here, and in *How to…* Guide Ten which accompanies this fable, we apply this thinking, by considering how each of these identified weaknesses can be addressed – or, to put it another way, performance influencing factors positively harnessed – so as to help secure the optimal level of operational control.

Putting it bluntly, the key message to take from this fable, which applies to any organisation that calls upon operatives to carry out safety critical tasks, is:

'Don't allow them to be too stressed, stupid, overwhelmed, tired, bored, weak or – *dare I say it?* – devious to get things right.'

Or, to coin the names of the imps…

'Don't let them be like *Stressy, Bumbler, Spent, Drifty, Idle, Weedy* or *Sly.*'

And why is this message important? It's because left unchecked, these *imps* will compromise the effectiveness of operational control, by decreasing the performance of barriers and stopping them from functioning in the way they should, which can ultimately lower an organisation's immunity against process safety incidents. They can also threaten the personal safety, health and wellbeing of the operatives who perform tasks, and sometimes that of others with whom they have cause to interact. And, whilst individuals displaying any such characteristics have a part to play in addressing these, the clear responsibility for dealing with them – and encouraging the right behaviours too – ultimately rests with organisational management, right up to the level of its senior leaders.

Approaches taken towards risk, and the role people play in controlling it, differ widely – some are highly reactive, whilst others are heavily weighted towards the proactive end of the spectrum. It's often the case that an organisation's risk strategy will feature both proactive and reactive elements, with even those that adopt a predominantly proactive approach towards controlling risk still needing to make an effective reactive response on the occasions when incidents do occur. Where organisations take an approach that is proactively biased, this tends to see them using knowledge about the reliability (or unreliability) of human performance to inform the design of their risk controls, which is a good thing. A mainly reactive approach, on the other hand, typically means weaknesses in human performance are reactively identified, being corrected retrospectively, for instance through addressing the learning points and recommendations which flow from incident investigations.

It's often the case that, in the aftermath of an incident, an organisation will take the opportunity to identify where human involvement could have been improved or, to use the analogy from the fable, to say that one or more of the *imps* were *at play*. For barrier performance to be high or, to put it another way, for barriers to function well – particularly for the active and procedural types – organisations need to be confident that the human operatives for whom they are responsible aren't too stressed, stupid, overwhelmed, tired, bored, weak or devious to get things right. This might seem like a negative, blunt or even impolite message. *I have some sympathy with this view.* But it's worth paying attention to the intrinsic properties of each performance influencing factor in turn, given that it's likely to have been these – possibly with others thrown in too – which permitted or, in the case of 'violations', even directly caused an incident. Indeed, their relevance within the realm of safety critical task performance cannot be overstated – a point borne out by the fact that they are often viewed as significant 'contributory factors' in incident investigations[278]. This also holds true for 'near miss' incidents, albeit that the data from these tends to be less publicised, largely due to these events not being as newsworthy as circumstances in which a catastrophic outcome results. With all this in mind, organisations need to be satisfied that they can call upon workers like the *Get It Right Sprites* instead. These sprites can be viewed as the antitheses to the imps featured in this fable. And, whilst these are sprites to whom we

---

278. The characteristics displayed by the imps featured in this fable typify the sorts of factors responsible for creating the *trajectory through the cheese* (see the explanation of Reason's 'Swiss cheese model', provided in the context of *the porridge pot fable*).

are never properly introduced here, they embody the sorts of qualities that any organisation should welcome as traits in the operatives within their workforces. It's these sprites to whom they look to *save the day...*

To *Strong* who, unlike *Weedy*, is able to carry out assigned tasks within the limits of his personal physical capability and is supported by an effective organisational approach to the assessment and control of 'manual handling' risks.

To *Alert* who, unlike *Spent*, is vigilant and able to notice new or abnormal events, being adept at problem-solving and decision-making, and is supported by an organisational approach which maintains optimal staffing levels, ensuring 'workload' is kept at the right level, particularly crucial for the conduct of safety critical tasks.

To *Active* who, unlike *Idle*, adopts a dynamic approach and remains attentive, maintaining mental agility even when there is little work to do, and who is supported by an organisational approach which optimally allocates workload, ensuring roles, tasks and activities offer a sufficient level of interest for those carrying them out.

To *Rested* who, unlike *Drifty*, has opportunities for periods of good quality sleep or relaxation, including sufficient time in which to rest, and who doesn't allow productivity or personal issues to conflict with these goals. This needs to be backed up by an organisational approach which champions effective 'fatigue' risk management and fair workload allocation, and also caters for the support and welfare needs of its 'workers', rather than being purely productivity-focused.

To *Calm* who, unlike *Stressy*, is able to manage the pressures of a fair workload, backed up by the necessary pro-active organisational support measures which place a positive focus on mental wellbeing and the management of 'stress', and which detect circumstances in which work demands have the potential to become excessive, before they become problematic.

To *Smart* who, unlike *Bumbler,* has the right skills, knowledge and attitude – or 'competence' – to carry out allocated tasks and assigned duties, so as to be able to reliably perform them to agreed standards, whether set by an organisation, legislation, industry, external bodies, or any combination of these.

To *Honest* who, unlike *Sly*, shows willingness, openness and integrity, and has the confidence to speak up whenever things go wrong or not as planned, or when in possession of knowledge of poor practice, 'non-compliances', or 'violations' of standards by fellow operatives.

To exhibit one or more of the traits embodied by Not-Quite's imps in this fable (or 'performance influencing factors', to use Health and Safety Executive terminology) not only has potentially grave implications for the conduct of safety critical tasks, but also carries with it significant personal health and safety risks for those involved, and others with whom they work and interact. It's often the case that specialists in the process safety domain set out quite different priorities to those within the occupational health and safety sphere. In reality though, it should be perfectly possible for their goals to be achieved in tandem. The process safety specialists don't want operatives to mess up their shiny machines and processes. The occupational health and safety specialists, on the other hand, don't want the use of shiny machines and processes to mess up the miraculous machines that are the bodies of the human operatives tasked with using them. The reality is that optimal performance arises when operatives, together with the processes, systems and machines they operate, are all working well.

This fable has highlighted the importance of the factors influencing reliable human performance, by taking a look at each of them in turn.
    The lead character was intentionally called Not-Quite, because the initial scenario depicts strong (negative) influencing factors at play – as shown by the imps – which, independently or in combination, conspire to prevent him from performing at his best. In the safety critical arena – and particularly with reference to the performance of safety critical tasks – it's often the case that to nearly succeed isn't good enough. To give a basic example, completing 95% of valve maintenance scheduled is of no consolation if a valve failure falls within the 5% of valves which went without maintenance. Following the workshop exercise described in this fable, the suggestion is that by identifying the relevant characteristics (imps), their capacity to be optimised is achievable and capable of being harnessed, thus ensuring that the

desired performance level is a realistic goal – with the central character recast from *Not-Quite* to *Just-So*, and the imps' flaws addressed, as seen through their transformation into *Get It Right Sprites*.

In reality, of course, there can be – and indeed, often are – multiple performance influencing factors at play at any one time. It's well-known that where more than one factor is present, this can have a synergistic effect on those experiencing them; being tired or bored, for instance, is bad enough, but being both tired *and* bored can have a far more detrimental impact upon performance reliability than either one of these traits in isolation. It's an interesting exercise to consider each factor in turn, as has been done here, but in the real world what matters more is to think about the interplay between these factors and the critical barriers to which they apply, of which they form an essential component. At a basic level, this was highlighted by the workshop scenario that played out within this fable. For those barriers where the human contribution is significant or vital – often in *active* and always in *procedural* barrier types – it's essential to understand *how* the characteristics and behaviours of operatives can shape positive outcomes, thereby bolstering barrier strength. The consequences of failing to do so were highlighted vividly by the scenario depicted in *the porridge pot fable*.

FROM 'IMPISH INTRODUCTIONS'...
TO ACTION PLANNING FOR
RELIABLE HUMAN PERFORMANCE

Through each of the imps' introductions within this fable, we were afforded a brief look at the features of the *imp*-ediments to reliable human performance. This was a theme developed during the fable's workshop session, which saw each of them applied to the loss of containment case study, in a barrier discussion based upon the events of the earlier scenario from *the porridge pot fable*. It was this discussion which started to show how each of these factors – when uncontrolled – can undermine barrier effectiveness. Here, this thinking is progressed on a stage further, towards developing action plans which address each factor.

To produce a fully comprehensive human factors action plan would be an ambitious project and is one which falls outside the scope of this book. For a start, the development of any real-world action plan requires more information about the context within which activities are being undertaken than is provided by this fable. Nevertheless *How to...* Guide Ten, which accompanies this fable, can be regarded as a start point for anyone looking for an in-road to the discipline. This guide contains the imps' action plans referred to in the fable which, whilst not intended to be fully comprehensive, offer an introduction to each performance influencing factor (or *imp*), together with some accompanying basic practical steps as to how they might be addressed. These factors include both physical factors – relating to physical strength and capability – and mental factors, which can impair decision-making or result in non-desirable behaviours, including fatigue and sub-optimal workload allocation. As such, the type of information these plans contain should be of interest to those in charge or control of processes which require the performance of safety critical tasks.

When organisations take the time and trouble to understand and address the *imps* – commonly referred to as 'human factors' or 'performance influencing factors' – that pose potential problems for them, they can expect to enjoy improvements to their process safety performance, as well as to the safety and welfare of their workers. We've seen here how it's possible to look at each factor in isolation (of likely interest to an occupational health and safety expert), but also acknowledged the value of looking at how relevant factors can degrade the capability of barriers to prevent an operational incident or mitigate the consequences, should such an event occur (more the focus of a process safety specialist's endeavours). Barrier management was the subject of *the four little pigs' fable* and it's possible to apply the factors set out within the *How to...* Guide to this final fable, when seeking to improve the effectiveness with which active and procedural barriers, in particular, are managed.

There are undoubtedly differences in the extent to which real-world organisations choose to tackle performance influencing factors. The nature of their operations, the risks involved and budgetary constraints are just a few of the reasons that explain these differences. But whilst their approaches may be nuanced, organisations can reap clear benefits by simply addressing some basic elements for each factor. As such, the action plans featured in *How to...* Guide Ten contain actions which can be adopted in totality within organisations' real-world plans, adapted for their own purposes, or simply used to stimulate discussion.

Counteracting the influence of these factors has two key benefits. *First*, it reduces the likelihood of error and/or improves the reliability of individuals performing safety critical tasks, thereby reducing the likelihood of an incident occurring or mitigating its effects, if one does occur[279]. *Second*, it also delivers health benefits, due to the reduced reliance placed upon them, as individuals. The imps – and the performance influencing factors to which they are loosely connected – are complex and the issues to which they give rise cannot be corrected by a *one size fits all* approach. But taking the time to understand and address each of them offers organisations clear opportunities to secure the benefits of reliable human performance, as well as avoiding the risks created by any shortfalls in the ways in which people carry out safety critical tasks. When used to best effect, this approach can in turn help to shape a pro-active management strategy, allowing organisations to avoid the degradation of their risk controls – so called 'degradation factors' – which negative performance factors pose, if left unchecked.

Finally, it's important to remember that the consideration of personal factors (as epitomised by the imps) is just one of the three areas that organisations concerned about the performance of safety critical tasks need to address. Job factors and organisational factors are important too. And of course, it might be that there are other *imps* at play at any given time – or even that those considered here could be differently analysed or interpreted. It is, however, felt that sufficient types have been covered within this fable and in the accompanying *How to...* Guide Ten, so as to offer the necessary insights about their potential impacts and highlight how possible approaches can be developed, by way of response to them.

For the action plans relevant to each performance influencing factor or *imp*, reference should be made to *How to...* Guide Ten, which accompanies this fable. For each factor or imp, this guide contains, *first*, the reason it should be addressed; *second*, an overview of its effects, and *third*, some suggested management and mitigation measures to tackle it, with the context for each of the factors already having been given by the imps' personal introductions within the workshop featured in this fable.

---

279. See also the discussion of barrier principles in relation to the description of events given in *the porridge pot fable*, which considered the part played by basic human actions in preventing, and limiting the escalation of, incident scenarios.

CLOSING THOUGHTS

Putting the meaning of this final fable in a nutshell – and taking it in conjunction with the messages from previous tales – the reality is that people matter. They matter because they are people. *This is the moral bit.* They matter because the law says they matter too. *This is the legal bit,* reflected in *HSWA 1974* and all manner of supporting regulations. But, as this tale has sought to show, they also matter because of what they bring to the systems, processes and procedures organisations claim to have in place to make things work. *This is the practical bit.* Senior leaders need to be cognisant of this, always seeking to ensure that the procedures written on their watch are set out in a way which makes it far more likely that people (their 'users') will succeed rather than fail, with those who read them having clarity about what is expected of them, and acting accordingly. And, perhaps even more importantly, they need to ensure that their management systems are consistent with the tone they set for their safety culture, such that all those who work for them clearly understand how what they do and the way in which they act – including the reliability with which they perform tasks – contributes to successful outcomes. When senior leaders behave in a way that is consistent with the tone and which drives the culture that follows it, they are invariably rewarded by this permeating every other facet of risk management, across their organisations. It also follows that those organisations with a strong safety culture – in which there is close collaboration between senior leaders and all those who work for them – can typically expect to see this reflected in first-rate safety performance too.

This ultimate fable offered some important perspectives on the relationship between humans and the systems with which they interact. As well as the fable having considered the intrinsic nature of the factors (*or imps!*) influencing the reliability of human performance, it also – through the workshop scenario – showcased how they can be related to specific scenarios, with their presence compromising the effectiveness with which risk is controlled.

The fable looked at the protection of systems from humans.

There were four steps seen as valuable to the achievement of this outcome. *First,* identifying the major accident hazards, which require control; *second,* working out the tasks performed by people, in relation to the control of these major accident hazards; *third,* from this set of tasks, working out which are the most important – or 'safety critical' – ones, and *fourth* and finally, working out how to ensure that when people are called upon to perform safety critical tasks, they do so reliably well. Importantly, in looking at these steps, the fable considered the ways in which the different factors (or *imps*) might be addressed, to secure reliable performance from a process-safety perspective. As the fable highlighted, in this respect, the organisational emphasis should be placed firmly upon reducing the potential for human failure.

The fable also considered the protection of humans from systems.

This comprised a consideration of the various and variable physical and mental strengths and weaknesses of individuals. This aspect was tackled by looking at each separate factor (or *imp*) and the measures required to protect those directly affected or influenced by them – as well as others with whom they interact – from harm.

For a summary of practical points to take away,
based upon the topics and subtopics handled by this fable,
see *How to…* Guide Ten.

EPILOGUE

That just about finishes things, as far as the fables are concerned.

I hope that, in the course of compiling these tales, I haven't entirely destroyed the *magic* some readers might associate with the stories in their original forms. On the contrary, maybe I've succeeded in sprinkling a little *fairy dust* on to the surface of some areas of safety that have an unfortunate tendency to look shabby and old.

BEDLAM AND BEYOND

Life is full of optimistically dreamy *'what ifs...?'* and melancholy *'if onlys...'* And, for some lucky characters at least, fables and fairy tales end on an up-beat note. But, as we've seen, this isn't always the case. These fictional works – much like the fables spoon-fed to us during infancy – tend to be concluded at the extremes, following one of two paths. *On the one hand*, we witness euphoric endings, with marriages to princes and princesses instantly removing unassuming individuals with limited prospects from lives of dismal poverty. *On the other hand*, and often more interestingly, we see these stories terminated with the succumbing of central characters to grisly deaths or, for any remaining survivors, the enforced acceptance that they must endure the prospect of lifelong misery.

But no matter which of these two paths we are led down – to the destinations of Bedlam or Utopia – the fictional nature of the original versions was such that the consequences tended to be glossed over and the need for any kind of follow-ups dismissed out of hand. To some extent, we see equivalent endeavours to skirt around awkward outcomes in the tales here, but our frustrations with unsatisfactory endings to these modern versions should be greater. We learn of Pig One that '...*despite the efforts of medical staff to save him, his condition deteriorated and he passed away...*', that '...*the Pest Control Piper was never to be seen again...*', and that the three Goats Tough '...*knew in their hearts that they had been lucky...*', but what happens next? These are the kinds of bold narratives that those in the traditional fictional world seem to readily accept, but are flaws that these new versions unfortunately share in common – with the characters apparently reluctant to call out the need for more palatable endings. We remain unenlightened as to whether the big Giant Man made good on his promise to operate from lower level premises on a '...*happily ever after...*' basis. We aren't updated as to the survival rate of the community, in the wake of the Pest Control Piper's visit. Nor do we see mention made of the need for a post mortem on Pig One. There are no protracted claims for pain, suffering and loss. And on the strength of what we learn here, there's no need either for us to concern ourselves with the potential for tiresome wrangling with 'regulators'. But in a real-world context, the confident finality that accompanies such closing statements is, frankly, unacceptable.

So why should we demand more from these updated versions? It's because in real life – both in the workplace and the wider world – the attempted finality of 'ever afters', particularly where gruesome endings are involved, simply doesn't wash. A workplace death marks the end of life for the person who lived it, but it sets in train a range of consequences and collateral damage. The rebuilding of shattered lives begins. Heated debates rage on about enforcement decisions. Financially costly recovery strategies demand actuarial input. And the redesign of systems which should have been there to protect people from harm, and plant from damage, are given the resource that should have been assigned to them in the first place.

I said at the start that these fables were not true. *I stand by that.* But were there subsequently discovered to be some veracity to them, it's worth keeping in mind the real-world requirements of *the Reporting of Injuries, Diseases and Dangerous Occurrences Regulations 2013*[280] (*RIDDOR*) as well as other reporting expectations which would need to be met. A question often asked in the midst of a safety inspection, or as the follow-up to a reported incident which had the potential to

---

280. S.I. 2013/1471.

be more serious, is: *'What's the worst thing that could have happened?'* In the real world this matters. *Why?* Because to be a dreamer in a fairy tale is a perfectly honourable pursuit; to be one in the real world, however, is utterly unacceptable. And were there to be a sequel to any of these fables, we would no doubt learn of funerals for the deceased and hospital visits to the injured parties made by saddened relatives. We might also see inspections to damaged facilities and enforcement action imposed upon those who failed to meet the most basic of requirements. Not to mention details of the expensive environmental clean-up costs involved, for those who allowed off-site consequences to flow unchecked.

In order to address some of the unanswered, albeit hypothetical, questions that these works of fiction have posed, considered here are the more obvious examples of the worst things or consequences which might result, given equivalent real-world workplace scenarios. There is inevitably an element of repetition here, given that the potential for some types of incident crops up across multiple fables and, depending on your reading of these tales, there might also be a case for supplementary consequences to be added to those listed. That said, the events and their possible outcomes have primarily been evaluated against the requirements of *RIDDOR*, these being the regulations which put duties on employers, the self-employed and people in control of work premises (the 'responsible person') to report certain workplace accidents, occupational diseases and specified dangerous occurrences (near misses).

To date, as far as I'm aware, the goats, trolls, and fictional humans portrayed here have been fortunate in escaping the legal scope of the *Health and Safety at Work etc. Act 1974*[281] (*HSWA 1974*) and the associated regulations to which their real human counterparts fall subject. But, in harking back to the statement made at the beginning of this book – and by taking note of the actions of these characters, rather than any traits particular to the species featured – it remains a worthwhile exercise to look at the reporting requirements likely to have applied, had these instead been real-world events, involving real people.

So, here goes...

---

281. 1974 c. 37.

FATALITIES AND INJURIES

NOTE

In addition to the examples of specific injury types given here, there is also a requirement for any non-fatal injury arising '...*out of or in connection with*...' work which results in a worker being '...*incapacitated for routine work for more than seven consecutive days (excluding the day of the accident)*...' to be reported, under regulation 4(2) of *RIDDOR*, as soon as practicable, and at the latest within 15 days of the accident.

In *the goats' fable*, the Goats Tough were fortunate in not sustaining any injuries. But it's quite plausible that any of them could have become victims, had the angry troll's 'going to beat you up' threats been realised. In the real world, where such incidents result in a work-related death or fatality to 'any person' – with an accident including '...*an act of non-consensual physical violence done to a person at work*' (as defined within regulation 2) – this is *RIDDOR* reportable, being '*where any person dies as a result of a work-related accident*...' covered by regulation 6(1). And if a specified non-fatal injury is sustained by a worker – such as '...*any bone fracture...other than to a finger, thumb or toe.*' – this is *RIDDOR* reportable too, as the regulations require the reporting of specified non-fatal injuries sustained as a result of a work-related accident, which, as for fatalities, includes acts of non-consensual violence done to a person at work, covered by regulation 4(1)(a).

In *the piper's fable*, the outcome for the Pest Control Piper, the mayor and the community was left uncertain. But in the real world where '...*any person dies as a result of occupational exposure to a biological agent*...', of which *Leptospira interrogans* is just one example, this is *RIDDOR* reportable, as covered by regulation 6(2). *Leptospira interrogans* is listed as a causative agent of the bacterial infection, Weil's disease, under the *Health Protection (Notification) Regulations 2010*[282] (see schedule 2 to regulation 4(11) – 'Causative Agents')[283].

---

282. S.I. 2010/659.

283. These regulations contain a comprehensive listing of causative agents, to which SARS-CoV 2 and its accompanying notifiable disease COVID-19 have also been added, following an amendment made by *the Health Protection (Notification)(Amendment) Regulations 2020*; S.I. 2020/237.

Fortuitously, in *Ian's fable*, his venture into the mine did not lead to injury, or worse, but it's clear that things could have turned out very differently for him. Where a worker dies as a result of a work-related accident, this is *RIDDOR* reportable, being an example of *'where any person dies as a result of a work-related accident...'* covered by regulation 6(1). Additionally, if a worker suffers hypothermia or requires resuscitation or admittance to hospital for more than 24 hours due to *'...injury arising from working in an enclosed space...'*, this is *RIDDOR* reportable as an injury, as covered by regulation 4(1)(h). And if a worker experiences *'...loss of consciousness caused by head injury or asphyxia...'*, this too is *RIDDOR* reportable, as an injury, being covered by regulation 4(1)(g).

The swede-shifters in *the swede fable* didn't appear to suffer any injury, but given the haphazard nature of their approach towards vegetable removal and transfer, this would have been a distinct possibility for anyone involved. In the real world, where a worker suffers an injury such as *'...any bone fracture diagnosed by a registered medical practitioner, other than to a finger, thumb or toe...'*, as covered by regulation 4(1)(a), or *'any crush injury to the head or torso causing damage to the brain or internal organs in the chest or abdomen'*, covered by regulation 4(1)(d), these give rise to a need for *RIDDOR* reports to be made.

Zac's fable could so easily have ended differently, with either Zac or the big Giant Woman being struck by a harp, or falling from the beanstalk, resulting in one or more work-related fatalities. In the real world, where *'...any person dies as a result of a work-related accident...'*, this is *RIDDOR* reportable, as covered by regulation 6(1). Based on the account given in the fable, it was also foreseeable that the big Giant Woman could have been struck by a harp or fallen from the beanstalk, and that this would have resulted in injury. In the real world, if a specified non-fatal injury is sustained by a worker due to a dropped object or fall from height, this is *RIDDOR* reportable as an accident. The types of injuries flowing from such incidents, as covered by regulation 4, could conceivably include: *'...any bone fracture diagnosed by a registered medical practitioner, other than to a finger, thumb or toe...'*, under regulation 4(1)(a), or *'...any crush injury to the head or torso causing damage to the brain or internal organs in the chest or abdomen...'*, under regulation 4(1)(d), or *'...any degree of scalping requiring hospital treatment...'*, under regulation 4(1)(f), or *'...loss of consciousness caused by head injury...'*, under regulation 4(1)(g). Further possibilities, as picked out by the tale, might have involved Zac being struck by a harp (a dropped object) or his falling from the beanstalk (a fall from height), leading to injury. Injuries resulting from real-world dropped objects and falls from height are almost invariably of a severity requiring hospital treatment. Where a non-fatal injury is sustained by a non-worker requiring them to be *'...taken from the site of the accident to a hospital for treatment in respect of that injury...'* this is *RIDDOR* reportable, as is covered by regulation 5(a).

DANGEROUS OCCURRENCES

The fictional leptospirosis (Weil's disease) diagnosis described in relation to *the piper's fable* arose following exposure to the bacteria *Leptospira interrogans*. In the real world, where there occurs *'...any accident or incident which results or could have resulted in the release or escape of a biological agent likely to cause severe human infection or illness...'* notification of a dangerous occurrence must be made via the reporting procedures set out under *RIDDOR,* with a report of diagnosis needing to be sent without delay. This covers confirmed cases of Weil's disease, together with other diseases attributable to occupational exposures to biological agents, as required by regulation 7 (see also 'Dangerous Occurrences' schedule 2 to regulation 7, Part 1, paragraph 10 – 'Biological agents').

In *Ian's fable*, it was fortuitous that the dust within the mine was not ignited, given the nature of the activities described, with two notable examples including the rubbing of the ring and the use of a non-approved lamp. In the real world, where a worker's actions result in *'...the ignition of any gas (other than in a safety lamp) or dust below ground...'* this is *RIDDOR* reportable, as a 'dangerous occurrence reportable in relation to a mine', as covered by regulation 7 (see 'Dangerous Occurrences' schedule 2 to regulation 7, Part 3, paragraph 31 – 'Fires or ignition of gas').

The release of porridge from the porridge pot in *the porridge pot fable* led to a farcical scene of mess and chaos but where, in a real-world workplace setting, there is an *'...unintentional release or escape of any substance which could cause personal injury to any person other than through the combustion of flammable liquids or gases...'* this is *RIDDOR* reportable as a 'dangerous occurrence', as covered by regulation 7 (see also 'Dangerous Occurrences' schedule 2 to regulation 7, Part 2, paragraph 27 – 'Hazardous escapes of substances').

In *Zac's fable*, the story left ambiguous both the nature of the physical structure at the top of the beanstalk and whether the workplace was still under construction – a distinct possibility, given that it appeared to spring up overnight! It's unclear how the harp came to fall, but one possibility is that this was due to the big Giant Man taking insufficient measures when working near 'fragile surfaces' at the top of the beanstalk, a factor covered by regulation 9 of *the Work at Height Regulations 2005*[284] ('*the Work at Height Regulations*'). In the real world, where a 'structural collapse' occurs, being '...*the unintentional collapse or partial collapse of...any floor or wall of any place of work, arising from, or in connection with, ongoing construction work...whether above or below ground*', this is *RIDDOR* reportable as a 'dangerous occurrence' under regulation 7 (schedule 2 to regulation 7, Part 2, paragraph 23(b) – 'Structural collapse').

OCCUPATIONAL DISEASES

In *the swede fable*, reference was made to the harvesting of just one over-sized vegetable, but if the work of the super-sized swede-shifters had involved the harvesting of multiple smaller crops, the situation could have been very different. In the real world, a range of occupational diseases can result from this type of work. *First,* where work involves '...*prolonged periods of repetitive movements of the fingers, hand or arm...*' leading to a diagnosis of '*cramp in the hand or forearm*', this is *RIDDOR* reportable, as a case of 'occupational disease', being covered by regulation 8(b). *Second,* where work involves products used in agriculture, including certain plants, giving rise to '...*significant or regular exposure to a known skin sensitizer or irritant...*' and leading to a diagnosis of occupational dermatitis, this is *RIDDOR* reportable as a case of 'occupational disease', as covered by regulation 8(c). *Third,* where work involves exposure to, for instance, grain dust or animals, leading to '...*significant or regular exposure to a known respiratory sensitizer...*' and

---

284. S.I. 2005/735.

a diagnosis of occupational asthma, this is *RIDDOR* reportable, as a case of 'occupational disease', as covered by regulation 8(e). *Fourth*, where work involves tool use (which it clearly didn't here), this lessens the level of manual effort demanded from a worker, but where the '*...regular use of percussive or vibrating tools*' is included, this can give rise to a diagnosis of Carpal Tunnel Syndrome, which is *RIDDOR* reportable, as a case of 'occupational disease', as required by regulation 8(a).

In *Pixie-Locks' fable*, the aches and pains suffered by Small Bear might have been early indications of a more serious condition, for instance a work-related musculoskeletal disorder. In the real world, where work involves '*...prolonged periods of repetitive movement of the fingers, hand or arm...*' leading to a diagnosis of '*cramp in the hand or forearm*', this is *RIDDOR* reportable as a case of 'occupational disease', as covered by regulation 8(b).

A NOTE ON MAJOR ACCIDENT REPORTING

In *the four little pigs' fable*, reference was made to the need to control major accident hazards. There was no description of any incident having occurred at Pig Four's site, with his running of it apparently being exemplary! But in circumstances where real-world incidents occur at 'upper tier COMAH sites', of the type believed to have been operated by Pig Four, certain reporting requirements must be met. In the real world, Major Accident Hazards fall subject to *the Control of Major Accident Hazards Regulations 2015*[285] ('*the COMAH Regulations*') and any 'major accident' meeting the definition within regulation 2(1) must be reported to the competent authority. This requires the reporting of '*...an occurrence such as a major emission, fire, or explosion resulting from uncontrolled developments in the course of the operation of any establishment...*' to which the regulations apply, which leads to '*...serious danger to human health or the environment (whether immediate or delayed) inside or outside the establishment, and involving one or more dangerous substances.*' In such circumstances, reporting is just one aspect that needs to be fulfilled, with the other actions required following a major accident listed in regulation 26 of *the COMAH Regulations*.

---

285. S.I. 2015/483.

In England the competent authority is the Health and Safety Executive and the Environment Agency. In Scotland it's the Health and Safety Executive and the Scottish Environment Protection Agency. In Wales it's the Health and Safety Executive and Natural Resources Wales.

A NOTE ON ENVIRONMENTAL REPORTING

In *the four little pigs' fable,* a reference was made to firewater run-off. Whilst this was not fully explored by the fable, real-world organisations must take all reasonably practicable steps to minimise pollution resulting from firewater, including stopping it from entering surface waters such as rivers, streams, estuaries, lakes, canals or coastal waters or into the ground.

In England, the Environment Agency has wide-ranging powers of enforcement focused on achieving the best outcomes for the environment and for people, which include putting right environmental harm or damage, also known as restoration or remediation. Equivalent arrangements to those operated by the Environment Agency exist in Scotland and Wales, administered by Scottish Environment Protection Agency (SEPA) and Natural Resources Wales respectively, with available remedies including warnings, notices, powers, and orders to resolve and remediate any damage caused.

PART TWO

THE *HOW TO...* GUIDES

These *How to...* Guides draw upon the *modern meanings* of the fables to which they relate and should be of general reader interest. Additionally, organisations may elect to consider their contents insofar as they relate to particular workers and workplace settings. In deciding whether – and to what degree – these have relevance for their operations, organisations can choose to adopt the points they contain in totality or adapt them for their own purposes, or alternatively may deem that they are not applicable to their circumstances.

Those seeking to practically apply the points covered in these guides to specific workers and workplace settings should do so within the context of such Acts, regulations, guidance and other requirements to which their operations are subject. Furthermore, in their endeavours to meet or, better still, exceed these legal and other expectations, organisations should draw upon the support of competent persons whenever appropriate to do so, these being individuals who are able to recognise the risks involved in their activities, and who can advise and guide on the right measures to be applied, in order to control and manage them. Organisations should also ensure that consultation with employees and/or their representatives takes place, at the right times and to the level required, as relevant to the matters in hand.

HOW TO... LOOK AFTER LONE WORKERS

The goats' fable prompted consideration of lone worker safety, with a particular focus on violence and aggression risks. In order to ensure that their lone worker risks are addressed, organisations need to be satisfied they can answer questions about them, including: '*Who is working alone?*', '*What are they doing?*', and '*Are they okay?*' As such, and so as to practically control such risks and ensure the safety of their lone workers, they need to put in place and maintain management arrangements which incorporate considerations of task-based, location and social risks.

HOW TO... MANAGE TASK-BASED RISKS TO LONE WORKERS

This aspect is about making sure that workers know *why* they are going to a job, *what* the job involves, and what they might expect to find on arrival, which can alter according to *when* they are carrying out the work activity. It's important for them to be aware of any variability to the tasks they are required to undertake. There may, for instance, be different risks – or levels of risk – present between day-time and night-time hours. Wherever possible, workers should be provided with details about recent events or circumstances and also given guidance on how to react, should things not go as planned or expected.

In order to effectively manage task-based risks to their lone workers, organisations need to make sure they...

Take a zero tolerance approach towards any kind of violence and aggression. This requires the demonstration of clear management commitment by senior leaders, both towards preventing acts of violence and aggression against their workers, and through the taking of appropriate action whenever such incidents occur.

Carry out a lone working task-based risk assessment, where lone working is an identified risk. This includes: making sure the risk assessment undertaken is comprehensive; briefing workers on the tasks they are to carry out and the associated risks, and implementing all required control measures, advising workers of these and checking that they are following them. Note that lone working should be ruled out where certain types of risk exist including, for instance, confined spaces or working in the vicinity of exposed live electricity conductors. The risk assessment also needs to assess and, where required, appropriately control the negative impacts on workers' stress levels and mental health, as can potentially be brought about by their lone working.

Build capability to perform dynamic risk assessment amongst relevant workers. This applies where the task-based risks workers face have the potential to change rapidly, and includes making sure they are adept at switching between routine and dynamic modes, as necessary. Workers need to be provided with proper training in what to do, with appropriate support given for any decisions made as a result of their own dynamic assessment of the risks encountered. This skill is particularly invaluable for work environments or jobs where the potential for rapidly changing circumstances exists.

Train workers in the specific tasks they are required to perform. All workers need to be suitably trained, but for lone workers this is particularly crucial, as it can often more difficult for them to seek advice from others. It's important for them to understand the extent of the tasks they are able to perform and that they can readily identify circumstances which should motivate them to call for help or support.

Determine which jobs require double handling. This practice involves sending two or more workers to locations or jobs where violence and aggression are recognised as being a realistic possibility and the risk cannot be brought down to an acceptable level, by other means. For certain job types, locations or individuals, double handling may be deemed an appropriate control, on a routine basis.

Put suitable monitoring arrangements in place. It's important for the right balance to be struck between concerns for workers' welfare and other workload monitoring priorities. Particular care should be taken to ensure that workers don't perceive that more importance is attached to productivity monitoring, than monitoring efforts in support of their welfare. It's helpful for routine contact arrangements to be instituted, where supervisors regularly visit and observe lone workers. It's also crucial to implement and maintain effective sign-in and sign-out procedures, and for certain trigger points to be recognised, so that swift action can be taken where concerns for workers are raised. The use of a systems-based approach can often be helpful in supporting the effectiveness of monitoring arrangements, ensuring that knowledge of workers' whereabouts is kept up-to-date. Another important consideration is how alerts are to be communicated to relevant workers, in addition to the means by which workers can notify their supervisors that they are in difficulty. This includes the use of alarms, such as personal monitor alarms, personal attack alarms, panic buttons, and so on. In setting up their monitoring arrangements, it's important for organisations to dedicate a sufficient level of resource to the provision of an agreed, appropriate and reliable response, upon activation of any such devices. Whatever approach is taken, it's vital that workers understand the monitoring systems and procedures involved.

Provide appropriate levels of supervision for the tasks involved. Supervision levels should be commensurate both with the risks and the capability of individuals to recognise and deal with health and safety issues. There should be a particular focus on those lone workers who could require increased levels of supervision. It might be that they lack experience, as is true for trainees. There might be specific risks involved. The situations might be new to the workers concerned. Or they could be classified as vulnerable workers.

HOW TO... MANAGE LOCATION RISKS
TO LONE WORKERS

This aspect is about making sure that workers know *where* they are going – including how they are to get into locations safely, ensuring their safety throughout the duration of their visit, and how they are to get out again safely – noting any difficulties particular to the environment in question.

In order to manage location risks to their lone workers, organisations need to make sure they...

Understand the varied challenges posed by different work locations. It might be that the locations lone workers are required to visit are, for instance, rural or isolated, therefore calling for specific arrangements to be put in place to counteract any difficulties in relation to communication or access.

Share learning and knowledge proactively with them. In addition to ensuring the effectiveness of internal communications, it can also be invaluable for external knowledge-sharing arrangements and dialogue to be built and developed with other stakeholders, including external bodies and the emergency services, as appropriate. This is particularly relevant where information is held on risks at specific assets and/or locations, where there are clear potential benefits to knowledge being collectively harnessed and shared. Key to the success of internal knowledge-sharing is the need for workers to be educated on the importance of their inputting the necessary information into, and extracting it from, systems. Additionally, there are some clear safety advantages to be gained from external collaboration, even with organisations that would otherwise be viewed as competitors.

Arm workers with the knowledge and skills to enable them to escape from locations. This is relevant for locations where there is a perceived threat to worker safety, with particular attention needing to be paid to any high-risk locations. Plans should be developed to cover alternative routes in and out, with the actions to be taken in case of an emergency being agreed and communicated to workers in advance of any such situation arising.

HOW TO... MANAGE SOCIAL RISKS
TO LONE WORKERS

The focus of this aspect is upon making sure workers know *who* they are going to see, as well as equipping them with any relevant knowledge about *why* they are going to see them, and *what* they might find on arrival. There might be specific up-to-date information on the people they are visiting, which may act as a trigger for them to modify their approach, or cause them to adopt a different mindset than would routinely be the case. It's also about anticipating what *might* happen, and recognising the potential for lone workers to be subject to stress, or for their mental health and wellbeing to be negatively impacted if the risks involved are poorly managed. This can be addressed by adopting a range of measures including: keeping in touch with workers, by setting down and maintaining effective contact arrangements; monitoring the health of lone workers, and seeking and acting upon medical advice for those with health conditions, or who are subject to specific health risks.

In order to manage social risks to their lone workers, organisations need to make sure they...

Prepare workers for the unexpected! This means providing them with guidance on how to handle emergency and evacuation situations, ensuring they understand what to do – including how to escape from difficult situations – before they face any such circumstances. This aspect can be addressed by setting out simple steps which are easy for workers to remember and follow, particularly in the heat of the moment, where a swift and effective emergency response is needed. Additionally, if a risk assessment indicates that lone workers should carry first-aid kits and/or that first-aid training is required, these must be provided. For further detail on this aspect, reference should be made to *the First-Aid Regulations,* which set out the requirements for employers to make provision for first-aid and to inform employees of their first-aid arrangements.

Train workers in how to handle uncertain situations. This is about empowering workers to manage and/or withdraw from situations where violence and aggression are encountered, should they feel their safety or that of others to be compromised in any way. This should be supplementary to any training provided to workers about the tasks they are expected to perform, the focus here being upon developing and maintaining a situational awareness skillset amongst lone workers. These skills are particularly important where it's conceivable that difficult clients or members of the public will be encountered. It includes developing workers' skills – with a particular focus on personal safety and violence prevention – enabling them to recognise circumstances where they feel at risk and to adopt conflict-resolution techniques by way of response, to defuse situations. Such training should also include discussions about emergency procedures and may extend to addressing particular concerns including the handling of money and off-site visits. Depending on the location, it might also include some simple practical measures, such as a requirement to lock doors before counting money, keeping all money in a safe, checking in with a 24-hour reception, and logging visits via an agreed method.

HOW TO...
HANDLE HAZARDS TO HEALTH
(AND CONTRACTORS TOO)

The piper's fable showcased the efforts of a strange piping fellow to manage a health hazard – the bacteria *Leptospira interrogans* – and his inept handling of a Weil's disease health risk. In the circumstances the tale portrayed, it should have been obvious to the Pest Control Piper that the rats hosted such a risk – the very risk he had been called upon to manage – but his total failure to adopt suitable control measures for dealing with the infestation was indicative of an approach which was flawed from the start. By bringing to light the troubles that engaging the Pest Control Piper's services created for the mayor and his town, the fable also surfaced the need to control contractors – effective management of contractors being a vital concern for many a real-world organisation.

The events of the fable prompted the consideration of two strategies – a three-step approach for managing exposure to a health risk and a five-step approach for managing a contractor risk. Controlling health risk exposure requires assessment of the risk it poses, the adoption of suitable control measures, and a review of the risk. Whilst the nature of the health risk in this tale involved a zoonotic disease, the approach to managing the risks to health extends to other types of substance too. Effective management of a contractor, on the other hand, requires careful planning, picking the right contractor in the first place, providing information to those working on site, keeping a check on them, and reviewing their performance, once the job is done. From a client's point of view, it's crucial to be clear about the difference between directly managing a risk and engaging a person or organisation to manage that risk, because each approach is subject to a different control strategy, as summarised here.

HOW TO... EFFECTIVELY MANAGE A HAZARD TO HEALTH RISK

The focus of this type of strategy is upon assessing, controlling and reviewing the risks associated with hazards to health. The fable showcased the example of a bacteria (germ), namely *Leptospira interrogans* which causes Weil's disease, but there are many other types of substances hazardous to health covered by *the COSHH Regulations* and other substance-specific regulations. Included amongst these are chemicals and chemical containing products, fumes, dusts, vapours, mists, and gases and, whilst the form in which they arise varies, the control requirements attaching to them are fundamentally the same. There's always a need to think about which activities cause hazardous substances to be generated or encountered, how they could cause harm, and how the risk of harm to which they give rise can be removed or, if not, reduced to acceptable levels.

In order to reduce the risk of harm and effectively manage a hazard to health, a three step approach needs to be taken by the person or organisation directly responsible for it. Referred to by the Health and Safety Executive as the assess-control-review model, this is summarised here.

STEP #1 – HOW TO... ASSESS THE HEALTH RISK

Put a plan in place. This should identify the health hazards in substances used or encountered. It's important to make sure that the right people are involved, including those whose work requires them to use, or could cause them to encounter, the substances concerned.

Identify the potential health hazards. This includes hazards both linked to, and encountered in the course of, the work being undertaken.

Assess the health hazard exposure risk. The assessment of the risk should relate to the tasks being undertaken, with both the likelihood of exposure and the severity of harm needing to be determined in order to evaluate the level of risk.

Involve workers. It's important that those who face a risk to health, and others seeking to control it, are directly involved in the ongoing development of the assessment and control strategy. They will have critical insights about practical issues, and their participation in developing the strategy makes it much more likely that they will buy into the control measures ultimately put in place, thus protecting them and others from harm.

STEP #2 – HOW TO...
CONTROL THE HEALTH RISK

Prevent the risk of exposure to substances hazardous to health, wherever possible. This includes the use of different work methods and the prioritisation of engineering controls.

Where it's not possible to prevent the risk of exposure, the following action should be taken to control the health risk...

Apply control measures to address the health risk. This requires use of the hierarchy of control, to restrict the extent to which individuals are exposed to the health risk. It also means limiting the numbers of workers who are exposed (*or rotating those who are*), minimising the time spent in areas known to be contaminated (*including taking breaks away from the area*), and using PPE and RPE, where residual risk remains.

Train workers to complete job tasks in the right way. This includes making sure that they use control measures – the administrative controls – as intended, by maintaining equipment, using PPE and RPE where required, and taking the right actions in response to dynamic circumstances, or in situations where things go wrong.

STEP #3 – HOW TO...
REVIEW THE HEALTH RISK

Supervise workers. This includes checking that they know what they are doing, are using control measures as intended, and feel able to raise any concerns. Individuals and groups requiring additional support – such as inexperienced workers, trainees or other vulnerable workers – need to be identified, with extra guidance and supervision provided for them, as and when needed.

Maintain control measures. This means making sure equipment is still working, that workers still know what to do, and that they are continuing to carry out activities as agreed. Proactively maintaining control measures enables changes to be made where concerns about their effectiveness arise, in the course of their active use.

Carry out monitoring. This should include monitoring exposure levels and reports of ill health. It also includes sampling, as well as routine monitoring on working methods and the use of PPE and RPE.

Make sure people know what to do. They need to know the right action to take to put things right quickly and efficiently when faced with a health risk, including how to use administrative controls – which can help to prevent or limit the extent of an incident – and how to avoid escalation scenarios. The opportunity should also be taken to review the level of risk, both in the immediate aftermath of an incident and on a longer term basis. This approach requires the backing of a supportive organisational culture, with all workers encouraged to speak up at any point, without fear of reprisal if they feel risks are being inappropriately managed, this being invaluable feedback for any review process.

HOW TO... EFFECTIVELY MANAGE
A CONTRACTOR RISK

Using contractors is a common practice when organisations are faced with a need for work to be undertaken which is not core to their routine business, or where it would be inefficient for them to maintain in-house expertise for the carrying out of certain activities, of which pest control is just one example. The effective use of contractors can be highly beneficial, because it transfers the risk for managing the activity to a contractor. It does, however, replace the need to manage an activity risk with the need to manage a contractor risk instead, which calls for organisations to have an effective contractor management strategy in place.

Taking on contractors in no way permits client organisations to delegate their health and safety responsibilities – they remain ultimately responsible for the risks generated by their activities. In managing the risk of contractors, therefore, client organisations need to ensure that they: appoint competent contractors with relevant expertise, via an effective contractor selection and management process; have a clear scope of work; co-ordinate any separate works taking place, requiring engagement with the contractors in question, and work co-operatively with contractors – from the planning stage and for the entire duration of the job – checking that risks are reliably well managed, on a sustained basis.

When seeking to take on a contractor, following the five steps set out here should ensure that the associated contractor risk is effectively managed, as well as providing a client organisation with good oversight of any contractor they engage to undertake activities on their behalf.

REMEMBER!

Contractual curiosity is a good thing! Asking the right questions helps clients to ensure that their control of contractors is robust and allows any weaknesses to be addressed. Included against each process step here, are examples of questions clients can ask to check the effectiveness of their control of contractors.

STEP #1 – HOW TO...
PLAN THE JOB

Define the job clearly. This ensures that all parties are clear as to what is expected of them under the contract, including aspects for which one party has exclusive responsibility, and others where co-operation between the parties is required.

Identify the hazards associated with the activity. This includes making sure that these are understood by all involved.

Assess the risks involved. This includes both the risks associated with the work itself, and those introduced by the way in which it is to be undertaken.

Eliminate risks, wherever possible. Where this is not possible, risks need to be reduced to a level which is as low as reasonably practicable.

Set out health and safety conditions clearly. This includes determining *how* work is to be done safely.

Discuss the scope of the work. This requires the active involvement of all concerned and helps to iron out any issues before contractual agreement is reached, ultimately enabling an evaluation to be made as to whether the proposed contractor is a suitable choice to carry out the work.

Questions for client organisations to consider, to check their contractor planning arrangements, include:
- *'What arrangements do you put in place to discuss a job's scope with a potential contractor?'*
- *'Do you ask to have early sight of a potential contractor's risk assessments and method statements?'*
- *'Do you share with potential contractors your own risk assessments and method statements, relevant to the particular location and job type being considered?'*
- *'Do you discuss basic health and safety conditions and targets with contractors at the planning stage?'*
- *'Do you pass on details about job complexity and the level of risk relevant to the work type and location being considered?'*
- *'Do you suggest and arrange joint site visits to the location(s) involved?'*

STEP #2 – HOW TO...
PICK A SUITABLE CONTRACTOR

Set out upfront the safety and technical competence requirements. Deciding this in advance avoids the need for there to be a rush or panic to agree and set requirements, in cases where an urgent need arises to engage a contractor to carry out work.

Seek evidence. The purpose of this is to show whether, and to what degree, the potential contractor meets organisational requirements. This includes getting testimonies from internal and external stakeholders – via both formal mechanisms and informal networks.

Run through site rules with contractors. This ensures that everyone involved is clear about site standards and other expectations, right from the start.

Request a method statement. This should preferably be for the job in question or, if not, for a similar job. This gives an indication as to whether a contractor has a sound approach to risk, with their working methods for the type of work being considered clearly of particular interest.

Decide whether sub-contracting is allowable. If this is to be permitted, the arrangements the main contractor has in place to vet the sub-contractor's delivery of performance need to be checked, including their capability to comply with legal requirements and to conform to the client's rules, working methods and procedures.

Questions for client organisations to consider, to check their contractor selection arrangements, include:
- *'Do you ask to view and check the details of risk assessments carried out by a contractor, and how do you evaluate the quality of these?'*
- *'Do you check the arrangements contractors have in place to supervise their workers?'*
- *'Do you ask about a contractor's recent health and safety performance?'*
- *'Do you ask contractors to supply a current copy of their health and safety policy?'*
- *'What safety and technical competence is needed, in order to carry out the proposed work, and how do you check that a potential contractor has the capability to fulfil these requirements?'*
- *'What arrangements do you have in place to validate any claims made by a contractor as to workforce competence, prior to awarding a job to them?'*
- *'What checks do you carry out on contractors' claims to prior experience of a certain job type and/or location?'*

STEP #3 – HOW TO...
INDUCT A CONTRACTOR

Set down the site sign-in and sign-out arrangements. This includes the required methods by which contractors are to sign in and out.

Provide the name of a designated site contact. This means contractors know who to get in touch with, whether on a routine basis or if problems arise as work progresses. The site contact plays a pivotal role in the formation and maintenance of an effective contractual relationship, throughout the job's lifecycle.

Brief out health and safety information, and site rules. This should take place in the course of site inductions, such processes being instrumental to ensuring workers are briefed on site conditions, facilities, safety rules and any other particular expectations. It can also be beneficial to repeat this information, particularly where jobs are of lengthy duration, or are of a dynamic nature.

Check the job. This should be done before work is formally allowed to start on site, to the satisfaction of all parties.

Put a formal timetable of reviews and checks in place, to start as soon as work begins. This includes scheduling in when inspections, audits and meetings are to take place, as well as agreeing on the contents of any performance indicator reports, together with submission timescales and intervals.

Questions for client organisations to consider, to check their contractor induction arrangements, include:

- *'How do you advise contractors on the requirements for signing in and out of site?'*
- *'Do you identify a lead site contact and provide contractors with their details, as the person to approach routinely, or if changes to the job or site conditions make them uncertain as to what they should do?'*
- *'Do you brief contractors on site rules, including any safe working methods, ensuring all the appropriate arrangements are in place in advance of work commencing?'*

- *'Does the site induction you provide include information on the key site hazards and risks contractors might face and any other health and safety information? How is this information passed across to contractors at induction and, where required, what arrangements do you have in place to update them on an ongoing basis?'*
- *'What control measures have you put in place to mitigate any identified site risks, including the requirement to wear PPE, where residual risk remains?'*
- *'What information do you provide to contractors about handling emergency situations?' (this should include making contractors aware of any action they are required to take in an emergency, including the requirements of the emergency procedures, what alarms look or sound like, how they are expected to respond in the event of an alarm being raised, and any applicable first-aid arrangements).*

STEP #4 – HOW TO...
CHECK-IN WITH A CONTRACTOR

Work out the degree of contact needed. This decision should be based upon factors including job complexity, the level of experience possessed by the contractor, and the nature of the relationship between the parties.

Check that work is going as planned. This includes making sure work is being carried out safely and as agreed, as set out at the planning step.

Check up on incident reports or other performance concerns raised. This can include checks being made on incident reports and records, as well as on performance data. Any incidents or other performance concerns need to be followed up and addressed and, if necessary, a decision made about required action, including either temporarily or permanently halting work. In cases where work is stopped, it should only be allowed to resume once issues and concerns have been resolved to the satisfaction of all parties.

Check to see whether any changes to personnel have taken place. This is particularly important where changes fall outside agreed contractual arrangements, triggering concerns about the way in which a job is being carried out. It's important that, in such cases, any concerns are addressed and the necessary action taken.

Where required, put in place special arrangements. These might be needed due to changes in timing, out-of-hours working or weekend working, but could also be for any number of other reasons, which will vary from contract to contract, and should be considered on a case-by-case basis.

Questions for client organisations to consider, to check their contractor supervision arrangements, include:

- 'How do you determine the degree of contact required for contractor workforces on site, and how do you ensure that this level of contact actually takes place?'
- 'Does the contractor in question have a health and safety management system in place and is this being followed effectively, with the contractor working safely?'
- 'What general checks do you make to see that a job carried out by a contractor is progressing as expected, with people working safely and in line with what was agreed with them in advance?'
- 'If incidents occur, how are these recorded and investigated, and how are any recommendations implemented and followed up?' (including short term arrangements to stop jobs, as well as the triggering of longer term adjustments to site practices and ways of working)
- 'How are changes to personnel or the introduction of new workers to site communicated, and what measures are put in place to ensure they receive any additional support they might need?'
- 'What factors would trigger special arrangements for a job, what might such arrangements involve, and how might these factors impact upon your usual checking arrangements?' (such factors could include job timings, out of hours working or weekend working).
- 'Where jobs are of high risk (rather than routine or lower risk), what effect does this have upon the level of contact or other arrangements?'
- 'Where the circumstances of a job or site have the potential to change rapidly what impact, if any, does this have upon your checking arrangements?'

STEP #5 – HOW TO...
REVIEW A CONTRACTOR'S WORK

Upon completion, review how the job went, noting how the contractor performed. It's generally considered beneficial for this to be recorded and shared with the contractor. It's at this point that a decision can be reached about whether the activities and tasks involved would be approached in the same way in future. As such, the focus here is upon how well the job was done and the contractor performed overall, with the opportunity being taken to provide them with any feedback. The style of review will vary according to the scale of the organisations involved and the nature of the job in question, but common to all such reviews is the need to include suggested amendments or additions to procedures or working practices, so as to inform the quality of future contracts, provide critical insights for future jobs, and thus drive up performance levels. As such, this step of the process gives all parties a formal opportunity to think about what went well and to reflect upon what could have gone better, enabling lessons to be learnt from any incidents which have occurred, and allowing areas for improvement to be readily identified and applied to future contracts. When carried out effectively, this step of the process offers a positive opportunity for those involved to evaluate all aspects of the job and contractual arrangements. Furthermore, when such reviews are well performed, they are invaluable to the *check* and *act* steps of an effective risk management cycle.

Revisit the planning step. This last step offers a useful opportunity to check the effectiveness of the planning arrangements, with the benefit of hindsight. Furthermore, forming a view as to whether the job was performed as intended can help to shape the way in which the planning step of the process is administered for similar jobs in the future. Practically speaking, reviews and other such methods enable clients to apply any learning points, in response to anything that went badly on a given job – but equally, to transfer any good practice – and in turn to feed improvements through into the *plan* and *do* parts of the following round of the risk management cycle. This can prove invaluable when they are next seeking to engage a contractor or supplier to undertake work for them, with any lessons learnt helping to inform future decisions about whether a particular party might be re-engaged in a similar capacity.

Questions for client organisations to consider, in order to check the performance of a contractor, at the point of contractor review, could include:

- 'How did the contractor perform?'
- 'Were there any health and safety problems, which arose from the way in which the contractor performed the work?'
- 'Would the contractor be accepted back on site again?'
- 'Did action need to be taken against the contractor?'
- 'Did the contractor need to be taken to task about anything?'
- 'How good was the contractor's standard of housekeeping?'
- 'Would the contractor be given a reference in future?'
- 'Is enough known about the contractor to justify their inclusion within an approved contractors' list?'

Questions for client organisations to consider, in order to check how a job went, at the point of contractor review, could include:

- 'How did the job go overall?'
- 'Was the planning for the job and contractor effective?'
- 'Was hazard identification and risk assessment adequate?'
- 'Did the contractor do the work as agreed and as per contract, in accordance with any agreed method statements?'
- 'Have any required monitoring tests been carried out, with the results checked and recorded?'
- 'Have any remaining actions been agreed and taken into account?'
- 'Has the outcome of the review been recorded, so that if similar work is undertaken in the future, the review outcomes can inform and drive improvements to the next round of the planning process?'

REMEMBER!

There are lots of questions that can be asked about the contractor and the job in any such review process, for this fifth and final step. The answers to many of these questions will probably seem obvious immediately after a job has been completed, but it's always an invaluable exercise to think through all aspects of contractual performance, with the benefit of hindsight – reflecting upon what went wrong and recognising what went well – as this helps to inform decisions about whether a particular contractor would be re-engaged, or a job differently carried out, in the future.

HOW TO... GET LIGHT RIGHT

Ian's fable saw some poor lighting choices and other ill-judged decisions being made by the characters involved which, in turn, introduced dangerous substances and explosive atmosphere risks, and other risks too. With an element of *theatre*, it included a *prop* (the lamp), a *cast list* (featuring a mine owner, a mine operator and a worker), some *extras* (Procurement Prince Paul and Disposal Duke Dave), and a dimly lit *backdrop* (mine). And it was only down to luck that there were no *special effects* involved!

In response to the events of the fable, five key principles were derived, addressing: *first*, getting lighting basics right; *second*, making sure confined space risks are understood and well controlled; *third*, making sure lighting doesn't introduce explosive atmosphere risks; *fourth*, making sure lighting and other equipment is procured in the right way, and finally, *fifth*, understanding how to responsibly dispose of equipment, including lighting, at the end of its useful life. These five principles are set out here.

HOW TO... GET
LIGHTING BASICS RIGHT

Good lighting is essential for both safety and human health reasons.

In order to achieve good (general) lighting conditions, organisations need to make sure they...

Provide lighting which helps workers to see properly. Good lighting assists people in identifying hazards and assessing risks, including their being able to differentiate between colours, thereby promoting good personal safety.

Provide lighting which offers sufficient illumination for workers' tasks and activities. The lighting needs to be appropriate for the environments and locations within which workers use it, which includes checking the sufficiency of lux levels.

Provide suitable emergency lighting, where required. Circumstances calling for emergency lighting need to be identified and any lighting selected needs to show people where to go in an emergency, when ordinary lighting could fail to function.

Select lighting which doesn't cause harm to individuals or create undesirable effects. This means avoiding types which cause glare, flicker, or stroboscopic effects, or which introduce any additional health and safety risks.

Choose lighting which meets the requirements of all those who need to use it. This includes accounting for the needs of particular individuals, including those with specific eyesight requirements or who have other health needs, as well as meeting the routine needs of all users.

HOW TO... ADDRESS CONFINED SPACE WORKING RISKS

Alongside lighting basics and the use of lighting within potentially explosive atmospheres, the location described within the fable highlighted a confined spaces' risk. The points listed here are of general application to all confined spaces.

Where a confined space risk exists, work must always be safely controlled, which means risks must be appropriately considered,

assessed and addressed and that safe working methods must be adopted.

In order to ensure that confined space working is safely undertaken, organisations need to make sure they...

Avoid the need for workers to enter a confined space, wherever possible. Where achievable, work is to be conducted outside a confined space, thereby avoiding or, if not, minimising the need for entry.

...and if entry cannot be avoided, organisations need to make sure that they...

Remove hazards. Hazards must be removed wherever practicable and any risks – including any industry-specific or work activity-specific risks – controlled. This also includes the banning and enforcement of bans on unsuitable lighting and other equipment, as well as the bringing of personal items into confined spaces (and potentially confined spaces) which could generate a spark, including remotely operated key fobs, some types of clothing, cigarettes, lighters, and so on.

Appoint a supervisor. The supervisor's role is to ensure that the necessary precautions are taken, which includes the checking of safety at each stage. Where deemed necessary, a supervisor must remain physically present for the entire duration of the work activity.

Check that those carrying out the work are competent and fit to do so. Competence is paramount and anyone working within a confined space must be adequately trained and fully aware of all associated procedures. As such, any confined spaces' training given needs to cover: how to enter them safely; how to work safely within them, and how to exit them safely (including in emergency situations). Checks must be carried out to ensure that workers are competent to perform the work required of them, including whether they hold the right experience, and also that they are of suitable build, where the physical layout of the environment imposes constraints. Furthermore, where workers could be exposed to risks including, e.g. fatigue or temperature extremes, the supplementary controls required would variously include: the postponement of work, where worker fitness is in doubt; the management of working time spent within the environment, and hydration management.

Establish a safe system of work, including any permits-to-work, where required. A permit-to-work ensures that all the elements of a safe system of work are in place prior to workers entering or working in a confined space, which must cover the full duration and scope of the work, and is a vital tool to ensuring effective communication takes place – between managers, supervisors and workers – throughout the course of a hazardous work activity.

Set down and check emergency arrangements. These need to cover the necessary equipment, training, and practice drills, and must be regularly tested and reviewed, to ensure they remain effective. The emergency arrangements – which will vary according to the particular circumstances – need to be verified and could include, for instance, the positioning of a person outside the space to keep watch, who is capable of communicating with those inside and also able to swiftly raise the alarm in case of emergency, as well as being competent to take overall charge of rescue procedures if needed.

Check that communication arrangements are effective. This means making sure that clear dialogue is able to take place between people inside and outside the confined space. This is particularly important in emergency situations, where the need might arise to summon help and interact with the emergency services.

Check that entrances (access) and exits (egress) are adequate. This means ensuring there is sufficient space, so as to allow workers to enter and exit in safety. It also includes making sure that all necessary equipment can be carried in and out safely, with ergonomic aspects being a key consideration.

Carry out air testing and monitoring. Air needs to be confirmed to be free of toxic and flammable vapours, as well as being fit to breathe, which requires the checking of oxygen levels. Such testing variously includes atmospheric testing, purging and ventilation, together with the removal of any residues.

Where required, isolate equipment. If equipment could otherwise operate or be inadvertently operated, arrangements need to be made to ensure it is isolated.

Where required, ensure the suitability of arrangements for equipment cleaning. If the cleaning of equipment is required, this should be carried out prior to entry, so as to avoid the development of fumes from residues, in the course of work taking place.

Provide appropriate respiratory protective equipment (RPE), e.g. respirators. This is additional to any other personal protective equipment, with which it needs to be compatible. RPE is essential if the air inside the space cannot be made fit to breathe – due to any gases, vapours or fumes that are present, or a lack of oxygen – in order to militate against the risk of asphyxiation.

Provide rescue equipment. This includes rescue harnesses, with lifelines attached, running back to a point outside the confined space, such that the rescue of stranded (possibly injured) persons can be easily achieved.

HOW TO... INTRODUCE LIGHTING FREE FROM EXPLOSIVE ATMOSPHERE RISKS

It's fundamentally important to ensure that the lighting selected is appropriate for any tasks being carried out, as well as checks being made as to its suitability for the environment within which it is to be used. This is particularly crucial where there are other risks present, for instance, where dangerous substances and explosive atmospheres are involved; in these circumstances, care needs to be taken to ensure that an effort to control one risk doesn't – even inadvertently – introduce or increase other risks. Where explosive atmospheres are a recognised risk, the equipment used by workers must be intrinsically safe.

In order to address lighting requirements where dangerous substances and explosive atmosphere risks exist, organisations need to make sure they...

Carry out a risk assessment. This requires the likelihood of an explosive atmosphere occurring and its persistence to be determined, as well as that of ignition sources – including electrostatic discharges – being present and becoming active and effective. This is additional to the other aspects which need to be addressed by the risk assessment, such as the hazardous properties of the substance(s) and the circumstances of the work, with a focus on activities such as maintenance, which involve a high level of risk.

Eliminate or, failing that, reduce risk. This means putting the necessary management arrangements in place, which follow the 'hierarchy of control' principle, and include: *first,* reducing the quantity of any dangerous substance to a minimum; *second,* avoiding or minimising its release; *third,* controlling its release at source; *fourth,* if it's not possible to prevent release, preventing the formation of an explosive atmosphere; *fifth,* if prevention isn't possible, collecting, containing and removing or otherwise rendering substances safe; *sixth,* avoiding ignition sources, including electrostatic discharges and adverse conditions, and finally, *seventh,* segregating incompatible dangerous substances.

Classify areas where potentially explosive atmospheres may exist into zones. This means first classifying areas where potentially explosive atmospheres may exist into hazardous and non-hazardous places, before further classifying the hazardous places into zones.

Select suitable equipment, based upon the requirements of the area classification. This includes lighting, personal lamps and clothing. Having classified and marked zones, the next stage is for appropriate equipment to be selected (see also 'How to… Buy Things Properly', in the next section of this How to… Guide).

Mark zones with appropriate warning signs. Having classified hazardous places into zones, these need to be appropriately marked, with warning signs positioned at the points of entry, alerting people to locations where an explosive atmosphere may occur. Where relevant, this needs to include multiple points of entry.

Provide fire fighting equipment. The control of ignition sources and use of intrinsically safe equipment should ward off the consequence of flammable and/or explosive substances being ignited. Despite this, it's imperative that fire fighting equipment is provided, in order to support the handling of emergency situations that could arise. For confined spaces, this needs to be situated at all entry points.

Train workers. This includes checking that they are aware of the right lighting to use and that they have a clear understanding of the safe working methods to apply within potentially dangerous and explosive atmospheres. Essentially, this means training workers on the appropriate precautions and actions they need to take, so as to keep themselves and others in the workplace safe, which includes how to handle emergency situations and use equipment, e.g. fire fighting equipment.

HOW TO... BUY THINGS PROPERLY

This is about making sure that suitable procurement processes are in place and followed, when seeking to obtain equipment.

In order to ensure the right kind of equipment is selected at the point of procurement, which is appropriate for the tasks carried out and the environment within which it is to be used, organisations need to make sure that they...

Check with the supplier to make sure it meets their requirements. This includes user needs, the demands of the tasks to be undertaken, the environmental conditions and any special requirements.

Only buy equipment which has been appropriately approved and correctly marked. Upon Great Britain's exit from the European Union, the requirements for the marking of products placed on the GB market changed away from the CE mark to the UKCA mark. The UKCA mark covers most goods which previously required the CE mark. With effect from 1 January 2021, and subject to a transitional period, equipment and systems for use in potentially explosive atmospheres – of which lamps and lighting are examples – need to be UKCA 'Ex', or *UKEX* – approved (formerly ATEX(Ex)-certified), as suitable for the specific zone(s) within which they are to be used. *Different rules apply in Northern Ireland.*

HOW TO... HANDLE WASTE
(AND GET RID OF IT PROPERLY)

Any equipment that has reached the end of its useful life must be handled appropriately, right up to the point of its final disposal. As well as being a fundamental legal environmental principle – the so-called 'duty of care' – this is the *right thing to do* morally, as a corporate citizen.

In order to achieve this, organisations need to make sure that any waste they produce is...

Transferred to the right people. Those who are authorised to handle or otherwise deal with waste include waste carriers (*who transport waste*), waste dealers (*who buy, sell and dispose of waste*) and waste brokers (*who arrange for others to buy, sell or dispose of waste*). Where doubt exists as to the capacity of anyone purporting to perform any of these roles, checks should be carried out to make sure that they are, in fact, appropriately registered.

Accompanied by the right documents. Documentation which includes an accurate description of the waste needs to accompany it from the point of its generation right up to its final disposal. The records need to be retained too.

Transported to the right place. This requires the carrying out of checks to ensure that waste is disposed of legally, including follow-up duty of care checks. In the waste management context, the duty of care starts at the point of the waste's creation and only ends with its final disposal.

HOW TO... GET A GRIP ON MANUAL HANDLING RISKS

The *pulling* (dragging/hauling) and *pushing* (rolling) activities carried out by a group of super-sized swede-shifters to move a giant vegetable in *the swede fable* provided a useful backdrop against which to highlight the three stage process for the risk assessment and control of any kind of manual handling. More broadly, the tale also led to the consideration of three key areas: *first,* the activity itself; *second,* relevant psychosocial factors, and *third,* the individual workers involved. The approach set out in this guide is one which applies across all manual handling types albeit that, in any given case, the filters, tools and overall assessment method will vary according to the nature and circumstances of the particular manual handling operation being assessed.

The effective assessment and control of manual handling risks is achieved by considering the nature of the activity, in addition to using the filters, the relevant tool (the example from this fable called for use of the RAPP tool), and the full risk assessment outcomes, as appropriate. Where organisations believe they may have a problem with manual handling, line managers should observe the activities carried out by their workers – making sure they account for differences associated with the time of day or particular locations – and talk to those involved, so that the challenges they face can be more fully understood. Taking this kind of approach, when supported by an effective management response to resolve any identified issues, invariably leads to risk being better controlled.

STAGE #1 - HOW TO... APPROACH
MANUAL HANDLING RISK ASSESSMENT

It's clear – even from the definition provided in *the Manual Handling Regulations* – that 'manual handling' covers a broad range of activity types. It's important to differentiate between types, as it's the type that should steer the assessment process and ultimately, the selection of appropriate control measures for the risks involved. The identification of tasks and risk avoidance opportunities are prerequisites that need to be attended to, before any kind of risk assessment is undertaken.

In order to ensure that a manual handling activity and the risks it involves can be suitably understood, assessed and addressed, organisations need to consider the following three assessment levels...

LEVEL #1 – **Check the filters**. Filters vary, but their common purpose is to help to distinguish low risk tasks from higher risk ones. There are filters available for *pushing and pulling, lifting and lowering,* and *handling whilst seated.* These enable assessors to filter out low risk manual handling operations, and so help to steer their decision as to whether a more complex assessment is required, for the given circumstances.

LEVEL #2 – **Use the appropriate risk assessment tools**. The tools' outputs and associated findings can help with the development and prioritisation of actions to control risk. The nature of the manual handling operation being considered should inform the decision as to which one (or more) of the risk assessment tools within the Health and Safety Executive's Toolkit for MSDs is the most appropriate for use in the circumstances, to help identify high-risk activities and evaluate the effectiveness of any accompanying risk reduction measures. The tools include:

- **The MAC tool**, which helps to identify high-risk workplace manual handling activities;
- **The V-MAC tool**, which helps to assess multiple manual handling operations, where load weights vary;
- **The ART tool**, which helps to assess manual handling tasks which are repetitive in nature, and,

- **The RAPP tool**, which helps to assess manual handling risks in pushing and pulling operations, involving whole body effort.

NOTE!

As this book goes to press, an integrated version of the MAC, ART and RAPP tools has just been made available, being embedded within an MSD assessment tool – an all-in-one digital solution, provided by the Health and Safety Executive.

LEVEL #3 – **Conduct a full manual handling risk assessment, if required.** A full risk assessment is needed where the relevant risk filters and risk assessment tools highlight the need for one, *and/or* if there are any vulnerable workers involved in the activity, *and/or* if there are other factors pointing to one being required. Where used, the filter and risk assessment tool outcomes should be evaluated first and referenced within the full risk assessment. A full manual handling risk assessment is a more detailed assessment type, which includes consideration of the tasks being performed, the particular workers undertaking them, the nature of the load, and the environment within which the activity is being carried out.

STAGE #2 – HOW TO... ACCOUNT FOR PSYCHOSOCIAL FACTORS

It's important for organisations to incorporate consideration of psychosocial issues within any assessment of their manual handling risks. These are factors which affect workers' psychological reactions to work and the environment.

In order to ensure psychosocial factors have been appropriately considered and addressed, organisations need to make sure they...

Identify psychosocial issues and put measures in place to counteract them, where required. These are best addressed by involving workers and making improvements to the work environment and other aspects, in conjunction with measures in support of their wellbeing. Senior leaders need to be mindful of external and internal factors which can have negative psychosocial impacts and should ensure that their working cultures are intolerant to any form of harassment towards workers.

Give workers the opportunity for some degree of control and input. This should include taking on board workers' comments about preferred working patterns (including shift patterns) and work methods, always remembering that the scheduling of working hours must be approached with health and safety in mind, rather than from a purely financial perspective. By having a degree of control and input over their working arrangements, workers are better able to play their part, by ensuring that they have a good work-life balance, including opportunities for rest and relaxation, following periods of physical effort.

Give workers the opportunity to make full use of their skills, wherever possible. This can promote good mental health amongst workers, by helping them to feel valued and respected for their capabilities.

Involve workers in making decisions that affect them, wherever possible. Those engaged in activities are often best placed to describe the issues and challenges they face, and are likely to be able to provide a clear steer as to practical solutions which would be beneficial for all concerned. Gaining upfront workforce buy-in from the start also makes it more likely that a high level of compliance will be achieved, in the long run.

Give workers the opportunity to carry out a variety of tasks. It's important to ensure that tasks allocated are not solely of a repetitive and/or monotonous nature. Varying the types of tasks assigned to workers can be helpful in maintaining their mental and physical agility. This can be advantageous even if all of the different tasks involved are physically challenging, because alternating between tasks is likely to use different muscle groups – rather than causing repetitive strain on one set – which is beneficial for the overall health of those performing them.

Enable workers to work at a pace which suits them. This can sometimes be achieved by avoiding work types which are machine– or system-paced, and by replacing dissatisfactory monitoring tools with others which positively endorse safe working methods.

Set work demands which are reasonable, not excessive. These should be accompanied by realistic targets. This can be particularly challenging where there is a time-limited window, for instance where the work is of a seasonal nature, e.g. crop harvesting. It's important to ensure there is sufficient workforce capacity to safely deliver the required level of output, even where demands fluctuate, with due account taken of peak times and workloads, so as to avoid workers being placed in a state of work overload. Where work demands are ineffectively managed, the likelihood of workers experiencing physical and/or mental harm increases, which can also result in negative organisational impacts including raised levels of sickness absence and workplace stress. In the longer term, this can negatively impact upon productivity levels and work output.

Design payment systems which enable workers to take sufficient breaks. Workers should be discouraged from working too quickly or missing rest breaks, and work practices which link pay solely to piecework should be avoided.

Put in place work systems which provide sufficient opportunities for social interaction. This can be particularly helpful in ensuring that worker wellbeing and mental health is protected.

Balance demands for high levels of effort with sufficient rewards. Rewards vary and can include resources, remuneration, and status, all of which tend to have a generally positive effect on the self-esteem of workers.

STAGE #3 – HOW TO... ADDRESS THE NEEDS OF VULNERABLE WORKERS

Consideration of the needs of vulnerable workers is important across the range of activities undertaken by people at work. These needs are particularly pronounced in relation to the carrying out of manual handling activities, however, due to these often calling for particular physical strength requirements to be met, in order that they can be safely performed.

In order to ensure vulnerable workers' needs have been appropriately considered and addressed, organisations need to make sure they...

Account for the different and diverse needs of vulnerable workers. This includes migrant workers, young workers, and those with pre-existing medical conditions.

Look out for older workers. These are workers who have more life experience but may, in some cases – though by no means all – have declining physical strength. Some might have specific health issues or pre-existing conditions, and in these cases medical advice should be sought and acted upon. But there are many older workers who have an equivalent or better level of capability and fitness than their younger peers. In any event, older workers often have vital knowledge and experience, which should be readily drawn upon.

Recognise and address the challenges faced by migrant workers. The use of different communication tools should be considered to assist these workers, utilising appropriate approaches through induction, training and briefing processes, and the like. It's also important to ensure that the equivalence of any qualifications they have obtained elsewhere is appropriately taken into account.

Provide increased support for young workers. They might be less risk-aware and need more mentoring, support, supervision and instruction, than is true for others. Particular attention should be paid to situations where they might feel under pressure to perform outside limits which are comfortable for them, for instance, due to a desire to impress their colleagues. In relation to manual handling risks, this could include attempting to lift more than is safe for them to do so.

Conduct a separate risk assessment for new and expectant mothers, where appropriate. There is no legal obligation to carry out a separate risk assessment where risks have already been sufficiently assessed as part of the general risk assessment called for by *the Management Regulations*, but it is good practice to do so. The needs of new and expectant mothers vary widely and, depending upon both the individuals and the work types involved, some may face no additional risk. It is, however, important to recognise the needs of each individual and for these differences to be reflected within risk assessments. Specifically, in the context of physically tough work, the additional pressure placed upon the joints, lower back and muscles can cause harm to a new and expectant mother, as well as posing a risk to the health of her unborn child. The assessment should be reviewed on a periodic basis, including within the third trimester, as factors which may not influence assessment outcomes in the early stages can have an increased impact, with the progression of the pregnancy.

REMEMBER!

Here the needs of vulnerable workers have been considered in the context of manual handling activities, but these must be taken into account when risk assessing *any* activity, where relevant to do so, including where specifically required by legislation.

HOW TO... EMBRACE ERGONOMIC PRINCIPLES

From its humble bear-based beginnings, it soon became apparent that *Pixie-Locks' fable* was about more than petty porridge pilfering and trivial discussions about spoon size. Importantly, its focus was upon two key principles, these being *protection of the system from the user,* and *protection of the user from the system,* both of which should lie at the heart of any ergonomic endeavour.

Summarised here are the four key ergonomic considerations which flowed from this ostensibly simple tale. Taken collectively, these support both principles and, when put into practice, can help organisations address concerns and reap rewards for their users on the one hand, and their products, systems and processes on the other. The advantages gained by designing safety critical systems which minimise the chance of user error and prevent accidents are generally well understood, but addressing broader user experience concerns can yield other benefits too. In seeking to win acceptance for ergonomic solutions, the challenge for ergonomists is to create compelling business cases for their adoption. The ergonomic endeavour is, however, one which reaches beyond factors of a solely commercial nature, extending as it does into the ethics which sit behind developing products, systems and processes that are both inclusive of, and accessible to, as broad a range of users as might need or want to use them.

HOW TO... ADDRESS USABILITY CONCERNS

'Usability' concerns the extent to which something can be successfully used by a target population to meet certain goals. Usability is most successfully achieved when due account is taken of the ease with which products, systems and processes can be used by users, from the design stage onwards. When appropriately considered and applied, usability principles directly support improved user experience and engagement by, for instance, making things easier to see, reach and understand.

A good organisational approach which addresses usability concerns will...

Consider the full range of users and their different needs and desires. This approach – *so called 'inclusive design'* – is best applied right from the start, at the design stage, continuing throughout the course of user testing and user trials and beyond, right up to the stage at which products, systems and processes are reviewed and updated or improved.

Apply the findings from user testing and trials, to inform product, system and process design. This is relevant not only when products, systems and processes are introduced, but also when modifications and enhancements to them take place.

Use workshops and other collaboration methods. These help to support the roll-out and implementation of products, systems and processes in the field by building, embedding and maintaining user engagement – including generating their buy-in for, and take-up of, products, systems, and processes – which ultimately helps to drive up compliance levels.

Evaluate the success of implementation programmes, post roll-out. This means building in reviews and further opportunities to gather feedback from users, using their insights to continually drive future improvements to products, systems and processes.

HOW TO… DESIGN IN
USER EXPERIENCE (UX) CONSIDERATIONS

'User experience (UX)' concerns the methods and processes by which products and services are designed to satisfy users. The application of good ergonomic design principles to high-end goods and luxury goods often leads to an improved user experience, resulting in higher levels of user satisfaction with products. But even where a product or service has a primarily utilitarian purpose, there are still benefits to be won from creating a positive user experience. When something is straightforward, logical and intuitive to use, user satisfaction levels tend to be higher, which positively influences user experience and in turn increases the likelihood that user compliance levels will be better and error rates lower, too. This can have a consequentially positive impact on safety.

A good organisational approach which incorporates user experience concerns will…

Consider emotional, cognitive and experiential factors, as well as functional considerations. This is about the totality of what users *see*, *think* and *feel*. Even for lower end functional products, systems and processes, those which are attractive to users are more likely to inspire their engagement, when contrasted with others which are not pleasurable to use.

Build user satisfaction aspects into development trials and workgroup discussions. This helps to secure the early-stage buy-in of those who are actually going to use the products, systems and processes. 'User Acceptance Testing' (UAT) can prove particularly useful in gauging ease of use amongst a target population, including identifying and fixing any problems – whether for an initial product, system or process launch, or following modifications or enhancements – before full deployment takes place.

HOW TO... DESIGN THE USER INTERFACE (UI)
FOR CONTROL PANELS AND ROOMS

Regarded as a subset of total user experience (UX), the 'user interface (UI)' is essentially about what the user *sees*, in terms of the ways in which products or systems are presented to them. When well-designed, user interfaces can support the carrying out of safety critical tasks, where overall system states require ease of user understanding and action. From a process safety perspective, this is arguably the most important of the ergonomic principles set out here. An effective control panel, control room or other workspace design can lead to improved job design and reliability, as well as delivering other benefits. An example of user interface design principles being well applied is where a positive decision is made not to locate an emergency stop button next to a start-up control. *A strong user interface design makes the right things easy to do and the wrong things difficult to do!*

In order to ensure user interface factors have been addressed within control panel and control room design, organisations should...

Consider users' needs for all types of operating conditions. This should include abnormal and emergency operating conditions, as well as normal and routine situations. Effective control panel and control room layouts should optimise system use and facilitate effective communication between users at all times.

Solicit user feedback from the start of any design or redesign. Engaging users at an early stage of the process, and factoring in the outputs of task and workload analysis, invariably provides them with the best opportunity to influence the final design and drives all involved to pursue the optimal solution. Specialist input is often needed in these circumstances and enlisting the support of a qualified ergonomist can be helpful in working out where and how improvements can be made.

Recognise that adopting good ergonomic design principles doesn't necessarily increase costs. It might be, for instance, that fewer screens are deemed to be required, if they don't aid control. It could also be the case that savings on installation and maintenance are achievable, whilst at the same time improving user experience and acceptance.

And of course, any costs involved should be considered in the context of the financial savings achievable through the avoidance of potentially catastrophic outcomes which can flow from basic design failings or shortfalls.

HOW TO... CARRY OUT
EFFECTIVE WORKSTATION ASSESSMENTS

The goal of any 'workstation assessment' should be to ensure the safety and comfort of users, which includes avoiding equipment and practices with the potential to lead to harm or ill health. When an effective workstation assessment is carried out, and followed up with relevant improvements, this increases wellbeing, making for a higher quality of user experience and better working conditions. This shows that the incorporation of adjustability considerations is consistent with, and supportive of, a more inclusive design approach. It's important to understand that workstation assessment is not a *one size fits all* exercise and that, when it's carried out methodically with control measures put in place to address any findings, it can bring about marked improvements in user productivity too. For the specifics about how to ensure users' workstation set-up needs are met, refer to *the DSE Regulations*.

In order to ensure their approach to workstation assessments is effective, organisations should...

Dedicate sufficient time to observing users carrying out their activities. This is about gaining an understanding of what users need to do – across the full range of tasks they perform – which includes looking at the equipment they use and the environments within which they operate, as well as observing any variability to the activities they perform within a shift, or across different shifts, as appropriate.

Recognise that some users will require more detailed assessments than others. For many users, workstation assessment is a straightforward process but there will be others who will require a more detailed or bespoke assessment, for various reasons. It's important to consider users who may have particular needs, on either a permanent or transitory basis, including: vulnerable workers; those who are significantly shorter, taller, wider or narrower than the core population; those who have medical conditions, such as circulatory problems, and pregnant employees. For these users, any specific needs, requirements, and associated control measures should be noted within the assessment, on top of those recorded for users covered by standard assessments. Additionally, some individuals may require more frequent assessment or review than others. In such cases, a risk-based approach should be taken, which not only draws upon the outcomes of their individual risk assessments, but also addresses the requirements of any other relevant legislation and procedures, as appropriate.

Put in place appropriate control measures. This not only includes putting in place control measures which address workstation outcomes for all users, but also making suitable adjustments for individuals with particular medical needs. For those with such needs, adjustments should be bespoke to them and also address any recommendations and advice given by their medical practitioners.

Don't forget home workers! Workstation assessments need to be carried out within domestic settings for those who use display screen equipment as part of homeworking arrangements, and any risks identified must be controlled, just as is true for other workers.

HOW TO... BUILD AND USE
BASIC BOW TIE MODELS

The ostensibly simple problem of too much porridge described in *the porridge pot fable* set the context for explaining how to develop bow ties, with a focus on their value in defining a risk ('top event'), showing what could cause and result from it ('threats' and 'consequences') and what is – or should be – in place to stop it ('barriers'). The simple 'loss of containment' scenario within the tale helped to promote the value of the bow tie model approach, but the broad principles derived from the tale – as featured in this *How to...* Guide – can be used to steer the development and building of bow tie models for any top event (risk) type, which typically align to the risks found documented within organisational risk registers.

The fable's overflowing porridge pot provided useful context within which to show how bow tie models can help to address three vital questions, namely, *first,* the risk question – '*What could possibly go wrong?,*' *second,* the operational management question – '*How will we stop it and will it work?*', and *third,* the assurance question – '*How will we know that what we want to stop it, will do so?*' Bow tie models that are well-constructed can be used to support organisations' judgments about how effectively risks are being managed, inform decisions about where future improvements might be required, and help to foster improved risk understanding throughout their workforces. There are five '*How to...*' principles set out here. The first three link to the three vital questions just noted, which should be applied when developing any real-world bow tie model. The fourth and fifth principles handle how these models can be put to good practical use, as part of a broader assurance-based approach. Some suggested questions have been included here, being of the type used as part of an equipment inspection (*How to*...check equipment does what it needs to do), and in the course of a health and safety management system audit (*How to*...check people do what they need to do).

HOW TO... USE BOW TIE MODELS TO SHOW WHAT COULD GO WRONG

Addressing *the risk question*, the focus here is on the need for organisations to recognise the adverse events that might play out, in relation to the activities they perform and processes they operate, and on deepening their understanding of these, through the building of a risk picture. This requires them to be clear about what could go wrong – the things they don't want to happen – which helps to define their top events, a top event being the core around which a bow tie model is built.

In order for organisations to make effective use of bow ties, to help them show what could go wrong across their operations, they should...

Develop models for potential risk scenarios – so-called *top events*. These top events can be identified in relation to their operational activities and/or as a result of other risks to which they are subject. For those involved in high-hazard activities, this information will often be available from existing assessment methods, but models of this kind typically add a further layer of insights, by providing a clear visual demonstration of any given risk scenario. Integrating other sources of information within such models – including internal incident data, industry data, and information from other high-risk sectors – can make for a richer understanding of any given risk and positively influence decision-making about risk control. Some risk scenarios, even those drawn from a different industry context, may provide useful inputs for risk models. Also, anecdotal workforce comments about risk should never be ignored. Being closer to the action at the sharp end, operatives are more likely to know about, and be able to describe, *what risk looks like* in reality. Developing such models can clearly show the risk controls believed to be in place – which is particularly important for the really big risks – allowing the models to be used as the basis for judging the control of risk *as is*, set against how it should be, or the control of risk *as desired*.

Precisely define the *hazard, top event, threat* and *consequence* components of barrier models. Top events should reflect the risks that materialise from the activities carried out, or from concerns arising from other external factors. The threats that could cause each top event should be identified. Next, the consequences should be determined, these being impacts which could flow in circumstances where the averting of the top event is unsuccessful. Internal data – particularly incident investigation and near miss data – can also be invaluable here, especially where it has been shown that specific barriers have previously averted catastrophe or limited potential consequences or, on the flip side, where the absence of such barriers has led to more severe outcomes than might otherwise have been the case.

Link bow tie models (and/or other risk models) to risk registers. The top events that sit at the centre of bow tie models should largely mirror the risks identified within risk registers. When used effectively, a bow tie model – including its validation – should give confidence that barriers are in place to both lower the likelihood of a top event occurring in the first place and to prevent or mitigate the consequences, should one occur. Where bow tie model components are used to proactively inform organisational practice, this should be observable in improved risk register ratings and marked by increased levels of confidence in the overall control of risk, at the sharp end. On the flip side, where risk register ratings are unchanged or worsening, this should act as a prompt for risk models to be revisited – with them being updated, where necessary – to ensure that risks have been comprehensively analysed, understood and addressed.

HOW TO... SHOW WHAT'S IN PLACE
TO STOP THINGS GOING WRONG

Addressing *the operational control question*, this is about organisations developing dynamic bow tie models, which accurately reflect what they have in place to stop things going wrong.

In order to be confident about the arrangements they put in place to stop things going wrong, it's advisable for organisations to...

Put *prevention barriers* and *mitigation barriers* in place. Prevention barriers stop threats from leading to top events, whilst mitigation barriers limit or mitigate consequences, to address circumstances in which top events do occur. The choices made about which barriers to put in place should logically flow from, and correspond to, the outputs of risk identification and evaluation processes.

Put multiple barriers in place, wherever possible. This helps to prevent given threats from leading to top events, and top events from leading to consequences. Using multiple barriers should mean that, in circumstances where one barrier fails, another fills (or at least partially fills) the gap it leaves, thereby blocking a top event, or preventing or limiting the extent of a given consequence. It's important to have confidence in the selected barrier(s) being able to block the trajectory of failure (*or the path through the cheese!*).

Regularly maintain and test any critical equipment forming part of a barrier. This includes safety critical equipment, such as gauges, alarms and shut-off valves, these being examples of types of safety critical instrumentation. Maintaining and testing equipment should help to ensure it works at the point and time of need.

Educate operatives about their roles in managing and/or maintaining barriers. This can include their role in terms of stopping top events, through their involvement in prevention barriers, and/or the part they play in limiting consequences, through their involvement in mitigation barriers. Often referred to as 'barrier ownership', this is about people understanding where responsibility for barriers and their upkeep sits, being allocated to designated operatives or functions. This means making sure they have the appropriate level of understanding, and are clear as to the actions they are expected to take to make barriers effective – including monitoring gauges, responding to alarms, and shutting valves, right through to the steps they need to follow under emergency plans to mitigate consequences – for instance, limiting the extent of any spill following a loss of containment incident. It also includes ensuring that any responsibilities forming part of, or connected to, their day-to-day roles are clearly assigned, examples of which include performing maintenance activities, reporting incidents – even low-level ones, and attending to any necessary remedial action. For active barrier types, operative action is sometimes needed, whilst for procedural barrier types, this is always required. For further details on barrier types, as well as what the type means in terms of the corresponding actions required from operatives, refer to *the four little pigs' fable* and *How to...* Guide Seven, which accompanies it.

HOW TO... GAIN CONFIDENCE THAT WHAT'S IN PLACE WILL WORK AS PLANNED

Addressing *the assurance question*, this is about organisations using barrier management to ensure the delivery of effective operational performance. This means testing what's in place, or what's believed to be in place, so as to have confidence in it actually working at the time and point of need.

In order for organisations to make best use of assurance methods – which check the robustness of their arrangements for controlling risk – it's advisable for them to...

Use performance data to check that barriers are working well. Barriers need to perform as intended, and when required. Performance data includes failure data from incidents and failed maintenance, as well as proactive data from audits, inspections and safety tours, which highlight good practice. When used effectively, the insights from both failure and proactive data should drive improvements to existing barriers and/or prompt the introduction of new ones, this being an example of pro-active barrier management working in practice.

Use bow tie models and/or other barrier models to set the direction for barrier-based audits. This means: *first,* recognising the threats that could cause a top event, as well as how top events might lead to one or more consequences; *second,* identifying the components the model asserts are in place to stop a top event (prevention barriers), and *third,* identifying the components the model asserts are in place to limit consequences which flow when a top event occurs (mitigation barriers). It's from these bow tie model insights that audit questions can be developed to evaluate barrier effectiveness, and so assist with testing whether the barriers actually work.

Carry out a range of assurance activities, appropriate to the nature and scale of their operations. These activities vary, but will typically include audits and inspections, alongside other methods. A responsible and forward-looking approach will often see a range of methods being used to positively validate (or *check* and *act* upon) the arrangements for managing risk, these forming key steps within a *plan-do-check-act* cycle and being vital to effective safety risk management.

The last two '*How to...*' points within this guide – '*How to...*check equipment does what it needs to do' and '*How to...*check people do what they need to do' – are based upon a loss of containment example, analogous to that which was profiled in *the porridge pot fable.* Their purpose is to indicate how *the assurance question* might be practically addressed, by real-world organisations.

HOW TO... CHECK EQUIPMENT DOES WHAT IT NEEDS TO DO

These are indicative barrier-based inspection questions, as might feature within inspections of equipment. They have been framed around the types of equipment typically required to achieve successful containment (and so, prevent the risk of loss of containment), but the four aspects to the approach could be readily applied to equipment used to help prevent and/or control other risk types too.

In order to check the effectiveness of their equipment arrangements for preventing loss of containment scenarios, organisations typically need to address the following aspects, as part of their inspection activities...

ASPECT #1 – Check that equipment is in place.

Questions to be asked about the equipment required, where loss of containment is an identified risk, could include:
- *'Have gauges (level indicators) been fitted?'*
- *'Have high level alarms been fitted?'*
- *'Have shut-off valves been fitted?'*

ASPECT #2 – Check that the equipment is right for the process it needs to control, and is tolerant of any variations to environmental conditions.

Questions to be asked about gauges could include:
- *'Are they right for the conditions?'*
- *'Are they able to tolerate any extreme or stressful conditions to which they might be subject, for instance, extreme heat or cold?'*

Questions to be asked about high level alarms could include:
- *'Has the operation of sensors been checked pre-start up?'*
- *'Has the operation of safety devices been checked pre-start up?'*

Questions to be asked about shut-off valves could include:
- *'Are they designed such that 'valve-open' and 'valve-closed' positions are easily distinguishable?'*
- *'Are they designed to fail to safety?'*
- *'Are they being operated within design parameters?'*

ASPECT #3 – Check that the equipment and the process function it supports continue to work.

The over-arching question to be asked here is: *'Is the overfill prevention system effective?'*

Questions to be asked about gauges could include:
- *'Are they legible?'*
- *'Are level transmitters reliable?'*

- *'Is the maintenance regime being adhered to?'*
- *'Are they performing reliably in situ?'* (i.e. where and how they are used, not just in laboratory conditions)
- *'Do they continue to perform accurately, even in adverse conditions, such as in bad weather, or in circumstances of temperature or pressure fluctuations?'*
- *'Are they flushed out, if clogging is identified as a problem?'*

Questions to be asked about alarms could include:
- *'Are they useful and relevant?'*
- *'Are they functioning as intended?'*
- *'Are they checked on a routine basis?'*

Questions to be asked about shut-off valves could include:
- *'Are they used as directed?'*
- *'Are their seals intact and not worn?'*
- *'Is there a process in place for cleaning them, including checking for debris and clogging?'*
- *'Are they kept sufficiently lubricated?'*
- *'Are they replaced as needed?'*

ASPECT #4 – Check that operatives know and do what is required of them, in relation to the equipment they need to use, ensuring that they understand and operate it in the right way.

Questions to be asked about gauges could include:
- *'Do operatives know how to read them, what they mean and what action to take, based on the readings given?'*
- *'Are operatives able to take readings without distractions or conflicts with their other responsibilities?'*

Questions to be asked about alarms could include:
- *'Are operatives clear about what they mean, including display layouts?'*
- *'Is guidance provided to operatives, which makes clear to them the responses/actions they are expected to take upon alarm activation, and with the terms used in alarm situations being obvious and meaningful to them?'*
- *'Do alarms alert, inform and guide operatives about the right response and allow adequate time for them to carry out the expected response?'*

- 'Does the alarm handling process take account of human limitations?'
- 'Are suitable measures in place to prevent high level alarms from being overridden or defeated?'
- 'When carrying out alarm monitoring/handling responsibilities, are operatives free of other tasks which might distract them?'
- 'Do operatives understand the action to take in response to alarms, including how to prioritise them, in cases where multiple alarms activate?'
- 'Do operatives encounter 'alarm flooding' or nuisance alarms (large numbers of alarms needing to be acknowledged in quick succession) and how are these circumstances managed?'
- 'Are suitable measures in place to prevent alarms being turned off?'

Questions to be asked about shut-off valves could include:
- 'Do operatives know how to activate manual valves?'
- 'Are suitable measures in place to prevent operatives from tampering with or defeating shut-off valves?'

HOW TO... CHECK PEOPLE DO
WHAT THEY NEED TO DO

It's not enough simply to have the right equipment in place. People matter too and, whilst the fable did not dwell on levels of responsibility, in equivalent real-world circumstances, *what* they do is a vital consideration. The types of questions which follow here are invaluable for checking the effectiveness of the barriers with which people are involved (the active and procedural barrier types, further explored in the context of *the four little pigs' fable*), and are pitched at senior leader, process manager and operative levels, all of whom have key roles to play in the effective operation of any health and safety management system arrangements. These are typical of questions used by organisations within management system audits, which check health and safety management system arrangements and activities. They are based upon checking the effectiveness of containment arrangements – and what people need to do to prevent loss of containment scenarios for processes, facilities or functions within their remit – but the three levels of the approach shown here can be readily applied to the control arrangements required for other risk types.

In order to check that people do what they need to do to control risk, organisations should typically ask the following types of question...

SENIOR LEADER LEVEL QUESTIONS

Questions to be asked of senior leaders, to check the areas for which they are accountable, could include:

- *'What do you know about the risk?'* including previous audit reports, outstanding audit findings, and so on;
- *'Who is in charge of the risk?'* including competent persons, those who are accountable, those with responsibilities for the operation, process or location in question, and those who have specific responsibilities in case of an incident;
- *'What sorts of things might go wrong if this operation or process fails?'* including potential major incident scenarios, escalations from minor to major incidents, and so on;
- *'What's in place to stop things going wrong?'* including the aspects of the risk that have been designed or engineered out, the safety critical equipment in place, the approach to maintaining plant and equipment, and the methods by which any identified problems are resolved;
- *'What could happen if the risk isn't controlled and what should be in place to stop it from happening or limit its effects?'* including recognition of potential incident and near miss event types, as well as appropriate prevention barrier and mitigation barrier types;
- *'What procedures are in place to cover the control of the risk?'* to ensure effective containment is maintained;
- *'Who takes overall charge in the event of an incident, and what procedures are in place to cover incident management, reporting and investigation, including how these are communicated to the relevant people?'* covering all the different types and levels of incident that might occur, and the required action to be taken, together with investigation arrangements, the communication of any learning, and the completion of actions and follow up points;
- *'What arrangements are in place for alarm management?'* including alarm design, handling, prioritisation, and shelving arrangements;
- *'What training is in place for those with responsibilities for safety critical processes, and how is the right balance struck between the need for control and engineered systems, and operative knowledge?'*

including how competence is demonstrated and maintained, and how systems allow for intervention and detection, avoiding exclusive reliance being placed upon systems, and

- 'What steps do you take to create and sustain a positive safety culture?' including any action taken to build workforce understanding about why and how to report incidents or raise any safety concerns and challenge unsafe behaviours, and/or to invite their suggestions for improvement, whether relating to plant and equipment, or to wider cultural initiatives.

PROCESS MANAGER LEVEL QUESTIONS

Questions to be asked of process managers, to check their understanding about what they need to do, could include:

- 'How do you go about identifying, assessing, recording and reducing on– and off-site risks?' including the steps taken to ensure that risk is reduced to a level which is ALARP;
- 'How do you identify the risk controls required to prevent loss of containment in major accident hazard event scenarios?' including how these are communicated and briefed to workers who need to know about them;
- 'Are documented procedures available for all safety critical tasks for which you are responsible, and is there a method in place to invite operatives' suggestions for improvement, in cases where they are found to be unclear?', including whether examples are available and whether these clearly document the procedural steps in a way which is obvious to those who are expected to, and need to, follow them;
- 'Do you know the start-up and shut-down processes that are in place, including for interventions to stop tasks that are not progressing as intended?' including triggers for validation, and authorisation of start-ups, shut-downs and interventions;
- 'Can you explain the planned preventative maintenance that takes place?' including the current status of the programme and how any actions from it are tracked through to completion, in a timely manner;
- 'Do you know and understand the operating limits of all plant and process equipment that you are required to use, or upon which your activities rely?' including whether these are marked on the equipment and noted within relevant documentation;

- *'Do you know and understand any tank filling procedures in place?'* including what these require and how overfill situations are avoided and managed;
- *'Do you know and understand the process for alarm management and handling?'* including how alarm management is carried out, what the process is for updating and managing alarms and trip settings, how often alarms activate, whether alarm rates are acceptable in routine/normal, abnormal and emergency operating circumstances, the process for alarm prioritisation or reduction in circumstances where the number of alarms is unacceptable, how alarm override situations are managed and who is competent to authorise these, and how alarm shelving is handled, where this is permissible;
- *'How do you build and maintain the necessary understanding amongst your team?'* including knowledge of the safety critical elements of plant and equipment design, and how these function to keep the process contained and people safe;
- *'How do you deal with circumstances in which people do the wrong thing, whether errors, deliberate acts or violations?'* including investigations, recommendations and follow-ups to any actions following such occurrences (immediate and long term), and,
- *'How do you help to foster a positive safety culture, amongst your team?'* including the methods used to communicate with them; the types of incidents they need to report, to whom, the method for so doing and why it's important; how they can raise any safety concerns and with whom; how to challenge any unsafe behaviours they observe, and the vital part they can play in putting forward suggestions for improvement, whether relating to plant and equipment, or as part of any wider workplace cultural initiatives.

OPERATIVE LEVEL QUESTIONS

Questions to be asked of operatives, to confirm their understanding about what they need to do, could include:

- *'How do you confirm a task is safe to start, ensure it is performed safely throughout, and is safely completed?'* including what would trigger you to stop it at any point and how you safely perform tasks independently, or with others, depending upon the nature of the task;
- *'How do you ensure you safely operate any process equipment or plant you need to use?'* including what you know about the

operating limits of any process equipment or plant, what action needs to be taken if it approaches the limits, and who provides authorisation for its operation outside the limits;

- *'Do you know the required actions to take for all circumstances you might encounter?'* including for gauge monitoring tasks, in the event of an alarm sounding, in response to any overfill situation, and in circumstances where plant or equipment shut-down is required;

- *'Do you know what to do if you suspect a given barrier is failing to control risk to the level expected?'* including gauges, alarms, or valves not performing as intended or, if required, the actions of people falling short of the expected standard;

- *'Do you know the right action to take to prevent an incident or minimise its impacts?'* including the reporting processes you need to follow, in the wake of any minor and major incidents, and

- *'In circumstances where you believe others may be doing the wrong thing, whether in error or as a deliberate act, do you know how to raise safety concerns or to challenge unsafe behaviour?'* including to whom this should be reported and the type of feedback that can be expected, by way of response.

HOW TO... MANAGE BARRIERS EFFECTIVELY

The *four little pigs' fable* depicted a [hostile dragon attack on pigs' homes] top event, providing a useful example from which to explore in greater detail the barrier – *or risk control* – principles highlighted by the previous *porridge pot fable*. It prompted a more detailed look at the importance of matching the type of barrier to the threat it seeks to prevent and/or the consequences it aims to block or mitigate, and saw a greater focus placed upon the range of consequences that can spring from the same top event. It also looked at the concept of emerging risk, using the example of *wolf-targeted* protection measures becoming outmoded, in the face of a present danger which is *dragon-based*, the reason being that something which works against *huffing and puffing* wolves won't necessarily be effective against *smoking and flaming* dragons! In so doing, the fable highlighted the importance of organisations keeping their level of risk knowledge up to date.

The fable built upon the basics for developing bow tie models, a technique outlined in the context of the previous *porridge pot fable*. It was in relation to this earlier tale that the approach for developing bow tie models was explained, their purpose being to clearly define a risk (the top event), showing what could cause and result from it (the threats and consequences) and what is, or should be, in place to stop it (the barriers). Having enlarged upon these basic principles, the *four little pigs' fable* gave rise to three '*How to...*' points of its own about how to manage barriers effectively. These are *first,* how to select and install barriers, taking account of barrier purpose and function; *second,* how to maintain and test barriers, including the role played by assurance, and *third,* how to make sure both on- and off-site effects are sufficiently considered.

Summarised here are three key principles for organisations to follow, in order to manage their barriers effectively...

HOW TO... SELECT AND INSTALL BARRIERS

In choosing and putting in place barriers, organisations need to make sure that those they select will serve to stop bad things happening and – if bad things do happen – that they will stop or limit the effects of these upon the operatives, assets, other people, or the surrounding environment, that they have the potential to reach.

When selecting and installing barriers – which act to block threats in the case of prevention barriers, or stop or limit consequences in the case of mitigation barriers – organisations should make sure that they...

Select barriers capable of preventing identified threats and/or mitigating possible consequences. It's important that barriers are not regarded as a generic tool for controlling risk, but that they fulfil their purpose, being well-matched to the threats or consequences they seek to block.

Select barriers which are both fully functional and independent. The fully functional aspect means they need to be fully capable of delivering their intended function, whilst the independent aspect means they don't depend upon other barriers for their success.

Don't over-rely on one – or too few – barriers. In situations where one barrier is protecting against several different threats or consequences, this is likely to be placing too much reliance upon it, due to the negative outcomes which can flow if that barrier fails. The use of one barrier only is regarded as creating a single point of failure and additional barriers should be considered in these cases, with the ownership of different barriers being assigned to different parties, so as to better the chances of warding off unwanted outcomes.

Know the difference between passive, active and procedural barrier types. This includes ensuring that 'barrier owners' are clear as to the purpose and function of the barriers selected, as well as anything they personally need to do to make them work. It's important to make sure operatives know about the passive, active and procedural barriers (*or walls, buzzers and plans!*) put in place, for which they carry responsibility, which includes understanding the different ways in which they work, and any accompanying action required from them for their upkeep. Every barrier selected should have a valid role to play in controlling risk.

HOW TO... MAINTAIN AND TEST BARRIERS

Once barriers have been selected and installed, it's important for them to be maintained and tested, to ensure they continue to work, on an ongoing basis. A sign that maintenance and testing is effective is seen where negative effects are prevented, for instance, where bad things are blocked from reaching operatives, neighbours, properties, or the environment, or where plant damage is successfully avoided.

In order for their barrier maintenance and testing arrangements to be effective, organisations should make sure that they...

Understand the problems that gaps in barriers cause. In the case of weak prevention barriers, gaps can allow a top event to occur, whilst weak mitigation barriers can lead to a range of consequences. The root of this issue often lies in shortfalls at the initial design stage, but gaps can also develop due to weaknesses in planned or reactive barrier maintenance arrangements. Examples of weaknesses include walls not being maintained, sensors going unchecked, or emergency plans untested, which can result in them failing to work as intended. *REMEMBER!* As well as looking out for gaps in barriers, there may be some occasions on which barriers are entirely absent!

Correctly design, maintain, routinely inspect and monitor passive barriers. They don't have an activation method that needs testing, but should still be checked to make sure they remain sound, for example, checking that walls are intact and are not showing signs of crumbling.

Design active barriers to fail-safe. The method for testing an active barrier can vary, with them either being self-tested or regularly tested by a human operative but, whichever method applies, sensors and actuators need to be checked, to ensure they will continue to function on demand, at the time and point of need.

Test procedural barriers regularly. This means checks need to be made that communication between key stakeholders – both internal and external – is effective, which focus on making sure that operatives know what to do. The need to check operative understanding of their procedural barrier actions is an ever-present one, with these expectations being initially set out, and updated on a refresher basis, following any change to site requirements, in response to emerging risks, or for any other reason.

Actively encourage feedback from those with barrier responsibilities. It's important to make clear to operatives with barrier responsibilities that this extends to circumstances in which they believe any given barrier is failing to deliver the expected standard of risk control. The insights gained from frontline operatives can prove particularly invaluable, as they are often best placed to say whether the expected level of risk control is actually being delivered at the sharp end.

HOW TO... ADDRESS THE EFFECTS OF ON– AND OFF-SITE INCIDENTS

The focus here is upon making sure internal and external incidents are managed and that, if a bad thing happens, the consequences – including any off-site effects – are minimised, thereby averting injuries to other people, or damage to assets or the environment.

Organisations need to ensure they are not only equipped to deal with day-to-day running, but are also able to respond appropriately when unexpected events occur. This can be achieved through the adoption of operative-centred approaches – such as risk and reliability assessment, scenario generation and testing, and emergency plan testing – activities which help to ensure the right level of workforce preparedness and capability to respond, in the wake of any incidents. Whilst this fable supplied only limited details, Pig Four was assumed to have been the 'operator' of an upper tier COMAH site, meaning he would have been subject to wide-ranging obligations under *the COMAH Regulations*, including in relation to off-site effects. In a domestic context, such behaviours might simply be regarded as good neighbourly, but these regulations clearly set out specific requirements for certain sites which must be fulfilled, these being locations at which dangerous substances are present in quantities above stipulated thresholds. Of particular relevance to this tale was the adequacy (or inadequacy!) of emergency response: *it pays to remember that one pig's firewater can become another's floodwater, if not managed correctly!*

This section of the *How to...* Guide makes reference to aspects specifically covered by *the COMAH Regulations*. Direction to specific regulations has therefore been provided, where relevant.

In order to achieve the effective management of off-site effects and control major accident hazards, operators subject to the COMAH Regulations need to ensure such requirements as are applicable to their site(s) are understood and met. This requires that they...

Take all reasonable measures to prevent major accidents and limit consequences to human health and the environment. This includes showing to the competent authority that all necessary measures have been taken to comply with the regulations, cooperation with its inspections and investigations has been forthcoming, and any necessary information supplied. It also requires that particular details have been provided to the competent authority, so as to enable it to fulfil its obligations to make certain information available to the public, including: the name of the operator, confirmation that a site falls subject to *the COMAH Regulations*, the activities undertaken at the site, details of any dangerous substances which could give rise to a major accident, details of what the public are expected to do in the event of a major accident or where the information can be accessed, the date of the last site visit carried out as part of a routine inspection programme, and where further information can be obtained (see regulation 5 of *the COMAH Regulations*).

Prepare a Major Accident Prevention Policy (MAPP). This document shows that all necessary measures have been taken to prevent major accidents, detailing the arrangements for controlling major accident hazards, to limit consequences to human health and the environment (see regulation 7 of *the COMAH Regulations*).

and additionally, operators of upper tier COMAH sites are required to...

Prepare a safety report, which includes the MAPP. The safety report needs to include a comprehensive description of the site and its surroundings, together with details of the associated hazards and risks, and the control measures in place. Information also needs to be sent to the competent authority to demonstrate to it that all the required actions have been taken to prevent major accidents, with major accident risks having been methodically considered, and the necessary measures put in place to both prevent accidents, and limit the consequences to human health and the environment of any that do occur (see regulations 8 – 10 of *the COMAH Regulations*).

Prepare, review and test an internal emergency plan. The preparation of this document shows that the potential on-site consequences of a major accident have been considered and appropriate measures put in place to minimise these, as well as arrangements having been instituted for the plan's review and test. This includes engaging with relevant external parties, as well as with workers at the site (see regulation 12 of *the COMAH Regulations*).

Supply information to the local authority. This enables the local authority to prepare external emergency plans (see regulation 13 of *the COMAH Regulations*).

Provide additional information to the public. This is supplementary to the information required for all COMAH sites. It applies specifically to those people likely to be affected by a major accident at an upper tier COMAH site, detailing the dangerous substances, possible major accidents and their consequences, together with what to do in the event of an accident, drawn from the contents of the external emergency plan. Information provided to the public should be written in easy-to-understand terms, avoiding complex technical jargon. The clarity of emergency instructions and structures plays a vital part in securing a successful response to safety critical incidents. In addition to ensuring the safety of operations, this positively protects individual and societal wellbeing, as well as the environment (see regulation 18 of *the COMAH Regulations*).

HOW TO... AVOID DROPPED OBJECTS, FALLS FROM HEIGHT, AND LEGAL CONSEQUENCES

Zac's fable showed the importance of managing the specific risks of dropped objects (*falling harps!*) and falls from height (*falling people!*). The fable also offered up key insights on some of the many different legal claims and actions which might be pursued, given equivalent real-world scenarios.

NOTE

As this fable's accompanying *modern meaning* makes clear, it's important to recognise that all cases are different. The avenues of legal redress open to aggrieved or injured parties in any real-world scenario will always depend upon the nature of the events and circumstances, as well as the relationships between those involved. It's in a bid to highlight these various options that references to Acts and Regulations have been included within this guide, to support and illustrate the *How to...* points made here.

Summarised here, in the context of work at height activities, are three key aspects for organisations and individuals to consider when seeking to control the risks to people. Additionally, under a fourth aspect, this *How to...* Guide offers some suggested practical steps that can be taken more broadly, to avoid or limit the possible prosecutions and claims which can flow, in circumstances where the control of risk fails. As such, this *How to…* Guide covers: *first,* how to ensure trespassers are protected; *second,* how to ensure the health, safety and welfare of employees and others; *third,* how to ensure work at height activities are safely carried out – including the control of fall from height and falling object risks, and *fourth,* how to ensure the effective management of health and safety and so avoid the risk of prosecution for corporate manslaughter, gross negligence manslaughter and other offences.

HOW TO… PREVENT CIVIL CLAIMS

This is about what occupiers, including organisations, need to do to avoid a civil claim being brought against them under *OLA 1984,* for failing to protect uninvited visitors (trespassers).

In order to control risks to uninvited visitors and avoid the potential for civil claims, or limit their liability under OLA 1984, occupiers of premises need to…

Carry out effective risk assessments and regularly review them.

and, in circumstances where the risks they identify cannot be eliminated…

Formulate a strategy for dealing with identified risks. This includes either making them safe or better still, inaccessible – for instance, by fencing off dangerous parts. Particular attention needs to be paid to things that might seem exciting to children, where the priority must be to stop them getting near such dangers in the first place. Occupiers also need to devote particular attention to high-risk work activities – of which work at height is just one example – making sure people are kept away from the activities and any associated work traffic, and taking extra steps to prevent unauthorised access.

Recognise that a higher duty of care exists towards children. Their risk perception skills are likely to be lower than those of an average adult, which means that any control measures put in place need to reflect the higher duty of care owed to them. This should include ensuring that everyone in the work area knows to stop work immediately if they spot a child trespasser in the vicinity. Work should only resume once the situation has been safely resolved and the all-clear given.

Provide effective signage to warn against any residual risk which cannot be fully removed. The provision of signage alone is, however, unlikely to be viewed as sufficient, especially where children are involved. Where warning signage is provided, making sure this is easily understandable and that what is depicted makes the nature of the risk obvious to a trespasser is really important. The threshold of obviousness will vary according to the type of trespasser – heavily-worded warning notices might be adequate for most adults but not for children, or others who may be unable to read, or to fully appreciate the nature of the danger they warn against. Children are likely to find visual images more understandable than excessively wordy signage.

Carry out regular workplace inspections. Inspection programmes need to be supported by effective processes for remedying any identified defects within appropriate timeframes, as based upon the degree of urgency recognised.

HOW TO... PREVENT PROSECUTIONS FOR BREACHES OF GENERAL DUTIES

The focus here is upon what organisations need to do to meet their general duties under *HSWA 1974* to protect the health and safety of employees (section 2) and others (section 3), so as to avoid the risk of injury and thus, the potential for prosecution. Prosecutions for dropped object and fall from height events are commonly brought under this legislation, because the general nature of the *HSWA 1974* duties makes them harder for organisations to defend against than those contained within *the Work at Height Regulations* and other risk-specific regulations. Highlighted here are the specific points the fable brought out in relation to sections 2 and 3 of *HSWA 1974*, but real-world organisations need to consider these provisions in their entirety, to ensure they do all that is required of them to fully meet these duties.

In order for employers to control risk and avoid the potential for criminal prosecutions being brought under HSWA 1974 for failing to protect employees, they need to...

Provide safe systems of work and safe plant. These are to be provided and maintained such that they are, so far as is reasonably practicable, safe and free from risks to health. This includes, for instance, methods of lowering and raising objects and materials, and covers administrative controls too, such as prohibiting the throwing of materials into uncontrolled areas, and keeping material storage to a minimum. Where it's not possible to eliminate the risk of materials falling or being ejected, areas need to be fenced off or demarcated, with only authorised people being allowed to enter and access strictly controlled so as to, wherever possible, avoid times where the risk of people being struck remains (see section 2(2)(a) of *HSWA 1974*).

Put arrangements in place to ensure that articles and substances are safe and free from health risks. This includes ensuring that the ways in which articles and substances are used, handled, stored and transported are, so far as is reasonably practicable, safe and free from risks to health. This applies to workplaces at height, just as it does to any other workplace (see section 2(2)(b) of *HSWA 1974*).

Make sure workers are competent. This includes providing them with any information, instruction, training and supervision necessary to ensure, so far as is reasonably practicable, their health and safety at work. Just as is true for other work activities, those who work at height must be provided with appropriate information, instruction, and training, as well as being appropriately supervised for the work they are required to carry out (see section 2(2)(c) of *HSWA 1974*).

Provide and maintain workplaces, which are safe and free from health risks. Workplaces – including means of access (*ways in*) and egress (*ways out*) – need to be provided and kept in such a way as to be safe and free from risks to health. In circumstances where materials could fall into pedestrian areas, this means identifying areas of risk, instituting protected walkways and putting up warning signs (see section 2(2)(d) of *HSWA 1974*). For signage requirements, refer to *the Safety Signs and Signals Regulations*.

In order for employers to control risk and avoid the potential for criminal prosecutions being brought under HSWA 1974, for failing to protect non-employees, they need to...

Protect them from risks to their health and safety. This means ensuring that activities do not, so far as is reasonably practicable, expose non-employees to risks to their health and safety (see section 3 of *HSWA1974*). In addition to taking practical steps to prevent them being exposed to risk, this includes a requirement to provide information to non-employees about any remaining risk. As such, this means making sure that safe areas are appropriately demarcated, as well as displaying appropriate signage highlighting danger areas and explaining the dangers present. Just as is true for employees, the signage provided for the benefit of non-employees also needs to meet the requirements of *the Safety Signs and Signals Regulations*.

HOW TO... PREVENT PROSECUTIONS FOR BREACHES OF SPECIFIC DUTIES

Organisations need to ensure they comply with any specific duties to which their operations fall subject. *The Work at Height Regulations* are a good example of legislation creating a distinct regulatory regime for a particular work type. Here, the focus is upon what to do to control the risks to employees working at height – including dropped objects and falls from height – so as to avoid the potential for prosecution under the regulations.

In order to control work at height risks, organisations must make sure that...

Work is properly planned and organised. This needs to take place from the start, continue throughout the duration of the activity, and account for any changes as work progresses. It needs to address aspects including, as appropriate, the instituting of safe systems of work, together with the establishment of exclusion zones, and storage, emergency planning, and rescue arrangements (see regulation 4 of *the Work at Height Regulations*).

Those involved in work at height are competent to carry it out. This is additional to the general duty to ensure that workers are competent, as required under section 2(2)(c) of *HSWA 1974*. Workers need to have the right level of knowledge, understanding and experience relevant to their work at height activities. And inexperienced workers need to be supervised, until such time as they reach the required level of competence (see regulation 5 of *the Work at Height Regulations*).

The risks involved in work at height are properly assessed and effectively controlled. This means avoiding work at height if it's possible to carry out the work in a different way. In cases where work at height is the only option, falls are to be prevented. Where falls cannot be prevented, the distance and consequence of any that could occur is to be minimised (see regulation 6 of *the Work at Height Regulations*).

The right work equipment is selected, in good working order and well maintained. In cases where falls cannot be prevented, work equipment is to be selected which minimises the distance and consequences of falls, with collective measures (which protect groups) prioritised over personal ones (which only protect individuals). This should include: *first*, collective protection; *second*, collective mitigation; *third*, personal protection, and finally, *fourth*, personal mitigation/restraint (see regulations 7, 8, and 12 of *the Work at Height Regulations*).

The risk of dropped objects is managed effectively. The preferred approach is to stop objects from dropping in the first place, by: *first*, checking to make sure there are no fragile surfaces, and using toe boards, handrails, and tethering systems to reduce the risk of objects or materials falling; *second*, planning how materials will be raised and lowered, and finally, *third*, eliminating the risk of dropped objects striking people by establishing and enforcing danger areas, with these being clearly demarcated as such, and securely fenced and monitored. Where it's not possible to entirely eliminate the risk of objects or materials falling or being ejected, there's a need to: *first*, fence off or demarcate the area, restricting access to authorised people only and controlling their access to avoid times when there is a risk of them being struck; *second*, make sure no materials or objects are thrown into uncontrolled areas; *third*, institute protected walkways, if there remains a risk of materials or objects falling into pedestrian areas and *fourth*, and finally, identify areas of risk and put up warning signs (falling objects are handled by regulation 10 of *the Work at Height*

Regulations, danger areas are covered by regulation 11 of *the Work at Height Regulations*, and signage requirements are covered by *the Safety Signs and Signals Regulations*).

The risks of working on or near fragile surfaces are properly controlled. Platforms need to be able to bear the weight of any loads, as well as being capable of supporting the weight of workers, so as to prevent the risk of their falling. If the risk of a person passing across or near, or working on, from or near a fragile surface cannot be removed, suitable and sufficient platforms are to be provided to take loads, and to minimise the distance and consequence of any falls, where the risk of falling remains. If working near fragile surfaces is unavoidable, suitable warning notices – or other means – are to be provided, making employees aware of the danger (see regulation 9 of *the Work at Height Regulations*).

HOW TO... PREVENT PROSECUTIONS FOR OTHER OFFENCES

The responsibility for the effective management of health and safety is a collective one. Organisations have corporate responsibilities, requiring them to consider how their undertakings are managed, as well as their interactions with external stakeholders. But individuals – in various different capacities – also have a part to play, and their responsibilities are summarised here too.

Organisations need to recognise that they are expected to do the right things to protect the health and safety of employees and others who may be affected by their activities, as an essential part of managing risk effectively. This requires their senior leaders to show clear leadership. If organisations fail to take their obligations for managing health and safety seriously, and a fatality results, they run the risk of prosecution and ultimately, conviction for corporate manslaughter, under *the Corporate Manslaughter Act*, leading to penalties including unlimited fines, remedial orders and publicity orders. In circumstances where organisations are prosecuted for corporate manslaughter, consideration will be given to the extent to which they breached their health and safety requirements, including the seriousness of any such failings.

In order for organisations to demonstrate that they take their health and safety responsibilities seriously, and prevent prosecutions for corporate offences, they need to make sure that they...

Appoint the right people into senior management positions. As well as any other management qualities they may have, these individuals need to be capable of showing strong and active leadership on health and safety matters – this being vital in setting the right tone for organisational culture. Effective leadership helps to demonstrate that legal health and safety obligations are taken seriously. Furthermore, an organisational approach which shows zero tolerance towards attitudes, policies, systems or accepted practices that encourage any serious management failure (or which allow this to occur), reduces the likelihood of any conviction for a charge of corporate manslaughter being successful.

Have access to, and take on board, competent advice. This should include the instituting of effective processes, which facilitate compliance with any applicable health and safety legislation.

Identify, assess, manage and review health and safety risks. This needs to include all the risks relevant to operations as may pose a threat to workers and others, with appropriate steps taken to eliminate or reduce risk to acceptable levels.

Put in place robust health and safety management systems, practices and standards. These need to cover the full scope of their operations and be communicated to, and understood by, those who have responsibilities detailed within them, as well as being rigorously enforced, and regularly reviewed. When supported by planned assurance methods – such as monitoring, reporting and review activities – this allows checks to be made on how effectively risk is being controlled, and any identified shortfalls to be resolved, which extends to the way in which activities are planned, managed and organised by senior management.

Build and foster a competent workforce. This includes making sure that workers at every level are competent in the tasks they are expected to perform. It is also about empowering them to speak up, where they identify unsafe or inadequate working practices and want to raise a safety concern. Making sure that workers feel actively engaged with organisational values and culture, as well as providing them with appropriate levels of training and supervision to help them work safely, are key steps in driving workforce competence. Taking these steps supports the identification and control of risks to a level which is as low as reasonably practicable, both to workers themselves and others with whom they come into contact.

Having considered what organisations need to do, to ensure the effective management of health and safety and avoid prosecution under *the Corporate Manslaughter Act*, there remains a need to consider the requirements placed upon individuals. They have responsibilities too, ranging from those to which senior managers at the top of organisations are subject, right down to workers at the sharp end.

In order for directors, managers and other officers to play their part, and thus avoid being prosecuted as individuals, they need to...

Take senior management responsibilities seriously. This means they must not show '*...consent or connivance...or neglect...*' for any breaches of *HSWA 1974* and *the Corporate Manslaughter Act* committed by their organisations. If they fail to take this responsibility seriously, they can be found personally liable for so-called 'offences by bodies corporate' under section 37 of *HSWA 1974*. Furthermore, the test of '*neglect*' relates to what they should have known, not what they actually knew – and simply turning a blind eye to an offence having been committed is enough for them to be found to have fallen foul of the legal requirements. As individuals, they also need to make sure they don't run the risk of being found guilty of the sister offence to 'corporate manslaughter', namely that of 'gross negligence manslaughter'. Where organisations are found guilty of corporate manslaughter, in order for individuals to avoid prosecution for this offence, they must prove that their conduct did not fall short, so as to '*...be so bad in all the circumstances as to amount to...a criminal act or omission*' in the jury's view. It takes a lot to prove a case of gross negligence manslaughter, but it's worth noting that where the requirements for the offence are met, it's not only those in senior management positions who can be convicted, but also anyone connected in some way to a workplace death.

In order for employees to play their part, and thus avoid being prosecuted as individuals, they need to...

Do the right things. Essentially, this requires them to show that they behaved in a reasonable and conscientious manner. If they fail to do so, they could be convicted of an offence under *HSWA 1974* and/or their employer could successfully defend a prosecution. This means they must make sure they understand and comply with any relevant requirements including, for instance, using machinery and equipment in accordance with any training given and wearing any personal protective equipment as required, as well as reporting any dangerous work situations (see section 7 of *HSWA 1974*). They also must not intentionally or recklessly interfere with anything provided by their employer to satisfy the requirements of *HSWA 1974* or other relevant legal provisions. If they fall foul of this obligation – the purpose of which is to ensure that work can be carried out safely and that employees are protected – they could be found guilty of an offence, which would cover circumstances such as interference with work equipment or PPE provided by their employer (see section 8 of *HSWA 1974*).

HOW TO... HARNESS THE POWER
OF PERFORMANCE INDICATORS

The cuckoo's fable highlighted some key principles for managing the development, implementation and maintenance of a robust set of performance indicators, *or nest of golden eggs!* Performance indicators are widely used across the corporate world, with the safety management arena being no exception. They have a particularly significant part to play in service of effective process safety management – by providing organisations with confidence in the effectiveness of the control offered by the barriers they put in place to prevent things going wrong – of obvious importance in relation to major accident scenarios. When used to best effect, an effective two-way relationship will be observable. *First,* upward communication of performance indicator outcomes will inform and guide the decisions about action required – including budgets and resourcing – made by senior leaders. *Second,* downward communication of performance indicator outcomes will percolate from the top, right down into the organisation, helping to drive cultural change and disseminate messages, including sending signals about any action needed at the sharp end.

The performance indicator principles derived from this fable were to: *first,* develop a set of performance indicators which is inherently sound; *second,* make sure the links between the performance indicator set and relevant desired safety outcomes/process controls are robust, and *third*, preserve the quality of the performance indicator set over time. As such, summarised here are some practical measures that organisations can adopt in order to develop performance indicators which are intrinsically sound, logically link to their respective desired safety outcomes and process controls, and have the power to endure, weathering any changes to their operational activities or indeed, other shifts in concerns seen across the broader risk landscape. There's a *fourth* point here too, which looks at how to keep the value of performance indicators in perspective, by balancing the structured approach that sits behind their development and maintenance, with a softer approach derived from picking up and reacting to other organisational signals.

HOW TO... CREATE
GREAT PERFORMANCE INDICATORS

Addressing the intrinsic quality of the set of performance indicators – *or clutch of golden eggs* – this principle is concerned with how to choose and/or devise measures which provide key insights and an at-a-glance view on the true health of an organisation's health and safety management system.

In order to select appropriate performance indicators, which reflect the nature, scope and scale of their operations, senior leaders within organisations need to ensure that they...

Question the quality of existing data sets. Where their existing data sets are perceived to be weak, nominating a risk champion – for instance, a safety advisor – to set up a working group, with the aim of developing performance indicators which are reflective of the organisation's risks and align to its risk profile, is a good place to start. A risk champion should be given the authority to challenge existing, and recommend new, performance indicators from an unbiased perspective. This can require collaborative efforts with external as well as internal stakeholders, for instance where there are industry requirements supplementary to the organisation's own, which might call into question the adequacy of organisational performance indicators and prompt their revision.

Define precisely the scope of performance indicators. This paves the way for relevant data to be collected, particularly when supplemented with periodic checks to ensure that what is measured remains appropriate over time. The aim here should be to reflect the whole organisational risk profile, whilst ensuring that the number of performance indicators is kept at a sensible level. It's crucial to solicit input from the right people when seeking to set performance indicators, these being individuals who are fully conversant with potential incident scenarios and the risks involved, who show clear-sightedness about what could go wrong and who are capable of identifying any immediate and underlying causes, such that they are able to confirm the appropriateness and sufficiency of the chosen indicators. This activity should typically involve risk owners, with efforts coordinated by a risk champion. A great data set should always be relevant to risk profile and not unduly burdensome in terms of data provision, collation or interpretation.

Keep the number of performance indicators manageable and avoid over-measuring. Where the number of performance indicators becomes excessive or the data unnecessarily detailed, this can be symptomatic of a failure to pinpoint areas of organisational vulnerability. *It's certainly not true to say that the higher the number of performance indicators, the better the control of risk will be!* On the contrary, putting in place a small number of carefully selected performance indicators, which map to the organisation's risk profile, can provide a more targeted focus for management attention and action.

Don't over-rely on failure data, at the expense of pro-active data. Failure data, including accident and injury rates, is important as it provides insights as to what has already happened (where the control of risk has failed), but an organisation with a progressive approach to effective safety management should seek predictive insights too.

HOW TO... BUILD STRONG
PERFORMANCE INDICATOR BONDS

Regarding the linkages between *first,* process controls and leading indicators, and *second,* desired safety outcomes and lagging indicators – or the principle that *golden eggs need golden threads* – the concern here is with making sure that there are effective parent-child relationships between process controls/desired safety outcomes and performance indicators. It's only by taking this kind of approach that an organisation can claim confidence in the value of its performance indicators as robust assurance tools and, more specifically, in their ability to report accurately the health of process controls and desired safety outcomes. Furthermore, well connected performance indicators have a significant role to play in adding to the effective functioning of a risk management cycle (the *plan-do-check-act* cycle), seen as vital in securing good safety risk management. This is achieved through effective upward communication which, when supported by all lower organisational levels, ensures accurate performance indicator information finds its way up to the right places, including to senior leaders. It's also achieved through effective downward communication, which facilitates the dissemination of messages from senior leaders, percolating down into the right organisational levels and driving the required cultural change.

In order to ensure that performance indicators link to process controls and/or desired safety outcomes, senior leaders within organisations need to make sure they...

Set performance indicators which are, and remain, reflective of risk profile. The chosen performance indicators should directly relate to their current risk priorities and risk profile. Looking at risk registers can help to highlight whether the performance indicators are driving the right behaviours – where successful, this should be reflected in improved risk scores and ratings. Ensuring that the data collated is the appropriate data – rather than that which has historically been provided, but has subsequently become outdated – poses a constant challenge for many organisations. If they are not careful, it can be the case that such information is supplied because it is easier to provide, rather than being in service of the effective control of risk.

It's particularly important for high-hazard organisations to get this right, with a priority focus placed upon those performance indicators which report on the quality of the organisation's major accident hazard control.

Understand what the change in status of a performance indicator says about the control of risk. This includes anticipating the types of recovery activity required where sub-optimal performance is recorded against a performance indicator. Performance indicators which enable early-stage detection of even small changes to performance can give vital insights to risk owners, before any deviation from acceptable levels occurs. And, where deviations do occur, risk owners need to understand what these mean, as well as the types of actions that might be required from them by way of response, in order to address these. This makes it crucial to set the right thresholds for performance indicators in the first place, and for there to be a clear and consistent understanding of the tolerance levels for performance deviation, as well as the implications of such deviations in each case.

Check that any risk register linkages remain intact. It's important to remain mindful of the possibility of these becoming compromised, due to ineffective change management or *indicator drift*, where once good indicators cease to be fit for purpose. Where linkages have become invalid or outmoded, ensuring that collaboration takes place with those responsible for overarching risk registers – which often contain safety risks alongside other risk types – and making any necessary adjustments, can reverse this issue, by realigning performance indicators to risk profile.

HOW TO... MAINTAIN PERFORMANCE INDICATORS

The focus of this third principle is upon defending performance indicators and data linkages or *golden threads* on an enduring basis – or *defending the nest of golden eggs and the parent-child relationships*. This means making sure that the connection between *first*, process controls and leading indicators, and *second*, desired safety outcomes and lagging indicators, remains strong, rather than degrading over time.

In order to maintain the quality of performance indicators over time, senior leaders within organisations need to make sure they...

Recognise the role played by performance indicators as a vital tool for controlling risk. This ultimately means having a deep understanding of the organisation's risks in totality, knowing what is being measured and why, and making sure that there is a clear and continuing logical link between risks and the performance indicator data being collated and analysed.

Review the full set of performance indicators, on a regular basis. This should ensure they continue to reflect the organisation's main risk management vulnerabilities. Just because performance indicators and the linkages between them were once sound, doesn't mean that this will remain the case on an enduring basis; if the risk register has moved on, so too should the performance indicators. Also, where the data itself has shown consistently good control over a sustained period, this might justify the removal of some performance indicators, reduction in the frequency of data collation, or replacement of the current performance indicators with others which have become a higher priority – where it's less clear that the risks are well controlled. The practicalities of ensuring performance indicators remain valid over time are such that it's sensible to schedule in periodic reviews of the risk register and consequential updates of the indicator set accordingly. Adopting a 'risk-based reporting' approach is a good way of avoiding the onset of *indicator fatigue*, through keeping the focus on priority issues of concern and preventing the dilution of report benefits. When an organisation approaches risk on an enduring basis – of which the refreshment of performance indicator reporting forms an integral part – this informs key players, sends meaningful signals back to senior leaders and risk owners, and ultimately helps to drive any required change.

Support the activities performed by data analysts. If the data they input is accurate, any challenges should be made directly to risk owners, rather than at data analyst level. This can be achieved by assigning responsibility for the performance reporting of safety critical tasks to risk owners, together with any associated remedial actions, in circumstances where the performance indicator data reveals shortfalls.

Observe improvements in the control of risk, as a result of gathering performance indicator data. There is little benefit to be gained from collating data, if risk owners aren't prepared to act when in receipt of poor performance ratings. If negative performance results don't translate into action being taken by risk owners to improve performance, this should prompt the organisation to question its overall approach. This might mean that the performance indicators aren't the right ones. Alternatively, and more worryingly, it might be that pervasive cultural issues exist – whether at the very top of an organisation, at the sharp end, or in pockets throughout it – which are preventing improvements from being achieved, in the wake of reported deficiencies. Where this is the case, the need to institute cultural change must be addressed.

HOW TO… KEEP PERFORMANCE INDICATORS IN PERSPECTIVE

It's important to keep in mind that instituting and maintaining an effective set of performance indicators offers a good way of keeping a watchful eye on risk, but it's by no means the only way. Even those organisations that have highly structured methodologies for developing performance indicators – and other well-established assurance tools – should remain wary about the effectiveness with which their risks are being controlled, regularly sense-checking whether performance indicators and other routinely used assurance methods are collectively providing them with the full picture.

In order to keep performance indicators in perspective, senior leaders within organisations need to make sure they…

Maintain a healthy cynicism – or chronic unease – about how well risk is being controlled. *REMEMBER!* Systems and plant are unlikely to be perfectly safe. Designs are unlikely to cater for every contingency. Procedures may not be complete, correct, available and usable for every occasion. People sometimes don't behave as expected, or in line with training given. And a score of 100% against a given performance indicator is unlikely to mean that what is being measured is 100% safe. *It might even mean the performance indicator itself is wrong!*

Act on weak signals. This means being ever-alert to signs of potential failure – as well as being careful to avoid the development of a perception that only good news will be tolerated, due to commercial pressures driving the wrong behaviours – ensuring this is reflected in effective and timely interventions being made within risk assessment and decision-making processes, when needed. There is little doubt that robustly reporting against a well-defined set of performance indicators is invaluable, but those who also: seek out and act on weak signals that indicate the potential for adverse events to occur; encourage and highlight the value of reporting; ask the right questions and seek a variety of perspectives; use systems consistently and reliably, and move quickly to mitigate or minimise upset conditions, are far more likely to be successful in managing risk on an enduring basis.

HOW TO... ACHIEVE
RELIABLE HUMAN PERFORMANCE

By embodying performance influencing factors within the imp characters at its heart, *Not-Quite's fable* highlighted the importance of securing reliable human performance, this being particularly crucial for those activities which require the carrying out of safety critical tasks. It also showed that by taking the time to understand the range and variability of human traits, characteristics, strengths and weaknesses – and accounting for these when designing and putting in place workplace control measures – organisations can protect the personal health, safety and wellbeing of their workers.

Organisations commonly lay claim to having well-established management systems and processes in place. It's also the case that they often speak to having positive safety cultures, with strong senior leaders, supportive line management, and workforce buy-in throughout. But even where this is true, it remains essential for organisations to recognise that errors can still occur for all sorts of reasons, meaning the challenge of achieving reliable human performance is an ever-present one. The delivery of reliable performance by frontline workers carrying out sharp end operational activities is particularly crucial. With this in mind, the purpose of this guide is to outline how organisations might tackle each of the identified factors to help them meet this challenge, not only to secure the integrity of their safety critical processes and operations, but also to ensure workforce safety and welfare.

In seeking to further explore the theme of controlling major accident hazards *the porridge pot fable* had highlighted, *Not-Quite's fable* looked more broadly at *why* it's important for organisations to secure reliable performance from those operatives responsible for undertaking safety critical tasks. It set about doing this by examining in more detail the different human failure types through the imp characters at its heart – a group collectively encompassing the range of factors which, in real-life contexts, make negative outcomes more likely than positive ones, when not kept in check. From a proactive perspective, the fable's *happy ending* suggested the steps needed to control these – or improve operative reliability when performing tasks – most notably the safety critical ones. The earlier *porridge pot fable* had presented an opportunity to highlight safety critical tasks as the most important aspects of high-risk processes, with the carrying out of these being crucial to achieving process control and preventing incidents and associated outcomes. The workshop exercise featured within *Not-Quite's fable* provided the vehicle for this to be progressed a stage further, by showing how identifying and controlling specific human failure types can make for the development of organisational strategies focused on the avoidance of negative outcomes (or poor control of risk), whether these are top events or consequences. The analysis of each imp's characteristics served to demonstrate how the safety and welfare of the operatives involved – and those with whom they interact – might be achieved in the first place, and defended on an ongoing basis.

Of course, whilst the pursuit of reliable human performance from operatives in the quest for a positive safety culture is an entirely legitimate goal, it's fundamental for those leading organisations to understand the role they personally play in setting the right tone for this to be achieved. When senior leaders clearly communicate their vision for organisational culture – as well as directing their workforces as to how they intend to get there – there is a far greater chance of them securing buy-in and thus, of safety targets and objectives being achieved, and even surpassed. Organisations want those who work for them to apply their knowledge and skills consistently and correctly every time, but senior leaders must fulfil their part of the bargain too, by being receptive and responsive to workforce views, opinions and feedback. This requires them to make sure they have the basics covered, including providing the right equipment, instructions, information and training to workers, and showing them what they need to do to stay safe. But, arguably more importantly, it's about senior leaders building trusted relationships with those who work for them, by taking action in response to any health and safety concerns they raise, escalating these to the right level to be resolved when necessary, and regularly communicating with the workforce on a planned, as well as *ad hoc*, basis. Where appropriate, this should include the use of formal consultation methods. Furthermore, when senior leaders are seen to be crediting workers by praising good behaviours, rather than only ever addressing poor practice, this invariably leads to more positive outcomes.

The fable looked at the importance of reliable human performance for the good of the processes for which people carry responsibility, with an emphasis on the importance of controlling major accident hazards.

The approach encouraged by this fable followed on from the first stages of effective process control highlighted by *the porridge pot fable*, in which the need was identified to determine the hazard, understand the risk (or top event), decide on the barriers required, and define the safety critical tasks forming an integral part of those barriers. *Not-Quite's fable* demonstrated that in order for organisations to have confidence in their standards of process control, they need not only to underline the importance of operatives doing the things expected of them to deliver reliable performance, but also to show them what can happen in circumstances where these expectations are not met.

Specifically, organisations need to...

- **Identify potential failures associated with the safety critical tasks people perform.** This requires them to work out the points within processes at which things could go wrong, because of what operatives might do or fail to do. Crucially, organisations need to focus on critical transition points within processes – for instance, times of shift handover – where what operatives do or don't do ultimately influences the degree to which a risk is effectively controlled;

- **Identify the factors that make failure more likely – which, left unchecked, could lead to a risk – and propose and develop strategies to prevent failure (and ultimately stop the risk being realised).** Which factors are the most important will vary on a case-by-case basis, but this information can be derived from risk register insights, horizon scanning, incident investigations, recommendations and findings, and so on, and,

- **Develop contingency plans for the circumstances in which risks occur and secure more successful error recovery, by blocking or reducing consequences.** Again, this will vary on a case-by-case basis, but it's important to ensure that sufficient resource is reserved to remedy post-top event outcomes, covering circumstances in which avoidance of the top event is unsuccessful. It's commonplace for pro-active, forward-thinking organisations to allocate more resource to preventing incidents from occurring in the first place – through their use of pre-top event risk controls – but even where this kind of approach is taken, it's fundamental for them to set aside sufficient resources to apply to mitigation efforts, should the worst case scenario occur.

Additionally, the fable looked at the importance of reliable performance being achieved by human operatives for their own good, as well as for the benefit of those with whom they interact and anyone else who might be affected by what they do, thereby preventing the risk of injury and promoting workforce and wider societal wellbeing.

Experiencing just one of the factors embodied by the imps in *Not-Quite's fable* can have safety, health and/or welfare implications for individuals displaying these characteristics but additionally, where multiple factors are at play, this can lead to synergistic effects being seen in those who are subject to them. It's important for organisations to understand the effects of any of these factors upon the particular individuals concerned – together with the motives and reasons behind their behaviours – as well as seeking to prevent any negative impacts which could result if they are present. Taking such an approach not only has benefits for the operatives involved, but is also good for the systems they operate and the processes within which their actions form an integral part.

HOW TO... ADDRESS
PERFORMANCE INFLUENCING FACTORS
AND SECURE RELIABLE HUMAN PERFORMANCE
The Imps' Action Plans

In a bid to offer some suggestions as to how the problems posed by performance influencing factors might be addressed, the action plans which follow here can be used to inform organisational thinking in two different ways – *first,* to help address specific factors that might affect the effective performance of safety critical tasks, so as to reduce the likelihood or magnitude of a real-world incident, equivalent to the fictional one in *the porridge pot fable,* and *second,* to help them address specific factors which drive individuals to act in a particular way which, if left unchecked, might cause harm to them or others.

There is inevitably some duplication between these action plans. This is unsurprising, because some actions are geared towards achieving a common outcome. In real-world circumstances, organisations can reap benefits from assigning joint ownership of action plans to those for whom the outcome is recognised to be a shared goal. An example of this would be that an action to *put in place an effective workload strategy,* when supported by the necessary arrangements, addresses the need to achieve an optimal workload outcome, by looking at workload allocation as a whole. *And how does it do this?* Well, in circumstances of 'work underload' (as shown by *Idle,* in the fable) it might lead to the allocation of more workload, whilst in 'work overload' circumstances (as shown by *Spent,* in the fable) it might necessitate workload reduction or redistribution. It's suggested that, by adopting such an approach, each imp's action plan can be independently viewed, whilst recognising the added value achievable from the plans being read concurrently. This approach transfers to a real-world context too. By viewing the factors collectively, rather than one-by-one, organisations can ensure that any solutions put in place to resolve the issues of one factor don't – even inadvertently – lead to an uptick in the failings associated with one or more of the others.

Having highlighted the importance of ensuring human performance reliability for the good of both people and processes, the predominant focus of this final *How to...* Guide is upon the practical steps that can be taken to address each of the seven factors (or each of the *imps*). The symptoms or signs associated with the factors (or *imps*) are to be found within the fable itself, but summarised within the *How to...* Guide for each factor is *first*, an outline of why the given factor matters and needs to be tackled, supported by references to Acts and regulations, where appropriate; *second*, an overview of the effects of that factor, and *third*, some practical management and mitigation measures to help control it, these being examples of the types of action which would also be suitable for inclusion within real-world action plans.

Essentially, therefore, this seven-part *How to...* Guide contains hints and tips for dealing with each of the seven factors. It is suggested that incorporating the types of action linked to the factors here within real-world action plans – when supported by the downward communication of appropriate and correctly targeted messages from an organisation's senior leaders – should help to secure reliable human performance, invariably bringing about positive safety culture change too.

Not-Quite's fable showed that, in order to achieve reliable performance, for the good of the people involved and the processes they operate, organisations should make sure they...

- **Address physical strength and capability concerns**...which means making sure that people aren't too physically weak to get things right (*Weedy's* action plan);
- **Address work overload concerns**...which means making sure that people aren't too mentally overwhelmed to get things right (*Spent's* action plan);
- **Address work underload concerns**...which means making sure people aren't too bored to get things right (*Idle's* action plan);
- **Address fatigue concerns**...which means making sure people aren't too tired to get things right (*Drifty's* action plan);
- **Address stress and low morale concerns**...which means making sure people aren't too stressed to get things right (*Stressy's* action plan);
- **Address competence concerns**...which means making sure people aren't too stupid to get things right (*Bumbler's* action plan). *This might come across as a particularly blunt message!* But it's about organisations ensuring that those who work for them have the right level of knowledge, understanding and experience to competently perform the tasks they are required to undertake, and,

- **Address concerns about motivation to carry out designated functions, roles or tasks**...which means making sure people aren't too devious, distracted or misguided to get things right, and is of particular importance where health and safety priorities may appear to compete or conflict with other priorities on organisational agendas (*Sly's* action plan).

So, without further ado, here is the *How to...* Guide (*or what might colloquially be regarded as the imps' action plans*), covering the seven factors.

HOW TO... ADDRESS LACK OF PHYSICAL CAPABILITY, SUITABILITY OR CONDITION
Weedy's Action Plan
'Don't be too physically weak to get things right!'

In this fable's workshop-based application of the porridge pot scenario, it was identified that Weedy might have been unable to exert enough manual effort to close a shut-off valve, due to his lacking in physical strength.

WHY IT MATTERS

As the first of the *workload imps*, relating to physical capability, suitability and condition, Weedy highlights an important aspect to address in terms of human performance. Many industrial tasks involve high physical workload, whether through lifting, lowering, carrying, pushing and pulling, other sustained physical effort, or the performance of a high number of physical actions or movements within a restricted timeframe. The effects to which Weedy might have been subject would have included: physical fatigue, injury, and ill health, resulting in his consequential reduced ability to do work, as well as associated personal financial implications[286]. Work related musculoskeletal disorders – already considered in the context of *the swede fable* and *Pixie-Locks' fable* – can be avoided by attending to the factor epitomised by this imp. Reflecting back upon *the swede*

---

286. For statistics on manual handling injuries and ill health, refer to *the swede fable.*

fable, the learning from that tale focused upon the approach to assessing manual handling activities, much of which applies here too. Regulation 4 of *the Manual Handling Operations Regulations 1992*[287] (*'the Manual Handling Regulations'*) sets out the hierarchy of control for employers to adopt in order to assess and control the manual handling activities performed by their employees, and requires that they avoid, assess and reduce the associated injury risk, including providing information on loads to those who carry them out. Central to this is the need for employers to ensure that they have appropriately considered the physical capabilities required of those called upon to perform such activities, a factor which merits attention alongside the others to be looked at here. But of additional relevance to this factor in the context of this fable – over and above the attention it was given in connection with *the swede fable* – is the importance of it being considered in relation to the performance of safety critical tasks.

OVERVIEW OF EFFECTS

Health conditions associated with excessive physical workload can arise from certain types of activity, as identified in *the swede fable,* the questions posed there having been principally framed around agricultural push and pull manual handling operations. The questions asked in the context of this fable are broadly similar, although the emphasis here is subtly different, being upon the ease with which operations can be performed by operatives – including those that involve the performance of safety critical tasks – as well as the potentially negative impacts they can have upon them, as individuals too.

The types of questions organisations might ask to help them identify if they have a problem in relation to potentially excessive physical workload demands being placed upon workers could include: '*Are loads too heavy and/or bulky, placing unreasonable demands on those carrying them out?',* '*Do loads have to be lifted from the floor and/or above the shoulders?', 'Do tasks involve frequent repetitive lifting?', 'Do tasks require the adoption of awkward postures, such as bending, twisting, or excessive reaching?', 'Is it impossible to grip loads properly?', 'Are tasks performed under time pressure?'* and '*Do the tasks, as designed, incorporate too few rest breaks?'*

---

287. S.I. 1992/2793.

As well as having implications for the effective performance of safety critical tasks, if not appropriately controlled, these types of activities can directly cause physical injuries to the individuals performing them – to their lower backs, arms, hands and fingers – and can indirectly contribute to an increased risk of slips, trips and falls injuries too.

MANAGEMENT AND MITIGATION MEASURES

In circumstances where the physical capability, suitability and condition demands placed upon workers pose problems for organisations, they need to address this by putting in place appropriate management and mitigation measures.

In order to address the problems associated with this factor, organisations need to...

Put a manual handling strategy in place. This should cover the assessment and control of the risks, with a focus on avoidance as the first priority, including designing out the need for manual handling, wherever possible. The strategy needs to address workplace aspects, together with the activities, processes and substances which could injure individuals or harm their health. Depending on the extent of the risk identified, there might be further benefits to be gained by conducting workload analysis, including user trials, in order to analyse the scale of the problem. Efforts also need to be made to ensure that manual handling activities can be performed satisfactorily by the majority of reasonably fit and healthy workers.

Review organisational data. This includes looking at whether trends identified within incident reports and performance indicator reports highlight manual handling as a cause for concern, with steps being taken, where necessary, to address these and any other specific findings accordingly.

Focus upon safety critical tasks which require particular physical strength. An example of this would be manual valve operations, where the expectation would be that anyone recruited and assigned to any such activities and tasks should be capable of performing them safely. This is important not only for the effective and reliable performance of the activities and tasks themselves, but also for the protection of the personal safety, health and wellbeing of those involved in undertaking them.

Risk assess manual handling activities. It's sensible to use the Health and Safety Executive's Toolkit for MSDs as a start here, with the adoption of a three stage approach to the assessment process being advised[288]. Remember that for risk assessment to be effective, it's fundamental for the resulting control measures to be understood and adopted by frontline workers, who actually need to use them. This includes providing lifting and handling aids, where identified as an appropriate control measure by risk assessment, supported by the provision of suitable information, instruction, training and supervision to make sure such aids are used as intended.

Address the particular needs of vulnerable workers. This includes checking whether they have any special requirements. Those classed as vulnerable include new and young workers, migrant workers, new and expectant mothers, those with disabilities, temporary workers, contractors, home workers, and lone workers. The approach taken towards addressing such needs should be driven by an understanding as to why a given activity might cause specific issues or be more challenging for some individuals or groups, than is the case for other workers. It should also account for the possibility of physical capability varying with age, due to possible decline as part of the ageing process (albeit that age, of itself, need not be an issue given the variability between all individuals). It's important for particular attention to be paid to those who have a physical weakness. Where there's deemed to be a problem, personal monitoring and the adoption of work physiology measures should be considered. And, where individuals are known to have health conditions, efforts should be made to reduce the physical demands of heavy jobs, so that tasks can be safely performed by a wider range of individuals. Ultimately, the solution here is to either adapt the tasks or to redeploy those identified as vulnerable to other alternative tasks, which are within their physical capability.

---

288. The three stage approach to manual handling risk assessment was summarised in the context of *the swede fable* and in its accompanying *How to...* Guide, together with references to the relevant Health and Safety Executive manual handling publications.

Involve workers. They are often best placed to gauge what the hazards are and may notice things that are not obvious, as well as having some good ideas about how best to control manual handling risks. A further reason for seeking their involvement in the development of strategies which help to control the risks is that this increases the likelihood of compliance, through the securing of their early-stage buy-in.

Look at manufacturers' instructions for equipment. These can be helpful in determining hazards and often give guidance on safe manual handling arrangements too, providing useful information such as *two person lift,* with the equipment itself also stating the weight of the load, on its face.

Manage organisational change effectively. This often brings with it increased levels of risk, and introduces a need to review risk assessments and control measures, with these being adapted where necessary.

HOW TO... ADDRESS
MENTAL WORK OVERLOAD
Spent's Action Plan
'Don't be too mentally overwhelmed
to get things right!'

In this fable's workshop-based application of the porridge pot scenario, it was identified that Spent might have misread a gauge or failed to respond to a high level alarm due to 'alarm flooding'. Spent's state of mental exhaustion could also, of itself, have been the reason behind his having failed to distinguish between the *valve open* and *valve closed* positions.

WHY IT MATTERS

As the second of the *workload imps*, Spent can be seen as the embodiment of excessive mental workload – sometimes referred to as 'cognitive overload'. People vary widely in their capacity for, and vulnerability to, high workload, but too much workload is widely recognised as being a primary cause of high stress. This can have a consequence of seriously degrading human performance, often observable through reduced accuracy levels – a major implication for those involved in safety critical tasks, where operative 'vigilance' is of paramount importance. Poor quality problem solving and decision-making can lead to errors being made. And errors involving poor judgments invariably result in inappropriate plans being made and incorrect actions taken, ultimately leading to accidents and/or incidents. Other effects can include detrimental mental health outcomes, including stress, anxiety and depression. These sit alongside other issues, including general dissatisfaction, low morale and reduced commitment to job roles, often reflected in a consequential rise in absenteeism and/or high levels of staff turnover.

OVERVIEW OF EFFECTS

The key feature of this factor is excessive mental effort demanded from human operatives, either at a single point in time or over a whole shift. Most typically this arises in tasks which demand more attention than they have available, and can result in those affected – often subconsciously – continually adjusting their working methods to keep their mental workload within limits. Individuals affected by this factor can sometimes be observed to be devoting more attention to tasks or information they consider to be important, albeit that their judgment may not be correct or valid. This is because of the natural tendency of those faced with such situations to focus on information sources which are easiest to see and their defaulting to using strategies requiring the least mental effort. Often these are the best learned, but they may not be the most appropriate for the situation at hand. By pitching their attention at too high a level, people can miss important events or workflow trends. When faced by cognitive overload scenarios they may also, unintentionally, get locked into a single approach, thereby impeding their capability to make the optimum decision for the circumstances or to maintain accuracy on a sustained basis. They might miss important information due to their visual system being overloaded, or because the circumstances in which they find themselves drive them to divide their attention, with their attempts to multi-task leading to information being missed and errors occurring. Continually changing work methods can assist with keeping mental workload within limits, but by far the best method is for organisations to design interfaces, workplaces and jobs so as to minimise the occurrences of work overload arising in the first place.

Organisations need to identify and measure any activities or tasks where cognitive workload is high and to put in place control measures, where this is seen as problematic. The mental demands placed upon people can be both diverse and complicated, and the types of questions organisations might ask to help them identify whether this factor poses issues for them could include: *'Are individuals required to diagnose and develop an effective solution to a problem, which could be complex, or one of many problems needing to be solved?'*, *'Do individuals need to process multiple sources of information and make difficult decisions?'*, *'Do the activities undertaken by individuals require them to apply fine judgment or discrimination?'* and *'Are individuals expected to remember (store) or recall (retrieve from memory) lots of facts or pieces of information?'* Another question to ask might be: *'Do individuals need to apply sustained attention, vigilance or monitoring, or to maintain a high level of situational awareness of the current status of a process, and are they called upon to choose the correct response, if the status of plant or equipment changes?'*

MANAGEMENT AND MITIGATION MEASURES

In order to manage work overload situations, organisations should address any problems highlighted by their investigation of the issues particular to their operations. Additionally, they need to be aware of tasks being made more difficult if subject to one or more of the following aspects: *first*, if they are performed under time pressure; *second*, if operatives are required to multi-task; *third*, if operatives are not yet fully competent; *fourth*, if activities are performed in abnormal operating conditions or emergency situations; *fifth*, if information is unclear, ambiguous, provided late or requires conversion or pre-processing; *sixth*, if the result of the activity is critical to safety, environmental protection or financial success, and finally, *seventh*, if the operative is fatigued or distracted, for instance due to work environment or personal factors.

In order to address the problems associated with this factor, organisations are advised to...

Put a workload strategy in place. An effective workload strategy will design interfaces, workplaces, jobs and systems to facilitate an operative's function, so as to minimise the occurrences of work overload. Applying user-centred design principles at the design stage makes it possible to use workload prediction and measurement techniques to identify likely problem areas, determine the potential for automation to reduce work overload, and define operative roles accordingly. Where effective, a workload strategy can provide a good basis for decision-making about function allocation, task and role design, team design and user equipment interface design. By pro-actively designing interfaces, workplaces, jobs and systems – including carrying out early-stage user trials – workload problems can be prevented from arising in the first place. Techniques which can be helpful here include holding interviews with users and the testing of prototype interfaces and work schedules.

Review organisational data. This might include incident data which implicates work overload as a root cause. The checking of incident reports and performance indicator ratings can be invaluable for the detection of concerning trends, where cognitive overload might have been a contributory factor, which can in turn help to inform where improvements are required. It can also be helpful to refer to occupational health records, which could highlight excessive workloads as having a detrimental impact on the health and wellbeing of particular individuals or groups, or indeed upon their performance of certain tasks and activities.

Identify safety critical tasks, emergency situations and abnormal operating conditions. These are activities and circumstances where it's essential for operatives to be fit, rested and alert. Even if the extent of work overload as an organisational problem isn't fully known, where identified as an issue, it makes sense to prioritise these types of tasks and situations. This is particularly important, given the gravity of the outcomes for the systems and processes involved, as well as the operatives who use them, as can result when there are shortcomings in the conduct of safety critical tasks, or the adequacy of responses to emergency situations.

Identify and control situations involving high cognitive workload. This includes: where there are complex or multiple problems; where problems need to be diagnosed and solutions developed; where it's necessary to process multiple sources and make difficult decisions; where there's a need to apply fine judgment or discretion; where there's a need to remember (store) or recall (retrieve) lots of information; where there's a need to apply sustained attention or vigilance, or where a high level of situational awareness needs to be maintained.

Recruit and retain sufficient numbers of people for roles. Having the right numbers of operatives helps to ensure the required tasks can be performed and identified workload demands met, without safety standards being compromised. In seeking to ensure that there is a sufficient level of resource available, account needs to be taken of abnormal and emergency operating conditions, as well as routine circumstances.

Choose the right people. The selection process should, in part, be based upon the aptitude of individuals to deal with potentially large workloads. The aim should be to choose individuals who are best able to strike the right balance between maintaining sufficient focus on monitoring for incoming information on the one hand, whilst being alert to changes to the expected environment, on the other.

Make sure people are able to do what they need to do. This means training and briefing them, including 'overtraining' them, where appropriate. This should ensure that they are routinely capable of working to a higher or more intense level when needed, albeit that this may not be demanded from them on a daily or frequent basis. Giving operatives more training than they apparently need to pass end of training tests can often prove effective because it gives them the opportunity to practise what they have learnt, such that their skills become more intuitive, which is of particular assistance for equipping them to respond rapidly in emergency situations.

Involve workers. This helps to identify workload problems. As well as considering the basic concern of workload being too high, this can also include exploring other issues with them, such as the comfort of their working positions, reports of personal discomfort, and their level of satisfaction with working arrangements. In seeking to address such issues with workers, efforts should be directed towards ensuring that any machines and equipment provided are appropriate for the tasks involved, easy to use and well-maintained, as well as focus being placed upon resolving error frequencies and incident report findings, where high workload is perceived to have been an initiating factor.

Foster a positive safety culture. A key feature seen in proactive team cultures is that workloads are anticipated and back-up is provided, or alternative work found. This means scheduling operatives' hours of work and shifts, so as to allow for sufficient periods of rest both within and between them, helping to minimise workforce fatigue levels and maximise their attentiveness and effectiveness. It also means taking opportunities to plan workload, so as to ensure there is an equitable allocation, and considering the automation of tasks, where possible, even after the design stage, which reduces the volume of tasks required to be undertaken and enables operatives to focus on achievable output levels. Where workload issues are well-handled, this should avoid a perception developing amongst those involved that the best jobs or more favourable workload levels have been allocated to one group, or particular individuals, thus avoiding feelings of resentment, demotivation or dissatisfaction setting in. Encouraging a culture of co-operation should prevent the emergence of feelings that one group is receiving preferential treatment over another.

Manage organisational change effectively. This often brings with it increased levels of risk, and introduces a need to review risk assessments and control measures, with these being adapted where necessary. It's important to note that this should apply not only to major organisational restructures that take place, but also to smaller incremental changes which can occur over time and have the effect of eroding initially effective workload planning and resource allocation.

HOW TO... ADDRESS
MENTAL WORK UNDERLOAD
Idle's Action Plan
'Don't be too bored to get things right!'

In this fable's workshop-based application of the porridge pot scenario, it was identified that Idle might have failed to distinguish between *valve open* and *valve closed* states, in large part due to his mental workload having been too low, which in turn resulted in his failure to notice important events.

WHY IT MATTERS

This factor, as epitomised by Idle – the third of the *workload imps* – is one which is generally less well understood than is true of the physical capability and mental work overload factors, albeit that there is growing acceptance of its relevance. 'Cognitive underload' refers to the state in which an individual's mental workload is too low, where they experience lower arousal levels and suffer consequential drops in their performance levels, as can be brought about by the carrying out of unstimulating or repetitive tasks. As was noted for Spent, sub-optimal workload allocation is a big problem where operatives perform safety critical tasks, but here it is for the opposite reason, due to their lack of activity creating the potential for them to become bored and inattentive, with observable loss of job satisfaction, demotivation and consequential errors. This can also result in those affected displaying thrill-seeking behaviours, or in operatives generating inappropriate tasks for themselves, so as to make their work more stimulating. Alternatively, it can simply be that they fail to perform effectively, perhaps due to their designated tasks being of a mundane or repetitive nature. If left unchecked, lack of practice or mental exercise can also lead to the deskilling of once competent operatives.

OVERVIEW OF EFFECTS

Underload theory identifies an 'optimal performance zone' within which an individual should operate. According to this theory, there are several performance effects observable in individuals subject to a state of work underload, the most notable of which is the impact on their execution of safety critical tasks. Work underload is to be avoided in these circumstances, as vigilance is imperative when carrying out this type of activity. Other effects noted in work underload situations can include slower response times, a failure to notice new events, an increase in the number of performance errors, and an increased probability of operatives failing to respond appropriately to environmental stimuli.

This factor is becoming increasingly relevant, as can be seen across the transport sector, where the choreography between the respective roles of driver and vehicle is changing. The advent of 'intelligent transport systems' – across road, rail and air – is giving cause for these industries to broaden their focus beyond simply recruiting good drivers, towards hiring those who show vigilance, in cases where smart vehicles and infrastructure behave outside anticipated or desired 'performance envelopes'. Those who have historically been high performers in physically driving vehicles often need to adjust their skills when redeployed to activities such as the accurate and timely monitoring and intervention (or detection and correction) of self-driving vehicles, where these do not behave as predicted or intended.

Whilst perhaps not ordinarily as significant an issue for their operatives as that of high cognitive workload, there remains a need for organisations to identify circumstances in which cognitive workload is low, and for them to decide whether such a state poses a problem for the conduct of activities, particularly those of a safety critical nature. As such, a relevant question to be asked here is: *'Are those individuals who are subject to ordinarily low cognitive workload still able to react with the desired accuracy and speed of response when called upon to do so, however rarely this might be required from them?'*

MANAGEMENT AND MITIGATION MEASURES

In circumstances where organisations identify low cognitive workload as an issue for their workforces – and particularly where this has implications for the conduct of safety critical tasks – they need to put in place appropriate management and mitigation measures.

In order to address the problems associated with this factor, organisations are advised to...

Put a workload strategy in place. This was one of the points also listed to address problems of work overload. Here, however, for the workload strategy to be effective, it needs to minimise circumstances of work underload, with a possible solution being to redistribute work away from those experiencing work overload, and towards those in a state of work underload. This may not work in all cases, however, as it's dependent upon the skill sets of the operatives involved. It might therefore require the reskilling of those in a work underload position to a satisfactory level first, in order to enable them to take on additional work from those in a work overload situation.

Review organisational data. This helps to highlight if there are trends, problems or incidents in which low workload is implicated as a root cause. The checking of incident reports and performance indicators can be invaluable in detecting concerning incident trends, where cognitive underload might have been a contributory factor. The adverse effects of low workload can be manifested in workers perhaps displaying signs of boredom or creating distractions which are inappropriate for the operating conditions. It can also be helpful to refer to occupational health records, which could highlight low workloads as having a detrimental impact on the health and wellbeing of particular individuals or groups, or indeed upon their performance of certain tasks and activities.

Choose the right people. In a similar way to the work overload situation, selecting the right people includes determining the operative numbers and capabilities required, and the designing of appropriate solutions. In these circumstances, however, the focus is upon preventing occurrences of work underload amongst operatives. Staffing levels should be appropriate for routine operating conditions, with a sufficient number of individuals being available to carry out all required tasks. If the work type being considered allows for situations of work underload and is of a type suited to the operatives in question, what matters most in the context of performing safety critical tasks is that they are capable of switching into dynamic mode at the crucial moments. This means that they need to be able to maintain vigilance, even after protracted periods of little change, or where they are ordinarily subject to low workload demands.

Make sure people are able to do what they need to do. This means training and briefing them, including 'overtraining' them, where appropriate. This ensures that the operatives selected are capable of working at higher intensity when required, even in situations where this is a rarity and something they may not be called upon to do during every shift or day. This is particularly key where workloads are ordinarily low or moderate. It's a similar consideration to that looked at for work overload situations, but here it matters more because operatives who ordinarily have too little to do or to occupy themselves are likely to deskill faster, lose reaction speed or respond less quickly than required, when called upon to act. This is of particular importance in relation to the performance of safety critical tasks, for which a range of different measures can be considered to help maintain or increase alertness levels. The work environment can be altered, either temporarily or permanently, for instance by changing lighting levels or work positions. Also, memory aids can be used by operatives, so as to maintain their mental agility. Additionally, provided it is carefully managed, caffeine can be used, so as to temporarily boost the concentration levels of individuals at identified low points, although, as already noted, this has the effect of masking tiredness, thus blocking rather than addressing the root cause.

Involve workers. Talking to workers helps to identify workload problems. The action here is equivalent to that identified for work overload, but here the problems identified are likely to differ, ranging from boredom and dissatisfaction with the work allocated to them to a sense that, as individuals, their skills are not being used, or that they are being underutilised. It's important to recognise the wide variety of workload problems, as a first step towards identifying how best to remedy them.

Foster a positive safety culture. A key feature seen in proactive team cultures is that workloads are anticipated and back-up is provided or alternative work found. This is a similar action to that identified for the high workload scenario, but here, ensuring the equitable allocation of workload means operatives in a work underload state taking work from those who are experiencing work overload. It's important that teams work collaboratively in these circumstances, with managers sanctioning workload reallocation only where those taking on additional work are sufficiently skilled and in a state of readiness to do so, without the control of tasks being compromised. Where such issues are well-handled, this should avoid a sense developing amongst operatives that the *best* jobs or more favourable workload volumes have been allocated to certain groups or individuals, thus avoiding feelings of resentment, demotivation or dissatisfaction creeping in. Encouraging a culture of co-operation should prevent the emergence of a perception that one group or certain individuals are receiving preferential treatment over others.

Consider the quality of the user experience. Attention should be paid to the particular type of work being undertaken, with improvements made where necessary. Where the quality of the user experience is high, this makes doing the right thing easier and more enjoyable. Efforts to improve user experience in a work underload context can include the designing in of 'haptic feedback', where users experience physical feedback through touch, for instance by using vibrating joysticks, which assist with the maintenance of alertness levels. Another alternative can be to introduce interactive secondary tasks, such as the verbalisation of actions or risks, which can help to lower the likelihood of error. Finally, on this point, 'gamification' elements can be introduced to the tasks carried out, providing increased challenge, performance feedback, social approval and incentives for operatives to take the correct action.

Manage organisational change effectively. This often brings with it increased levels of risk, and introduces a need to review risk assessments and control measures, with these being adapted where necessary. It also includes being mindful of circumstances in which change is incremental, as over time this can degrade the effectiveness with which safety critical tasks are performed. In circumstances where organisational downsizing is taking place, consideration still needs to be given as to how all operational functions are to be carried out, so that a work underload situation does not suddenly become a work overload situation, for the remaining workers.

HOW TO... ADDRESS FATIGUE
Drifty's Action Plan
'Don't be too tired to get things right!'

In this fable's workshop-based application of the porridge pot scenario, it was identified that Drifty might have been poor at gauge monitoring due to his not being in a fit, rested and alert state. His lack of alertness might also have contributed to him being confused between *valve open* and *valve closed* states.

WHY IT MATTERS

Fatigue is a major factor, and one which it's vital for organisations – particularly high-hazard organisations – to address, not least because the requirement to manage fatigue is a legal one. For employers to show that they have performed an effective risk assessment, they must assess the risks to employees from work activities, and commit to introducing such measures as are 'reasonably practicable' to remove or control them, as is called for by *The Management of Health and Safety at Work Regulations 1999*[289]('*the Management Regulations*'). This includes the number of hours worked and how these are scheduled. But legal requirements aside, there are many other compelling reasons for addressing this factor. It's a known fact that when the human brain or body is fatigued, the risk of errors being made increases significantly. Fatigue can result in errors being brought about through confusion, indecision and panic – these obviously being undesirable states for both the processes being controlled and those individuals subject to them – and poses particular problems where there's a need for safety critical tasks to be undertaken. Operatives who tend to be more prone to fatigue include those whose work is machine-paced, complex or monotonous.

The risks posed by fatigue, both for personal wellbeing and for process safety – as highlighted by Drifty in this fable – should not be underestimated. The risk might manifest itself in slower reaction times, or in a reduced ability to process information being observed amongst those affected. Or in memory lapses, absent-mindedness or decreased awareness. Other undesirable traits which might become apparent – and of particular concern in those to whom safety critical tasks are assigned, where alertness is key – can include lack of attention, poor risk estimation and reduced co-ordination. But what is perhaps of greatest importance is that, however it manifests itself, left unchecked, fatigue can lead to increased errors and violations. A tragic example of this was seen in the *Clapham Junction* rail disaster, mentioned in the *prologue* to *the porridge pot fable*, which clearly highlighted how the factor can compromise reliable human performance, and the consequences which can flow when it isn't proactively addressed. It's well-known that this factor has a significant impact as a root or underlying cause of incidents – as is borne out by the findings of many a major accident investigation report – with a fatigued person more likely to exhibit poor decision-making capabilities. Simply put, as fatigue levels increase, the risk of an incident occurring rises, with

---

289. S.I. 1999/3242.; this requirement is set down in regulation 3.

sometimes devastating consequences. It's for these reasons that it's vital for organisations to be proactive in managing this factor.

OVERVIEW OF EFFECTS

Whilst lacking in clear definition, those suffering from fatigue can exhibit a range of effects, arising due to their working excessive hours or being subject to poorly designed shift patterns. Fatigue can be the result of either prolonged or excessive exertion, and the impacts on the human body can be both physical and mental in nature. The indications of fatigue being a problem can be subtle, complex and varied, with the symptoms or observable traits and behaviours in those subject to it including: a feeling of tiredness and an inability to perform work tasks effectively; reduced alertness and a compromised ability to process information within required timeframes; disinterest in tasks, and slower reaction times, when compared with those who are well-rested. In terms of workforce impacts, this factor can be felt through: unexplained or frequent absences; behavioural change; drops in productivity; increased accidents and near misses, and performance or conduct issues amongst those affected.

The types of questions organisations can ask when seeking to identify whether they have a problem with fatigue include: 'Are staffing levels sufficient for the workload required?', 'Is fatigue implicated – directly or indirectly – as a causal factor in incident reports, or as a theme in near miss data?', 'Do workforce sickness levels point to fatigue being a problem?', 'Are individuals subject to personal factors, for instance in their home lives, which are adding to their personal levels of fatigue?', and 'Is the organisation – even indirectly – prioritising productivity goals over safety goals, for instance, by allowing excessive overtime in order to meet output targets?'

MANAGEMENT AND MITIGATION MEASURES

Both the prevention strategy and the required management action for this factor are complex, as fatigue is comprised of both short and long term elements and is influenced by both workplace and individuals' home and other life aspects. Clearly, the measures suggested here won't necessarily be feasible across all work settings, but it's worth highlighting that even small changes made by organisations can benefit individuals' sleep patterns and home lives, and potentially have a big pay-off in the workplace too, marked by decreased levels of fatigue and improved levels of work output.

For their part, operatives should be encouraged to develop good sleeping habits. This is because, at a personal level, good sleep is restorative and carries with it a wealth of benefits, including the repair of the immune system and positive impacts for mental wellbeing. From an organisational perspective, on the other hand, being well-rested brings advantages in terms of reducing the likelihood of the performance of safety critical tasks being compromised by those required to undertake them. This should compel organisations to follow some basic principles, including: ensuring the regularity of shift schedules; making sure operatives have sufficient rest periods between shifts; scheduling in rest days, and restricting the number of shifts – especially night shifts – in a row. Applying a shift rotation approach is important too – specifically forward rotation (mornings, followed by afternoons, followed by nights), rather than the other way around. Looking at, and making adjustments to, start and end times can also make a big difference, helping to reduce disruption to the sleep schedules of individuals, and perhaps enabling them to avoid rush-hour traffic, or difficulties with child-care or other domestic arrangements. Even moving early shift starts an hour later can be helpful in reducing the impact of this factor, as can limiting the number of successive early starts in a row. Another measure that can be taken is to shorten the length of shifts which involve early starts, so as to counteract the potentially detrimental impact of fatigue onset, in the latter stages of a shift.

Additional practical steps which can be taken to support with the moderation of this factor include the avoidance of long shifts and too much overtime, arrangement of quality breaks during the working day, and consideration of personal preferences – some people are morning people (*larks*), whilst others are night people (*owls*). Further work design aspects can also be considered, such as the permitting of napping at work to restore performance – depending on the role and job type – but this carries with it some risks of its own: for example, it has been shown that an individual's effectiveness can reduce for the period immediately following a nap. Another approach can be to arrange for more interesting and varied work to be done at night and at other low points but, in doing this, it should be ensured that tasks are not too demanding, monotonous or repetitive in nature.

In order to address the problems associated with this factor, organisations are advised to...

Involve workers. Talking openly can help to identify whether, and to what extent, fatigue is problematic for the workforce. There might be warning signs which suggest it isn't being well controlled. In setting the tone for a collaborative and honest culture, senior leaders must – through their decisions, actions and behaviours – be alert to the multiple causes of fatigue, and develop an approach which spans the entire range of operational activities performed by their workforces, as the first step to ensuring that these are effectively assessed, addressed and managed.

Develop and implement a working hours' policy. The overriding purpose of such a policy should be to ensure that working hours are not too long, covering aspects such as: daily work hours, maximum average weekly hours (typically 48 hours, averaged over a 17-week period), on-call work and work-related travel. The policy should make clear the arrangements to manage and limit excessive working hours – which could include placing restrictions on the number of hours worked, overtime and shift-swapping – with any supporting procedures being implemented and rigorously enforced. The policy also needs to include a requirement for the provision of adequate and regular breaks, so as to allow workers the opportunity to rest, eat and rehydrate too.

Review organisational data. This includes making sure fatigue is considered as a potential causal factor, when conducting accident and incident investigations. The proactive use of this data can help to inform fatigue risk management, on an ongoing basis.

Focus upon individuals involved in the control of major accident hazards and safety critical work. Operatives involved in these work types should be prioritised for fatigue monitoring, given the vital role they play in controlling process safety risks and applying mitigation measures too. These individuals should be made aware of the process safety implications if their fatigue risk is not well-controlled or managed, with it also being explained to them that they have a personal responsibility to ensure they are well-rested. Furthermore, it's essential to make sure that these workers, in particular, understand the implications of alcohol intake and the use of medication (whether prescribed or over-the-counter, and short or long-term) for their fatigue levels. The use of drugs and alcohol often brings into play organisational expectations, for example, the need for workers to declare any new or changed medication. Given that drugs and alcohol are a common cause of fatigue, as well as other problems, requirements relating to them will often feature prominently within a 'drug and alcohol policy' (sometimes part of an overall health and safety policy), supported where appropriate by 'drug and alcohol screening and testing' arrangements. These requirements should be clearly and specifically communicated at induction and before operatives are set to work on safety critical tasks, so as to ensure they do not, even inadvertently, fall short of the expected standards.

Conduct a specific fatigue risk assessment. Where appropriate, this needs to include consideration of the effects of shift work. A review should be carried out prior to any proposed change to working hours taking place. The risk assessment should: *first,* consider the risks of shift-work and the benefits of effective management; *second,* establish systems to manage the risks of shift-work; *third,* assess the risks of shift-work in the workplace; *fourth,* take action to reduce these risks, and finally, *fifth,* regularly check and review shift-work arrangements. There are tools available which may be of assistance here, including for instance, the Health and Safety Executive's 'Fatigue Risk Index'[290].

Take a proactive approach to planning. This means overstaffing key posts, to build in resilience, so as to effectively manage workload volumes, including circumstances in which fluctuations arise, for instance due to absenteeism or other changes in operational priorities.

Fill vacant posts efficiently. This is particularly important in areas of high demand. The need to maintain a relief pool of staff should be considered, where appropriate.

---

290. Further information on how to manage fatigue, as compiled by the Health and Safety Executive is available at: https://www.hse.gov.uk/humanfactors/topics/fatigue.htm [viewed 1 May 2021].

Promote and develop flexible working and/or remote working approaches. Where the work type permits, using alternative arrangements such as meeting virtually rather than face-to-face avoids unnecessary travel time, which can be helpful in reducing instances of physical fatigue. Flexibility should also be provided to allow access to on-call workers to cover unplanned leave, emergencies or unexpected workload increases.

Manage the fatigue risk, irrespective of personal preferences. The duty placed on employers to manage it is a legal one and managers should be made aware of the key facts about fatigue, together with the appropriate actions they can take to reduce the impact of work-related causal factors upon their team members. Employers should put in place management processes for working hours, work scheduling and roster design, and avoid work arrangements or reward systems which might, even inadvertently, incentivise operatives to work excessive hours. These processes can be complemented by efforts to manage overtime, shift-swapping and on-call duties and the instituting of arrangements which handle accrued leave balances and leave requests, for instance by the setting of maximum limits on leave accrual, so as to encourage operatives to use it. First and foremost, it's important to make sure that the fulfilling of the legal duty to manage fatigue isn't compromised, in the course of entertaining requests by operatives to work extra hours or accommodating their preferences for certain shifts for social or personal reasons. Moreover, the choices of individuals should not be allowed to prevail where the reliability with which they perform safety critical tasks would be negatively impacted, the proper management of risk compromised, or their personal health and wellbeing adversely affected.

Schedule work appropriately. This means avoiding the scheduling of demanding, dangerous, monotonous and/or safety critical work during the night, early morning, towards the end of long shifts and during other periods of low alertness. It's important to note that body clocks tend to vary between individuals, being based on so-called *circadian rhythms* – the natural internal processes which run in the background of the human brain and regulate sleep-wake cycles – switching between sleepiness and alertness at regular intervals.

Monitor working hours accurately. It's important to approach the monitoring of working hours from a health and safety risk perspective, rather than solely with financial costs in mind. Where applicable, such monitoring needs to include the robust checking of: working hours and shift patterns; the taking of scheduled breaks, and overtime analysis. Monitoring plays a valuable role where high numbers of incidents and injuries have been recorded amongst operatives. And it goes without saying that those who are night shift-workers, work successive shifts, or work long shifts should be prioritised within monitoring programmes. It's also key to factor in the impact of commutes and travel times on overall fatigue levels, within fatigue risk management programmes.

Educate people on self-help strategies for managing personal fatigue. It's often beneficial for this to be included as an element of workplace induction at the point at which operatives join an organisation as well as thereafter, to refresh their knowledge at appropriate points. Examples of things that operatives can do to help themselves include the taking of breaks and making sure they get enough quality sleep between shifts. It's really important for shift workers to understand that shift patterns can run counter to the natural human sleep-wake cycle, as well as the practical steps they can take to help ensure that the sleep they get is of a high quality. But whilst there are things operatives can do themselves, the need remains for a supportive organisational culture to be fostered and maintained.

Manage organisational change effectively. This often brings with it increased levels of risk. It's important to manage even apparently minor changes associated with workload and work-pace variability which can be caused by, amongst other things, planned or unplanned machinery breakdowns. Change can be major or minor, short or long term, and incremental or rapid, in nature. Whatever the nature of the circumstances, care should be taken to ensure that individuals who have a well-managed workload do not suddenly or gradually become subject to unmanageable workload levels. Where it is proposed that changes are to be made to employees' working hours and/or shift patterns, they or their representatives should be provided with information on how these might impact upon their health and safety at work, under formal consultation arrangements, prior to these being implemented.

Consider and, where necessary, improve workplace environmental factors. This includes factors such as temperature and lighting, which can potentially impact upon individuals' alertness levels, as well as other aspects including adverse weather, which might place increased physical strain upon them, for some types of work activity.

HOW TO... ADDRESS
STRESS AND LOW MORALE
Stressy's Action Plan
'Don't be too stressed to get things right!'

In this fable's workshop-based application of the porridge pot scenario, it was identified that Stressy might have misread a gauge or been unable to make a decision regarding the high level alarm at the critical moment, when ordinarily he would have been able to work accurately or respond appropriately.

WHY IT MATTERS

Workplace statistics produced by the Health and Safety Executive highlight the extent of the problem of stress[291]. Data for the year 2020/21 indicated that 822,000 workers were suffering from work-related stress, anxiety or depression (new and long-standing cases), with a staggering 17.9 million working days lost due to this cause. The total annual costs to Britain of work-related injury and new cases of work-related ill health in 2018/19 was £16.2 billion, with ill health representing the biggest proportion of total annual costs at around 65% (£10.6 billion). To give some idea of the scale of the problem, the *stress, depression or anxiety* category accounts for 50% of all work-related ill health cases, with 55% of all working days lost to ill health

---

291. The stress statistics provided here are based upon self-reports from the Labour Force Survey (2021) and are as quoted in *Health and Safety at Work – Summary Statistics for Great Britain 2021*. Health and Safety Executive, and in *Work Related Stress, Anxiety or Depression Statistics in Great Britain 2021*. Annual Statistics (data up to March 2021). Health and Safety Executive (published 16/12/2021). This is with the exception of data on working days lost and economic costs, the figures for which were only available from the previous year's report at the time of going to press (Labour Force Survey (2020), as quoted in *Health and Safety at Work, Summary Statistics for Great Britain 2020*). This is due to statistics for the year 2020/21 having been impacted by the Coronavirus (COVID-19) pandemic.

being attributable to this cause. These figures highlight the seriousness with which this factor should be treated.

OVERVIEW OF EFFECTS

It's widely felt that some pressure can be a positive thing for workers, creating challenges, opportunities and interest for them, in the workplace and beyond. When these demands become excessive however, this factor can have a deleterious effect on both the mental and emotional wellbeing of individuals, and the reliability with which they perform tasks. Defined by the Health and Safety Executive as 'the adverse reaction people have to excessive pressure or other types of demand placed on them'[292], stress is now recognised as impacting upon individuals, in addition to having negative connotations in the context of performing safety critical tasks, which has potentially severe consequences in major hazard settings.

From an individual perspective, the impacts of stress may not be as readily apparent as, say, those for someone suffering a workplace injury, but the workplace statistics cited here underline the gravity of the problem. Also, from an organisational perspective, people who are stressed are more prone to making mistakes. It's this which makes it crucial for those leading organisations to ensure that they don't allow an urgency culture to develop amongst those who work for them. Where such a mindset is allowed to proliferate amongst those required to complete safety critical tasks, this can push individuals into displaying undesirable, thoughtless behaviours, brought about by their thinking being impaired. Even hints about the need to *speed up* being made by managers and peers can lead to individuals feeling pressurised to complete tasks in a rushed fashion, with an increase in the numbers of errors made being seen as a result. Demands for urgency may be justifiable under emergency operating conditions, but these should never be made simply on the basis of a desire to drive excessive productivity from workers. In cases where target levels of output are prioritised above all else, this can be a major source of stress for operatives – which might be manifested in their becoming

---

292. This definition, together with a wealth of other information on how to manage work-related stress is to be found at: https://www.hse.gov.uk/stress/ [viewed 1 May 2021].

confused, indecisive or panicked – and as well as being deleterious to their health, are clearly negative traits in those who are required to perform safety critical tasks. The causes of stress – as called out by Stressy's account in this tale – are multiple and complex and, in gauging its effects upon workers, organisations need to take time to understand the challenges particular to their workplace settings.

The types of questions organisations are required to consider, in seeking to address this factor, include: *'Are workload levels an issue?' (importantly, this includes circumstances where messages about the urgency with which work is expected to be completed might lead to individuals' thinking being impaired), 'Do people feel unsupported?', 'Are there pockets of violence, threats or bullying within the workforce, which are being inadequately managed?', 'Are changes to workplaces or work activities being poorly handled or communicated to affected individuals?'* and *'Are there environmental factors present – whether natural or artificial – which raise the levels of stress experienced by workers?'.*

MANAGEMENT AND MITIGATION MEASURES

The measures an organisation puts in place to address stress concerns should form part of its wider workplace wellbeing agenda. The emphasis of such an approach should be upon positively identifying the signs and symptoms of poor mental health, including developing organisational awareness of the causes, and supporting with the treatment of any conditions seen as a result. Additionally, attention should be paid to the development of stress recognition and management skills amongst the workforce. An effective management strategy needs to be backed up by robust management policies and guidance, the risk assessment of work-related stress amongst teams, and a willingness amongst senior leaders to implement the right control measures, which could include job redesign, supported by appropriate resourcing levels for stress identification and management training programmes.

The first line of defence against the impact of stress relates to prevention, including risk assessment. Organisations have a clear duty under health and safety law to manage psychological health at work, with the risk assessment of stress being central to any such management strategy. This should include consideration of various elements such as demands, control, support, relationships, clarity about job roles, and change management[293], together with environmental factors, which can make work activities more challenging or workplace comfort levels sub-optimal. Where these elements are not properly managed, this can make for negative health impacts, reduced productivity, and a rise in accident and sickness absence rates.

When looking at work demands, organisations should make sure operatives have the right amount of work to do, that breaks are taken, that the right type of training is provided, and that any problems with the work environment are avoided. Control, on the other hand, relates to the degree of autonomy an operative has towards the way in which their work is carried out and their involvement in decision-making, accompanied by the right support being in place which allows them to use their skills to best effect. The support aspect includes the encouragement, sponsorship and resources provided by employers, managers and co-workers to help with the striking of a healthy work-life balance. Relationships are important too, with the promotion of positive working so as to avoid conflict and dealing with unacceptable behaviour being central to addressing some of the key root causes of stress. Additionally, the taking of simple steps to clarify roles and ensure no conflicts exist between different role aspects is helpful. Effective management at the point at which change takes place can also be invaluable in lessening the impact of disturbance to operatives' duties, thereby ensuring a smooth transition is achieved. And it's important for organisations to educate operatives as to how they can help themselves with regard to non-work related aspects too, for instance, by extolling the personal benefits of enjoying a good work-life balance.

In developing an approach to managing stress amongst their workforces, organisations need to identify the particular issues relevant to their operations, being mindful of signals which implicate stress as a problem and regularly taking stock of the situation. Some issues can change in magnitude and others can newly arise, which makes it vital

---

293. *ibid.* These are the aspects addressed by the Health and Safety Executive's 'Management Standards', which encompass six areas of work design. When these areas are effectively handled, this allows organisations to tackle work-related stress and ultimately, to achieve compliance with the law.

for the handling of stress as a factor to sit at the heart of any workplace wellbeing strategy.

In order to address the problems associated with this factor, organisations are advised to...

Secure leadership engagement with the mental wellbeing agenda. This should include: developing an appetite for change, backed by policy and practice; a commitment to make cultural and workplace improvements, where necessary; a willingness to assess and address any weaknesses in the current approach, and the allocation of appropriate resources, including the necessary support for line managers and individuals alike, which is of particular importance at times of functional, or indeed wider organisational, restructures.

Put a stress prevention strategy in place. This needs to include the implementation of clear policies and guidelines on stress at work, for instance, a wellbeing policy and guidelines on absence management. A key part of this is the carrying out of regular risk assessments of work-related stress amongst teams, using methods such as questionnaires and focus groups and – where possible – removing stressful aspects of work, including through task redesign, which can help to lessen the pressure on individuals. Efforts should also be directed towards providing help which proactively manages the risk of stress in advance, thereby reducing the incidence of stress reports. The strategy should recognise the direct link between leadership and management behaviours, and mental wellbeing.

Put in place a supporting training plan, which underpins the strategy. This should include specific training provision for managers, together with workshops and similar activities focused on responsibilities, consideration of how managers can help their teams, and the arrangement of targeted training for individuals – a key component of which could be the development of coping skills and self-help strategies. These activities should help sell the benefits – from an individual, as well as an organisational perspective – of nurturing good mental health.

Build a stress treatment management plan, where cases of stress are highlighted. Such plans can include the provision of access to professional treatment, where required, alongside other occupational health services and confidential counselling arrangements. These elements will often be supported by a range of other wellbeing initiatives.

Provide effective support to workers who are absent for stress-related reasons. In terms of facilitating returns to the workplace, this can be offered on a phased basis, which needs to be backed up by a supportive culture, to ensure that the necessary understanding is fostered amongst colleagues in the period following the return of an absent worker.

Involve workers. Encouraging individuals to adopt self-help strategies can help to reduce their stressors, but this needs to be complemented by organisational stress management arrangements. An open culture should be fostered which allows the workforce to report concerns, as well as stress being recognised as a possible contributory factor within incident investigations, without individuals fearing adverse personal implications. A self-help strategy will typically include: *first,* taking action on personal pressure points – showing people what they can do about stressors in their home lives; *second,* educating people to build their own resilience, including developing confidence and assertiveness, and making time for non-work activities – family, hobbies and so on; *third,* educating people about how to reduce their own and others' stress, including recognition of the signs of stress and learning stress management techniques, and finally, *fourth,* providing an explanation of the support available and how to access it, when needed. It's important to note that training for individuals should focus on coping mechanisms, with access to professional occupational health services being signposted, where available.

HOW TO... ADDRESS LACK OF COMPETENCE
Bumbler's Action Plan
'Don't be too stupid to get things right!'

In this fable's workshop-based application of the porridge pot scenario, it was identified that Bumbler may not have known how to read the gauge or have misread it. He also might have lacked the 'competence' or confidence to make the right decision in response to the sounding of the high level alarm. A further possibility was that he was confused as to the difference between *valve open* and *valve closed* states, with this state of confusion carrying with it the potential for him to make a poor decision.

WHY IT MATTERS

Lack of competence or an 'inability to deal with circumstances' is typified by Bumbler, the sixth imp. It might sound trite to say *'don't be too stupid to get things right'*, but ultimately this factor highlights the clear responsibility placed upon organisations to ensure that operatives are equipped with the right knowledge, understanding and experience to carry out their work as expected. Competence is important not only in terms of what is needed for an individual's day-to-day work, but also for hazard recognition and controlling risk. Having competent workers is critical to the safe running of an organisation's operations and basically requires selecting the right people, training them, and assessing them at key stages, on a continuous basis. And, whilst competence of itself doesn't guarantee safety, when taken seriously it does improve the predictability of good performance being delivered.

The start-point for any organisation seeking to address workforce competence is the general duty set out in *the Management Regulations*[294], which requires them to have access to 'competent persons' to help meet such legislative health and safety requirements as are applicable to their operations. But on top of this duty, there is a raft of more specific requirements contained within *the Control of Major Accident Hazards Regulations 2015*[295] ('the COMAH Regulations'), which apply to those organisations in control of operations involving major accident hazards. Under these regulations, it's first necessary to identify the relevant hazards on site, before considering the safety critical tasks linked to them, including what operatives need to do to keep hazardous materials contained, as well as what they are expected to do if they are released. Next, it must be checked that operatives have the necessary skills, knowledge and experience to carry out their safety critical tasks. It's through ensuring they have competent

---

294. Regulation 7 of *the Management Regulations* sets out this requirement.
295. S.I. 2015/483.

workforces that organisations protect themselves against the wrong decisions being made in safety critical situations, abnormal operating conditions and emergency situations, as well as in circumstances which are routine in nature. Where *the COMAH Regulations* apply, an effective 'competence management system' has particular importance, providing organisations with a vehicle through which to control, in a logical and integrated manner, the cycle of activities which assures and further develops the competent performance of work by their workforces. In the context of major accident hazard control, the use of a competence management system also has connectivity with other important documents and entities, informing as it does 'safety reports' and 'major accident prevention plans', as well as fulfilling the requirement to demonstrate competence to a 'competent authority'.

Competence in the health and safety aspects of a role is gained in part through training and also, specifically, through organisations instituting a structured 'competence assurance' process, which helps operatives to gain the requisite skills, knowledge and attitudes, so that they are able to perform their tasks effectively. Training can include off-the-job, group or individual instruction, but also includes on-the-job coaching too. Regardless of the format it takes, when carried out effectively, it gives operatives the capability and confidence to deal with circumstances – whether routine, non-routine or exceptional – and prevents their acting in a way which endangers themselves or others. Furthermore, in addition to being critical to the running of a safe operation, having competent operatives ensures the smooth running of day-to-day work and fosters a good safety culture, where all those involved in the operation of safety critical processes understand what is required, as well as being adept at hazard recognition and controlling risk.

OVERVIEW OF EFFECTS

Where competence requirements are not taken seriously, typically observable organisational shortcomings include failures to analyse processes in sufficient depth, and to identify the safety critical tasks required to keep hazards contained. Another failure – which sometimes leads on from these first two – can be an omission to base training on defined operative needs, for instance, what they are personally expected to do to achieve the control of major accident hazards. An observable trait in those subject to this factor tends to be their lacking in knowledge about what to do if a hazard is released. In these circumstances, individuals become more prone to slips, lapses, mistakes and other errors, thereby reducing an organisation's capability to prevent or mitigate risk.

The types of questions organisations might ask to help them to identify if they have shortfalls in their competence arrangements could include: *'Are competence requirements clearly set out at the point of operatives joining the organisation and are these checked at key points, including, for instance at times of role transfer, organisational change, or where a need for periodic review is identified?', 'Is lack of competence cited as a causal or underlying factor within incident investigations?', 'Are there certain safety critical tasks to which specific competence requirements attach, and are these always met?' and 'Are there signs of operatives failing to act in accordance with set down procedures, or not complying with safe working methods, or indications that they are choosing to adopt unsafe approaches, due to shortfalls in training and supervision arrangements?'*

MANAGEMENT AND MITIGATION MEASURES

In a bid to avoid the problems associated with this factor and fully address their competence requirements, many organisations will look to set out a clear management strategy for competence management, which comprehensively covers workforce capability. Such strategies can be delivered through instituting a 'competence management cycle', as a key part of a competence management system, with phases including: *one,* define its scope; *two,* design it; *three,* implement and operate it; *four,* assess and maintain it, and finally, *five,* verify and test it. Links should be made to relevant internal and external requirements, for instance those that are variously set at industry level and by regulators.

In order to manage workforce competence through the use of a competence management system, organisations should seek to address the components of each of the following phases...

PHASE #1 – **Define its scope.** *This should include its purpose, as well as the identification and assessment of the activities and risks involved, which will in turn form the basis upon which competence standards are selected.*

The elements to be covered during this phase should include: procedures, methods and work instructions for the system's operation, including those for safety critical tasks; 'competence standards' and assessment criteria; training, development and assessment arrangements, together with the 'competencies' and responsibilities of those who are to manage and operate it. There needs to be an emphasis on safety critical tasks, because these are the tasks where the competence of operatives involved in controlling risks is particularly important. This is why the analysis of them forms the basis upon which standards are selected and roles and responsibilities within job specifications defined. Thinking more broadly, this analysis, together with any applicable legislative and organisational requirements, as well as those of industry parties, should inform the practical, technical and behavioural skills required, and the level of expertise needed to perform tasks competently. By creating a list of safety critical tasks which need to be consistently well-performed to avoid major accident scenarios, and considering all types of operating condition, this paves the way for standards to be selected, and roles and responsibilities to be defined within job specifications, across all relevant functions, which support the consistent control of risk.

PHASE #2 – **Design its structure and contents.** *This should include setting competence standards and determining how each of these is to be met, assessed, achieved and recorded, accompanied by training, development and assessment requirements.*

The setting of competence standards should be informed by the analysis of safety critical tasks, together with other site, process and job specific standards, reflecting the risk profile of the site, with particular reference made to safety critical tasks and the control of major accident hazards. Competence standards serve multiple purposes, at different points in time, including for contractor selection, onboarding new recruits, and for workforce assessment, re-assessment and development. But irrespective of their particular purpose, they should focus upon what operatives are expected to do to consistently and reliably control risk. In determining how each competence standard is to be met, assessed, achieved and recorded against each role type, the following details should be specified: the nature of the assessment; the assessment type; the scope, location and expected duration of the assessment; the parties involved in the assessment process, and the frequency of the assessment and reassessment cycle. The assessment method selected needs to be appropriate to the work activity being assessed, and can include: direct observation; indirect information gathering; simulation; written and verbal questions; open questions, and multiple choice questions.

PHASE #3 – **Implement and operate it.** *This should include measuring and verifying the competence of operatives against the defined competence standards.*

Having set down standards during the previous phase, it's here that operatives – particularly those who perform safety critical tasks – need to be trained, developed and assessed against the competence standards, before being deemed competent to carry out a job role unsupervised. This requires an evaluation to be made as to whether operatives possess knowledge of all the hazards which could arise for every task they carry out which is, to a large extent, based upon the outputs of processes for identifying and managing risks. It also requires control processes to be established to ensure that operatives only undertake work in which they are competent. For those already deemed competent, the emphasis of this phase is upon gaining proof of their competence.

PHASE #4 – **Assess and maintain it.** *This should include monitoring, reassessing and maintaining operative competence, and ensuring gaps are closed.*

The primary focus here is upon the assessment and reassessment of competence of those required to carry out safety critical tasks, such that performance is consistently maintained. A combination of methods can be used during this phase, including scheduled full and partial observations and assessment, and non-scheduled spot observations and assessments. Infrequent events and emergencies also provide opportunities to monitor the performance of inexperienced individuals, to ensure the full range of operating conditions they might encounter has been captured. The frequency of reassessment should reflect the criticality of the tasks involved, external regulatory requirements, incident response and organisational change, any or all of which could trigger a need for the competence standards themselves to be updated. It's also during this phase that the output and impact of the competence management system upon performance indicators should be reviewed.

PHASE #5 – **Verify, audit and test it.** *This is about checking the performance of the system, as a whole.*

It's here that feedback on the system as a whole can be collectively derived through audit and verification processes, as well as from the use of performance indicators. Carrying out audits allows gaps to be identified in the system, whilst verification processes highlight how well the assessments themselves are carried out and the degree to which the assessment process is successfully applied, and performance indicators can be used to check the overall effectiveness of the competence management system. When well-applied, the use of these techniques in combination serves to support the continuous improvement of the competence management system.

and finally...

It's important to make sure that the contents of any other procedures and safety information are supportive of, and consistent with, the competence requirements set by the competence management system. This means ensuring that any information provided is: easy-to-use, read and understand; comprehensive, including all the details that operatives need to know; not in conflict with other information or at odds with other organisational requirements; available at the point and time of need, and delivered in a style which suits the intended audience.

HOW TO... ADDRESS POOR MOTIVATION
Sly's Action Plan
'Don't be too devious, distracted or misguided to get things right!'

In this fable's workshop-based application of the porridge pot scenario, it was identified that Sly might have fully understood the criticality of plant and equipment involved, but still have wilfully chosen to interfere with the high level alarm due to a personal desire to prioritise production over safe operation, or to get the work done faster, being motivated by money. Or he could have chosen to subvert or sabotage the valve out of malice or thinking he could get the job done more quickly. This type of human failure is clearly of a non-compliant type, rather than being error-based in nature.

WHY IT MATTERS

The majority of workers want to get things right, by looking up to leaders they respect, doing a good job, complying with standards and procedures, and following instructions. Very few of them want to get things wrong, or to interfere with things going well. *But some do.* And it's vital for organisations to pick up on the reasons why this is the case, given their particular operating circumstances and the individuals involved. The problem of poor motivation to carry out designated functions, roles or tasks, as set down in organisational standards – including those of a safety critical nature – is epitomised by Sly. This factor covers violations and, unlike other types of human failure such as errors (including slips, lapses and mistakes), it includes circumstances in which deliberate action is taken by someone who knows it is incorrect or to be acting in contravention of procedures or rules, perhaps for their personal benefit or even for reckless reasons. There can be many reasons for this factor arising as an issue for an organisation. It might be that it stems from individuals harbouring feelings of mistrust towards managers, or more broadly towards those that employ them. Alternatively, it can be that they are indifferent to the risk it poses to themselves or others, or, arguably worse still, that they simply don't care about it.

Much of what has been said for the foregoing six *imps* or factors relates to obligations placed upon employers. But employees have responsibilities too and the behaviours of the type shown by this imp are often indicative of an individual failing to take their personal obligations seriously. Employees are required to take reasonable care for themselves and others who may be affected by their acts or omissions whilst at work, including co-operating with their employers in respect of duties placed upon them[296]. An example of this would be that an employer has a responsibility to supply and instruct employees on the use of PPE, but this is matched by a corresponding responsibility placed upon the employee to wear and use it, in accordance with the employer's instructions (this was a point noted in relation to *the piper's fable*). Added to this, there is a legal requirement placed upon employees not to intentionally or recklessly interfere with or misuse anything provided in the interests of health, safety or

---

296. Section 7 of *HSWA 1974* sets out the general duties of employees at work.

welfare[297]. Examples of actions caught by this section would include wilful interference with alarms, or the subverting or sabotage of safety valves by employees.

OVERVIEW OF EFFECTS

The outcome of this failure type is to impair the reliability of human performance. The planned behaviour of these operatives is incorrect (despite their being fully aware of it being contrary to procedures), their actual behaviour is as planned, and the result is a deliberate non-compliance by them. This means their intention is to do a wrong thing, and a wrong thing is done. The problem, for both the individual concerned and for others affected, is that this involves the operative making a judgment about the risk involved. If this judgment is incorrect or flawed, the results can be disastrous and far-reaching.

The types of questions organisations might ask to help them to identify if they have a problem with poor workforce motivation – as highlighted by Sly – could include: *'Is there evidence of operatives choosing to behave in a certain way, due to their thinking that breaking rules is in the real or assumed interest of the organisation?', 'Is there evidence of operatives being motivated by the potential for personal reward, or the thought of it being less effort, faster or more exciting for them to break the rules than to follow them?', 'Is it possible that their behaviour is driven by a desire not to let people down?'* and *'Do there appear to be instances of reckless violations, with operatives seeming to break the rules, despite their knowing of the dangers this poses for them personally and for others?'*

MANAGEMENT AND MITIGATION MEASURES

It's important for organisations to adopt a firm stance towards this factor whenever it's identified as an issue for them, taking action as necessary but, as a pre-requisite, it's important that they understand *how* this factor arises as an issue in their particular circumstances. There are specific actions organisations can take to help to reduce

---

297. Section 8 of *HSWA 1974* sets out the duty of employees not to interfere with or misuse anything provided by their employer in the interests of health, safety and welfare.

the likelihood of operatives wanting to violate set standards or agreed methods of working. One way of achieving this is for them to make it clear that those found to have broken rules or regulations will be subject to disciplinary procedures, including sanctions and punishments. Another, more positive, way is to make sure that any set down rules, regulations or procedures are easy to follow and supported by the appropriate user guides, tools and equipment, so as to prevent a mindset developing in some individuals that it is more convenient, less trouble and quicker to flout requirements, than to comply with them. Typically, an organisation should seek to adopt a combination of both types of action, in order to limit the likelihood and extent of violations within their workforce.

In order to address the problems associated with this factor, organisations are advised to...

Recognise the diverse ways in which human failure can occur. This is especially important in the context of safety critical task performance. Senior leaders need to identify the particular types of failure which pose a problem for them and do all that they can to reduce the likelihood that they will occur, including learning from incident investigation reports, where violations are recognised as having contributed to adverse outcomes.

Establish and maintain effective hazard assessment and risk control practices. These should be supported, where necessary, by risk and reliability assessment. A good application of these techniques can help to narrow the possibility of operative failure, irrespective of motivation, and thus, drive high reliability.

Ensure systems are tolerant to failures by people. This means that systems should allow for continuous safe operation, whilst avoiding process interruption. It also means they should not be capable of being defeated through one rogue action by an operative, that they should allow for recovery, and that they should not fail to danger.

Foster a positive safety culture. One characteristic of such cultures is their intolerance towards violations of safety requirements, which is particularly important in the context of safety critical tasks. Where senior leaders promote and drive an open culture, this tends to be felt through increased operative understanding of the need to report problems with procedures and tasks, rather than their seeking to work around them or take short cuts. It's often advantageous for this kind of approach to be complemented by instituting programmes which welcome and positively consider suggestions from operatives, with ideas developed and improvements implemented wherever appropriate to do so.

Set out clearly the organisation's goals, rules and procedures to teams and individuals. People need to understand why these are important. It's crucial for operatives to understand how their following of requirements contributes to better safety standards, and even to broader business success. When these messages are pitched in the right way by senior leaders and linked to wider safety cultural initiatives, operatives tend to feel more emotionally connected with organisational values, which in turn feeds better levels of compliance. It's also key to make operatives aware of the potential consequences of rule-breaking behaviour, both for them as individuals and for operations as a whole. Again, this can be supported by cultural aspects, by making sure that any problems or safety concerns raised by operatives – including any difficulties they cite in relation to complying with procedures – can be freely reported, aired, and swiftly addressed, with amendments being made, where required.

Design and apply procedures in a logical and consistent manner. This means taking care to make them workable and usable, and avoiding conflicts and inconsistencies with other procedures or requirements. It also means being alert to contrary signals – even subtle ones – as may exist within organisational culture, suggesting that productivity goals are to be prioritised above safety goals.

Make sure people are able to do what they need to do. This means it's vital for them to be competent in all the tasks they are required to perform. Making sure that operatives have the necessary knowledge, understanding and experience to perform tasks means it's less likely that uncertainty as to what to do will act as a trigger for them to deviate from expected practice.

Foster workforce understanding of the consequences of flouting safety critical task procedures. This can variously encompass personal, organisational and societal consequences. It's also important to be clear on the circumstances under which disciplinary action will be invoked.

Put in place clear disciplinary procedures. This ensures that operatives understand the personal consequences of breaking rules, regulations or procedures. Invoking disciplinary procedures where violations occur allows them to be effectively addressed and helps to prevent a future recurrence. Where it's identified or suspected that a rule, regulation or procedure was broken, breached or not followed – due to it being more convenient, less trouble or quicker to pursue an alternative course of action – it's important to ensure that lessons are learnt from this, that follow-up checks are carried out and, where necessary, processes and procedures are revised, updated and communicated accordingly.

This *How to...* Guide shows just some of the varied challenges that the complexities of human performance can present for organisations and highlights the accompanying need for these factors to be managed in subtly different ways.

Humans are brilliant, but they can fail too!

The broad ranging nature of these aspects – which form just a part of the human condition – requires organisations to clearly identify and address the specific types of human failure relevant to their operations, not only by taking the time to understand each factor, but also by accounting for them whenever designing or improving processes. When organisations successfully manage these – often diverse – aspects, they can be confident that safety critical tasks are safely and reliably performed by operatives, and also that they have done all that is expected, to protect the personal safety, health and welfare of those who carry them out, on their behalf.

APPENDICES

Factor	Description	Rating Thresholds and Scoring			
B-1 Activity/Load weight (kg)	For Activity/Load weight: identify the work activity and if two or more activities are to be performed, e.g. rolling and dragging, do an assessment for each type of activity; find out the weight of the load to be moved (e.g. from any labelling provided, by asking the workers, or by weighing); if two or more loads are to be moved at a time, assess the total weight to be moved, and if moving different loads, assess the heaviest load.				
	Dragging/hauling or sliding.	< 25kg **Low GREEN/0**	25-50kg **Medium AMBER/2**	50-80kg **High RED/4**	> 80kg **Very High RED/8**
	Rolling.	< 400kg **Low GREEN/0**	400-600kg **Medium AMBER/2**	600-1000kg **High RED/4**	> 1000kg **Very High RED/8**
B-2 Posture	Observe the general positions of the hands and the body during the operation.	Torso is largely upright, *and* torso is not twisted, *and* hands are between hip and shoulder height. **Good GREEN/0**	Body is inclined in the direction of exertion, *or* torso is noticeably bent or twisted, *or* hands are below hip height. **Reasonable AMBER/3**	Body is severely inclined, or worker squats, kneels or needs to push with their back against the load, or torso is severely bent or twisted, or hands are behind or on one side of the body or above shoulder height. **Poor RED/6**	
B-3 Hand grip	Observe how the hand(s) grip or contact the load during pushing or pulling. If the operation involves both pushing and pulling, assess the hand grip for both actions.	There are handles or handhold areas which allow a comfortable power grip for pulling, or comfortable full-hand contact for pushing. **Good GREEN/0**	There are handhold areas, but they only allow a partial grip, e.g. fingers clamped at 90°, or partial hand contact for pushing. **Reasonable AMBER/3**	There are no handles or hand contact is uncomfortable. **Poor RED/2**	
B-4 Work pattern	Observe the work, noting whether the operation is repetitive (five or more transfers per minute) and whether the worker sets the pace of the work. Ask workers about their pattern of breaks and other opportunities to rest or recover from the work.	The work is not repetitive (<5 transfers per minute) *and* the pace of work is set by the workers. **Good GREEN/0**	The work is repetitive, *but* there is opportunity for rest or recovery through formal and informal breaks or job rotation. **Reasonable AMBER/1**	The work is repetitive *and* no formal/informal breaks or job rotation opportunities are provided. **Poor RED/3**	

Appendix A
Assessment Guide: Risk Assessment of Pushing and Pulling Tool
– rating classifications for loads without wheels

Compiled using Health and Safety Executive Guidance document (2016);
Risk Assessment of Pushing and Pulling (RAPP) tool (INDG478), pages 10-13

Factor	Description	Rating Thresholds and Scoring		
B-5 Travel distance	Determine the distance from start to finish for a single trip. Where the operation is not repetitive, do an assessment for the longest trip. Where the operation is repetitive, determine the average distance for at least five trips.	2m or less **Short** **GREEN/0**	2m – 10m **Medium** **AMBER/1**	> 10m **Long** **RED/3**
B-6 Floor surface	Identify the condition of the surfaces along the route and determine the level of risk using the criteria.	Dry and clean, and level, and firm, and good condition (not damaged or uneven). **Good** **GREEN/0**	Mostly dry and clean (damp or debris in some areas), or sloping (gradient is 3° - 5°), or reasonably firm underfoot, or poor condition (minor damage). **Reasonable** **AMBER/1**	Contaminated (wet or debris in several areas), or steep slope (gradient >5°), or soft or unstable underfoot (gravel, sand, mud), or very poor condition (severe damage). **Poor** **RED/4**
B-7 Obstacles along the route	Check the route for obstacles. Note if the load is moved over trailing cables, across raised edges, up or down steep ramps (gradient >5°), up or down steps, through closed/narrow doors, screens or confined spaces, around bends and corners or objects. Each type of obstacle is only to be counted once, no matter how many times it occurs.	No obstacles. **Good** **GREEN/0**	One type of obstacle, but no steps or steep ramps. **Reasonable** **AMBER/2**	Steps, steep ramps, or two or more other types of obstacle. **Poor** **RED/3**
B-8 Other factors	Identify any other factors, for example: the load is unstable; the load is large and obstructs the worker's view of where they are moving; the load is sharp, hot or otherwise potentially damaging to touch; there are poor lighting conditions; there are extreme hot or cold temperatures or high humidity; there are gusts of wind or other strong air movements; personal protective equipment or clothing makes pushing and pulling more difficult.	No other factors present. **None** **GREEN/0**	One factor present. **One** **AMBER/1**	Two or more factors present. **Two or more** **RED/2**

Assessor name:	Smug Little Mouse	Date:	Once upon a time...
Company name:	Big Farming Business	Location:	Super-Sized Swede Smallholding

Detailed description: pulling out of super-sized swede, by dragging/hauling it from ground (based upon a 54kg swede – UK and world record).				

Are there indications that the operation is high-risk? (enter YES in appropriate boxes)	
	The operation has a history of incidents (e.g. accident book records, RIDDOR reports)
YES	The operation is known to be hard or high-risk work
YES	Employees doing the work show signs that they are finding it hard (e.g. sweating)
	Discussions with employees doing the operation suggest some aspects are difficult
	Other indications. If so, what?

Identify the activity and insert the colour band, numerical score, and comments for each of the risk factors below

Factor	Dragging/Hauling		Comments
	Colour band	Numeric score	
B-1 Load weight	Red	4 High	Rated high, due to weight of 54kg. Dragging, hauling or sliding objects between 50kg and 80kg in weight is deemed to fall within high definition.
B-2 Posture	Red	6 Poor	Rated poor, due to hands being above shoulder height; severe bending/twisting of the torso shown by some of those involved in the activity.
B-3 Hand grip	Red	2 Poor	Rated poor, due to there being no natural handles or handhold areas, preventing a comfortable power grip for pulling from being achieved.
B-4 Work pattern	Green	0 Good	Rated good, due to this not being a repetitive activity (less than 5 transfers per minute) and pace of work being set by workers themselves.
B-5 Travel distance	Green	0 Short	Rated short (distance travelled to pull out swede less than 2 metres); operation not repetitive - one super-sized swede, one trip.
B-6 Floor surface	Red	4 Poor	Rated poor, due to: ground instability under foot; very poor ground conditions, and debris in several areas.
B-7 Obstacles on route	Red	3 Poor	Rated poor, due to two or more types of obstacle, e.g. other crops, raised edges.
B-8 Other factors	Red	2 Two + factors	Factors include: large and unstable load, workers facing away from direction of travel, clothing making pulling difficult, poor weather conditions.
Total score		21	

Note psychosocial factors and individual capability, e.g. vulnerable workers

Psychosocial factors: further information would be required, as difficult to judge on the basis of circumstances, as seen. Information would be needed on level of control over work and work methods, worker involvement in decisions affecting them, degree to which workers expected to carry out repetitive or monotonous tasks, whether work demands perceived to be excessive, whether payment systems encourage workers to work too quickly or without breaks, whether high levels of effort are balanced by sufficient reward (resources, remuneration, self-esteem, status).

Individual capability: vulnerable workers participating in the task include a new and expectant mother, a migrant worker, adolescent workers, and an individual with a pre-existing condition. Group of varied physique, e.g. height, reach, leading to poor posture when moving objects.

Appendix B
Completed Score Sheet: Pushing or Pulling Loads Without Wheels
Activity: pulling (dragging/hauling) super-sized swede from ground

Compiled using Health and Safety Executive Guidance document (2016);
Risk Assessment of Pushing and Pulling (RAPP) tool (INDG478), page 14

Assessor name:	Smug Little Mouse	Date:	Once upon a time...
Company name:	Big Farming Business	Location:	Super-Sized Swede Smallholding

Detailed description: pushing of super-sized swede, rolling it back towards smallholding cottage (based upon a 54kg swede – UK and world record).

Are there indications that the operation is high-risk? (enter YES in appropriate boxes)

	The operation has a history of incidents (e.g. accident book records, RIDDOR reports)
YES	The operation is known to be hard or high-risk work
YES	Employees doing the work show signs that they are finding it hard (e.g. sweating)
	Discussions with employees doing the operation suggest some aspects are difficult
	Other indications. If so, what?

Identify the activity and insert the colour band, numerical score, and comments for each of the risk factors below

Factor	Rolling		Comments
	Colour band	Numeric score	
B-1 Load weight	Green	0 Low	Rated low, due to weight of 54kg. Rolling objects less than 400kg in weight is deemed to fall within low definition.
B-2 Posture	Red	6 Poor	Rated poor, due to old farmer's body being severely inclined in order to the push the load and hands being above shoulder height.
B-3 Hand grip	Red	2 Poor	Rated poor, due to there being no natural handles or handhold areas, and hand contact being uncomfortable, when pushing.
B-4 Work pattern	Green	0 Good	Rated good, due to this not being a repetitive activity (less than 5 transfers per minute) and pace of work being set by workers themselves.
B-5 Travel distance	Red	3 Long	Rated long (distance travelled to roll swede to smallholding cottage over 10 metres); operation not repetitive – one super-sized swede, one trip.
B-6 Floor surface	Red	4 Poor	Rated poor, due to: ground instability under foot; very poor ground conditions, debris in several areas, and steep slope (over 5° gradient).
B-7 Obstacles on route	Red	3 Poor	Rated poor, due to two or more types of obstacle, e.g. other crops, raised edges, as well as steep slopes (over 5° gradient).
B-8 Other factors	Red	2 Two + factors	Factors include: large and unstable load, obstructing workers' view of route, clothing making rolling difficult, poor weather conditions.
Total score		20	

Note psychosocial factors and individual capability, e.g. vulnerable workers

Psychosocial factors: further information would be required, as difficult to judge on the basis of circumstances, as seen. Information would be needed on level of control over work and work methods, worker involvement in decisions affecting them, degree to which workers expected to carry out repetitive or monotonous tasks, whether work demands perceived to be excessive, whether payment systems encourage workers to work too quickly or without breaks, whether high levels of effort are balanced by sufficient reward (resources, remuneration, self-esteem, status).

Individual capability: vulnerable workers participating in the task include a new and expectant mother, a migrant worker, adolescent workers, and an individual with a pre-existing condition. Group of varied physique, e.g. height, reach, leading to poor posture when moving objects.

Appendix C
Completed Score Sheet: Pushing or Pulling Loads Without Wheels
Activity: pushing (rolling) super-sized swede towards smallholding cottage

Compiled using Health and Safety Executive Guidance document (2016);
Risk Assessment of Pushing and Pulling (RAPP) tool (INDG478), page 14

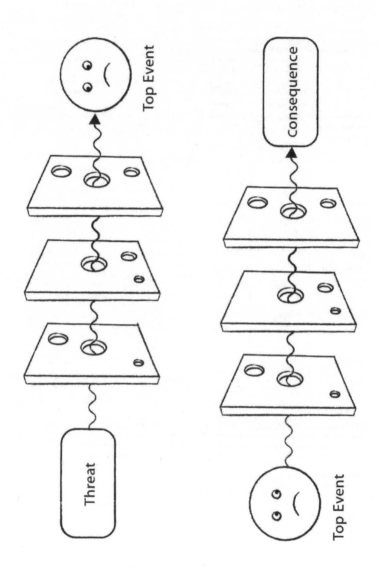

Appendix D
Simplified Depiction of James Reason's 'Swiss Cheese Model'

Appendix E
Indicative Bow Tie Model

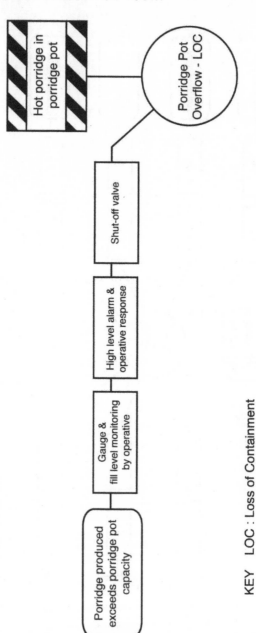

Appendix F
Bow Tie Model Extract:
Porridge Pot Overflow – Loss of Containment Top Event
left hand side – threat leg

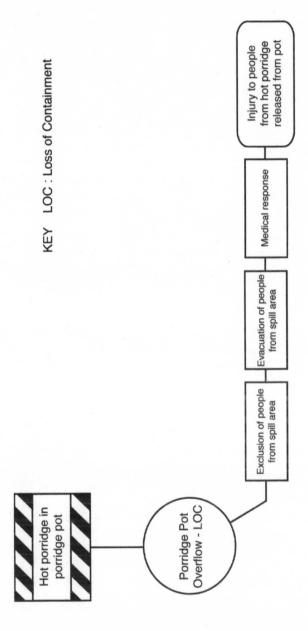

Appendix G
Bow Tie Model Extract:
Porridge Pot Overflow – Loss of Containment Top Event
right hand side – consequence leg

GLOSSARY

abnormal operating conditions – circumstances in which operating parameters exceed their design, outside specified limits. These are not regarded as emergency operating conditions, but they do demand prompt correction so as to avoid threats to life, or plant operation.

accident – *'an event that results in injury or ill health'* (Health and Safety Executive definition).

action level – *sometimes referred to as an 'action value'* – a level of exposure which, if exceeded, requires employers to take specific action. Examples of hazardous agents for which action levels are set down by regulations include noise, vibration, and some chemicals.

active barrier – a barrier type, the function of which is delivered by equipment or systems. In order to deliver its function, this type of barrier is required to move from one state to another, in response to a change in a measurable process property, examples of which include pressure, temperature, or a signal from another source, such as a switch. In order to ensure the continued effectiveness of this type of barrier, functional checks are required, including checking that sensors and activation measures are working. This barrier type contains *'sense-decide-act'* elements, not requiring human intervention in order to be effective, with activation being possible by other means. Examples of questions used to help verify the effectiveness of this barrier type include: *'Do sensors work?'* and *'Are activation methods working?'*

active indicator – *see 'leading indicator'*.

active monitoring – a form of monitoring which provides feedback on performance before an incident occurs, for example an inspection or audit, or the use of leading indicators.

acute – an effect which is short term and severe, developing immediately – or shortly after – exposure.

administrative control – the type of control that is to be put in place only after efforts have been made to avoid the risk, work in a way that is less hazardous, and use 'engineering controls'. Examples of administrative controls include: procedures which help people to work safely; reducing the time workers are exposed to risks through task rotation; prohibiting the use of mobile phones in hazardous places, and putting in place safety signage.

'after the fact' indicator – *see 'lagging indicator'*.

alarm – a device or call to warn of danger, usually indicated by a visual or audible signal.

alarm, high/low level – a point established within a control system, which identifies when a condition has reached a high/low limit, an example being the level of liquid in a tank, triggering an alarm, usually via an audible or visual warning.

alarm flooding – a state in which the volume of alarms presented to an operative exceeds their capacity to respond with the expected action. This could be due to a range of factors including: an excessive alarm rate, unclear rules for deciding priority levels, or an ineffective organisational strategy for dealing with site alarms.

alert – a type of communication given when there is a specific issue which, without immediate action being taken, could result in harm to people, process interruption, or environmental damage. An alert generally activates before alarm activation, the purpose being to reduce the disruptive impact of false alarms, and give opportunities to investigate, whilst avoiding endangerment of human life.

anthropometrics – the practice of collecting data and applying human body measurements. This practice can be put to good effect in relation to product design, an example being that anthropometric data can be used to inform the locating of alarm buttons – such that these are positioned within the easy reach of all users/operatives – which shows positive application of ergonomic design principles, and supports the broader goal of achieving reliable human performance.

app – an application, especially as downloaded by a user to a mobile device.

Approved Body – *see 'United Kingdom Approved Body'.*

Approved Code of Practice (ACOP) – a document with special legal status which gives practical advice on how to comply with the law, by describing preferred or recommended methods that can be used – or standards to be met – to comply with regulations and the duties imposed by *HSWA 1974*. It is not essential to follow this type of document, but those prosecuted for breaching health and safety legislation who choose not to follow a relevant ACOP must be able to show that they complied with the law in some other better way, to avoid a Court finding them at fault.

approved contractors' list – a list of contractors who have met certain specified criteria, as laid down by an organisation or other body.

ART (Assessment of Repetitive Tasks) tool – a simple tool designed by the Health and Safety Executive to help assess repetitive tasks, involving the upper limbs, where multiple objects need to be moved on a repeat basis, within a fixed time period. The tool assesses some of the common risk factors that can lead to the development of musculoskeletal disorders, related to repetitive work.

as low as reasonably practicable (ALARP) – the level to which workplace risks are expected to be controlled; reasonably practicable requires a risk to be weighed against the time, trouble and expense needed to control it. The ALARP standard describes the level to which the Health and Safety Executive expects to see workplace risks controlled, thereby enabling it to set goals for duty holders, which form a key part of their duties under *HSWA 1974* and supporting regulations. It also helps policy makers, enforcers, and technical specialists to evaluate whether enough has been done by duty holders to fulfil their responsibilities. *See also 'so far as is reasonably practicable (SFAIRP)',* which is an equivalent term to this one and refers to the amount by which risk must be reduced, rather than the level to which it is expected to be reduced.

assess-control-review **model** – a cyclical three phase approach to managing workplace health risks, proposed by the Health and Safety Executive.

Associated Octel report – the report by the Health and Safety Executive into the chemical release and fire at the Associated Octel company, Ellesmere Port (*Great Britain, 1994*).

assurance – the means by which an organisation demonstrates that its arrangements and processes for health and safety management are being properly applied and are continuing to achieve their intended objectives, comprising the systematic and ongoing monitoring and recording of health and safety performance, together with the evaluation of health and safety management processes and practices. The objectives an organisation strives to meet can include those set by the requirements of legislation, industry practice, external standards or its own management system. Examples of assurance activities commonly undertaken by organisations include: audits, inspections and the collation and analysis of performance indicators.

assurance framework – a structured means of identifying and mapping the main sources of assurance activity operating within an organisation or other body, and co-ordinating these to best effect, often in support of other activities.

assurance tool – a tool used by an organisation to manage and monitor the activities of its health and safety management system. When taken collectively, such tools enable an organisation to gauge whether or not its health and safety management system is operating effectively.

ATEX – the abbreviation commonly used for the two European Directives, which set down requirements for the control of explosive atmospheres. *See 'ATEX Equipment Directive'* and *'ATEX Workplace Directive'*.

ATEX-certified – *sometimes referred to as 'ATEX(Ex)-certified'* – the certification applied to equipment certified for safe use in hazardous places, where explosive atmospheres are present, in accordance with the requirements set down in the ATEX Equipment Directive. Upon certification, equipment bears an ATEX logo. Following its exit from the European Union, with effect from 1 January 2021, Ex products placed on the market in Great Britain (England, Scotland and Wales) now need to be UKEX-approved, subject to transitional arrangements. *See also 'UKEX approved'*.

ATEX Equipment Directive – the set of European requirements designed to ensure the safety of equipment used within explosive environments.

ATEX Workplace Directive – the set of European requirements designed to ensure the safety of workers potentially at risk from explosive atmospheres within the workplace.

audit – a systematic, independent, and documented process, by which evidence is obtained and objectively evaluated, the purpose of which is to determine the extent to which management system criteria and other legal requirements have been fulfilled by an auditee (often an organisation), and to identify any gaps in arrangements, requiring action.

bacteria – a microscopic living organism, usually one-celled, which can pose a danger to human health, for instance by causing infection, an example being legionella.

Baker report – the report of the BP US Refineries Independent Safety Review Panel, which conducted a review of the organisational failings that led to the Texas City incident (*United States, 2005*) and made recommendations for improvements to be made to organisational safety culture, health and safety management systems and corporate safety oversight.

barrier – *sometimes referred to as a 'risk control'* – a functional group of safeguards, which can include primary containment, process equipment, engineered systems, operating procedures, health and safety management system elements, or operative capabilities designed to either prevent a top event – for instance, loss of containment – or mitigate any potential consequences, should a top event occur. A group of barriers can also be referred to as a *'risk control system'*. In the context of a bow tie model, barriers appear on both sides of the top event. Barrier type can be classified as 'passive', 'active' or 'procedural', and as 'prevention' or 'mitigation'. *See also separate entries for 'active barrier', 'mitigation barrier', 'passive barrier', 'prevention barrier', 'procedural barrier', 'risk control system'*.

barrier, active – *see 'active barrier'*.

barrier, mitigation – *see 'mitigation barrier'*.

barrier, passive – *see 'passive barrier'*.

barrier, prevention – *see 'prevention barrier'*.

barrier, procedural – *see 'procedural barrier'*.

barrier action – an action required to make a barrier effective, relevant to active and procedural barrier types; *see also 'barrier maintenance'*.

barrier-based assurance – a type of assurance methodology, relating to the barriers within barrier models, which verifies that safety critical tasks and critical systems are functioning effectively.

barrier-based audit – an approach to audit, the focus of which is upon whether barriers (risk controls) are effective, and functioning as intended.

barrier-based inspection – an approach to inspection, the focus of which is upon whether barriers (risk controls) are effective, and functioning as intended.

barrier-based risk management – a pro-active methodology concerned with ensuring, on a systematic and continuous basis, that barriers are relevant, effective and robust, for the threats/consequences against which they are intended to defend.

barrier-based thinking – the use of barrier models – for instance *'bow tie models'* – to stimulate discussions about the management of risk. Often used in the context of process safety, these visual tools can help those leading organisations to demonstrate the sufficiency of the barriers (risk controls) believed to be in place for daily operation and maintenance, and thus enable them to evaluate whether further barriers are required to prevent a top event and/or mitigate its consequences.

barrier effectiveness – the level to which barriers are successful in blocking threats from becoming top events or top events leading to consequences.

barrier failure – circumstances in which a barrier is unsuccessful in delivering its intended function and, therefore, ceases to act to block threats and/or consequences. Barrier failure can be total or partial.

barrier function – *how* a barrier works to provide risk reduction, through preventing, controlling or mitigating undesired events or incidents. This describes *why* a barrier is there or needed, for instance, the function of an active barrier, such as a sprinkler system, is to move rapidly in detecting and evaluating damage and in countering its continuation and extension.

barrier installation – the process of putting barriers in place. Examples include putting in place physical hardware in the case of passive or active barriers or, for procedural barriers, the full implementation of procedures, such that those who are required to carry them out understand what they need to do to make them work.

barrier loading expectation – *see 'barrier performance expectation'*.

barrier maintenance – any action required to ensure a barrier remains effective. Maintenance varies according to barrier type. A passive barrier – such as a wall – might require routine visual inspection and remediation, whilst an active barrier – for instance, a sprinkler – might require the checking of sensors and activation methods. A procedural barrier – such as an emergency plan – requires more subtle forms of maintenance. This includes regular drills taking place with the operatives required to perform the actions forming an integral part of the barriers (their *'barrier actions'*), to ensure they know what they need to do to carry them out effectively, on an enduring basis.

barrier management – the management process by which an organisation ensures that the risk controls it intends and expects to protect against threats, or mitigate consequences, are actually capable of doing so, and are properly implemented, supported and maintained, so as to function as expected, on demand.

barrier model – a type of risk model which assists in the identification, control and management of risk, by depicting risk controls as a series of barriers. The development of this type of model is based on the principles of the 'Swiss cheese model' proposed by James Reason (*see 'Swiss cheese model'*). A popular example of a barrier model is the 'bow tie model' (*see 'bow tie model'*).

barrier modelling – the practice of developing a barrier model, to illustrate a top event – typically involving an organisation – together with the threats and consequences which lead to it, and the risk controls (barriers) in place to prevent it, or, if realised, block or mitigate the consequences which would otherwise flow from it.

barrier owner – an operative, function or department with barrier ownership responsibilities.

barrier ownership – the assignment of responsibilities for delivery of barrier actions to operatives, functions or departments, which contribute wholly or partially to barrier success; visualisation of the distribution of barrier responsibilities facilitates the monitoring of their handling, whether management or workforce-owned.

barrier performance expectation – *sometimes referred to as 'barrier loading expectation'* – the quantum of load a barrier needs to withstand in order to be effective, for instance the force against which it needs to defend.

barrier purpose – the reason a barrier is required, which should link to the preventing of one or more threats which lead towards, or the blocking or mitigating of consequences which lead away from, a top event.

barrier selection – an activity, the purpose of which is to determine the choice of barriers, to prevent threats leading to a top event or, a top event having occurred, block or mitigate the consequences which would otherwise flow from it.

barrier testing – an assurance activity, the focus of which is upon checking that barriers work as intended.

barrier thinking – an approach to safety management which views the prevention of incidents as being achievable through the use of barriers (passive, active and procedural) which act to prevent a top event or, a top event having occurred, to block or limit consequences that would otherwise flow from it. This approach is based upon James Reason's 'Swiss cheese model'; *see also 'Swiss cheese model'*.

barrier type – a method of classifying barriers, an example of which is the 'passive', 'active' and 'procedural' distinction. *See also separate entries for 'active barrier', 'passive barrier', 'procedural barrier'*.

'before the fact' indicator – *see 'leading indicator'*.

best practice – the quality seen in a working method, procedure or standard, which is accepted as being optimal or most effective. Typically, where something is recognised as being best practice, it exceeds the legal minimum expected and is regarded as a superior approach to that associated with other ways of doing it. Best practice goes beyond good practice (*see also 'good practice'*).

beyond reasonable doubt – the standard of proof used to convict defendants charged with criminal offences. Where a court decides that a defendant is guilty as charged, a conviction will follow. Where this standard is not met, the defendant will be acquitted.

biological agent – a micro-organism, cell culture, or human endoparasite, whether or not genetically modified, which may cause infection, allergy, toxicity or otherwise create a hazard to human health; examples include bacteria, viruses, parasites and fungi.

body corporate – an organisation that is considered to have its own legal rights and responsibilities.

bow tie model – a specific type of barrier model, in widespread use across high-hazard organisations, the purpose of which is to assist with the identification, management, communication and understanding of risk. It is referred to as a bow tie because of its visual appearance, with the model's central knot representing a top event e.g. loss of containment, dropped object, and the threats and consequences that lead up to and away from it featuring on the left and right hand sides respectively. The barriers which feature on both sides of the model serve to prevent the top event occurring (prevention barriers) and/or to block or limit the consequences, in cases where a top event does occur (mitigation barriers). The types of barrier put in place can relate to equipment, processes, procedures or people, or a combination of these.

Buncefield report – the report into the underlying causes of the Buncefield explosion and fire (*Great Britain, 2011*).

cause – *see 'threat'*.

CE mark – the mark which appears on many products traded on the single market in the European Economic Area, which: demonstrates that the manufacturer has checked that the product to which it is affixed meets European Union (EU) safety, health or environmental requirements; is an indicator of a product's compliance with EU legislation, and allows the free movement of products within the European market. Note that, following the UK's departure from the EU, the UKCA mark now covers most goods which previously required this mark. The CE mark – or the UKNI mark – will, however, continue to be used for goods placed on the Northern Ireland market. Furthermore, UKCA and UKNI marks are not recognised within the EU market, and the CE mark will continue to be the requirement for goods sold there. *See also 'UKCA mark' and 'UKNI mark'*.

chronic – an effect which is a long term syndrome and is slow to develop, following exposure.

chronic unease – a state of constant wariness towards the management of risk, achieved where a culture is created in which humans are alert to weak signals, and effective and timely interventions are made in risk assessments and decision-making (*see also 'weak signals'*).

churn, to (verb) – to move violently.

civil claim – an action pursued by an individual seeking damages, which succeeds in cases where it can be shown they suffered harm as a result of a duty holder's negligence. Where an individual suffers loss – injury, ill health or death – the victim or their dependents are entitled to sue for damages, in the form of compensation through the civil courts.

civil law – the part of the law that relates to personal matters, rather than criminal ones; the body of rules that delineates private rights and remedies.

claim – *see 'civil claim'*.

classified area – *see 'hazardous area classification'*.

client – a person or organisation using the services of another professional person or organisation. Note that, whilst not explored in the context of the fables in this book, this term also has a specific meaning in relation to regulation 2 of *the CDM Regulations*, which defines it as *'any person for whom a project is carried out'*.

CLP – the European Regulation (EC) no. 1278/2008 on the classification, labelling and packaging of substances and mixtures which came into force on 20 January 2009 in all

EU member states, including the UK, as a member state at that time. This regulation adopted the United Nations Globally Harmonised System (GHS) on the classification and labelling of chemicals across all EU countries. As a voluntary agreement, GHS has to be adopted through a suitable national or regional legal mechanism to give it legal effect. *See also 'GB CLP'.*

cognitive overload – a state in which an operative has too much work to do; a situation in which an operative is given too much information or too many tasks to undertake simultaneously, resulting in them being unable to process the information, or their processing the information inadequately or inefficiently. The workload demands in a state of cognitive overload exceed the mental processing capability of the operative involved.

cognitive underload – a state in which an operative has too little work to do; the reverse of cognitive overload, this refers to a state in which the demands of an operative's tasks are so low that their performance is impaired, for instance due to loss of focus, distraction by other activities, or boredom.

collective control measure – *also known as a 'collective protection measure'* – a control measure which protects more than one user at any one time, not requiring their intervention in order to work effectively. An example of a collective control measure is a guardrail system.

COMAH site – a location at which a dangerous substance is present in a quantity in excess of certain thresholds and which is therefore subject to *the COMAH Regulations*. The requirements to which these locations are subject vary according to the quantities of such substances stored. *See also 'lower tier COMAH site', 'upper tier COMAH site'.*

COMAH site, lower tier – *see 'lower tier COMAH site'.*

COMAH site, upper tier – *see 'upper tier COMAH site'.*

community order – a non-custodial sentence, requiring an offender to perform community service, observe a curfew, or undergo treatment, rather than their being imprisoned for an offence.

compensation order – a requirement imposed by a court on an offender to pay compensation for injury, loss or damage, resulting from an offence, either in preference to, or as well as, a fine.

competence – the ability to reliably perform a specific role, function or task, or undertake activities to an expected standard. In settings where the control of major accident hazards is required, the competence of individuals to undertake safety critical tasks is crucial.

competence assurance – an assessment process, which measures the knowledge and skills of an individual or team against expected standards. When well-applied, such processes can help to identify skills gaps before adverse consequences occur.

competence management cycle – the integration of a number of related competence management activities within a logical cyclical process.

competence management system – a structured risk-based process which demonstrates the capability of an organisation's workforce to carry out the tasks that they are required to perform, and includes: clearly defined multi-level competence standards; training, development and assessment arrangements, including assessment criteria; monitoring methods, and arrangements for addressing sub-optimal performance.

competence standard – the articulation of an established method which ensures individuals are able to do what is required to consistently and effectively control risk, being of particular importance in relation to the carrying out safety critical tasks.

competency – the skills and underpinning knowledge that enable an individual to perform a task.

competent authority – the statutory body responsible for the enforcement of regulations, which differs according to the particular regulations being enforced. An example is *the COMAH Regulations*, which are enforced by a competent authority comprising the Health and Safety Executive, or the Office for Nuclear Regulation, for nuclear establishments, acting jointly with the appropriate environmental agency.

competent person – someone with sufficient training and experience or knowledge and other qualities to allow them to ensure that health and safety responsibilities are being met. This includes the ability to recognise hazards associated with tasks, and the authority and ability to mitigate them. The level of competence required is dependent upon the complexity of the situation being considered and the particular help needed to ensure risks are robustly controlled.

confined space – any space of an enclosed nature where there is a risk of death or serious injury from hazardous substances or dangerous conditions, an example being lack of oxygen. Some confined spaces are fairly easy to identify, for instance enclosures with limited openings. Examples include: mines; storage tanks; silos; reaction vessels; enclosed drains, and sewers. Others may be less obvious, but can be equally dangerous, with examples including: open-topped chambers; vats; combustion chambers in furnaces; ductwork, and unventilated or poorly ventilated rooms. Some enclosed spaces will always be designated as confined spaces, whilst others may become confined spaces during the course of work activities undertaken or because of the substances used within them. Workers involved in these work activity types need to be skilled in dynamic risk assessment, so that they can readily identify when a situation, condition or environment is deteriorating from *safe* to *unsafe*, and has the potential to involve or become a confined space.

conformity assessment – a set of processes which shows that a product, service or system meets the requirements of a standard, typically before it is placed on the market, which can include activities such as testing, inspection and certification.

consequence – an outcome, which results from a top event. There can be more than one consequence for every top event. On a bow tie model these feature on the right hand side, at the end of consequence legs. Consequences can be identified by asking the question: *'If the top event occurs, what are the possible results that could flow from it?'*

consequence leg – a component of a bow tie model, which depicts the flow from a top event to a given consequence. Typically, along a consequence leg, an organisation will put in place a number of mitigation barriers, each with a purpose of either fully blocking or partially mitigating a given consequence.

construction work – the carrying out of any building, civil engineering or engineering construction work. For examples, refer to the definition given within regulation 2 of *the CDM Regulations*.

consultation – the process by which employers provide employees with information, as well as listening to them and taking on board what they say, before reaching any health and safety decisions, allowing sufficient time to consider the matters being raised and provide them with sufficient responses.

continual improvement, *also referred to as 'continuous improvement'* – the ongoing effort applied by an organisation to improve its products, services, and/or processes.

contract management system – a system which manages the production and management of contracts.

contractor – any individual or organisation entering into an agreement – written or verbal – with a company to provide goods or carry out services. Contractual relationships vary from case to case, for instance, a contractor can be managed as part of a client company's own workforce or be subject to the direct supervision of the contractor company.

contributory factor – a close causal element which influences the chain of events leading towards or flowing from an incident. These can be positive or negative in nature. Where positive, they mitigate or minimise the extent of a risk (top event) or the consequences which flow from it.

contributory negligence – a defence available, where it is proved that a claimant's own actions or omissions contributed to their loss or damage. Where this defence fully or partially succeeds, following a claimant's successful claim, this leads to a proportionate reduction of the damages they receive.

control measure – a measure which prevents, controls, or limits exposure to a defined risk or consequence.

control panel and control room design – the area of ergonomics which includes consideration of the layout, displays, controls and interactions, and alarms, on control panels or within control rooms.

control strategy – *see 'risk control strategy'.*

conviction – the verdict reached by a court, when a defendant is found guilty of a criminal offence.

Coronavirus disease (COVID-19) – an infectious disease caused by Coronavirus (a large family of viruses that cause human illnesses ranging from common colds to more severe diseases, including MERS and SARS).

corporate citizen, *sometimes referred to as a 'good corporate citizen'* – an organisation that displays the values of corporate citizenship, which comprises its responsibilities towards society, the goal of which is to provide a higher standard of living and quality of life for the communities around it, whilst still maintaining profitability for its owners.

corporate homicide – the Scottish law equivalent to the English law offence of corporate manslaughter.

corporate manslaughter – the offence of which an organisation is guilty if the way in which its activities are managed causes a person's death and amounts to a breach of the relevant duty of care owed by the organisation to the deceased. In order for an organisation to be found guilty of this offence, the way in which its activities are managed or organised by senior management needs to constitute a substantial element of the breach (section 1 of *the Corporate Manslaughter Act*).

COSHH (Control of Substances Hazardous to Health) assessment – the systematic examination of a task or process that involves the use, or encountering, of one or more hazardous substances; a form of risk assessment, specifically focused on the control of hazardous substances.

criminal law – the area of law which deals with breaches of legislative requirements; judge-made law, derived from judicial decisions of courts and similar tribunals. This is law which arises as precedent.

criminal prosecution – the instituting and conducting of legal proceedings against an accused, in respect of a criminal charge, leading to trial. A defendant found guilty by a judge will be convicted, whilst one found not guilty will be acquitted.

critical task – *see 'safety critical task'.*

damages – a form of monetary remedy paid to someone by a person or organisation found to be responsible for causing them injury or loss.

danger area – an area designated by a duty holder around works, such that persons not engaged in the work are prevented from entering it, thereby stopping them from being exposed to danger. An example – in the context of work at height – would be an area within a workplace which, owing to the nature of the work, gives rise to a risk of any person at work falling a distance or being struck by an object (regulation 11 of *the Work at Height Regulations*). *See also 'exclusion zone'.*

dangerous occurrence – a specific reportable adverse event, examples of which include: lifting equipment collapse, overturn or failure; pressure system failure; fires or explosions; fires or ignition of gas within a mine (for the full listing of dangerous occurrences, see schedule 2 to regulation 7 of *RIDDOR*).

dangerous substance – this term is used in two different contexts in this book. *First,* in the context of the definition given within regulation 2 of *DSEAR*, it includes *'...any dust, whether in the form of solid particles or fibrous materials or otherwise, which can form an explosive mixture with air or an explosive atmosphere...'* (NB: whilst not directly considered by this book, there are other types of dangerous substances listed within regulation 2). *Second,* in the context of the definition given within regulation 2 of *the COMAH Regulations*, it includes substances and mixtures specifically listed, present in certain quantities, e.g. Ammonium Nitrate, Chlorine (see column 1, Part 2, schedule 1), and substances or mixtures in 'CLP' categories, present in certain quantities, e.g. acute toxic (H1), oxidising gases (P4), various flammable liquids (P5a, P5b, P5c), which bring with them certain responsibilities for operators of COMAH sites, and vary according to the tier classification. *See also 'CLP'.*

dashboard – an informal management tool, which visually tracks, analyses and displays performance indicators, the purpose of which is to monitor the health of a department, process or function within an organisation. This type of tool is usually customisable to meet specific departmental or organisational needs.

data analyst – someone who analyses data.

data architect – someone who builds and maintains an organisation's data architecture – the models, policies, rules and standards which set out the types of data collected – which includes making decisions about how it is stored, arranged, integrated and put to use, and determining any enhancements that need to be made.

data harvester – someone who collects data from online sources.

data lake – a centralised repository which allows an organisation to store all its structured and unstructured data until it is needed.

data miner – someone who sorts through large data sets to identify patterns and establish relationships, in order to solve problems through data analysis processes, allowing future trends to be predicted by an organisation.

degradation factor – *sometimes called an 'escalation factor' (effectiveness can be degraded or the risk of failure escalated).* In relation to a bow tie model, this is a condition which does not directly cause a top event or consequence, but which increases the likelihood of a scenario progressing due to the degradation or failure of associated risk controls.

depot manager – an individual who holds responsibilities for managing a depot location for an organisation, which can include the management of day-to-day operations, or the management of a location which serves as a collection and drop-off point for products and materials, such as scrap metal, fuels and oils.

design envelope – *see 'performance envelope'*.

desired safety outcome – the desired safety condition that a risk control system is designed to deliver. Given the need to discover weaknesses in risk control systems – and irrespective of whether major damage, injuries or incidents result from them – an organisation will often gauge the degree to which this is achieved through the use of lagging indicators, a form of reactive monitoring; see also *lagging indicator*.

disease – an illness in a human, animal or plant.

display screen equipment – *'any alphanumeric or graphic display screen, regardless of the display process involved.'* (as defined by regulation 1(2) of *the DSE Regulations*).

Display Screen Equipment (DSE) assessment – *see 'workstation assessment'*.

doctrine of precedent – *see 'precedent'*.

domino effect – *sometimes referred to as an 'escalation scenario'* – a sequence of incidents in which a, sometimes small, primary incident (usually a fire or explosion) triggers a further secondary incident(s), with an overall escalation of the event consequences, the outcome being more severe than that directly generated by the primary event. In the context of *the COMAH Regulations*, this is manifested in an increase in the risk or consequences of a major accident because of one or more of the following factors: the geographical position of sites; the proximity of sites to each other, or inventories of dangerous substances held (see regulation 24 of *the COMAH Regulations*). *See also 'off-site scenario'*.

downward communication – the process by which information flows from the upper level of an organisation (e.g. senior leaders) to its lower levels.

drag, to (verb) – the action of pulling something forcefully or with difficulty.

drop height – how high an object is dropped from.

drop zone – an area at ground level within which it is foreseeable that items would land if they were dropped, or to fall, from a structure.

dropped object – any item or object that falls or has the potential to fall from its previous position, which can be further classified as 'static' or 'dynamic' (*see also 'dropped object, dynamic' and 'dropped object, static'*).

dropped object, dynamic – any object that falls, the failure for which may be attributed to applied forces, including from the impact of equipment, machinery or other moving items, severe weather or manual handling.

dropped object, static – any object that falls from its previous static position under its own weight, due to gravity, without any applied force. Such failures can be due to: corrosion, vibration, or inadequate securing. These are the most common types of dropped object, being objects at rest which fall from their original position under their own weight – for instance, a dislodged nut on a wind turbine, or a tool falling from an operative's hand.

drug and alcohol policy – an organisation's agreed position against workforce drug and alcohol misuse, commonly forming part of its overall health and safety policy. Such a policy will often: state what an employee can do if they feel they have a drug or alcohol problem; document what help and support is available, following an employee request; address the use of prescribed and over-the-counter medication, as well as drug and alcohol misuse, and highlight the disciplinary or other action that the organisation will take where an employee is found to have fallen foul of its requirements. Some drug and alcohol policies – in particular, those for organisations with workforces carrying out safety critical tasks – also set out accompanying screening and testing arrangements. Where such arrangements are instituted, they must be properly applied and followed, with the consent of the employees who are subject to them.

drug and alcohol screening and testing – arrangements put in place by organisations, particularly those where workers perform safety critical tasks, the primary purpose of which is to prevent the compromising of safety standards, due to drug or alcohol misuse. An additional purpose of such screening and testing can be to support wider workforce health and wellbeing initiatives.

dual assurance – a methodology by which activity and outcome performance indicators complement each other. For instance, improved gauge monitoring and operative response (activities) may reduce loss of containment incidents (outcomes). Further reviews may still be needed to better understand situations and validate connections in circumstances where leading and lagging indicator results appear to be in conflict, for instance, where all gauge monitoring staff have received better training, but loss of containment incidents continue to show an upward trend.

duty holder – a person who holds a duty or duties under legislation, for instance, an employer is a duty holder under *HSWA 1974*. Irrespective of the legislation, the general expectations of duty holders are for them to: *first*, systematically identify hazards; *second*, assess the risks and the consequences of those hazards being released, and *third* and finally, put in place suitable procedures and measures to control the risks.

duty of care – a moral or legal obligation to ensure the safety or wellbeing of others, an example being that which employers have towards their employees.

duty of care (waste) – the obligation requiring anyone who deals with waste to keep it safe, make sure it is dealt with responsibly, and only give it to others authorised to take it.

dynamic dropped object – *see 'dropped object, dynamic'*.

dynamic mode – the desired state for workers to adopt, when confronted by rapidly changing work activities, circumstances or environments, in order that they are able to make the right decisions and take the right actions to control risks to themselves and others.

dynamic risk assessment – the type of process required in rapidly changing situations, where decisions are made in fast-moving circumstances, with often incomplete or inaccurate information at a worker's disposal. This type of risk assessment is made at the time and location of undertaking the activity, and takes into account the actual risks as well as any changes to the working conditions or fitness of those involved. It can address issues that may arise as work progresses, together with possible courses of action, including cut-offs that might have been identified by generic risk assessment. This requires workers to make operational decisions for themselves, based on risks which could not necessarily have been foreseen or addressed at an earlier stage of the process, for instance, at the point of an initial or generic risk assessment having taken place.

dynamic risk model – a model of risk which has the flexibility to be changed or adapted by an organisation, in response to new or developing risks.

edge protection – a type of collective fall protection, which protects persons from the risk of a fall, examples of which include toe boards, guard rails and intermediate rails.

EH40/2005 – the environmental hygiene guidance document for workplace exposure limits, for use with *the COSHH Regulations*. Last updated in 2020, it includes new and revised workplace health exposure limits (WELs), introduced by European Commission Directive (EU/2017/2398) and guides those responsible for controlling workplace hazardous substance exposure.

electrostatic discharge – the release of static electricity that takes place when two objects touch each other. This occurs when two charged surfaces pass over each other, with the sudden recombination of the separated positive and negative charges creating an electric arc. The effect is created due to there being a difference in charge between objects, the protection from which can be achieved through the proper handling of components and application of basic precautions. Sources can include people, equipment and charged insulators. Methods of protection can include zoning (defining boundaries with physical barriers and suitable signage) and the provision of effective methods for grounding people, including wrist straps and dissipative flooring with suitable footwear.

electrostatic risk – a risk generated *either* by flammable vapours, gases or dust clouds being present, such that static electricity is able to provide an unexpected ignition source and cause a fire or explosion, *or* where static charge builds up on workers, equipment or materials, resulting in unpleasant electrostatic shocks to workers in the area. One activity where the potential for an electrostatic risk exists is during refuelling operations, which can present a particular danger. If fuel passing along a hose is allowed to build up a static charge, a resulting spark might ignite the fuel contained within it. This risk is controlled by the earthing of hoses, which prevents this from occurring.

emergency operating conditions – circumstances under which a disaster or emergency is imminent or in progress. In these conditions, emergency support locations should be fully activated and support functions mobilised or in a state of readiness to be deployed.

emergency (response) plan – a document which handles the methods by which an organisation responds to an emergency situation, which should include, as appropriate: *first*, protective actions for life safety; *second*, incident stabilisation, and *third*, property conservation. The requirement for an emergency plan can be driven by legislation – an example being *the COMAH Regulations* – or where stipulated by other external requirements, or an organisation's own identification of need.

emergency plan, external, *sometimes referred to as an 'off-site emergency plan'* – a plan which specifies the emergency measures to be taken outside a site, should an emergency situation occur. Where an organisation is subject to *the COMAH Regulations*, the requirements for the preparation of this type of plan are handled by regulation 13.

emergency plan, internal, *sometimes referred to as an 'on-site emergency plan'* – a plan which specifies the emergency measures to be taken inside a site, should an emergency situation occur. Where an organisation is subject to *the COMAH Regulations*, the requirements for this type of plan are handled by regulation 12.

emerging risk – a new and unforeseen risk, where the potential for harm or loss is still not fully known or has yet to be determined.

employee – someone who is employed by a person or organisation. For the purposes of employment rights, this is someone who works under a contract of employment (see section 230 of the *Employment Rights Act 1996* c.18).

employer – a person or organisation that employs people.

energy theft – the action of interfering with a gas or electricity supply, which bypasses a meter, such that actual usage cannot be measured or recorded. For electricity, this is a criminal offence, being contrary to section 13 of *the Theft Act 1968*, which is committed where a person '*...dishonestly uses without due authority or dishonestly causes to be wasted or diverted any electricity...*' In cases where energy theft is suspected – and it is believed that gas, electricity or both are being stolen – this can be anonymously reported via www.stayenergysafe.co.uk

enforcing authority – an authority responsible for enforcing laws or obligations within its remit.

engineering control – the type of control which acts to protect a worker(s) by removing hazardous conditions or by placing a barrier between them and the risk. This can include, for instance, local exhaust ventilation, which captures and removes airborne emissions, or machine guards which act to shield workers. This form of control needs to be put in place before administrative controls are considered, in accordance with the hierarchy of control principle.

Environment Agency – an agency, the purpose of which is to protect or enhance the environment, taken as a whole, creating better places for people and wildlife, and supporting sustainable development; an executive, non-departmental public body, sponsored by the Department for Environment, Food and Rural Affairs (DEFRA).

equipment category – a classification which determines the type of equipment, meeting specified integrity requirements, appropriate to the location (zone) within which it is to be used. Equipment is built to a level of protection known as a category, which matches the level of risk.

equipment group – a designation of equipment which is in turn sub-divided into equipment category in accordance with the area in which it is to be used. Group I is relevant to atmospheres found underground in mines. Group II is intended for use in all other places with potentially explosive atmospheres (as defined by regulation 2 of *the EPS Regulations*).

equipment integrity requirements – the criteria that must be met by equipment used within 'zones', covering use within the circumstances of normal operation, together with the likelihood of malfunction. The higher the probability of an explosive atmosphere occurring and persisting, the higher the equipment integrity requirements will be (as set out in schedule 3 to regulation 7(2) of *DSEAR*).

ergonomics – the scientific discipline concerned with the understanding of interactions amongst humans and other elements of a system, and the profession that applies theory, principles, data and methods to design in order to optimise human wellbeing and overall system performance. The term can be used interchangeably with 'human factors', although 'ergonomics' is often used in relation to the physical aspects of the environment, such as workstations and control panels, whilst 'human factors' tends to be used in relation to the wider systems within which people work.

ergonomist – an expert in the field of ergonomics.

escalation factor – *see 'degradation factor' (the risk of failure can be escalated, or effectiveness degraded).*

escalation scenario – *see 'domino effect'. An 'off-site scenario' is an example of an escalation scenario.*

Essential Health and Safety Requirements – the broad objectives for health and safety, stating how designers and manufacturers should construct applicable products. At the time of this book going to press, Great Britain's essential requirements are substantially the same as EU essential requirements, which apply under equivalent EU law (as specified in EU Product Safety Directives), albeit that this position may diverge over time.

European Economic Area – the area consisting of European Union Member States, together with three countries of the European Free Trade Association (Iceland, Liechtenstein and Norway).

EU CLP – *see 'CLP'*.

Ex sign – a sign that warns of a danger of explosive atmospheres.

exceptional operating conditions – operating circumstances in which the work involved is unusual, or non-routine tasks are undertaken, requiring performance in exceptional conditions. An example of these conditions would be work in confined spaces.

exclusion zone – an area within which workers or members of the public are not safe from the risks of work activities; an area where people are not allowed to go, or where they are not allowed to do a particular thing, because of the danger which exists there. This is one example of a control measure to prevent people being injured, which operates by keeping them away from identified risks. NB: In *the Work at Height Regulations*, the term used for an exclusion zone is a 'danger area', which needs to be set up in circumstances where it is not possible to stop objects from falling.

explosion pressure relief – the method by which a safety device – of which vents and rupture panels are examples – operates to protect equipment or buildings against excessive internal, explosion-incurred pressures. The relief of pressure occurs as soon as the opening pressure has been exceeded.

explosion protection system – a system designed to suppress, isolate and vent combustible dust or vapour.

explosion suppression equipment – an equipment type designed to suppress or extinguish an explosion or fire at its onset, reducing pressure build-up which, if left unchecked, would rupture a process vessel or conveying duct.

explosive atmosphere – a mixture, under atmospheric conditions, of air and one or more dangerous substances – in the form of gases, vapours, mists or dusts – in which, after ignition has occurred, combustion spreads to the entire unburned mixture (as defined by regulation 2 of *DSEAR*).

external emergency plan – *see 'emergency plan, external'*.

face covering – something which safely covers the nose and mouth, and which is intended to protect others, rather than the wearer, against the spread of infection, e.g. viruses, by blocking routes of transmission. These coverings are not classified as PPE, which is used in workplace settings to protect wearers against specific hazards and risks. In the UK, the increased use of face coverings in public followed in the wake of the Coronavirus disease (COVID-19) outbreak of 2020.

fail to danger – an equipment fault which would inhibit or delay automatic shut-off should this be required, and which has a direct and detrimental effect on safety.

fall energy – a measurement of impact force, calculated as follows:
mass (kilograms) * height (metres dropped) * gravity (9.8m/s).

fall from height – a fall from a distance liable to cause personal injury or worse to an individual.

fall prevention – collective fall protection – a work equipment system or existing feature which provides fall prevention for a group. Examples include tower scaffolds, guard rails, toe boards, and safety barriers (see regulation 7(1)(a) and schedule 2 of *the Work at Height Regulations*).

fall prevention – personal fall protection – a work equipment system or existing feature which provides fall prevention for an individual; a work restraint system which stops a worker getting into a fall position. An example is a valley gutter frame walker, this being a mobile safety cage, which stops them from falling in the first place by restricting their movement (see regulation 6(3) of *the Work at Height Regulations*).

fall protection – collective protection – a work equipment system or existing feature which provides fall protection for a group, minimising the distance and consequences of any such fall. These are forms of fall mitigation, being physical measures which, if successful, lead to a reduction in the severity of the hazards and risks associated with falls. Examples include nets and airbags, which can catch groups who have fallen. These do not prevent falls, but operate to arrest falls safely (see regulation 8(c) and schedule 4 of *the Work at Height Regulations*).

fall protection – personal protection – a work equipment system or existing feature which provides fall protection for an individual, requiring them to act for it to be effective. These are forms of fall mitigation, being physical measures which, if successful, lead to a reduction in the severity of the hazards and risks associated with falls. An example would be a fall arrest system using a high anchor point, or a safety harness which is correctly put on and connected, via an energy absorbing lanyard, to a suitable anchor point, and which could be effective in circumstances where other types of work equipment are deemed not to be reasonably practicable (see regulation 8(d) and schedule 5 of *the Work at Height Regulations*).

falling object – an item falling from above ground level.

fatigue – a state of extreme tiredness, resulting from mental or physical exertion, or both, and which can be short or long term.

fatigue risk index – a tool designed by the Health and Safety Executive, the primary intention of which is to compare different shift schedules but which can also be used to identify any particular shift within a given schedule that might be of concern to an organisation.

firewater – water that has been used for the purpose of fire-fighting, and which subsequently requires disposal.

first-aid – treatment for the purpose of preserving life and minimising the consequences of injury until help from a medical practitioner or nurse is obtained, and the treatment of minor injuries which would otherwise receive no treatment, or which do not need treatment by a medical practitioner or nurse (see *the First-Aid Regulations*).

fully functional – a term used in bow tie modelling, as related to barrier (risk control) properties, which means a barrier should be fully capable of preventing a top event or mitigating consequences.

functional manager – an individual who manages people with specific skills, together with different resources within a department or section, in order to meet functional objectives. Individuals who perform this role are typically responsible for overseeing the operation of an entire unit of an organisation.

gamification – the application of typical elements of game playing – for instance point scoring, competition with others, or rules of play – to other areas of activity, with the purpose of encouraging engagement or compliance with products, services, safety rules and so on.

gauge, *also referred to as a 'level indicator'* – an instrument which detects the level of liquids, fluids and fluidised solids, including slurries, granularised materials and powders, which exhibit an upper free surface. Such instrumentation can be designed using a variety of sensing principles, depending upon application, and performs an important function in a variety of consumer and industrial contexts.

GB CLP – the regulations put in place in order to ensure Great Britain's independent adoption of the 'GHS' post-EU exit, which secure the continued effective regulation of the classification, labelling and packaging of substances and chemicals on the GB market (England, Scotland, Wales). There are a number of consequential changes following the move from EU CLP to GB CLP, but the main duties to classify, label and package remain, the Health and Safety Executive has become the relevant GB CLP agency, overseeing GB CLP functions for substances and mixtures placed on the GB market, and the GB CLP Regulation now applies to GB-based manufacturers, importers, downstream users and distributors supplying the GB market. Different rules apply on the Northern Ireland market.

general duties – duties contained within *HSWA 1974*, which apply to everyone. Employers have two general duties under *HSWA 1974*. Section 2 requires them to ensure so far as is reasonably practicable the health, safety and welfare of employees, whilst section 3 requires them to conduct their undertakings in such a way as to ensure so far as is reasonably practicable that non-employees affected are not to be exposed to risks to their health and safety.

generic risk assessment – the type of risk assessment covering the risks inherent in an activity and control measures that must be followed for that activity whenever it is undertaken. A single assessment or safe system of work that is suitable for an activity performed regularly in a similar manner, across different locations and/or departments within an organisation, this type of assessment is particularly suitable for repeatable jobs. The main benefit of this form of risk assessment is that it avoids repeating the same assessment many times, when the level of risk and applicable precautions would be identical as between assessments. The output is a set of standard control measures and precautions applicable to similar activities, provided these are undertaken in a similar way and under similar conditions on each occasion. This form of assessment is good for activities which are repeated with little change – but there remains a need to check that these are appropriate for the particular circumstances, on every occasion it is used.

gig economy – a labour market characterised by the prevalence of short-term contracts or freelance work, as opposed to permanent jobs.

Globally Harmonised System (GHS) – a single worldwide system developed by the United Nations for classifying and communicating (labelling) the hazardous properties of industrial and consumer chemicals.

good practice – a standard for controlling risk which has been judged and recognised to satisfy the law when applied to particular circumstances in an appropriate manner, the scope and detail of which reflects the nature of hazards and risks, the complexity of the activity or process, and the relevant legal requirements. Sources of good practice can include Approved Codes of Practice, and Guidance produced by the Health and Safety Executive, and are useful to regulators when judging the adequacy of compliance and deciding whether standards such as 'practicable' and 'reasonably practicable' legal tests have been met. Many organisations will seek to exceed good practice, by striving to adopt 'best practice'. *See also 'best practice'.*

gross breach – circumstances where the conduct alleged to amount to a breach of the duty of care falls far below what can reasonably be expected of an organisation (see section 1(4)(b) of *the Corporate Manslaughter Act*).

gross negligence manslaughter – an offence committed where the death which occurs results from a grossly negligent – though otherwise lawful – act or omission on the part of the defendant.

Hand Arm Vibration Syndrome (HAVS) – a syndrome caused by exposure to vibration at work, which is preventable, but irreversible, once damage is caused.

haptic feedback – a feedback response based on the experience of touch, by applying forces, vibrations or motions to the user/operative.

haul, to (verb) – to pull or drag with effort.

hazard – something in, around or part of an organisation with the potential to cause harm, including: ill health and injury; damage to property, products or the environment; production losses, or increased liabilities.

hazard group – a group assigned to a biological agent in accordance with the classification system for biological agents. Classification is made on the basis of the answers to four key questions: (1) *'Is it pathogenic for humans?'* (2) *'Is it a hazard to employees?'* (3) *'Is it transmissible to the community?'* and (4) *'Is effective prophylaxis or treatment available?'* (see schedule 3 to regulation 7(10), Part 1, paragraph 2 of *the COSHH Regulations*).

hazardous area – *see 'hazardous place'.*

hazardous area classification – a process carried out as an integral part of *DSEAR* risk assessment, the purpose of which is to analyse and classify the environments where explosive gas atmospheres may occur. The process results in the identification of places where control over ignition sources is needed ('hazardous places') and those where it is not ('non-hazardous places').

hazardous place – *sometimes referred to as a 'hazardous area';* any location in which an explosive atmosphere may occur, in quantities such as to require special precautions to protect the safety of workers. Ignition sources must be controlled in such locations, which are in turn sub-divided into zones, the precise requirements for which are dependent upon the designated zone classification; *see also 'zones'.*

hazardous substance – an umbrella term for substances including: chemicals, chemical containing products, fumes, dusts, vapours, mists, the outputs of nanotechnology, gases and asphyxiating gases, biological agents, and germs that cause disease, such as leptospirosis or legionnaires disease (see regulation 2 of *the COSHH Regulations* – 'substance hazardous to health'). Other substances which are hazardous to health – but not covered by *the COSHH Regulations* – include lead, asbestos, and radioactive substances, which have their own regulations.

hazardous waste – a term applied to waste which, owing to the nature of the material or substances it contains, is harmful to humans or the environment. Examples include: asbestos, batteries, solvents, pesticides, and some chemicals.

health and safety document – the document required under *the Mines Regulations 2014*, prepared by a mine operator, which shows that risks to workers in mines have been assessed and adequate control measures put in place to ensure their health and safety.

Health and Safety Executive (HSE) – the independent regulator that operates within Great Britain, the mission of which is to prevent work-related deaths, injuries and ill health.

The Executive provides free guidance and advice, and arms businesses and employers with information on how to correctly manage risk, helping them to boost productivity, support the economy, and contribute to a fairer society. It performs the central policy role for the regulation of health and safety at work in Great Britain and helps workers to understand how they can keep themselves and their co-workers safe and well.

health and safety management system – a set of inter-related or interacting arrangements – including procedures and processes – used by an organisation to deliver its health and safety policy, such that occurrences of work-related injury and ill health to workers are prevented, and safe and healthy workplaces are provided and maintained. When such a system is well-delivered by an organisation, a systematic and proactive approach to managing health and safety risks will be evident, with supporting risk management activities including the identification of safety issues, risk assessment and risk mitigation. Further evidence of an effective health and safety management system is seen where an organisation institutes a strong assurance function, which monitors compliance and performance, as well as managing change. Underpinning any such system should be the direction and support of strong leadership, including that shown by senior leaders.

health and safety policy – a document which sets out an organisation's commitment to managing health and safety effectively, and what it wants to achieve. This needs to include *first*, a statement of intent; *second*, responsibilities for health and safety and *third*, their arrangements for health and safety.

health surveillance – *'a system of ongoing health checks, which may be required by law for employees who are exposed to noise or vibration, ionising radiation, solvents, fumes, dusts, biological agents and other substances hazardous to health, or work in compressed air'* (Health and Safety Executive definition).

Hidden report – the investigation report, led by Hidden, A, QC and published by the Department of Transport, following the rail incident at *Clapham Junction (1989)*.

hierarchy of control – an approach taken to reduce levels of risk to the lowest level reasonably practicable, by taking preventative measures in order of priority. This approach is commonplace across health and safety legislation, for a range of risk types, with examples including hazardous substances, manual handling, work at height, and confined spaces. Typically, this type of approach includes: *first*, elimination; *second*, substitution; *third*, engineering controls; *fourth*, administrative controls, and *fifth*, and finally, personal protective clothing and equipment.

high-hazard organisation – an organisation which conducts activities or operates processes that carry with them the potential for harm or death to result to large numbers of individuals, or to cause significant damage from single events including fires and explosions.

high level alarm – *see 'alarm, high level'*.

home worker – a worker performing duties under a homeworking arrangement; *see also 'homeworking'*.

homeworking – an arrangement whereby a worker and employer agree that some or all of a worker's duties can be performed from home.

horizon scanning – the systematic examination of information sources – internal and external to an organisation – to identify potential threats, risks, emerging issues and opportunities. Once identified, this information can be exploited (and threats, risks and issues mitigated through risk and policy-making processes), paving the way for better organisational preparedness, which thereby secures the best chance of the most positive outcome being achieved.

hot-desker – a worker who uses a shared desk or workstation, through the practice of hot-desking; *see also 'hot-desking'*.

hot-desking – the practice whereby multiple workers use a single physical workstation or surface during different time periods.

human error – something done which was not intended by the actor, which can include a deviation from intention, expectation or desirability; error types can be categorised in various ways, one such distinction being between slips, lapses and violations.

human factors – *see 'ergonomics'*.

ignition risk – *see 'ignition source'*.

ignition source – an object, process or event capable of igniting or transmitting a medium to prompt combustion, resulting in a fire or explosion. Examples of ignition sources include: open flames, sparks, static electricity, and hot surfaces.

immediate cause – the basic reason for an incident occurring, examples being where a guard is missing or a worker slips. There can be many such reasons identified in relation to any one incident.

impact force – *see 'fall energy'*.

incident – an occurrence, other than an accident, associated with an organisation's operations which affects, or has the potential to affect, the safe conduct of its operations.

inclusive design – the approach which applies the understanding of user diversity to inform decisions throughout the development process, in order to better satisfy the needs of more users.

independent – a term used in bow tie modelling, as related to barrier (risk control) properties, meaning that a barrier should be capable of operating by itself, not depending upon other barriers within the same threat or consequence leg for its success in blocking threats or mitigating consequences. Barriers that are independent are free of common failure modes by design, being independent of other barriers and threats on the same threat or consequence leg. There is, however, no requirement for barriers or threats situated on different threat or consequence legs to be independent.

independent verification – a process for independently checking that a product, service or system meets requirements and specifications, and that it fulfils its intended purpose.

indicator drift – a state in which a performance indicator no longer delivers its intended purpose as an assurance tool, due to it having become outmoded or been misused.

individual control measure – *see 'personal control measure'*.

induction – *see 'site induction'*.

inhalable dust – the fraction of airborne material that enters the nose and mouth during breathing, which is therefore available for deposition in the respiratory tract.

inherently safe design – an approach which tries to avoid or eliminate hazards or reduce the magnitude, severity or likelihood of their occurrence, by prioritising design and layout. This approach places less reliance on add-on engineered safety systems and features, and procedural controls, which can and do fail.

inspection – a method of checking workplace standards; approaches to inspection are varied and can include safety tours, safety sampling, and safety surveys, as well as incident inspections carried out following an incident.

intelligent transport system – the application of technology to improve the safety, efficiency, environmental and journey experience for users. The purpose behind these systems is to optimise transport policy and operations, business models, user behaviour and safety, to help solve transport problems.

internal emergency plan – *see 'emergency plan, internal'.*

intrinsic safety – the design approach applied to electrical equipment and wiring, for hazardous locations. The technique is based upon limiting energy – electrical and thermal – to a level below that which is required to ignite a specific hazardous atmosphere mixture.

intrinsically safe – a required property of electrical equipment and wiring for use in hazardous locations. This design works by limiting energy – electrical and thermal – to a level below that required to ignite a specific hazardous atmosphere mixture.

job task analysis – an approach which involves the breaking down of a job into specific tasks, which assists with the development of effective procedures, to enable it to be carried out safely. The technique includes the methods used to collect, record and analyse information about practical tasks, in order to aid understanding about what operatives are required to do, and any changes that may be needed to improve human performance. Having identified safety critical tasks, these next need to be clearly defined and understood. This is achieved by carrying out a suitable task analysis, which could be as simple as a walk or talk through of the tasks – writing down what should be done, where and when it should be done, who should be doing it, how to do it and why it is important. For more complex tasks, the use of a formal human factors task analysis tool may be required.

Kegworth report – the report into the causes of the Kegworth air disaster (*Great Britain, 1989*).

lagging indicator – *also referred to as a 'reactive', or 'after the fact' indicator* – the type of indicator which measures an organisation's incidents, in the form of past incident statistics (it follows the top event). As a form of reactive monitoring – requiring the reporting or investigation of specific incidents and events to discover weaknesses in the system – this type of indicator represents a failure of a significant risk control system that guards against or limits the consequences of a major incident. This is the type of performance indicator traditionally used to indicate progress towards compliance with safety rules, being a bottom-line number which evaluates the overall effectiveness of safety at a facility or location. It typically records how many people got hurt or processes failed (*frequency*) and how badly (*severity*). It is an outcome-orientated retrospective indicator measure, describing events that have already occurred and which may indicate potentially recurring issues, for instance events meeting or exceeding an established severity threshold. It shows when a desired safety outcome has failed or not been achieved.

leading indicator – *also referred to as an 'active', 'before the fact' indicator* – the type of indicator used by an organisation which records precursors or indicators of future events (it changes before the top event). As a form of active monitoring, focused on a few critical risk control systems to ensure their continued effectiveness, this type of indicator requires a routine systematic check to be made that key actions or activities – process controls – are undertaken as intended. Focused upon future safety performance and continual improvement, indicators of this type are proactive in nature, reporting what is being done on a regular basis, to prevent injuries or loss of process control. An indicator of this type is forward-looking, measuring the performance of the key work processes, operating discipline or barriers that prevent incidents. It can be considered as a measure of the process or inputs essential to deliver a desired safety outcome.

Leptospira interrogans – a bacterial species (or germ) that contains over 200 pathogenic serovars (variations between immune cells of different individuals).

leptospirosis – *also known as 'Weil's disease'* – a serious, potentially fatal bacterial zoonotic infection, transmitted to humans via direct or indirect contact with infected rat urine, most commonly through contaminated water. Spread via the urine of infected animals – most commonly, rats, mice, cows, pigs and dogs – it can be caught if either soil or freshwater, e.g. from a river, canal or lake, containing infected urine gets into the mouth, eyes or a cut. This can arise from occupational activity – where there is human contact with an infected animal's blood or flesh from working with animals or animal parts – or through social pursuits, including kayaking, outdoor swimming, or fishing. It is very rare for leptospirosis to be contracted through contact with pets, other people or bites.

level indicator – *see 'gauge'.*

lifting and handling aids – aids which can remove or reduce the risk of musculoskeletal disorders and manual handling injuries, by lessening the human effort required to move a load. There are many types available, but those commonly used are 'powered assistance' and 'non-powered assistance' types (*see separate entries*).

line manager – an individual with direct managerial responsibilities for an employee or employees.

lone working – circumstances in which work activities are carried out by a worker in isolation, without the close, direct or immediate support of supervisors or colleagues.

Long Term Exposure Limit (LTEL) – a limit (8-hour time-weighted average, *or TWA*) placed on a hazardous substance to control the effects of prolonged or accumulated exposure, by restricting the total intake by inhalation over one or more work shifts, depending on shift length. This type of limit tends to be imposed for substances where effects are not seen after brief exposures, and for which Short Term Exposure Limits (STELs) are in place.

loss of containment – an unplanned or uncontrolled release of any material from containment, including non-toxic and non-flammable materials, for instance steam, hot condensate, nitrogen, compressed carbon dioxide, or compressed air. There are various levels of containment (and therefore levels of containment loss), examples of which include 'primary containment', which relates to the equipment in direct contact with the substances being stored or transported, and 'secondary containment', which involves equipment external to the primary containment system, and typically comes into play when the primary containment system fails. Primary containment examples include tanks and storage vessels, pipework, valves, pumps and associated management and control systems. Secondary containment acts as a barrier to limit the consequences which flow from a loss of primary containment, examples of which include dykes, curbing around process equipment, and the outer wall of double-walled tanks. When effective, it also provides limited storage capacity for firewater management, the need for which can arise following an escalation scenario.

low level alarm – *see 'alarm, low level'.*

lower tier COMAH site – an establishment subject to the lower requirements of *the COMAH Regulations*, based upon the quantities of dangerous substances present there.

lux – a unit of illuminance, which measures the intensity of light, as perceived by the human eye, that hits or passes through a surface (SI unit, equal to one lumen per square metre).

MAC (Manual Handling Assessment Charts) tool – a simple tool designed by the Health and Safety Executive to help identify high-risk workplace manual handling activities. This tool can be used to assess the risks posed by lifting, lowering, carrying, and team manual handling activities.

macro – a single instruction that expands automatically into a set of instructions, to perform a particular task.

macro level – large scale.

major accident – *'an occurrence such as a major emission, fire or explosion resulting from uncontrolled developments in the course of the operation of any establishment…and leading to a serious danger to human health or the environment (whether immediate or delayed) inside or outside the establishment, and involving one or more dangerous substances'* (see regulation 2 of *the COMAH Regulations*).

major accident hazard (MAH) – a hazard with the potential to cause a major accident.

Major Accident Prevention Policy (MAPP) – a document which sets out an organisation's policy with respect to the prevention of major accidents (see regulation 7 of *the COMAH Regulations*).

major accident scenario – a scenario which addresses the circumstances which could lead to, and follow, the occurrence of a major accident.

Management Standards – a set of conditions, developed by the Health and Safety Executive, a key purpose of which is to simplify the risk assessment of work-related stress for organisations by: identifying the key risk factors; placing a focus on the underlying causes and how to prevent them, and providing a yardstick by which performance can be gauged, in addressing the key causes. Additionally, they: demonstrate good practice, by taking a step-by-step approach to risk assessment; allow the current situation to be assessed through the use of pre-existing data, surveys and other techniques, and promote dialogue and a partnership approach with employees and their representatives, supporting decisions on practical improvements that can be made.

manager – an individual entrusted with responsibility for overseeing employees and/or processes within an organisation. *See also 'depot manager', 'functional manager', 'line manager', 'operational manager', 'performance manager', 'process manager', 'team manager'.*

manual handling operations – *also referred to as 'manual handling'* – any transporting or supporting of a load – including the lifting, lowering, pushing, pulling, carrying or moving thereof – by hand or bodily force (see regulation 2 of *the Manual Handling Regulations*).

manual handling risk filter – a simple filter designed by the Health and Safety Executive, which identifies manual handling tasks which are low risk, and distinguishes low risk tasks from those needing a more detailed assessment. If a task falls within filter values, there is not normally a need to do any other form of risk assessment, unless there are employees involved who may be at significant risk. Different filters apply to different types of manual handling, covering: lifting and lowering; carrying up to ten metres; handling whilst seated, and push and pull activities (*see also 'pushing and pulling risk filter'*).

manually operated valve – a valve which is activated by human intervention.

mass – how much stuff or matter is in an object.

method statement – a written document which describes in a logical sequence exactly how a job is to be carried out in a safe manner, and without risks to health. It includes all the risks identified by risk assessment and the measures needed to control them, and allows a job to be properly planned and resourced. Whilst the requirement for these documents is not legally set down, method statements are useful for higher risk, complex or unusual work and for providing information to employees about how the work should be done and the precautions to be taken.

micro level – small scale.

migrant worker – a person who moves to another country or area, in order to find employment, in particular work of a seasonal or temporary nature.

mine operator – a person who is in control of the operation of a mine; the principal duty holder (regulation 7 of *the Mines Regulations*).

(mine) owner – a person entitled for the time being to work in a mine; the owner must not appoint another person as mine operator, unless that person is suitable, and has sufficient resources to be able to operate the mine safely (regulation 5 of *the Mines Regulations*).

mitigation barrier – a barrier which acts to prevent or mitigate consequences, following a top (risk) event. Mitigation barriers feature on the right hand side of a bow tie model, occurring post-top event and, when fully effective, they ensure that escalation of the top event does not result in an actual impact (consequence). When partially effective, they serve to limit the consequences of the top event.

mitigation barrier action – an action required by an operative to make, or help make, a mitigation barrier effective.

mode confusion – the type of error which can occur when users – for instance, pilots – operate with many similar system modes, potentially with different levels of automation and support. Switching between systems can lead to confusion of modes, resulting in the formation of incorrect mental models and ultimately, the taking of the wrong subsequent actions – errors which may or may not be recoverable by users.

modern slavery statement – an annual statement which must be published by commercial organisations meeting certain criteria, setting out the steps they take to prevent modern slavery in their business and supply chains, as required under the *Modern Slavery Act 2015*.

MSD Toolkit – *see 'Toolkit for MSDs (musculoskeletal disorders)'*.

musculoskeletal disorder (MSD) – any injury, damage, disorder of the joints or other tissues in the upper limbs, lower limbs or back.

near miss – an event not causing actual harm, but which has the potential to cause injury or ill health, or damage. *Sometimes referred to as a 'near hit'*.

negligence – the breach of a duty of care, which causes damage.

new and expectant mother – a woman who is pregnant, has given birth within the last six months, or is breastfeeding.

non-compliance – a failure to act in accordance with a rule or regulation.

non-hazardous place – an area in which an explosive atmosphere is not expected to be present; a place where control over ignition sources is not needed.

non-powered assistance – a category of lifting and handling aid, examples of which include barrows and sack-trolleys.

non-routine operating conditions – circumstances in which plant or equipment is operated outside its design parameters. Examples include the start-up of a major unit operating with non-standard equipment, and non-routine testing of a critical device with the potential to shut down a unit.

normal operating conditions – *see 'routine operating conditions'.*

Notified Body – an entity that assesses the products of member countries against EU rules, and decides whether or not a product safety mark can be granted. Following the UK's departure from the EU, new entities granted 'United Kingdom Approved Body' status now perform the equivalent role to that of Notified Bodies. *See also 'United Kingdom Approved Body'.*

occupational safety – the discipline concerned with the safety, health and welfare of people at work.

occupational safety indicator – an indicator of occupational safety performance.

occupier – a person (or organisation) who occupies premises.

occupiers' liability – the duty owed by occupiers to those who come on to their land.

off-site emergency plan – *see 'emergency plan, external'.*

off-site scenario – a possible sequence of events envisaged by an organisation, outside its site, as could result from a major accident. This would typically be captured and addressed within an external emergency plan (see regulation 12 of *the COMAH Regulations*); *see also 'domino effect', 'escalation scenario'.*

on-site emergency plan – *see 'emergency plan, internal'.*

on-site scenario – the possible sequence of events envisaged by an organisation, inside its site, as could result from a major accident. This would typically be captured and addressed within an internal emergency plan (see regulation 13 of *the COMAH Regulations*).

onboarding – the action or process of familiarising a new employee with an organisation's policies, their role within it, and its culture.

operating conditions – the circumstances in which operations are carried out, which can be routine/normal, non-routine, exceptional, abnormal, or emergency. *See separate entries for: 'abnormal operating conditions', 'emergency operating conditions', 'exceptional operating conditions', 'non-routine operating conditions', 'routine operating conditions'.*

operational manager – *or operations manager* – an individual in charge of the planning and execution of the routine functions of an organisation. In the context used in this book, this has been taken as being someone with responsibility for managing those with frontline or sharp end responsibilities.

operative – a worker involved in carrying out practical sharp end tasks. In the context used in this book, this has been taken to apply to those directly responsible for, or involved in, the carrying out of safety critical tasks, being tasks directly connected to ensuring process safety. The reliability with which operatives perform such tasks is key to organisations ensuring the safe operation of plant and equipment and the meeting of legislative and other requirements.

operator – the person who is in control of the operation of an establishment. In the context of this book, examples include the person with responsibility for a site subject to *the COMAH Regulations,* and the person who is in control of the operation of a mine, under *the Mines Regulations*.

optimal performance zone – the zone within which the best performance for a specific activity is achieved.

overtraining – the training of operatives to a level above that which is required in routine/normal circumstances, so as to ensure that they are capable of performing in non-routine, exceptional, abnormal and emergency operating conditions, even where they are rarely called upon to do so. Adopting this kind of approach gives an organisation confidence in the capacity of its operatives to handle such circumstances and also avoids skill fade.

passive barrier – a barrier which does not perform a function in order to be operational, acting only by its presence, examples of which include walls, fences and dykes. This barrier type is either present or not present. Whilst it still requires maintenance in order to remain effective, this barrier type never requires human intervention in order to deliver its function.

pathogen – a bacterium, virus or other micro-organism that can cause disease.

performance envelope – *also referred to as a 'design envelope'*; the boundary of a design which is not to be exceeded, or strict limits within which an event can take place, or within which a vehicle or machine is to be operated.

performance indicators – a group of statistics which summarises an organisation's achievements, typically indicating the overall performance level of a process or system, as well as highlighting any change in performance over time. This information or data indicates an organisation's performance in managing their key risks – related to asset integrity, process safety and so on – measuring the status of operations, management or conditions. Performance indicators are also used to evaluate the success of an organisation, or of particular activities, such as projects, programmes, products or other initiatives, with which it is involved.

Performance Influencing Factors (PIFs) – a term coined by the Health and Safety Executive, which denotes the characteristics of the job, the individual and the organisation that influence human performance. Optimising PIFs reduces the likelihood of all types of human failure.

performance manager – an individual tasked with responsibility for continually improving performance, aligned to an organisation's strategic goals. The activities typically performed in order to accomplish this role include: setting individual and team goals which align to strategic goals; reviewing and assessing progress made towards them, and developing the knowledge, skills and abilities of individuals.

permit-to-work – a formal written system used to control certain types of work that are potentially hazardous, including work in confined spaces, and work at height. This form of documentation specifies the work to be done and the precautions to be taken, and forms an essential part of a safe system of work for many maintenance activities.

person at work – the term given in *the Mines Regulations* to a person working in a mine.

personal control measure – *also known as a 'personal protection measure' or 'individual control measure'* – a control measure which relies on PPE, and only protects the user. Most commonly, these measures are active, meaning that the user is required to do something to make them work effectively, for instance, attaching PPE to a fall prevention system. Examples include safety lines, rope access, and roof connection systems.

personal protection measure – *see 'personal control measure'*.

Personal Protective Equipment (PPE) – the equipment which protects the user/wearer against health and safety risks at work; this can include items such as safety helmets, gloves, eye protection, high visibility clothing, safety footwear and safety harnesses. It also includes respiratory protective equipment (RPE). It is to be regarded as the last line of defence in controlling risk, with engineering controls which design out risk having been applied first.

personal safety – *see 'occupational safety'*.

***plan-do-check-act* cycle** – a key practical methodology developed by the Health and Safety Executive which, when followed, ensures health and safety leadership duties are considered through each stage of the risk management cycle. In summary, this comprises an organisation setting out: *step one – plan*, detailing the direction for its health and safety management, forming a part of its culture, values and performance standards – what it will do; *step two – do*, setting out the practical steps it will take to reduce health and safety risks so far as is reasonably practicable to employees, customers and members of the public, as defined by an effective health and safety management system – how it will do it; *step three – check*, stating the ways in which it will measure how effectively it is controlling risks in reality and therefore, how it will know whether the measures put in place are working, for instance, specific reports on incident learning, and routine reports, as are contained within leading and lagging indicator data, and so on; *step four – act*, describing the actions it will take to address any weaknesses, responding to the lessons learnt from the *check* step – allowing it to show whether strong leadership, worker engagement, and assessment and review, have been embedded within the organisation, and thus, demonstrate the effectiveness with which the system is managing risk and protecting people. This stage should also inform the *plan* step for the next round of its cycle, and any other initiatives to control risk. For a comprehensive description of this approach, see Health and Safety Executive Guidance document (2013). *Managing for Health and Safety*. HSG65. Crown copyright.

portal – a website or web page, providing access or links to other websites.

potentially explosive atmosphere – an area where the possibility of an explosive atmosphere exists.

powered assistance – a category of lifting and handling aid, examples of which include lift trucks and drum or reel rotators.

pre-qualification questionnaire (PQQ) – a document that sets out a series of questions for potential contractors to answer regarding their experience, capacity and health and safety credentials and record. Typically completed in response to a request made by a client, the answers given by potential contractors to the questions contained within this document can be instrumental in a client's decision as to whether they are a party with whom they wish to enter into a formal contractual arrangement.

precedent – a judgment reached in a legal case, which can bind all subsequent cases, depending upon the seniority of the court. As such, case law becomes part of the law by either interpreting existing legislation or setting legal precedents where there is no legislation. This so-called *'doctrine of precedent'* is particularly important within common law jurisdictions, of which the UK is an example.

preferred contractor – a contractor that has already met a pre-defined minimum standard or set of criteria, proving they are capable of doing certain work, as set by an organisation and/or other body.

prevention barrier – a barrier which acts to prevent a loss of control, generally by interrupting a scenario – or blocking a pathway – so that an identified threat does not result in top event. Prevention barriers feature on the left hand side of a bow tie model, occurring pre-top event.

prevention barrier action – an action required by an operative to make, or help make, a prevention barrier effective.

proactive indicator – *see 'leading indicator'.*

procedural barrier – a barrier, the function of which is verified by testing its operation. Examples of questions which verify the effectiveness of this barrier type include: *'Does the emergency plan work?', 'Do people know what to do?'* and *'Is there adequate equipment available to deliver upon the requirements of the plan and make sure it works in practice?'* These barriers, like active barriers, contain *sense-decide-act* elements, but *always* require human intervention to be effective.

process – a set of actions, steps or other interrelated or interacting activities, which transforms inputs into outputs, in order to achieve a particular end.

process control – a physical or procedural control which ensures that a process is safe, predictable, stable and consistently operates at a target level or within set tolerances. Process controls include safety critical elements, such as instruments and alarms, together with the key actions or activities within risk control systems required to deliver desired safety outcomes, which are typically measured by leading indicators.

process manager – an individual who evaluates, designs, executes, measures, monitors and controls business processes, and who works to ensure that business process outcomes are being met and align to an organisation's strategic goals.

process safety – the discipline concerned with the prevention of harm to people, assets and the environment from major accidents, such as fires, explosions, releases of hazardous substances or stored energy. Generally focused on major accident hazards, associated with process industries – including petrochemical, chemical, oil & gas, mining and power generation – it can be characterised by substances being extracted, processed, or treated with the aim of readying them for some purpose, which is inherently dangerous or rendered so by the process. Examples of process industry activities falling subject to process control include those that involve: storing flammable gas, combustion, chemical reactions, reservoirs, kinetic or potential energy.

process safety culture – the combination of group values and behaviours that determine the manner in which process safety is managed. This is derived from multiple factors, which include: the quality of process safety leadership; employee empowerment; resources and distribution of process capabilities; incorporation within management decision-making, and any variations to custom and practice at operating locations.

process safety incident – an unplanned event – examples of which include uncontrolled releases of energy and/or hazardous substances – which either results in, or has the potential to cause, an injury, including illness, asset damage or environmental impact.

process safety indicator – an indicator of process safety performance.

procurement – the act of obtaining or buying something.

product – a good or service offered to the market, to satisfy a want or need.

prosecution – *see 'criminal prosecution'.*

protective system – a system which protects electrical power systems from faults, through the disconnection of faulted parts from the rest of an electrical network.

psychosocial factors – factors which may affect workers' psychological response to their work and workplace conditions, including working relationships with supervisors and colleagues. Examples of these factors include: high workloads, tight deadlines, and workers lacking control over their work and working methods.

publicity order – an order requiring an organisation convicted of corporate manslaughter or corporate homicide to publicise in a specified manner: the fact it has been convicted of the offence; the specified particulars of the offence; the amount of any fine imposed, and the terms of any remedial order made (see section 10 of *the Corporate Manslaughter Act*).

pull, to (verb) – to move something towards yourself, with great physical effort.

push, to (verb) – to use physical pressure or force, usually with the hands, in order to move something into a different position, usually one that is further away from you.

pushing and pulling risk filter – a type of risk filter used to assess the risk level of push and pull tasks.

RAPP (Risk Assessment of Pushing and Pulling) tool – a simple tool designed by the Health and Safety Executive, to help to assess the key risks in manual pushing and pulling operations, involving whole body effort.

reactive indicator – *see 'lagging indicator'.*

reactive monitoring – a form of monitoring which involves identifying and reporting on incidents, to check that the control measures in place are adequate, and identify weaknesses or gaps in risk control systems, and to learn from mistakes. A further example of reactive monitoring is the use of lagging indicators.

reasonably practicable – the requirement for a risk to be weighed against the time, trouble and expense needed to control it.

regulator – a body which determines whether organisations are effectively and proportionately managing their health and safety risks to workers and others.

reliability – the probability that a system or component will perform its intended function, whenever required, for a prescribed time and under stipulated environmental conditions.

reliable human performance – the quality required of people, in particular where they act as operatives, performing safety critical tasks. Simply put, its focus is upon people doing the right thing, in the right way, and at the right time. Where this is achieved, tasks are accomplished in line with agreed upon standards of accuracy, completeness and efficiency.

remedial order – an order requiring an organisation convicted of corporate homicide to take specified steps to remedy: the breach, any matter that appears to the court to have resulted from the breach and been a cause of death, and any deficiency as regards health and safety matters, in the organisation's policies, systems or practices, of which the relevant breach appears to the court to be an indication (see section 9 of *the Corporate Manslaughter Act*).

remotely operated shut off valve (ROSOV) – a type of valve designed, installed and maintained for the primary purpose of achieving rapid isolation of plant items containing hazardous substances in the event of a failure of the primary containment system, which includes, but is not limited to, leaks from pipework, flanges and pump seals. Closure of this type of valve can be initiated from a point remote from the valve itself, enabling emergency isolation of plant or equipment to be carried out from a safe location, without the necessity for manual operation, thereby avoiding the need for operatives to enter hazardous areas. Valves should be capable of closing and maintaining tight shut-off under foreseeable conditions following such a failure, which might include fire. For new installations, ROSOVs are normally the preferred option, unless there are good technical reasons why they are not appropriate.

representative of employee safety – *see 'safety representative'*.

rescue plan – a plan which handles the arrangements for rescue in an emergency situation. In the context of confined spaces, such plans need to consider and include: communication arrangements, rescue and resuscitation equipment, rescuer capability, process shutdown arrangements, fire safety and first-aid procedures, emergency service contact arrangements, and training.

respirable dust – the fraction of airborne material that enters the nose and mouth during breathing, and which is capable of penetrating the gas exchange region of the lung.

Respiratory Protective Equipment (RPE) – a particular type of PPE used to protect an individual wearer against the inhalation of hazardous substances in the air.

responsible person – a person in control of work premises.

reverse burden of proof – a circumstance in which the burden of proof falls to a defendant to establish a particular issue, reversing the normal situation in which the prosecution must prove the facts beyond reasonable doubt. This applies to health and safety offences, and means that where the SFAIRP/ALARP requirement applies, the duty holder has to prove it was not practicable or reasonably practicable to do more than they in fact did.

RIDDOR (*Reporting of Injuries, Diseases and Dangerous Occurrences Regulations 2013***)** – legislation which puts duties on employers, the self-employed and people in control of work premises (the 'responsible person') to report certain serious workplace accidents, occupational diseases, specified dangerous occurrences, and near misses.

risk – a measure of loss or harm, calculated as the product of the probability or likelihood of an event's occurrence and the magnitude or severity of its impact. The loss or harm caused by a risk can be seen in a range of outcomes, including to people, the environment, an organisation's reputation, assets or business performance. Risk can simply be expressed as: *Risk = Likelihood * Severity*. For the most part, the risks considered in this book are health and safety risks.

risk agenda – the means by which an organisation sets out its reasons for risk management, including the particular risk management activities it undertakes and the benefits it anticipates from carrying them out. When well-articulated, a risk agenda paves the way for effective risk-based resource allocation, and encourages the making of clear risk management decisions.

risk and reliability assessment – an evaluation method which allows for the systematic assessment of uncertainties relevant to the design and operation of equipment and systems and helps decisions to be made which account for consequences related to unexpected events.

risk assessment – the process by which risk is identified, analysed and evaluated and control measures are put in place. In carrying out this type of assessment, an organisation needs to give thought as to what might cause harm to people, assets, and the environment and make a decision as to whether sufficient steps are being taken to prevent harm, as well as addressing any shortfalls. The legal requirements to carry out risk assessment are set out in *HSWA 1974*, supported by regulation 3 of *the Management Regulations*, and other regulations relevant to specific risk types.

risk assessment, dynamic – *see 'dynamic risk assessment'*.

risk assessment, generic – *see 'generic risk assessment'*.

risk assessment, task-based – *see 'task-based risk assessment'*.

risk assessment tool – an umbrella term, which refers to the types of tool used to help assessors break down tasks, identify elements that could pose a risk to workers, and evaluate potential solutions or improvements. An example of a risk assessment tool is the 'Risk Assessment of Pushing and Pulling Tool (RAPP Tool)' – *see separate entry*. Manual Handling risk assessment tools are to be found in the 'Toolkit for MSDs (musculoskeletal disorders)' – *see separate entry*.

risk-based reporting – an approach to reporting which aligns to an organisation's risk profile. When effectively carried out, adopting this type of approach results in reports which are objectively compiled, delivering information that enables senior leaders to make risk-based decisions.

risk-based thinking – an intuitive approach to the evaluation of risk, often adopted by an organisation when establishing process controls and making improvements to its risk management strategy. The practical incorporation of risk-based thinking is often achieved through the use of risk registers and risk tools, which can include risk matrices, barrier models (such as bow tie models) and other assurance checks.

risk champion – an individual, usually distinct from a 'risk owner' who, by virtue of their expertise or authority, is responsible for promoting and championing aspects of risk management processes, including risk programmes. Organisations often appoint individuals to such roles to help embed risk management within functional areas by selecting workers from diverse backgrounds and with varied levels of experience, which facilitates a more holistic approach to risk.

risk control – *see 'barrier'*.

risk control strategy – a structured and coherent approach to the control of risk, the focus of which is to manage it to an acceptable level, through risk identification, assessment, management and control processes.

risk control system – a group of barriers, which collectively act to block threats that lead towards – or limit consequences which flow away from – a top event.

risk event – *see 'top event'*.

risk filter – *see 'manual handling risk filter'*.

risk governance – a structure through which an organisation's vision and commitment to the control of risk is set, the means of attaining objectives are agreed, the framework for monitoring performance is established, and compliance with requirements is ensured. Typically, this will include the organisation's arrangements to evaluate compliance with risk management systems and procedures, as well as those which provide assurance to both internal and external stakeholders.

risk lead – a person responsible for managing risks, on a day-to-day basis – at the sharp end – with frontline operatives.

risk management cycle – a four-point agenda for embedding health and safety principles, which helps an organisation to find the best ways to lead and promote health and safety, and therefore meet its legal obligations, including checking the continued sufficiency and effectiveness of the control measures it has in place and verifying that its risks are reduced to ALARP levels (*see also 'plan-do-check-act' cycle*).

risk management strategy – the approach taken by an organisation towards the identification, assessment and management of risk, in a structured and coherent way.

risk matrix – a tool which assists in defining the level of risk, by considering the likelihood and severity of an event, and determines risk scores, helping an organisation to prioritise its risk management activity, including the allocation of resource.

risk mitigation – the steps taken to reduce the adverse effects associated with a risk; the method by which a systematic reduction in the extent of exposure to a risk and/or the likelihood of its occurrence is achieved.

risk model – a model which depicts the extent of risk. In the context of safety risks, risk models assist with the identification of the risk, provide an assessment of what is in place to stop and mitigate it, and support the making of a determination of where, if any, further action needs to be taken, by answering questions including: *'What will potentially have the best result?'* and *'What is the priority?'* Such models can be applied to help support and drive improvements in the control of an organisation's health and safety risks, as well as having applicability to a broad range of other business disciplines. One type of risk model is a 'barrier model', and a specific type of barrier model is the 'bow tie model'. *See also 'barrier model', 'bow tie model'.*

risk modelling – the practice of developing risk models.

risk owner – the accountable point of contact (usually, although not always) at senior leadership level who co-ordinates efforts to mitigate or manage a particular risk(s), typically supported by various sub-ordinate individuals who own parts of the risk. Generally a risk owner has responsibility for articulating the risks owned by them within risk statements or registers.

risk perception – how a risk is envisaged by an individual, resulting from their assessment of the likelihood of a particular incident occurring to them, or the plant or systems they operate, and the level of concern they attach to it.

risk profile – the profile of an organisation which informs all aspects of its approach to leading and managing its health and safety risks. It examines: the nature and level of threats faced by the organisation; the likelihood of adverse events occurring; the level of disruption and costs associated with each type of risk, and the effectiveness of the control arrangements it has in place for managing those risks. Many organisations use the information contained in risk registers as the basis from which to derive their risk profile.

risk reduction measures – the measures taken to reduce risks associated with operational locations and activities – including the health and safety of operatives and others who may be affected by them – through reducing the probability and/or mitigating the consequences of failure.

risk register – an essential risk management tool used by an organisation for documenting its identified risks, logging the potential severity and likelihood of each, and deriving the level of risk in each case, as well as the plant, process, people and performance risk reduction measures put in place to manage and respond to them.

roll, to (verb) – to cause something to move somewhere by turning over and over, or from side to side.

root cause – an initiating event or failing, from which all other causes or failings flow. These tend to be failings relating to management, planning or organisational processes.

routes of exposure – the ways in which persons or other living organisms can come into contact with a hazardous substance. The four major routes of exposure are: inhalation (breathing), absorption (skin contact), ingestion (eating) and injection.

routine operating conditions – the circumstances which have been observed or taken from a reference source, and recorded as normal practice within standard operating procedures.

safe operating limits – the limits within which process conditions must be retained, for instance, the point at which alarms, sensors and level indicators are set, so as to ensure process conditions are kept under control.

safe system of work – a formal procedure, resulting from an organisation's systematic examination of an activity and its sub-division into tasks, in order to identify all of the associated hazards; an approach which sets out safe methods of working to ensure that hazards are eliminated or risks minimised, at each stage.

safety case – a logical and hierarchical set of documents which describes risk in terms of the hazards presented by a facility/site and its modes of operation, including potential faults and accidents, and the reasonably practicable measures that need to be implemented to prevent or minimise harm. It takes account of experience from the past, is written in the present, and sets expectations and guidance for the processes that should operate in the future, if the hazards are to be successfully controlled. As such, it provides the information required to enable a facility/site or activity to be safely managed, and demonstrates how risks are reduced to ALARP levels – often to a regulator – by communicating a clear and comprehensive argument that a facility/site can be operated safely, or that an activity can be undertaken safely.

safety critical element – any part of a facility or its plant – examples of which include instruments, alarms and computer programs – that has the purpose of preventing or limiting the effect of a major incident and the failure of which could cause, or contribute substantially towards, a major incident; *a subset of 'process controls'*.

safety critical equipment – any equipment, instrumentation, controls or systems, the malfunction or failure of which would cause or substantially contribute to the release of a hazardous material or energy, or whose proper operation is required to mitigate the consequences of such a release. Such plant and equipment is relied upon to ensure continued safe operation. It typically includes those items listed in a plant's planned preventative maintenance programme, such as: pressure vessels, storage tanks, piping systems, relief and vent devices, pumps, instruments, control systems, interlocks, emergency shutdown systems, and emergency response equipment.

safety critical instrument – *a type of 'safety critical equipment'* – a device which serves to regulate, monitor, shut down and/or isolate a safety critical system. Examples include gauges, alarms and shut-off valves.

safety critical instrumentation – *a type of 'safety critical equipment'* – a collective term for safety critical instruments.

safety critical system – *a type of 'safety critical equipment'* – a system, the failure of which could result in loss of life, significant property damage or environmental damage, or which could otherwise disrupt normal societal activity. Examples include the control systems that operate within aircraft and other transport systems, and other critical infrastructure, such as that found within communication, utility, and security networks.

safety critical task – an active, sharp end task, such as maintenance and modification which, if not carried out correctly, could lead to serious consequences. Consequences can be manifold, but failings or shortfalls in the performance of safety critical tasks could include operational error, corrosion or mechanical degradation. This is the kind of task associated with major accident hazards (MAH) where humans may initiate or fail to mitigate the consequences of a major incident. Such tasks need to be clearly defined and understood, through the carrying out of a suitable task analysis. *See also 'Safety Critical Task Analysis (SCTA)'*.

Safety Critical Task Analysis (SCTA) – a formal method of identifying the potential for error within safety critical tasks, and assisting with the development of appropriate risk controls, so as to reduce hazardous event risk to a level which is ALARP. In some cases, this can be as simple as walking through the tasks and writing down what should be done, where, when, by whom, how and why, although in some cases, specialist human factors tools may be required. This is an approach typically used by high-hazard organisations.

safety culture – *'the product of individual and group values, attitudes, perceptions, competencies and patterns of behaviour that determine the commitment to, and the style and proficiency of, an organisation's health and safety management'* (Health and Safety Executive definition).

safety management system – a term which, in the context of *the Mines Regulations*, describes the system a mine operator should put in place to address significant risks at a mine and provide the necessary control measures. *See also 'health and safety management system' which provides a generic definition of such a system.*

safety report – a report submitted by the operator of an upper tier COMAH site to demonstrate that they have taken all measures necessary to prevent major accidents and limit the consequences to people and the environment of any that do occur (regulation 8 of *the COMAH Regulations*).

safety representative – *commonly referred to as a 'safety rep'* – an individual with functions conferred upon them by law – either under *the Safety Representatives and Safety Committees Regulations 1977*, as a trade union health and safety representative, or by virtue of *the Health and Safety (Consultation with Employees) Regulations 1996*, as a representative of employee safety.

safety tour – a walk around a workplace or facility, the purpose of which is to gain a general understanding of the work environment and the safety practices undertaken there.

scenario modelling – the process of examining and evaluating possible events that could take place, by considering various feasible results or outcomes.

scorecard – a basket of measures, which provides an organisation with information on a range of health and safety activities.

self-declaration – a term used in relation to CE marks or UKCA marks, which applies to certain categories of products where there is no requirement for a third party assessment of conformity to be made.

senior leader – an individual at the highest level of an organisation, with day-to-day responsibility for its management. Typically a senior leader is someone with senior management responsibilities, which could include, but are not limited to, governance or directorial matters. These individuals often have a key role to play in collaborating with stakeholders internal and external to an organisation, with a view to endorsing, championing, delivering against, and influencing the future direction of its strategic goals.

senior management – someone within an organisation who plays a significant role in either: making decisions about how the whole or a substantial part of activities are managed or organised, *or* in the actual managing or organising of the whole or a substantial part of those activities (see section 1 of *the Corporate Manslaughter Act*).

sensor – a device which detects or measures the presence of, or changes to, a physical property.

Sentencing Council – an independent, non-departmental public body, which is part of the Ministry of Justice's family of arm's length bodies with responsibility for developing sentencing guidelines and monitoring their use, including assessing the impact of guidelines on sentencing practice.

Short Term Exposure Limit (STEL) – a limit (usually 15 minutes) applied to control hazardous substance exposure, for a substance recognised as being capable of producing effects after only a brief period of time.

simple filter – *see 'manual handling risk filter'.*

single point of failure – a part of a system or process, the failure of which will cause the whole system or process to stop working. This is undesirable for any system or process where high reliability is required and, in the context of risks controlled by procedural barriers, can include the things that people are required to do. The absence of backup arrangements to take the place of such system parts or processes, in cases where they fail to function, is the causal factor of a single point of failure.

site induction – *sometimes referred to as an 'induction'* – the process of ensuring that workers on a site are fully informed about its organisation and operation, and are cognisant of their responsibilities when working there. The primary focus of this type of process is upon safety aspects, including site hazards and risks, and the relevant control measures.

situational awareness – a person's state of awareness of what is happening around them, in terms of where they are, where they are supposed to be, and whether anything or anyone around them poses a threat to their health and safety; the state which determines a person's decision-making, what they do, and what they instruct others to do. Typically, those who operate within the emergency services have highly developed situational awareness skills, including fire fighters, police officers, and emergency first responders.

skill fade – the decay of human ability or adeptness over a period of non-use; skills getting rusty over time.

slide, to (verb) – to cause to move easily and without interruption over a surface.

so far as is reasonably practicable (SFAIRP) – a term denoting the amount by which risk must be reduced, rather than the level to which it is expected to be reduced (which is termed 'as low as reasonably practicable' ('ALARP').

social distancing – the taking of steps to reduce social interaction between people.

source-pathway-receptor model – a model often used in the context of environmental risk assessment. The basic principle of the model is that, for a risk to exist, there must be a hazard source, a receptor, and a pathway between the source and the receptor.

static charge – a set of circumstances in which the rate of charge accumulation exceeds the rate of charge dissipation. Metals are most likely to be at risk of static charge accumulation; this results from the imbalance between negative and positive charges in an object, which build up on its surface until they find a way to be released or discharged.

static dropped object – *see 'dropped object, static'.*

steering group – a group that oversees and facilitates the driving of management system standards, procedures and other expected practice throughout an organisation or industry.

stress – the adverse reaction people have to excessive pressures or other types of demands placed upon them. Whilst not an illness of itself, this is a state which, if it becomes too excessive or prolonged, can cause or contribute towards the development of mental and physical conditions.

structural collapse – the unintentional collapse or partial collapse of – (a) any structure, which involves a fall of more than 5 tonnes of material; or (b) any floor or wall of any place of work, arising from, or in connection with, ongoing construction work (including demolition, refurbishment and maintenance), whether above or below ground, or, the unintentional or partial collapse of any falsework (as defined in *RIDDOR*).

sub-contractor – an organisation or individual hired by a contractor to perform a specific task or work-type. The use of sub-contractors is often preferred by organisations seeking to engage particular specialists, or where specialist work types are required.

substance hazardous to health – *see 'hazardous substance'.*

'suitable and sufficient' – a quality expected of risk assessment, which means it should show that: a proper check has been made on the risk; those who might be affected have been considered; all obvious significant risks have been dealt with, including account having been taken of the numbers and types of people who could be involved; the precautions taken are reasonable and the remaining risk low, and workers or their representatives have been involved in the process. In order to be suitable and sufficient the level of detail in the risk assessment needs to be proportionate to the risk and appropriate to the nature of work.

supervisor – a person who is competent to monitor the work of another/others. This can include taking responsibility for the work of a person who is not yet competent, for instance where the person being supervised is a trainee.

Swiss cheese model – a model of accident causation which hypothesises that most accidents can be traced to one or more of four levels of failure, namely: organisational influences, unsafe supervision, preconditions for unsafe acts, and the unsafe acts themselves. Developed by Reason, J (1997), this is the theory upon which present day barrier models – including bow tie models – are based.

system – a set of things or components that are connected or work together.

task-based risk assessment – a method of risk assessment which assesses risks relative to the tasks undertaken by workers.

task rotation – a system of working in which a worker moves between two or more jobs or tasks, for a set period of time. Organisations often take this approach in order to manage the risks associated with repetitive work.

team manager – an individual who is responsible for the day-to-day activities and guidance of their team members, and whose responsibilities can include the setting of targets, the implementation of guidelines and assisting with any issues reported by their team members. The ultimate purpose of a team manager should be to ensure that all team members understand the team's objectives and are committed to work together to achieve them.

Texas City report – the investigation report into the refinery explosion and fire at BP's Texas City refinery, prepared by the US Chemical Safety and Hazard Investigation Board.

threat – *sometimes referred to as a 'cause'* – in the context of a bow tie model, this is anything which could cause a top event (risk) to result. There can be multiple threats for a given top event, which – on a bow tie model – are depicted on the left hand side, at the end of threat legs. Threats can be identified by asking questions such as: 'What *does a person – often an operative – actually do (or not do) to cause the top event?'* and *'Which piece of equipment or system failing causes the top event?'*

threat leg – a component of a bow tie model, which depicts the flow from a given threat to a top event. Typically, along a given threat leg, organisations will seek to put in place a number of prevention barriers, each with a purpose of either fully or partially preventing a given threat from resulting in a top event.

Time Weighted Average – a figure which gives the concentration of a hazardous substance in the air, averaged over a specified period of time.

Toolkit for MSDs (musculoskeletal disorders) – a collection of tools developed by the Health and Safety Executive to help employers and employees to identify common risk factors involved in manual handling operations. The tools cover high risk lifting and carrying (the 'MAC tool'), pushing and pulling (the 'RAPP tool'), repetitive tasks (the 'ART tool'), and variable manual handling (the 'V-MAC tool') – *see separate entries*. The basic principle common to all these tools is to help assessors to break down tasks, identify elements that could pose a risk to workers and evaluate potential solutions or improvements.

top event – *sometimes called a 'risk event'* – the unplanned or uncontrolled outcome of an organisation's operation or activity that has, or could have, contributed to an injury, illness or physical or environmental damage; the point at which control is lost over a hazard before the consequences occur; the release of the hazard; the first loss of control. In the context of a bow tie model, this is depicted as the central knot.

trade union – an organisation with members who are usually workers or employees, which looks after their interests at work by doing things including: negotiating agreements on better working conditions, including improved health and safety and pay; discussing big changes like large-scale redundancy; raising members' concerns with employers, and supporting members called to attend disciplinary and grievance meetings.

trespasser – a person who commits the act of trespass on a property, without the permission of the owner or occupier.

UKCA Mark (UK Conformity Assessed Mark) – a new product marking used for goods being placed on the market in Great Britain (England, Wales and Scotland), covering most goods which previously required the CE mark. The technical requirements ('Essential Health and Safety Requirements') that need to be met, as well as the conformity assessment processes and standards used to demonstrate conformity, are largely the same as for CE marking. This mark came into effect on 1 January 2021 but, in order to allow organisations time to adjust to the new requirements, the continued application of the CE mark is permitted for manufactured goods placed on the GB market up until 31 December 2022. From 1 January 2024, the permanent attachment of the UKCA mark to the products to which it applies will be required. NB: the UKCA mark alone cannot be used for goods placed on the Northern Ireland market, which require the CE mark or the UKNI mark to be applied.

UKEX (UKCA 'Ex') approved – the approval that confirms that the standards have been met for an Ex product (a product for use in hazardous locations) placed on the market in Great Britain and allows a UKCA Mark to be applied. This replaces 'ATEX certification' and is required for equipment and systems used in potentially explosive atmospheres.

UKNI Mark – a conformity marking for products placed on the market in Northern Ireland which have undergone mandatory third-party conformity assessment by a body based in the UK. This mark shows that all relevant EU rules relating to the placing on the market of manufactured goods have been met for any product to which it is applied. Where an EU conformity assessment body is used, the CE marking is to be used on its own. This is also the case for the placing of Northern Ireland goods on the market in the EU, where the UKNI mark is not recognised. For qualifying Northern Ireland goods placed on the GB market, either the CE mark, or the CE and UKNI mark in combination, must be applied. The UKNI mark is never to be used in isolation.

underlying cause – the systemic or organisational reason for an adverse event or incident occurring, examples of which can include: failures by supervisors to carry out pre-start-up checks, failures to adequately consider hazards via suitable and sufficient risk assessment, and productivity targets being prioritised over safety goals.

United Kingdom Approved Body (UKAB) – an entity which confirms the conformity of a product and allows the application of the UKCA Mark, prior to its acceptance on the GB market, upon completion of conformity assessment procedures. For example, products to be used within potentially explosive atmospheres must be UKEX (UKCA 'Ex') approved by a UKAB, prior to their acceptance on the GB market. This role is equivalent to that performed by a Notified Body for countries within the European Union, as was the case for the United Kingdom whilst a member country. Within the UK, as a conformity assessment body, a UKAB needs to be approved by the Secretary of State, who holds responsibility for assessing products for the GB market against GB Essential Health and Safety Requirements.

upper tier COMAH site – an establishment which, by virtue of the quantity of dangerous substances it holds, is subject to the most stringent requirements of *the COMAH Regulations,* including the preparation of a safety report (regulation 8), emergency planning arrangements (regulations 11 – 16), and the provision of information to anyone likely to be affected by a major accident (regulation 18).

upward communication – the process by which information flows from the lower levels of an organisation to its upper levels, including to its senior leaders.

usability – the extent to which a product can be used by specified users in order to achieve specified goals, with effectiveness, efficiency and satisfaction in mind, within a specified context of use.

user – a person who uses a product or process or who interacts with systems or an environment, an example being that someone who habitually uses display screen equipment as a significant part of their normal work is termed a 'DSE user'.

user acceptance testing (UAT) – a stage within a software development process – typically the final one – where the software is given to the intended audience, or a sample group, to test its functionality. The use of this approach ensures that the software can handle required tasks in a real-world scenario, in accordance with the design specifications, prior to its full deployment.

user-centred design – the application of methods and processes that focus on the end user throughout the design lifecycle.

user comfort – the state in which a user is protected from the systems or environments with which they interact, or in which they are situated.

user experience (UX) – the application of methods and processes that design for and assess the total user experience, including usability, user feelings, motivations and values, with respect to products and services; *'UX' is a term sometimes used by product developers, when referring to the user experience.*

user interface (UI) – the design of user interfaces for machines and software, e.g. computers, the focus of which is upon maximising usability and user experience; *'UI' is a term sometimes used by product developers, when referring to the user interface.*

user interface design – the design of user interfaces for machines and computer software, including task menus, with a focus on maximising usability and user experience.

user satisfaction – the attitude of a user to a system or product employed in the context of a work environment; *see also 'user experience'.*

user testing/user trials – a technique used in the course of a design process to evaluate a product, system, feature or prototype, which involves real users.

V-MAC (Variable manual handling assessment chart) tool – a simple tool designed by the Health and Safety Executive for assessing multiple manual handling operations where load weights vary; this tool is used in conjunction with the MAC tool.

valve – a device for controlling the passage of a substance through a pipe or duct which can be manually or automatically (remotely) activated. One example is a pressure relief valve which automatically releases, when the pressure or temperature exceeds pre-set limits. Valves should fail to safety and not place operatives in danger. Remotely operated shut off valves are generally preferred to those which are manually operated, for this reason.

valve, manually operated – *see 'manually operated valve'.*

valve, remotely operated shut off (ROSOV) – *see 'remotely operated shut off valve'.*

vigilance – the attention paid to a task by a worker for a period of time.

violation – an intentional failure to do the right thing, or deliberately doing the wrong thing. This type of human failure is one of the biggest causes of workplace accidents and injuries.

violence – any situation in which a person receives abuse, threats, or is assaulted, in circumstances related to their work, which can include verbal threats.

volenti non fit injuria (volenti) – the principle that *'no harm is done to a willing person'.* Where it can be proven that a claimant voluntarily put themselves in danger, this can be used as a defence by a defendant against a personal injury (negligence) claim. The essence of this legal principle is that anyone who knowingly and voluntarily consents to and takes on a risk cannot then ask for compensation for the damage or injury resulting from it.

vulnerable worker – an individual who is at risk of having their workplace entitlements denied, or who lacks the capacity or means to secure them. Health and safety should not be used as a basis upon which to discriminate against certain individuals or groups of workers. Examples of workers who might be regarded as vulnerable include: migrant workers, new and expectant mothers, those with a disability, older workers (in some cases) and those new to a job, such as trainees, who may have less risk-awareness than those with more experience.

warning sign – a sign giving a warning of a risk to health and safety (see regulation 2 of *the Safety Signs and Signals Regulations*).

waste broker – someone who arranges for someone else to buy, sell or dispose of waste.

waste carrier – someone who transports waste.

waste dealer – someone who buys, sells or disposes of waste.

waste management – an umbrella term covering the activities from waste inception, right through to its final disposal. As such, it includes the collection, transportation, disposal, recycling and monitoring of waste.

weak signal – an indication of safety standards which is more subtle than those derived from more structured methods, being intuition-led rather than fact-based. Typically this kind of indication is manifested in workers showing concern, which can arise as a result of factors including: mixed messages from senior leaders, inconsistent treatment of identified safety violations, and insufficient or excessive volumes of safety data being communicated.

Weil's disease – *see 'leptospirosis'*.

wellbeing – the state of being comfortable, healthy and happy.

work at height – the carrying out of work in any place, including places at or below ground level, where a person could fall a distance liable to cause themselves personal injury (see regulation 2 of *the Work at Height Regulations*).

work overload – *see 'cognitive overload'*.

work related musculoskeletal disorders (WRMSDs) – an umbrella term given to disorders associated with work patterns which include: fixed or constrained body positions, continual repetition of movements, force concentrated on small parts of the body such as the hand or wrist, and a pace of work which does not allow sufficient recovery between movements. Such disorders can develop in occupational settings, due to the physical tasks which individuals are required to carry out as part of their normal work activities.

work underload – *see 'cognitive underload'*.

worker – a person who works. Whilst this term is often used more generally in this book, for the purposes of employment rights this is someone who works other than under a contract of employment (see section 230 of *the Employment Rights Act 1996* c.18).

working group – a group that works with a cross-section of representatives on specific management system standards or allied work activities for an organisation or industry, as delegated to them by steering groups.

working platform – a platform traditionally seen as the fully-boarded type with handrails and toe boards, but which, since the introduction of *the Work at Height Regulations*, is now viewed as being virtually any surface from which work can be carried out, including a roof, a floor, a platform or a scaffold, a mobile elevated work platform (MEWP) or the treads of a stepladder.

workload – the effort demanded from people for the tasks they have to do. This can be at a single point in time, or over a whole shift, and can relate to physical or mental demands.

Workplace Exposure Limit (WEL) – a British occupational exposure limit, set in order to help to protect the health of workers, averaged over a specified period of time. The setting of such a limit means that within a specified reference period (often 8 hours, but sometimes as short as 15 minutes), an individual is only allowed to be exposed to a certain amount of a hazardous substance, as a maximum. Substances subject to WELs are contained within the Health and Safety Executive's *EH40* publication, which also sets out the method of calculating exposure. *See also 'Long Term Exposure Limit (LTEL)', 'Short Term Exposure Limit (STEL)'*.

workplace exposure monitoring – the process of measuring workers' exposure to named substances which can occur through inhalation, skin contact or swallowing, and can include personal monitoring which assesses a person's exposure, and/or static/background sampling of the workplace environment.

workstation assessment – an assessment which takes account of the design of the workstation, the design of the workplace and the user's role in helping to reduce risk, for instance, when using display screen equipment. The purpose of this type of assessment is to assess a workstation and to identify and resolve any issues which may affect user health. *A common type of workstation assessment is a 'display screen equipment (DSE) assessment'.*

young worker – a worker who has reached the compulsory school leaving age, but is under the age of 18.

zone – a classification given to a location based upon the risk level associated with it. In the context of *DSEAR*, this is based upon the persistence and duration of an explosive atmosphere within a 'hazardous place'. This follows on from 'hazardous area classification', as a further classification which distinguishes between places that have a high chance of an explosive atmosphere occurring, and those places where an explosive atmosphere may occur only occasionally or in abnormal circumstances. Gases, vapours and mists are covered by zones 0, 1 and 2; dusts are covered by zones 20, 21 and 22. Definitions of these zones (included in *DSEAR*) recognise that the chance of a fire or explosion depends upon the likelihood of an explosive atmosphere occurring at the same time as an ignition source becoming active. *For other examples of zones, see also 'exclusion zone' and 'drop zone', of relevance in the context of work at heights.*

zoonotic disease – an infection caused by bacteria, viruses and parasites that spread between animals and humans, e.g. Weil's disease.

BIBLIOGRAPHY

Information from Health and Safety Executive publications was referred to in the course of producing the Tables and Appendices in this book, as indicated here.

Table 1 – Classification of Biological Agents.

The classification of biological agents given within *Table 1* in *the piper's fable* is as set out in *the COSHH Regulations,* regulation 7(10), schedule 3 'Additional provisions relating to work with biological agents', Part I 'Provisions of general application to biological agents', at paragraph 2(2).

Table 2a – Classification of Places where Explosive Atmospheres may occur.

The information provided within *Table 2a* in *Ian's fable* is taken from schedule 2 to regulation 7(1) of *DSEAR* and is to be found within: Health and Safety Executive (2013) *Dangerous Substances and Explosive Atmospheres Regulations 2002, Approved Code of Practice and Guidance,* (L138) 2nd edition, pp74-75.

Table 2b – Criteria for the Selection of Equipment and Protective Systems.

The criteria for the selection of equipment and protective systems, appropriate for use in places classified as hazardous, provided within *Table 2b* in *Ian's fable* is taken from schedule 3 to regulation 7(2) of DSEAR and is to be found within L138, at p75.

Table 3 – RAPP Tool Risk Rating Classifications.

The RAPP tool risk rating classifications set out in *Table 3* in the *prologue* to the *swede fable* are taken from: Health and Safety Executive Guidance document (2016) *Risk Assessment of Pushing and Pulling (RAPP) tool,* (INDG478), at p2.

Appendix A – Assessment Guide: Risk Assessment of Pushing and Pulling Tool – rating classifications for loads without wheels.

The table of RAPP tool criteria provided in *Appendix A* is compiled from information contained within INDG478, pp10-13.

Appendix B – Completed Score Sheet: Pushing or Pulling Loads Without Wheels – activity: pulling (dragging/hauling) swede from ground.

The score sheet format used in *Appendix B* is based upon 'Score Sheet: Pushing or Pulling Loads Without Wheels' to be found within INDG478 at p14.

Appendix C – Completed Score Sheet: Pushing or Pulling Loads Without Wheels – activity: pushing (rolling) swede towards smallholding cottage.

The score sheet format used in *Appendix C* is based upon 'Score Sheet: Pushing or Pulling Loads Without Wheels' to be found within INDG478 at p14.

*The following sources were referred to in the course of preparing
this book and are acknowledged at the relevant points, within the main text
and/or in the supporting footnotes.*

Baker, JA (2007)., *The Report of the BP US Refineries Independent Safety Review Panel* ('The Baker Report').

Chemical Safety and Hazard Investigation Board (2007)., *US Chemical Safety & Hazard Investigation Board Investigation Report – Refinery Explosion & Fire – 'The Texas City Report'* [Report No. 2005-04-I-TX; March 2007]. United States.

Department of Transport, Air Accidents Investigation Branch (1990). *Report on the Accident to Boeing 737-400 G-OBME near Kegworth, Leicestershire on 8 January 1989.* Aircraft Accident Report 4/90. London: HMSO ('The Kegworth report').

Haddon Jr., W (1995). Energy Damage and the 10 Countermeasure Strategies. *Injury Prevention.* 1(1), 40-44. NB: this article first appeared in the *Journal of Trauma* (1973) 13, 321-31.

Health and Safety Executive (1996). *The Chemical Release and Fire at the Associated Octel Company Limited: A report of the investigation by the Health and Safety Executive into the chemical release and fire at the Associated Octel Company, Ellesmere Port on 1 and 2 February 1994.* ISBN 0-717-60830-1. Crown copyright.

Health and Safety Executive (2006). *Developing Process Safety Indicators: A step-by-step guide for chemical and major hazard industries.* HSG254 (First edition); ISBN 978-0-717-66180-0. Crown copyright.

Health and Safety Executive (2008). *Working in the UK from Overseas? Your health and safety at work in agriculture and food processing.* INDG410. ISBN 978-0-717-66241-8. Crown copyright.

Health and Safety Executive (2010). *Protecting Migrant Workers.* Guidance leaflet. Web-only version. [Viewed 01 May 2021].

Health and Safety Executive (2011). *Managing Contractors – A guide for employers.* HSG159 (Second edition). ISBN 978-0-717-66436-8. Crown copyright.

Health and Safety Executive (2011). *Buncefield: Why did it happen? The underlying causes of the explosion and fire at the Buncefield oil storage depot, Hemel Hempstead, Hertfordshire on 11 December 2005.* Report published on behalf of the Competent Authority for the Control of Major Accident Hazards. Crown copyright.

Health and Safety Executive (2012). *Leptospirosis: Are you at risk?* INDG84 (rev. 1). ISBN 978-0-717-66455-9. Crown copyright.

Health and Safety Executive (2013). *Managing for Health and Safety.* HSG65 (rev. 3). ISBN 978-0-717-66456-6. Crown copyright.

Health and Safety Executive (2013). *Ergonomics and Human Factors at Work – A brief guide.* INDG90 (rev.3). ISBN 978-0-717-66473-3. Crown copyright.

Health and Safety Executive (2013). *Consulting Employees on Health and Safety – A brief guide to the law.* INDG232 (rev.2). Crown copyright.

Health and Safety Executive (2013) *Young People and Work Experience – A brief guide to health and safety for employers.* INDG364 (rev. 1). ISBN 978-0-717-66471-9. Crown copyright.

Health and Safety Executive (2013). *Using Contractors – A brief guide.* INDG368 (rev. 1). ISBN 978-0-717-66467-2. Crown copyright.

Health and Safety Executive (2013). *New and Expectant Mothers who Work: A brief guide to your health and safety.* INDG373 (rev. 2). ISBN: 978-0-717-66530-3. Crown copyright.

Health and Safety Executive (2013). *Making the best use of Lifting and Handling Aids.* INDG398 (rev.1). Crown copyright.

Health and Safety Executive (2013). *Leading Health and Safety at Work.* INDG417 (rev.1). Crown copyright. ISBN: 978-0-717-66464-1.

Health and Safety Executive (2013). *Dangerous Substances and Explosive Atmospheres – DSEAR 2002 Approved Code of Practice and Guidance.* L138. Second edition. ISBN 978-0-717-66616-4. Crown copyright.

Health and Safety Executive (2015). *The Mines Regulations 2014. Guidance on Regulations.* L149. First edition. Amended 2020. ISBN 978-0-717-66647-8. Crown copyright.

Health and Safety Executive (2016). *.Risk Assessment of Pushing and Pulling (RAPP) Tool.* INDG478. ISBN 978-0-717-66657-7. Crown copyright.

Health and Safety Executive (2016). *Manual Handling: Manual Handling (Operations) Regulations 1992, Guidance on Regulations.* L23. Fourth edition. ISBN 978-0-717-66653-9. Crown copyright.

Health and Safety Executive (2020). *Workplace Exposure Limits. Containing the list of workplace exposure limits for use with the Control of Substances Hazardous to Health Regulations 2002 (as amended).* EH40/2005. Fourth edition. Amended 2020. ISBN 978-0-717-66703-1. Crown copyright.

Health and Safety Executive (2020) *Health and Safety at Work, Summary Statistics for Great Britain 2020,* data from Labour Force Survey, November 2020. Crown copyright.

Health and Safety Executive (2020) *HSE's Annual Statistics – Kinds of accident statistics in Great Britain, 2020* (published 04/11/2020). Crown copyright.

Health and Safety Executive (2020) *Work Related Stress, Anxiety or Depression Statistics in Great Britain, 2020.* Annual Statistics, published November 2020., data up to March 2020. Crown copyright.

Health and Safety Executive (2020) *Protecting Lone Workers: How to manage the risks of working alone.* INDG73 (rev 4). ISBN 978-0-717-66729-1. Crown copyright.

Health and Safety Executive (2020). *Manual Handling at Work – A brief guide.* INDG143 (rev 4). ISBN 978-0-717-66732-1. Crown copyright.

Health and Safety Executive (2021). Advisory Committee on Dangerous Pathogens. *The Approved List of Biological Agents.* Fourth edition. Crown copyright.

Health and Safety Executive (2021). *Health and Safety at Work, Summary Statistics for Great Britain 2021,* data from Labour Force Survey, December 2021. Crown copyright.

Health and Safety Executive (2021). *HSE's Annual Statistics – Kinds of Accident Statistics in Great Britain, 2021* (published 16/12/2021) – *provisional as at the time of going to press.* Crown copyright.

Health and Safety Executive (2021). *Agriculture, Forestry and Fishing Statistics in Great Britain, 2021.* Annual Statistics, published 16/12/2021., data up to March 2021. Crown copyright.

Health and Safety Executive (2021). *Work Related Stress, Anxiety or Depression Statistics in Great Britain, 2021.* Annual Statistics, published December 2021., data up to March 2021. Crown copyright.

Hidden, A., QC, Department of Transport., (1989). *Investigation into the Clapham Junction Railway Accident.* London: HMSO. ISBN 0-10-1082029 ('The Hidden Report').

Home Office (2020) *National Referral Mechanism and Duty to Notify Statistics, UK, End of Year Summary, 2020*; Home Office Statistical Bulletin 08/21. ISSN 1759-7005. Crown copyright.

Lewis, C.S., (2009). *The Lion, the Witch, and the Wardrobe – The Chronicles of Narnia, Book 2*. London: Harper Collins, 2009. ISBN 978-0-007-32312-8.

Orwell, G., (2021). *Animal Farm*. London: Harper Collins, 2021. ISBN 978-0-008-32205-2.

Reason, J., (1997). *Managing the Risks of Organizational Accidents*. Aldershot: Ashgate Publishing. ISBN 978-1-840-14105-4.

Shakespeare, W., *Romeo and Juliet*. Taken from *The Arden Shakespeare, Complete Works, Revised Edition*, edited by Richard Proudfoot, Ann Thompson, David Scott Kastan. London: Bloomsbury Publishing, 2019. ISBN: 978-1-4081-5201-0.

Sklet, S., (2006) *Safety Barriers: Definition, Classification and Performance*. Journal of Loss Prevention in the Process Industries. 19(5), 494-506.

The Office for Product Safety & Standards Guidance document, (2021). *Equipment and Protective Systems Intended for Use in Potentially Explosive Atmospheres Regulations 2016. As they apply to equipment and systems being supplied in or into Great Britain from 1 January 2021.* version 2. November 2021. Crown copyright.

The following on-line resources were accessed, in the course of preparing this book and are acknowledged at the relevant points, within the main text and/or in the supporting footnotes.

Department for Business, Energy & Industrial Strategy., (2021). *Historical Coal Data: Coal production, 1853 to 2020* [online]. DBEIS. [Viewed 08 January 2022]. Available from: http://www.gov.uk

Dropsonline. Dropped Objects Prevention Scheme Global Resource Centre. *For the DROPS calculator* [online]. [Viewed 01 May 2021]. Available from: http://www.dropsonline.org

Guinness World Records., (2021). *For the detail of the heaviest swede ever grown and the detail of the tallest beanstalk ever grown.* [online]. Guinness World Records. [Viewed 01 May 2021]. Available from http://www.guinnessworldrecords.com

Health and Safety Executive., (2021). *For the definition of 'vulnerable workers'.* [online]. Health and Safety Executive. [Viewed 01 May 2021]. Available from https://www.hse.gov.uk/vulnerable-workers/

Health and Safety Executive., (2021). *For information on how to manage fatigue.* [online]. Health and Safety Executive. https://www.hse.gov.uk/humanfactors/topics/fatigue.htm [Viewed 01 May 2021].

Health and Safety Executive., (2021). *For the definition of 'stress'.* [online]. Health and Safety Executive. [Viewed 01 May 2021]. Available from https://www.hse.gov.uk/stress/what-to-do.htm

Health and Safety Executive., (2021). *For information on the 'Management Standards' and other information on stress.* [online]. Health and Safety Executive. [Viewed 01 May 2021]. Available from https://www.hse.gov.uk/stress/standards/

Health and Safety Executive., (2021). *For the definition of, and other information on, 'safety culture'.* [online]. Health and Safety Executive. [Viewed 01 May 2021]. Available from http://www.hse.gov.uk/humanfactors/topics/culture.htm

Health and Safety Executive., (2021). *For information on the 'assess-control-review model'*. [online]. Health and Safety Executive. [Viewed 01 May 2021]. Available from http://www.hse.gov.uk/construction/healthrisks/managing-essentials/essentials.pdf

Health and Safety Executive., (2021). *For information on how to protect home workers.* [online]. Health and Safety Executive. [Viewed 01 May 2021]. Available from https://www.hse.gov.uk/toolbox/workers/home.htm

International Ergonomics Association., (2021). *For the definition of 'ergonomics'.* [online]. [Viewed 01 May 2021]. Available from https://iea.cc/what-is-ergonomics/

Office for Product Safety & Standards., (2021). *For information on the requirements to which those businesses placing equipment and protective systems intended for use in potentially explosive atmospheres on the market in Great Britain are subject, from 1 January 2021.* [online]. [Viewed 03 January 2022]. Available from https://www.gov.uk/government/organisations/office-for-product-safety-and-standards

Stay Energy Safe., (2021). *For details as to how to report energy theft.* [Viewed 01 May 2021]. Available from: http://www.stayenergysafe.co.uk

The Sentencing Council., (2021). *For details on the Sentencing Guidelines, introduced in 2016.* [Viewed 01 May 2021]. Available from: http://www.sentencingcouncil.org.uk

OTHER REFERENCE SOURCES

The fables in this book drew inspiration from the following sources.

Aesop. *The Hen that laid the Golden Eggs (no 87, Perry Index);* taken from Temple, O, (1998) *Aesop – The Complete Fables.* London: Penguin Books.

Anon, (18C). *Aladdin, from The Book of One Thousand and One Nights.* Added by Frenchman Galland, A, who acquired the tale from Syria.

Browning, R, (1842). *The Pied Piper, in Dramatic Lyrics.* Original Diyab, H, based on Verstegan, R's (1605) version of the tale (earliest account in English).

Dasent, Sir G W, (1859). *The Billy Goats Gruff, in Popular Tales from the Norse.* First English translation from the original, by Asbjørnsen, P C and Møe, J (1841-4). *Norwegian Folktales & Legends.*

Grimm. (19C). *Der Susse Brei, from Grimms Fairy Tales,* vol.2, as *Sweet Porridge.* Tale number 103. Translated to English by Hunt, M. *Grimms' Children's and Household Tales.*

Grimm (1812). *Snow White and the Seven Dwarfs,* from *Grimms' Fairy Tales (tale no.53).*

Halliwell-Phillips, J, (1886). *The Three Little Pigs,* included in *The Nursery Rhymes of England.* London and New York. First appeared in Jacobs J (1890) *English Fairy Tales.*

Roberts, J, (1734). *The Story of Jack Spriggins and the Enchanted Bean* from *Round About our Coal Fire* or *Christmas Entertainments* at pp35-48. 4ᵗʰ Edition.

Southey, R, (1837). *The Story of the Three Bears,* from volume of writings, *The Doctor.* Longman-Rees.

Tolstoy, A, (1910). *The Enormous Turnip.* Collected by Afanasyev, A. *Narodnye Russkie Skazki* (tale number 89), published in *Grimm's Fairy Tales (tale number 146).*